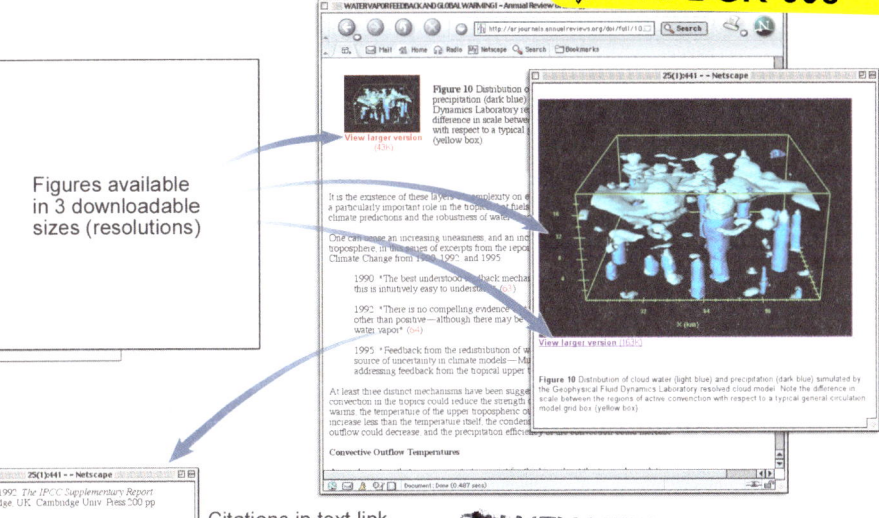

Figures available in 3 downloadable sizes (resolutions)

Citations in text link to references in bibliography

References in Annual Reviews chapter bibliography link out to sources of cited articles online

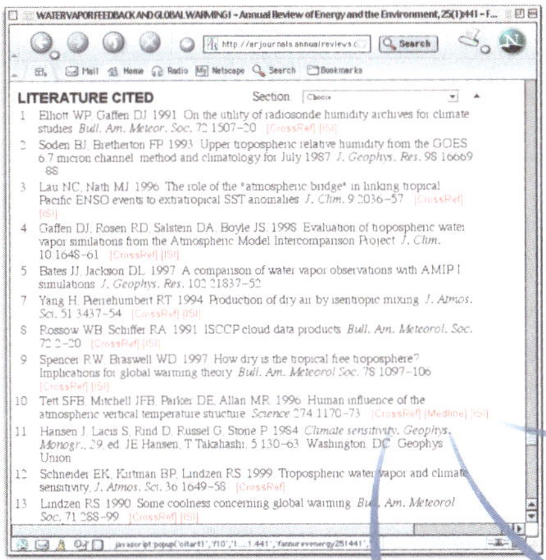

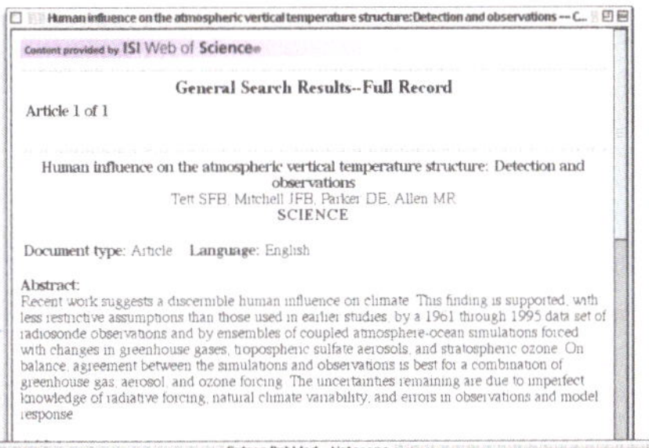

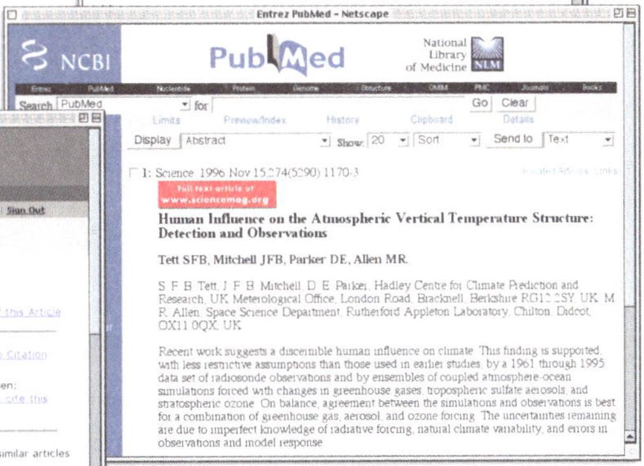

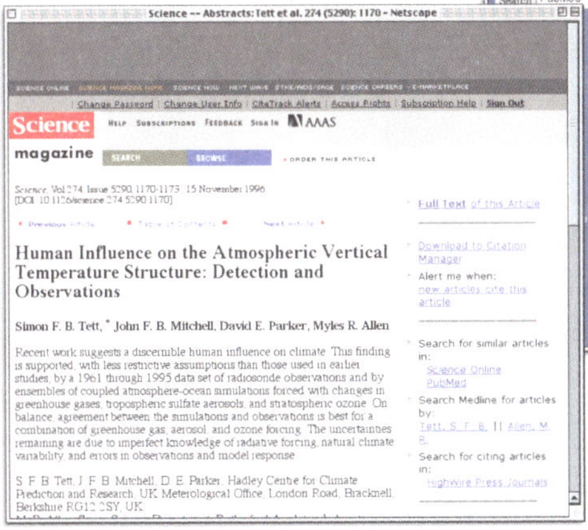

ANNUAL REVIEW OF ENVIRONMENT AND RESOURCES

EDITORIAL COMMITTEE (2004)

WILLIAM C. CLARK
ASHOK GADGIL
DANIEL M. KAMMEN
DIANA LIVERMAN
PAMELA A. MATSON
ROSAMOND L. NAYLOR
ISHA RAY
DAVID S. SCHIMEL

RESPONSIBLE FOR THE ORGANIZATION OF VOLUME 29 (EDITORIAL COMMITTEE, 2002)

WILLIAM C. CLARK
ASHOK GADGIL
PETER H. GLEICK
DANIEL M. KAMMEN
DONALD KENNEDY
DIANA LIVERMAN
PAMELA A. MATSON
DAVID S. SCHIMEL
PATRICIA HOLDEN (GUEST)
ROSAMOND L. NAYLOR (GUEST)

Production Editor: JESSLYN S. HOLOMBO
Bibliographic Quality Control: MARY A. GLASS
Electronic Content Coordinator: SUZANNE K. MOSES
Subject Indexer: BRUCE TRACY

ANNUAL REVIEW OF ENVIRONMENT AND RESOURCES

VOLUME 29, 2004

PAMELA A. MATSON, *Editor*
Stanford University

ASHOK GADGIL, *Associate Editor*
Lawrence Berkeley National Laboratory

DANIEL M. KAMMEN, *Associate Editor*
University of California, Berkeley

www.annualreviews.org   science@annualreviews.org   650-493-4400

ANNUAL REVIEWS
4139 El Camino Way • P.O. Box 10139 • Palo Alto, California 94303-0139

ANNUAL REVIEWS
Palo Alto, California, USA

COPYRIGHT © 2004 BY ANNUAL REVIEWS, PALO ALTO, CALIFORNIA, USA. ALL RIGHTS RESERVED. The appearance of the code at the bottom of the first page of an article in this serial indicates the copyright owner's consent that copies of the article may be made for personal or internal use, or for the personal or internal use of specific clients. This consent is given on the condition that the copier pay the stated per-copy fee of $14.00 per article through the Copyright Clearance Center, Inc. (222 Rosewood Drive, Danvers, MA 01923) for copying beyond that permitted by Section 107 or 108 of the US Copyright Law. The per-copy fee of $14.00 per article also applies to the copying, under the stated conditions, of articles published in any *Annual Review* serial before January 1, 1978. Individual readers, and nonprofit libraries acting for them, are permitted to make a single copy of an article without charge for use in research or teaching. This consent does not extend to other kinds of copying, such as copying for general distribution, for advertising or promotional purposes, for creating new collective works, or for resale. For such uses, written permission is required. Write to Permissions Dept., Annual Reviews, 4139 El Camino Way, P.O. Box 10139, Palo Alto, CA 94303-0139 USA.

International Standard Serial Number: 1543-5938
International Standard Book Number: 0-8243-2329-7

All Annual Reviews and publication titles are registered trademarks of Annual Reviews.

∞ The paper used in this publication meets the minimum requirements of American National Standards for Information Sciences—Permanence of Paper for Printed Library Materials, ANSI Z39.48-1992.

Annual Reviews and the Editors of its publications assume no responsibility for the statements expressed by the contributors to this *Annual Review*.

TYPESET BY TECHBOOKS, FAIRFAX, VA
PRINTED AND BOUND BY MALLOY INCORPORATED, ANN ARBOR, MI

WHO SHOULD READ THIS SERIES?

The *Annual Review of Environment and Resources* will be a useful resource for researchers and practitioners working on nature-society interactions who want and ought to know the current state of affairs on the topics reviewed, but who do not have the time to cover the individual articles in each of the dozen or so high-impact journals that would need to be read to keep up-to-date. We also hope this annual review will be useful to faculty and students presently using textbooks in environmental science and policy. It will update and provide the most recent take on many of the same issues covered more generally in such texts. In effect, we intend that *Annual Review of Environment and Resources* be used as a rolling textbook or desk reference about environment, resources, and society. Finally, we hope that this journal will count among its readership nonscientists who are professionally charged with making sense of changing environmental issues—for example, journalists, congressional and agency staff, and international organization analysts. We believe that these authoritative, up-to-date reviews will provide key background information at the intersections of science and policy.

Pamela Matson, William Clark, Ashok Gadgil, Daniel Kammen,
Donald Kennedy, Diana Liverman, Rosamond Naylor, and David Schimel

June 16, 2004

Preface

The *Annual Review of Environment and Resources* focuses on the emerging scientific and policy issues at the crux of sustainable development. In Volume 29, the second volume with this focus, we continue to assess critical scientific, policy, technological, and methodological issues related to Earth's global life support systems, sectors of human use of environment and resources, and the human dimensions and management of resources and environmental change. Our goal is for these reviews to provide scholars, practitioners, and policy makers in a range of fields with a thorough and fundamental analysis of the most critical and integrative issues and controversies in the environment and resource arena.

The reviews collected here survey and analyze emerging literature in fast moving and diverse fields. The chapters in the first major section—life support systems—reflect a second generation of critical global science issues. While greenhouse gases, their sources and sinks, and their relation to climate change were the focus of most attention in the first decade of global change research, aerosols have deservedly garnered considerable attention over the past decade. In this volume, Menon reviews the state of knowledge and areas of uncertainty for aerosol sources and dynamics, and he provides a guide to the range of direct and indirect mechanisms of climate forcing by aerosols. The past decade has also seen a blossoming of knowledge about marine ecosystems as well as a growing awareness and concern about the rapid loss of marine species, many of which provide food and economic opportunities for billions of the planet's inhabitants. Effective management of marine ecosystems has been one of the most difficult challenges of our time. In his review, Palumbi provides an integrative tour of current knowledge on population dynamics of marine species and the spatial dimensions of their ecosystems to both help explain the effectiveness of marine preserves and protected areas and to provide insights into better design for future reserves. The third review of this section expands the analysis of global elemental cycles far beyond those elements that have garnered most of the attention in the past several decades (i.e., nitrogen, carbon, phosphorus, and sulfur). Klee & Graedel provide a unique, comprehensive, and thoughtful analysis of the relative importance of anthropogenic versus natural mobilization of most of the elements in the periodic table.

The second major section delves into the patterns, drivers, and consequences of human uses of the environment and Earth's natural resources. In this volume, we present reviews on critical issues in four major sectors of human activity—energy, agriculture, industry and mining, and living resources. Anderson & Newell evaluate the range of options and prospects for carbon capture and storage from fossil-fuel energy sources. This controversial technology both holds the potential to reduce the direct impact of fossil-fuel combustion on global warming and to present new potential risks in terms of long-term sequestration and in terms of its effects on the development of far-reaching climate policies.

Issues of system efficiency and access are key components of the chapter on agricultural plant genetic resources written by Fowler & Hodgkin. The authors explore the state of the world's genetic plant resources—how many do we have, and how are they accessed and used. They conclude that although conservation strategies have been successful, these collections must now be secured and made accessible to a much broader range of users. Horvath discusses the state of knowledge in the area of current and advanced construction materials. He employs life-cycle methods to evaluate the relative economic and environmental costs and benefits of a range of materials, which are becoming increasingly important as the green building and sustainable architecture sectors rapidly expand. Bridge follows with a comprehensive review of mining that takes a social theory approach to a range of environment and sustainability issues, presenting a picture of an evolution, sometimes slow, toward better environmental management capacity and cleaner production techniques. His review evaluates institutional changes that would facilitate the capture of benefits for communities through processes that also lead to increasing corporate, social, and environmental responsibility.

The final chapter in this section focuses on the state of the world's grazing systems and their role in global and regional environmental change. Asner and his coauthors pull together a disparate and fascinating literature on managed grazing systems and the syndromes of change to which they are subject, ultimately presenting a picture of the surprisingly large footprint of these systems on the global environment.

In the third major section of this volume, three reviews explore several dimensions of the management, measurement, and human dimensions of environment and resources; in this year's volume, their common focus is energy. In the first, Kammen & Pacca present a review of the wide range of methods that are used to compute the costs of electricity from the many fuel and energy conversion technologies in use around the world. They pay special attention to the divergent costs that come from these different methods and to the ways these differences are often exploited by those making very different claims of the economic, social, and environmental costs of energy. The second chapter delves into methods and models for analyzing energy policy options. Worrell, Ramesohl, and Boyd explore the design and application of engineering economic models in evaluating the potential effects of policy choices on energy use and economic welfare. They outline the challenges that place new demands on policy analysis, and they argue for new modeling frameworks that extend methods to permit social and policy issues to be treated analytically.

The last two chapters of the volume explore intersections of energy resources with human health, security, and well-being. First, Ezzati and his coauthors provide an interdisciplinary review of the broad range of issues related to human health and energy use, which demonstrates again how pervasive energy uses and impacts are in human society. From the health impacts of traditional biomass cooking, to syndromes and illnesses connected to pollution in modern cities, the authors highlight the emerging set of methodologies available to assess energy-health linkages in both developed and developing nations. Farrell, Zerriffi, and Dowlatabadi review security in the world's oil, gas, electricity, and nuclear power energy systems. After an assessment of the major security issues in each of these areas, they discuss new design approaches toward "survivable systems," focusing on issues related to redundancy, diversity, resilience, decentralization, and distributed control.

These reviews grapple with the challenges and conflicts inherent in meeting people's needs while protecting the resources and environment that we, and future generations, must share. The authors focused on what we know from past research in natural and social sciences and in policy analysis; building on that, they offer suggestions for the way forward. We hope that their reviews foster communication not only among the disciplines that carry out research on issues of environment, energy, and resources, but also with the managers, policy makers, and public who must depend on such information to assist decision making.

Pamela Matson, William Clark, Ashok Gadgil, Daniel Kammen, Donald Kennedy, Diana Liverman, Rosamond Naylor, and David Schimel

June 16, 2004

Annual Review of Environment and Resources
Volume 29, 2004

Contents

I. Earth's Life Support Systems

Current Uncertainties in Assessing Aerosol Effects on Climate,
Surabi Menon — 1

Marine Reserves and Ocean Neighborhoods: The Spatial Scale of Marine Populations and Their Management, *Stephen R. Palumbi* — 31

Elemental Cycles: A Status Report on Human or Natural Dominance, *R.J. Klee and T.E. Graedel* — 69

II. Human Use of Environment and Resources

Prospects for Carbon Capture and Storage Technologies, *Soren Anderson and Richard Newell* — 109

Plant Genetic Resources for Food and Agriculture: Assessing Global Availability, *Cary Fowler and Toby Hodgkin* — 143

Construction Materials and the Environment, *Arpad Horvath* — 181

Contested Terrain: Mining and the Environment, *Gavin Bridge* — 205

Grazing Systems, Ecosystem Responses, and Global Change, *Gregory P. Asner, Andrew J. Elmore, Lydia P. Olander, Roberta E. Martin, and A. Thomas Harris* — 261

III. Management and Human Dimensions

Assessing the Costs of Electricity, *Daniel M. Kammen and Sergio Pacca* — 301

Advances in Energy Forecasting Models Based on Engineering Economics, *Ernst Worrell, Stephan Ramesohl, and Gale Boyd* — 345

Energy Management and Global Health, *Majid Ezzati, Robert Bailis, Daniel M. Kammen, Tracey Holloway, Lynn Price, Luis A. Cifuentes, Brendon Barnes, Akanksha Chaurey, and Kiran N. Dhanapala* — 383

Energy Infrastructure and Security, *Alexander E. Farrell, Hisham Zerriffi, and Hadi Dowlatabadi* — 421

Indexes

Subject Index — 471
Cumulative Index of Contributing Authors, Volumes 20–29 — 493
Cumulative Index of Chapter Titles, Volumes 20–29 — 497

Errata

An online log of corrections to *Annual Review of Environment and Resources* chapters may be found at http://environ.annualreviews.org

Related Articles

From the *Annual Review of Earth and Planetary Sciences*, Volume 32 (2004)

   Yucca Mountain: Earth-Science Issues at a Geologic Repository for High-Level Nuclear Waste, Jane C.S. Long and Rodney C. Ewing

   Multispectral and Hyperspectral Remote Sensing of Alpine Snow Properties, Jeff Dozier and Thomas H. Painter

From the *Annual Review of Ecology, Evolution, and Systematics*, Volume 35 (2004)

   Application of Ecological Indicators, Gerald J. Niemi and Michael E. McDonald

   Ecological Effects of Transgenic Crops and the Escape of Transgenes into Wild Populations, Diana Pilson and Holly R. Prendeville

   Landscapes and Riverscapes: The Influence of Land Use on Stream Ecosystems, J. David Allan

   Avian Extinctions from Tropical and Subtropical Forests, Navjot S. Sodhi, L.H. Liow, and F.A. Bazzaz

   Ecological Responses to Habitat Edges: Mechanisms, Models, and Variability Explained, Leslie Ries, Robert J. Fletcher, Jr., James Battin, and Thomas D. Sisk

   Regime Shifts, Resilience, and Biodiversity in Ecosystem Management, Carl Folke, Steve Carpenter, Brian Walker, Marten Scheffer, Thomas Elmqvist, Lance Gunderson, and C.S. Holling

From the *Annual Review of Entomology*, Volume 49 (2004)

   Long-Term, Large-Scale Biomonitoring of the Unknown: Assessing the Effects of Insecticides to Control River Blindness (Onchocerciasis) in West Africa, Vincent H. Resh, Christian Lévêque, and Bernhard Statzner

   Plant-Insect Interactions in Fragmented Landscapes, Teja Tscharntke and Roland Brandl

From the *Annual Review of Fluid Mechanics*, Volume 36 (2004)

   Vertical Mixing, Energy, and the General Circulation of the Oceans, Carl Wunsch and Raffaele Ferrari

From the ***Annual Review of Microbiology***, Volume 58 (2004)

Endangered Antarctic Environments, Don A. Cowan and Lemese Ah Tow

From the ***Annual Review of Political Science***, Volume 7 (2004)

What Does Political Economy Tell Us About Economic Development—and Vice Versa? Philip Keefer

From the ***Annual Review of Public Health***, Volume 25 (2004)

Emission Trading and Public Health, Alexander E. Farrell and Lester B. Lave

Issues of Agricultural Safety and Health, Arthur L. Frank, Robert McKnight, Steven R. Kirkhorn, and Paul Gunderson

The Current State of Public Health in China, Liming Lee

ANNUAL REVIEWS is a nonprofit scientific publisher established to promote the advancement of the sciences. Beginning in 1932 with the *Annual Review of Biochemistry*, the Company has pursued as its principal function the publication of high-quality, reasonably priced *Annual Review* volumes. The volumes are organized by Editors and Editorial Committees who invite qualified authors to contribute critical articles reviewing significant developments within each major discipline. The Editor-in-Chief invites those interested in serving as future Editorial Committee members to communicate directly with him. Annual Reviews is administered by a Board of Directors, whose members serve without compensation.

2004 Board of Directors, Annual Reviews

Richard N. Zare, *Chairman of Annual Reviews*
  Marguerite Blake Wilbur Professor of Chemistry, Stanford University
John I. Brauman, *J.G. Jackson–C.J. Wood Professor of Chemistry, Stanford University*
Peter F. Carpenter, *Founder, Mission and Values Institute, Atherton, California*
Sandra M. Faber, *Professor of Astronomy and Astronomer at Lick Observatory,*
  University of California at Santa Cruz
Susan T. Fiske, *Professor of Psychology, Princeton University*
Eugene Garfield, *Publisher*, The Scientist
Samuel Gubins, *President and Editor-in-Chief, Annual Reviews*
Steven E. Hyman, *Provost, Harvard University*
Daniel E. Koshland Jr., *Professor of Biochemistry, University of California at Berkeley*
Joshua Lederberg, *University Professor, The Rockefeller University*
Sharon R. Long, *Professor of Biological Sciences, Stanford University*
J. Boyce Nute, *Palo Alto, California*
Michael E. Peskin, *Professor of Theoretical Physics, Stanford Linear Accelerator Center*
Harriet A. Zuckerman, *Vice President, The Andrew W. Mellon Foundation*

Management of Annual Reviews

Samuel Gubins, President and Editor-in-Chief
Richard L. Burke, Director for Production
Paul J. Calvi Jr., Director of Information Technology
Steven J. Castro, Chief Financial Officer and Director of Marketing & Sales

Annual Reviews of

Anthropology	Environment and Resources	Physical Chemistry
Astronomy and Astrophysics	Fluid Mechanics	Physiology
Biochemistry	Genetics	Phytopathology
Biomedical Engineering	Genomics and Human Genetics	Plant Biology
Biophysics and Biomolecular Structure	Immunology	Political Science
	Law and Social Science	Psychology
Cell and Developmental Biology	Materials Research	Public Health
	Medicine	Sociology
Clinical Psychology	Microbiology	
Earth and Planetary Sciences	Neuroscience	
Ecology, Evolution, and Systematics	Nuclear and Particle Science	SPECIAL PUBLICATIONS
	Nutrition	Excitement and Fascination of
Entomology	Pharmacology and Toxicology	Science, Vols. 1, 2, 3, and 4

# CURRENT UNCERTAINTIES IN ASSESSING AEROSOL EFFECTS ON CLIMATE

Surabi Menon

Lawrence Berkeley National Laboratory, Berkeley, California 94720, and NASA Goddard Institute for Space Studies/Columbia University, New York, NY 10025; email: smenon@lbl.gov

Key Words carbonaceous aerosols, aerosol-cloud-climate interactions, climate change, climate predictions

■ **Abstract** The effect of anthropogenic emissions from activities, such as fossil-fuel, biomass, and biofuel burning; transportation; and land-clearing; have a profound impact on the climate system. The impact of these activities is manifested in observed changes in temperature, precipitation, sea-level rise, melting of glaciers, air quality, health, and agriculture yields, to name a few. The obvious question to ask is the role that these different processes play in affecting climate and what action could one impose to curtail or constrain adverse human impacts on climate. Greenhouse gases have long been studied, as they play a major role in changing climate. But over the past 10–20 years, aerosols have emerged as the other big contenders in climate change studies. This review focuses on the current understanding of the effects of aerosols on climate, with an emphasis on the thermodynamical and indirect aerosol effects. We also examine available measurements that could be used to decipher the aerosol influence on climate, with an outlook on how the uncertainties in aerosol effects may impact future climate predictions and policy changes.

CONTENTS

1. INTRODUCTION	1
2. AEROSOL SOURCES AND DISTRIBUTIONS	3
3. ESTIMATES OF AEROSOL EFFECTS ON CLIMATE	5
3.1. Direct Effect	5
3.2. Thermodynamical Effects	7
3.3. Semidirect Effects	11
3.4. Indirect Effects	12
4. OBSERVATIONAL EVIDENCE	14
5. UNDERSTANDING UNCERTAINTIES	15
5.1. Emissions/Distribution	15
5.2. Model Process Treatments	17
5.3. Satellite Retrievals	19
6. PREDICTING FUTURE IMPACTS	20

7. POLICY NEEDS 21
8. SUMMARY 23

1. INTRODUCTION

Human-influenced activity, such as burning of fossil fuel, biofuel, and biomass; land-cover changes; industrial activity; and transportation, can impact climate and may even exceed natural fluctuations within the climate system. However, the exact magnitude of these anthropogenic influences is quite uncertain. Although climate change estimates over the past million years have to be considered to place present-day impacts in context, most reliable estimates of climate change reported are for the past 150 years (the time from the preindustrial revolution to present day). This time period is of relevance because the warmth of the twentieth century appears to be unprecedented during the millennium (1), with several recent years reported to be the warmest on record for the late twentieth century (2). To reconcile temperature trends observed over the past 150 years, which indicate an increase of $\sim 0.6 \pm 0.2$ K, considerable attention was paid to the role of greenhouse gases [which has increased by $\sim 30\%$ since 1850 and continues to increase at $\sim 0.5\%$ to 1% per year over the past few decades (3)] in modifying climate. However, existing discrepancies between model projections of temperature change and surface observations suggest that other factors or processes may also exert significant influence. Solar and volcanic activity no doubt play a major role in influencing climate change over the past millennium, but over the industrial period, CO_2 effects, land-cover changes, and deforestation have become increasingly important (4). Over the past 20 years, however, more attention has been focused on the role of aerosols and aerosol-induced cloud changes as important contenders in the modification of the radiation balance of the Earth-atmosphere system and therefore in climate change scenarios.

Greenhouse gases, ozone, and black carbon (BC) aerosols are usually associated with global warming, whereas aerosols, such as sulfates and organic carbon (OC), and their interaction with clouds result in global cooling. Whereas global warming effects from greenhouse gases and ozone can be quantified fairly well, the magnitude of the effects of aerosols on climate still has a large uncertainty associated with it. The evaluation of the change in cloud properties, both microphysical and radiative, due to the interaction between aerosol particles and clouds presents one of the largest uncertainties in the quantification of the aerosol effects on climate. A large component of the uncertainty is due to the aerosols—sources (biomass, biofuel, and fossil fuel derived) and distribution. To predict the response of the climate to the various imposed forcings and to evaluate the changes in the forcings brought about by policy or emission changes, the primary tools relied on are models. However, model results may be subject to large uncertainties, and it is thus essential that climate change projections be presented more credibly by carefully identifying and quantifying aerosol effects on climate.

Comparing recent projections of greenhouse gas-induced changes (2.5 ± 0.5 W m^{-2}) with recent projections of aerosol-induced changes (0.5 to −4 W m^{-2}), and the change in temperatures since the preindustrial era to present (0.6 ± 0.2) (1) certainly lends credence to the argument that the uncertainty in quantifying the aerosol effect could be a key issue in predicting future temperature changes. Several approaches have been used to estimate the influence of aerosols on climate observationally and theoretically. The impact of volcanic aerosols on temperature records is one example of the effect of aerosols on climate. Several other examples in the past decade (modification of cloud properties in ship tracks, suppression of rainfall from satellite records in polluted air masses, etc.) suggest mounting evidence exists that aerosols are affecting climate in a significant way. Precipitation changes are easier to notice than are temperature changes, especially in arid regions. If aerosols do indeed alter circulation and precipitation patterns, as shown by some recent studies (5–10), it becomes essential for policy-making initiatives to take into account the role of aerosols on climate. To aid policy decisions, credible results that identify, quantify, and reduce the uncertainties in deciphering aerosol climate effects are needed. This review thus focuses on certain key processes that link aerosol effects to climate (primarily those related to the thermodynamical and hydrological processes), availability of related measurements, current uncertainties, future climate impacts, and policy needs. A more comprehensive review on climate change can be obtained from the Intergovernmental Panel on Climate Change (IPCC) report (1), which provides an assessment of climate change for the past, present, and future and is commonly used as a standard reference to understand climate change and its impacts.

2. AEROSOL SOURCES AND DISTRIBUTIONS

Aerosols of interest include sulfates, carbonaceous aerosols (OC and BC), nitrates, sea salt, and dust. Table 1 lists the primary aerosol sources and the range in atmospheric burdens compiled from different models (1, 11) from emission sources. Although carbonaceous aerosols from biofuel burning are prevalent in countries such as India, biofuel emissions are usually not separated from biomass or fossil fuel emissions. This issue will have to be addressed in future emission inventories. The wide range in atmospheric burdens of these aerosols can result in a wide range of forcing estimates that are not related linearly. To narrow the range in forcing estimates would require tighter constraints be placed on the source and distribution of aerosols. This can be quite formidable due to the complexities in quantifying emission sources and in determining the transformation of emissions to particles.

Carbonaceous (OC and BC) aerosols come from similar sources (incomplete combustion from biomass, biofuel, fossil fuel, and dung burning; emissions from diesel engines; etc.) but have different optical properties. OC aerosols are mostly hydrophilic and reflective except for some absorption in the ultra violet (UV) and visible region (12). BC aerosols are hydrophobic but can be hydrophilic as BC particles get coated with other particles as they age. However, unlike OC, BC is

TABLE 1 Range in estimated source strength (Tg aerosol year^{-1}) for present-day aerosols (1, 11)

Type	Source strength
Sulfate	
Industrial	65–92.4
Ocean	10.7–23.7
Aircraft	0.04
Biomass burning	2.0–3.0
Organic carbon	
Fossil fuel	10–20
Biomass	30–45
Black carbon	
Fossil fuel	5.8–6.6
Biomass	6.0–17.2
Nitrates	
Fossil fuel	0.3
Biomass	5.7
Other (human, soils, animal, agriculture)	74.5
Sea salt	
<2 μm	82
>2 μm	2583
Dust	
<2 μm	243
>2 μm	4859

mostly absorbing in the visible and UV region. It is this absorbing property of BC and its effectiveness in warming the atmosphere that could potentially offset, by a small amount, the cooling caused by the other aerosols. Although BC particles are estimated to have a small total global forcing effect of 0.4 to 1 W m^{-2} (13–16), their efficacy as a forcing agent can be high mainly due to their effects on snow albedo (17). Because BC aerosols can affect human health, agricultural yields, precipitation, temperature, and large-scale circulation through thermodynamical, radiative, and microphysical processes, their influence on regional and global climate can be quite significant, especially in areas where BC concentrations are high.

Several techniques and methods are used to detect trends in aerosol burdens. Deposition of aerosols on the surface serves as a useful proxy that can be used to extrapolate information for local aerosol loadings. Ice-core sampling, lake bed sediments, etc. present some evidence of the amount of aerosols present several centuries ago, though these are mainly useful to infer local trends. Estimating SO_2 emissions is relatively straightforward because these depend mostly on the mass of fuel burned and its sulfur content. However, obtaining estimates of BC emissions can be much more complicated. Being a product of incomplete combustion, the amount of BC emitted depends on how efficiently the fuel is burned in addition to the fuel amount. Thus, the mass of BC emitted per unit weight of fuel (emission factor) depends on fuel type (i.e., coal, diesel, and biomass) and other factors that influence the combustion efficiency. This makes BC emissions technology dependent. As an example, coal burned in inefficient stoves and furnaces produces orders of magnitude more BC than the same fuel burned in modern electric power plants. Similarly, coal use for space heating by individual household stoves results in much greater BC emissions than central heating. In industrialized countries during the past half century, moving coal consumption from inefficient to more efficient combustion was the main cause of decreasing BC emissions. Another example of technology effect on emissions is improvement in the diesel engine technology. Emissions from this source have been significantly reduced in many western countries as a result of improved engine design.

Thus, within the past 50 years, such changes in technology in the developed world have led to large reductions in aerosols emitted as compared to emissions in the developing world (18). Transfer of technology from the developed world to the developing world could lead to changes in future emissions that may be more difficult to quantify, thus possibly leading to some discrepancies when estimating changes in aerosol sources for future projections.

Once aerosol emissions are known, changes in particle radii, single scattering albedo as a result of aging, type of fuel burned, and combustion phase need to be quantified carefully (19) to estimate climate forcing. A multimeasurement approach from several platforms (satellites, laboratory, field observations) may serve to constrain the uncertainty associated with aerosol properties—physical and optical. Satellite-based retrievals that distinguish between fine and coarse particles can separate dust from pollution or smoke aerosols (20). Laboratory-based analysis of isotopic composition can also be used to gather information regarding the natural or anthropogenic origin of particles. To estimate past BC fossil fuel emissions, Novakov et al. (18) used annual consumption data for principal BC-producing fossil fuels and BC emission factors separated by source sectors: industrial, residential/commercial, power generation for coal, and transport for diesel fuel. These data sets, obtained for several countries and the rest of the world, were used to provide a time series of temporal trends in BC amounts from 1875 to 2000. The data show the increase from 1875 to 1950 for industrialized countries and their gradual decline in the past few decades in contrast to the data for developing countries (China and India), which indicate a general increase since 1950. Calculated single scattering albedos from Novakov et al. (18) agreed reasonably well with recent observations, and these values can be used to obtain an approximate measure of the degree of cooling or warming caused by aerosols.

3. ESTIMATES OF AEROSOL EFFECTS ON CLIMATE

Both aerosols and greenhouse gases modulate the energy and hydrological cycle. In general, greenhouse gases lead to warmer and wetter climates, whereas sulfates and OC tend to produce cooler and drier climates (21). Being absorbing, BC aerosols cause warmer temperatures (16), and their vertical distribution can affect the magnitude and sign of the surface temperature change and rainfall patterns through thermodynamical changes. Here, we examine the processes—direct, semi-direct, thermodynamical, and indirect—through which aerosols affect climate, paying more emphasis to the latter three, which are more uncertain. We also show some new results from the Goddard Institute for Space Studies (GISS) climate model that relate to aerosol vertical distributions and its impact on the thermodynamical process.

3.1. Direct Effect

The direct effect of aerosols was studied extensively in the late 1980s and early 1990s. This effect refers to the direct scattering or absorption of radiation by aerosol particles without the modification of cloud properties. From the optical characteristics (asymmetry parameter, optical depth, single scatter albedo, etc.) of the aerosols, their size distribution, and changes due to relative humidity effects, the radiative fluxes can be computed. This is relatively uncomplicated, although assumptions such as relative humidity effects on size, sphericity of the particles, transformation of the optical properties for aerosols due to it being internally mixed with other aerosols, vertical location of the aerosols, and the presence of clouds above or below the aerosol layer can affect forcing estimates. Among these, perhaps one of the greatest uncertainties is the increased absorption efficiency of BC when located inside a scattering particle (15, 22), which can change the single scattering albedo of the particle and thereby the sign of the aerosol forcing (18, 23).

Uncertainties in quantifying aerosol emissions and tranformation of emissions to atmospheric burdens, assumptions used in characterizing the physical properties of the aerosols, and the resulting optical properties can each affect estimates of direct forcing calculated by different models. The range of uncertainties associated with all these processes is not well known and hence cannot be characterized accurately. Nakajima et al. (24) found that the direct forcing estimates could vary as much as 40% depending on the optical depth and single scattering albedo used in the radiative transfer code. Their results were based on model simulations, surface radiation measurements, and satellite remote sensing. Variance in the aerosol size distribution was also thought to contribute to a 65% uncertainty in forcing estimates (1). These uncertainties produce wide ranges of forcings estimated by different models depending on the assumptions chosen.

Rather than compare the direct forcing estimates computed by different models, we compare the forcing efficiencies for aerosols, expressed as the ratio of forcing (W m^{-2}) to anthropogenic burden (g m^{-2}), which are given in Haywood & Boucher (11) for several models. These values can be used to estimate the efficacy [effectiveness of a forcing in producing a climate response (16)] of aerosols and thereby the changes that can be expected from controls on emissions of certain aerosol particles.

Forcing efficiency values for sulfate aerosols range from -125 to -460 W g^{-1}. (The direct forcing values range from -0.29 to -0.82 W m^{-2} for sulfate column burdens of 1.14 to 3.3 mg m^{-2}, with lower burdens producing lower forcing values in general.) One can expect that the values for OC are similar to that for sulfates because they are both mainly reflective in the visible spectrum. However, for fossil fuel BC aerosols, forcing efficiencies vary from 1123 to 3000 W g^{-1}. (The direct forcing for fossil fuel BC ranges from 0.17 to 0.42 W m^{-2} for column burdens of 0.13 to 0.16 mg m^{-2}.) Separate model estimates are not available for BC alone from biomass burning because these also include OC. The forcing efficiency for both BC and OC from biomass burning ranges from −80 to −210 W g^{-1}. (The direct forcing ranges from −0.14 to -0.74 W m^{-2} for column burdens of 1.76 to 3.7 mg m^{-2}.) Clearly, the forcing efficiency for BC surpasses that of sulfate and OC by several orders of magnitude.

Thus, it is not the abundance of the aerosols but their efficacy that provides an estimate of the change in forcing for given aerosol burdens. Sato et al. (23) find that climate forcing from BC, regardless of its mixing state, can be ∼1 W m^{-2}, most of which is anthropogenic. The authors base their estimates on a climate model with BC climatologies tuned to match the results from retrievals based on AERONET (a network of calibrated sunphotometers distributed globally) optical depths for aerosol absorption. The method used by Sato et al. (23) to validate model BC climatology for two aerosol transport models (based on the information of multiwavelength multiangle measurements from AERONET and Mie scattering calculations, which are used to obtain the spectral characteristics of the aerosols of interest) indicates that model BC climatologies and inferred absorption are lower than measurements by a factor of 2 to 4. Because knowledge of the atmospheric burden of BC as well as its optical properties can be quite uncertain, the methodology presented by the authors provides a rather useful measure to infer the degree of absorption present in the atmosphere and evaluate the ability of climate models to account for that absorption. This can be used to refine model estimates that may be incorrect either due to inadequate representation of physical processes that distribute BC or due to poor emission sources.

3.2. Thermodynamical Effects

For absorbing aerosols, changes in surface forcing relative to values of forcing at the top of the atmosphere can have a significant impact on evaporation, latent heating, and the hydrologic cycle. This feeds back to the aerosol distribution due to changes in aerosol scavenging through precipitation. Here, we discuss changes in the monsoon that may be attributed to aerosol effects. We focus on the Asian monsoon because it is a large dynamical system that affects a region with one third of the world's population. There have been several studies that have attempted to quantify precipitation changes for the Asian monsoon from doubled CO_2 or increased sulfates. For a doubled CO_2 scenario, increased rainfall and greater warming over the Asian continent than over the Indian Ocean was related to increased water content (horizontal transport and precipitation efficiency) rather than to changes in circulation (25), whereas a slight weakening (related to land-sea contrasts) for the

Indian summer monsoon was found if sulfate aerosols were included (first indirect effect only) (26). Based on observational data, Xu (27) linked the southward shift of the Chinese monsoon to the direct radiative effects of sulfate aerosols over China. Observational evidence from the Indian Ocean Experiment (INDOEX) field study by Ramanathan et al. (6, 21) indicate a regional scale warming of approximately 1 K in the lower atmosphere over the tropical Indian Ocean and land surface cooling of approximately 0.5 to 1 K. These changes and redistribution of heat within the boundary layer were thought to have a strong impact on tropical circulation and interhemispheric precipitation patterns, and they were related to the presence of absorbing aerosols over the Indian subcontinent (9). Another study found that the trends in summer precipitation over China—North China droughts, South China floods—considered to be the largest observed in several decades, were related to the increased aerosol emissions observed over East Asia in recent years (10). These trends were attributed to changes in vertical temperature profiles, stability, and vertical velocity fields from absorbing aerosols, which were thought to increase/decrease cloud cover and precipitation in the south/north of China.

Also of relevance are changes in surface fluxes. Meehl (28) suggests that greater forcings over land (due to lowered surface albedo) can enhance land-sea temperature contrasts and result in a stronger monsoon. However, results from Srinivasan (29) indicate that the monsoon can be adequately represented by three parameters, net radiation at the top of the atmosphere, evaporation, and the vertical stability of the atmosphere, without any dependence on land-sea contrasts. These results were based on a simple thermodynamic model. Thus, because the absorptive properties of BC aerosols can influence the net surface radiation budgets (30), and because the surface energy budget is a primary energy source for the Asian summer monsoon (31), accounting for BC aerosol effects on surface fluxes is important.

Since much less is known about aerosol vertical distribution than the horizontal distribution, theoretical investigations to illustrate the importance of aerosol vertical profiles have to be relied on. This has implications for aerosols released from fossil fuel use (mostly confined to the lower boundary layer but may be transported to higher levels owing to deep convection) and from biomass burning (where emissions often reach the midtroposphere). We used model simulations following a similar strategy as Menon et al. (10) wherein climate changes are calculated using the GISS GCM for simulations with aerosols distributed over China and India/Indian Ocean on the basis of inferred measurements compared with simulations with aerosols that have $\sim$0.1 optical depth. For simplicity, a single scattering albedo of 0.85 for aerosols composed of sulfates, organics, and BC was used, as in Menon et al. (10). This simulation is referred to as Exp A. The aerosol vertical distribution is that from Koch (32) (obtained from an aerosol transport model coupled to the GISS GCM). To illustrate the impact of the vertical distribution of aerosols on climate, we chose experimental setups (Exp L1 to L8) in which aerosols were completely confined in a single model layer, beginning with the first and extending up to the eighth model layer, i.e., eight different setups were used. Values for pressure and height corresponding to model midlevels for the first eight layers are

TABLE 2 Values of midlevel pressure and height for the different model vertical levels

Level	Pressure (hPa)	Height (km)
1	959	0.42
2	894	1.1
3	787	2.1
4	635	3.8
5	470	6.4
6	338	8.4
7	248	10.5
8	180	12.6

in Table 2. Results are confined to these levels because biomass burning emissions can extend up to 10–12 km (33) with peak values usually between 2–6 km.

Most of the Exp A results are in Menon et al. (10), and for brevity we describe the main results as applies to the intercomparison with Exp L1 to L8. We focus on Exp A, L1, L4, and L7 to illustrate key differences in simulations. Whereas surface radiation budgets and surface fluxes are negative for absorbing aerosols, top of the atmosphere fluxes are positive, and the atmospheric column gets heated (∼0.3 K/day) (10). The atmosphere is unstable for aerosols confined to the lowest model layer, with stability increasing as aerosols get distributed to higher levels. Depending on the location of the absorbing aerosol radiative heating/cooling rates, vertical motions, cloud cover, and convection respond quite differently, as we demonstrate below.

Evaporation, land-sea contrasts, surface fluxes, moisture convergence, and convective activity control the precipitation field to a large extent. However, in our simulations, increased summer precipitation over southeastern China is not accompanied by increased evaporation, except in Exp L1 (implying soil moisture does not increase); land-sea contrasts do not play a major role [shown in (10)]. The change in net surface heat flux (defined as the sum of the net surface radiation, latent and sensible heat fluxes, and cooling caused by melting/sublimation) indicate less heat flux for southern China (18–34 N) compared with northern China (34–50 N), with net radiation being the dominant contributor (mainly from reduced surface shortwave radiation). Larger negative values for aerosols at higher levels (<550 hPa) (Exp L5 to L8) correspond to cases with the largest increase and decrease in precipitation (Figure 1, see color insert). To aid the interpretation of the features in Figure 1, the change in the vertical profiles of cloud cover (Figure 2, see color insert) and temperature are examined. Whereas the overall cloud cover increases in Exp A, for Exp L1 to L8 cloud cover decreases in the layer where heating occurs [in conformation with the semidirect effect (34, 35)], except for aerosols at higher levels (<550 hPa). For Exp L1 and L2, reduced values of atmospheric heating and surface solar flux intensifies the low-level inversion that slows convection and cloud formation. For Exp L5 to L8, cloud cover decreases only in northern China, with overall increases in cloudiness at all levels for southern China. This is related to the strong updrafts (not shown) that dominate southern portions of China for aerosols at higher levels (<550 hPa), which also exhibit stronger heating gradients between the upper and lower atmospheres. Thus, strong convective activity appears to be the dominant mechanism that produces the precipitation patterns that are observed. Increased updrafts and the increased availability of moisture through circulation changes (not shown) result in increased vertical extent of convection, increased relative humidity, and increased precipitation. Observational evidence of changes in cloudiness due to smoke was also found for the 1991 Kuwait oil fire (36). The intense absorption of solar radiation by smoke induced convection and cloud formation, with roots at the top of the smoke layer that appeared to dominate the cloud evaporation caused by smoke-induced solar heating.

Values for the semidirect and direct effect (Exp A, L1, L4, and L7) over China and India are in Table 3. As can be seen for southern China, the magnitude of the semidirect effect increases as aerosols get distributed to higher levels, and the total forcing (semidirect + direct) for Exp A is ~-1.3 W m^{-2}. Positive semidirect forcings are obtained for aerosols at lower levels and negative values for aerosols at higher levels (<550 hPa) for all regions. For northern China and India, the total forcing remains positive for all cases and is $\sim+2.2$ W m^{-2} for Exp A (because cloud cover increase is not as much as over southern China). These findings agree with the results from Penner et al. (37), who found negative semidirect effects for aerosols confined at higher levels.

The above results imply that the strength of convection (caused by changes in the temperature profiles) and the enhanced BC absorption in the presence of clouds may compete with each other in a way that could either offset or enhance the presence of clouds, which in turn affects temperature and radiation. Observational or experimental verification of enhanced BC absorption either in clouds or when BC is mixed with other aerosols is not well known, and therefore more efforts

TABLE 3 Mean values of the semidirect and direct effects over China and India

Experiment	Semidirect (W m^{-2}) 2S–30N 60–100E	Semidirect (W m^{-2}) 18–34N 90–130E	Semidirect (W m^{-2}) 34–50N 90–130E	Direct (W m^{-2}) 2S–30N 60–100E	Direct (W m^{-2}) 18–34N 90–130E	Direct (W m^{-2}) 34–50N 90–130E
Exp A	−2.05	−8.04	−2.74	4.33	6.73	4.9
Exp L1	2.35	1.62	0.32	−1.20	−0.36	0.24
Exp L4	−1.53	−4.20	−7.28	6.29	8.40	8.33
Exp L7	−7.97	−33.8	−5.9	17.1	17.9	12.6

are needed to quantify these effects. Sato et al. (23) have found that existing BC inventories used in climate models to produce BC absorption optical depths do not match AERONET observations unless the absorption efficiency of BC is higher than currently thought, which suggests internally mixed BC particles.

Greater changes in simulated temperature, radiation, and precipitation for aerosols confined below ~550 hPa (above ~3700 m) suggest that climate effects of absorbing aerosols are stronger when they are located at higher levels in the atmosphere. This would apply to biomass emissions that are usually injected at higher altitudes, unless lower-level aerosol emissions get transmitted to higher levels through deep convection. High aerosol loadings at high altitudes observed over east Asia during the Aerosol Characterization Experiment (ACE)-Asia by Mader et al. (38) indicate that convective activity can enhance transport of the aerosols to higher levels, and because most of the Asian emissions are low-level fossil and biofuel generated (with a large proportion of BC) (39), they can have significant effects on climate. The role of convection is also of relevance in view of results from Fromm & Servranckx (40), who found that increased stratospheric aerosol amounts may arise from convective transport of boreal biomass burning. Model simulations of observed precipitation and temperature trends over China match observations mainly due to the effect of absorbing aerosols at higher levels, as was indicated by the series of simulations (Exp L1 to L8).

Thus, these results suggest that greater emphasis should be placed in obtaining realistic vertical profiles of aerosol distributions, which in turn determine the amount of energy and moisture available in the atmosphere.

3.3. Semidirect Effects

To differentiate between the direct (changes in radiation without cloud modification) and indirect (changes due to aerosol-cloud interactions) effect of aerosols on climate, we discuss two processes by which absorbing aerosols affect climate: (*a*) the effect that leads to the evaporation of clouds through solar heating of the boundary layer by absorbing aerosols such as BC, termed the semidirect effect (34), and (*b*) a process termed indirect soot forcing (17), which refers to the change in snow albedo due to BC aerosols. The semidirect aerosol effect has not been considered by IPCC (1) but may be quite significant based on the results of Hansen et al. (34) (who found an increase in radiation at the surface due to cloud evaporation that was important locally) and Ackerman et al. (35) (who found that daytime trade cumuli cloud cover could be reduced by almost one half due to solar absorption by aerosols). However, Penner et al. (37) point out that the negative longwave forcings of carbonaceous aerosol emissions (of which soot is a component) that are injected at higher atmospheric levels may cancel out the positive forcings usually associated with the semidirect forcing (because they can increase cloudiness at lower levels, which would decrease temperatures), and thus the semidirect effect associated with carbonaceous aerosols may not act to warm climate. To verify the positive or negative forcing associated with the semidirect effect requires better information on aerosol and cloud vertical profiles, which is only now being obtained as is discussed in Section 4.

Another potentially important climate effect of soot is its impact on snow albedo. Using a general circulation model and empirical data on soot amount in snow, Hansen & Nazarenko (17) estimate that soot effects on snow and ice albedos result in a forcing of ~ 0.3 W m^{-2} for the Northern Hemisphere and find the efficacy of this forcing to be approximately twice as effective as CO_2 in altering global surface air temperatures. Furthermore, they suggest that this soot effect may have contributed to the past century's global warming, melting land ice and permafrost, early arrival of spring in the Northern Hemisphere, and thinning Artic sea ice. The estimated subjective uncertainty in soot albedo forcing effects (accounting for the uncertainty in snow albedo and soot content measurements, absorption efficiency for internally mixed snow and soot, and relative contribution of the anthropogenic part of soot) could be factor of two. However, the authors argue that the soot-snow albedo effects are large because they exclude other factors (effects of darker surfaces in late winter and spring when higher overhead sun may magnify the absorption efficiency and prolong melt season) that may magnify soot snow albedo effects. Furthermore, they suggest that to avoid dangerous anthropogenic interference (DAI) levels within the climate system, additional global warming should not exceed 1 K. Thus, steps taken to reduce soot emissions will not only reduce surface temperatures but will also restore snow albedos to pristine values, thereby increasing the negative forcing effects of snow (17).

3.4. Indirect Effects

For climate change estimates, evaluating the dynamical, microphysical, and radiative changes in cloud properties due to aerosol-cloud interactions remains challenging. Hygroscopic aerosols that serve as efficient cloud condensation nuclei can increase cloud droplet number concentrations (CDNC) and reduce cloud droplet sizes if cloud liquid water content (LWC) remains unchanged (41)—the first indirect effect. Measurements from various field studies (42–47) and satellite retrievals (48–52) corroborate these effects. A consequence of smaller droplet sizes is that they do not grow large enough to participate in cloud droplet coalescence processes, inhibiting precipitation formation and increasing cloud liquid water path (LWP) and cloud lifetime (53)—the second indirect effect. However, it is not yet clear if the cloud water increases, decreases, or stays constant with increasing CDNC (51, 54–56). Satellite data analyses by Han et al. (55) indicate seasonal and regional variabilities. If LWP does not stay constant, the cloud susceptibility [change in the reflectivity of the clouds as a function of CDNC (57)] gets reduced, implying less sensitivity to pollution (55). Because most satellite-based estimates of the indirect effect are related to the change in cloud droplet effective radius (r_{eff}) with pollution, understanding causes of variability between cloud droplet radius and cloud liquid water (which are more controlled by dynamical changes) may be quite important when evaluating changes in r_{eff} with pollution (58).

The increase in precipitation due to the presence of large particles that can enhance the amount of precipitation-sized droplets and increase coalescence, or the decrease in precipitation due to the presence of small particles that do not grow to larger sizes, can have several notable consequences when determining cloud water budgets. Rosenfeld et al. (59) find that although increased pollution can suppress precipitation over land, for polluted deep-ocean clouds with high surface winds the presence of larger sea salt particles can act to cleanse the cloud of pollution by triggering precipitation [also corroborated by findings from Rudich et al. (60) based on satellite retrievals, which suggest that large salt-containing dust particles from the Aral Sea increase cloud droplets to sizes that are likely to precipitate, thus increasing rainfall in these regions] and reducing CDNC and cloud albedo. Rosenfeld et al. (59) suggest that this mechanism could be the likely cause for larger r_{eff} for the same aerosol index over land and ocean as reported by observational studies [such as that of Bréon et al. (61)].

Changes in LWP are an important consideration when evaluating the aerosol indirect effects. However, LWP and precipitation fields are often hard to predict because model parameterization of the autoconversion process (self-collection of cloud droplets) that determines the onset of precipitation is obtained from cloud-resolving models even though spatial scales vary dramatically. Multiscaling efforts required to treat these cloud physical processes in a GCM have not yet been explored adequately, leading to problems in most models when predicting precipitation fields (62).

Estimates of the indirect effects from the various climate models indicate a large range, from -0.5 to -4.4 W m^{-2}. Some of these higher values may be too large based on observed temperature changes over the past 150 years. Rotstayn & Penner (63) estimate climate sensitivity parameters for both the first and second indirect effect (from sulfates only) to be 0.78 and 0.7 K m^2 W^{-1}. These are comparable to the climate sensitivity parameters derived for the direct sulfate and $2 \times CO_2$ forcings of 0.69 and 1.01 K m^2 W^{-1} from the same model, and therefore these indirect effects are quite critical for climate change studies. In addition to these radiative and hydrological effects, the indirect aerosol forcing was also thought to substantially alter low-latitude circulation and rainfall based on results from Rotstayn & Lohmann (8), who used a mixed-layer ocean model coupled to an atmospheric model. They found that the near-global quasi-hemispheric pattern of contrasting SST (sea surface temperature) anomalies associated with trends in the drying conditions found in the Sahel may have some contribution from the indirect effect, although they only include sulfate aerosols in their analysis.

The magnitude of the first indirect effect is quite sensitive to the change in droplet concentration (64–69), whereas that of the second indirect effect is sensitive to model treatment of the autoconversion or precipitation parameterizations (64, 66, 67, 69, 70). Lohmann & Lessins (71) suggest that the combined value of the first and second indirect effect of -1.28 W m^{-2} over the oceans, predicted by their climate model, may be overestimated by as much as a factor of 1.3 based on slopes of r_{eff} and the aerosol index obtained from Polarization and Directionality of the

Earth's Reflectance (POLDER) (61). They cite a new global value of -0.8 W m^{-2} for the indirect effect. This is within the range of forcing (0 to -1.2 W m^{-2}) for the indirect aerosol effect based on observed historical surface temperature range or that derived from an analysis of observed changes and model predictions (72). However, these results can only be used to constrain indirect forcing estimates if they are based on physical mechanisms. Lohmann & Lessins (73) further point out that the difference in slopes over land and ocean that they obtained and corrected relative to satellite retrievals may be due to differences in cloud macrophysical properties (cloud LWP, cloud base, and thickness). Thus, using satellite retrievals to constrain model results is a worthy exercise provided caution is used when analyzing satellite retrievals, as is discussed in Section 5.3.

4. OBSERVATIONAL EVIDENCE

Analyses of estimates of changes in cloud properties based on satellite retrievals reveal several facets of the relationship that may exist between cloud top temperature, effective radii, CDNC, LWP, and cloud radiative properties such as cloud optical depth and cloud albedo.

Early investigations of the aerosol indirect effect from analysis of satellite retrievals concentrated on statistical means between cloud droplet effective radii, cloud optical depth, and column number concentration (49, 50, 74). Slowly, the importance of changing LWP gained prominence (as discussed in Section 3.4) as some studies (75) suggested a violation of Twomey's definitions of the indirect effect (smaller droplet sizes implying greater reflectivity). This was mainly due to variations in LWP that were not found to be constant but were found to vary depending on locations and seasons (52, 55), although other studies did not report such implied variability in LWP (51, 54). Furthermore, other studies report changing cloud top temperature along with LWP with increasing aerosol number concentrations (76). Rosenfeld (5, 77) provides some evidence of changing r_{eff} and cloud top temperatures for different cloud systems to link the increased pollution with smaller droplet sizes and decreased precipitation. Liu et al. (78) find that over the Indian Ocean region for similar values of cloud LWP, a north-south gradient in CDNC (a factor of $\sim$2.5 increase in CDNC for the north) is visible based on remotely sensed data collected by aircrafts during INDOEX, with decreases in radii of up to 2 μm for the north compared to the south. A more recent study from Sekiguchi et al. (79) does not find any correlation between cloud top temperature and aerosol number concentrations, although they do not preclude some correlation that may be more dependent on particle radius. They also found positive correlations between cloud optical thickness and cloud cover with aerosol number concentrations. Suzuki et al. (80), in their comparison of GCM cloud fields with that of Advanced Very High Resolution Radiometer (AVHRR) retrievals, found that the positive and negative correlations between LWP and aerosol concentration (N_a) may be balanced on a global scale due to the competing effects of increased cloud lifetime and increased aerosol scavenging, whereas LWP tends to have a negative correlation with N_a when using a parameterization that does not incorporate the cloud lifetime effect (i.e., when the precipitation parameterization does not have a dependence on the aerosols).

These results from various groups listed above present some contrasting evidence regarding aerosol effects on cloud microphysics and optics that may arise due to cloud sampling issues (56): assumptions used in the analysis of diagnostics, seasons, location, circulation effects, etc. What is clearly needed is a careful evaluation of cloud properties sampled in similar meteorological settings for a few locations around the globe where meteorology effects may be minimized so that some signal due to aerosol effects on clouds may emerge. This will help establish the nature of the changes in cloud properties solely due to aerosols.

The relationship and competition between cloud lifetime and aerosol scavenging by clouds are manifested locally, thereby precluding general conclusions on a global scale. Regional variability in aerosol distribution results in regional changes that are difficult to capture when using coarse resolution models. Previously, longer time-change climate integrations required coarse grid models due to the computational expense when running long simulations. However, as computational efficiencies improve, models can now use finer grid scales, and therefore future climate simulations should concentrate on comparing regional-scale changes with observations rather than solely investigating global-scale features. Although field studies are useful to compare with models, global coverage from satellite data are needed to verify the global impacts. Satellite data are available from late 1978 [International Satellite Cloud Climatology Project (ISCCP), Total Ozone Mapping Spectrometer (TOMS)] and can be used to decipher impacts over the past two decades. However, global-scale retrievals are not always feasible because some of the present-era satellites (e.g., AVHRR, available since the mid-1980s) provide valuable information mainly over oceans due to the difficulty in obtaining optical properties of land surfaces. Penner et al. (81) also found that three different analyses of optical depths from AVHRR differ by ~0.1 optical depth units mainly due to assumptions used in the retrievals. Cloud screening can also be an issue when analyzing satellite retrievals and could lead to different estimates (0.1 or larger for aerosol optical depths) for the same sets of retrievals (82). With the advent of polarization instrumentations, such as POLDER-1 and -2 (83) and the Research Scanning Polarimeter (RSP) (84) (which are able to provide more information regarding the size, shape, and refractive index of aerosol particles over land), accurate global-scale aerosol retrievals are becoming more feasible. Vertical information is usually more difficult to obtain, but for the first time vertical aerosol profiles will slowly be available through the NASA Geoscience Laser Altimeter System (GLAS) lidar measurements on the Ice Cloud and land Elevation Satellite (ICESat), which was launched in January 2003.

Encouragingly, an intercomparison of existing satellite products from MODIS (Moderate Resolution Imaging Spectroradiometer) or MISR (Multiple Imaging Spectroradiometer) with AVHRR, TOMS, POLDER, ATSR (Along Track

Scanning Radiometer), or GLI (Global Imager) can be performed to constrain aerosol climatology products (85). This is mainly possible due to the apparent lack of sensitivity of measurements to the time of the day (the lifetime of aerosols are of the order of a few days, and the relationship between aerosol loading and synoptic scale meteorological processes are largely independent of diurnal cycles) (85).

5. UNDERSTANDING UNCERTAINTIES

5.1. Emissions/Distribution

Accounting for sources, sinks, and transport of aerosol properties is complex, and therefore some uncertainty is bound to remain when estimating aerosol budgets, especially for carbonaceous aerosols. BC emissions are usually calculated from fuel consumption data differentiated by the utilization sectors and appropriate emission factors. Several compilations of sector-segregated BC emission factors have been published. Many of these emission factors were obtained from particulate mass and assumed BC mass fractions. Estimated uncertainties in these emission factors range from a factor of two to a factor of eight (86). Dickerson et al. (87) have found that BC estimated from fuel use and known emission factors yields values (0.7 Tg year^{-1}) that are much lower than those estimated from ambient concentrations (2–3 Tg year^{-1}). It is desirable to ascertain how realistic the emission factors are for BC emissions inventories. This can be accomplished by extensive direct source sampling and comparing model-derived and measured BC concentrations.

Directly measured BC emission factors have only recently been reported for a few related sources (88). These are, of course, characteristic of the technologies and locations where such measurements were done. It is difficult and perhaps even impossible to extend such measurements to all sources found in environments with different fuels and combustion technologies. Even if this were possible, the derived emissison factors would be applicable only to the present conditions and not those that have existed in the past. Several studies used BC emission inventories in global models to estimate BC concentrations and compared those with measured ambient values. Model-simulated and mean measured concentrations were generally within about a factor of two at some sites, with greater discrepancies at other sites (89). A more precise comparison is not feasible because of the lack of systematic BC concentration measurements worldwide because existing measurements were obtained at different time periods using different analytical methods.

To develop adequate mitigation strategies, consensus must be achieved regarding the uncertainty in aerosol radiative forcing estimates from either changes in aerosol distribution or aerosol physical process treatments. Considerable uncertainty exists in emission estimates for BC from biomass burning and can be even as high as $\pm 700\%$ (86). These uncertainties should be quantified separately among models that may use similar aerosol distribution to better separate the contribution to aerosol forcing from aerosol effects or from aerosol process treatment effects. However, a major complexity that may remain is the determination of the contribution of carbonaceous aerosols to forcing. The OC versus BC fractions that come about from fossil fuel, biofuel, or biomass burning will be a crucial factor in determining forcing estimate changes for the future and in developing climate mitigation strategies (90). Guazzotti et al. (91) found a 74% biomass/biofuel contribution to submicrometer carbonaceous aerosols for the Indian subcontinent, whereas for air masses from the neighboring Arabian Peninsula, there was a 63% contribution to the carbonaceous aerosols from fossil fuel use. Novakov et al. (39) also found greater fossil fuel contribution to the aerosols over the Indian subcontinent based on a two-week study during the INDOEX field study and suggests that seasonality may play a strong role in determining the contribution of fossil fuel or biomass/biofuel to the total aerosol burdens. This variability in aerosol source type has also been reported by several observationally based studies (92–95). Differences in fuel use lead to different ratios of, for example, sulfate to BC because sulfate emissions from biomass/biofuel are typically smaller than that from fossil fuel sources. Emphasis on detailed gas and particle phase measurements is required globally and on a temporal basis to account for regional differences in aerosol emissions and particles that form from them.

5.2. Model Process Treatments

Current uncertainties in model treatments of the aerosol effects include limitations in representing cloud-scale processes on model grid scales that are typically several times larger; effects of cloud updrafts on the activation of aerosol particles; relative humidity effects that affect the aerosol size distribution; knowledge of the optical properties of internally mixed aerosols; lack of thorough understanding of aerosol effects on ice nucleation processes; cloud droplet size dispersion effects (96); dynamical influences that may mask aerosol effects on clouds, which require decoupling feedbacks from forcings; and analyzing the extent that anthropogenic perturbations can influence natural dynamical changes, such as the El Niño and North Atlantic Oscillations (97), to name a few.

Here, we focus on the indirect effect because it has the largest uncertainty and is perhaps one of the largest contributors to climate change estimates. In Table 4, we indicate values from different models for the first and second indirect effect for different aerosol species. They range from -0.4 to -3.2 W m^{-2} depending on the process used in the models to represent the indirect effects. The difficulty in narrowing the wide range of the indirect effects predicted by the different models arises because model treatment of the coupling between aerosols and cloud droplet number, and in the parameterization of aerosol effects on precipitation, differ considerably. Differences exist between mechanistic and empirical treatments of cloud droplet number predictions (62), which may be partly related to inadequacies in model subgrid vertical velocity field diagnostics (which are usually derived from subgrid turbulence fields), although both methods are capable of providing an adequate treatment of cloud droplet number activated from aerosols. The IPCC (1) estimates almost a factor of three uncertainty in the indirect forcing estimate on

TABLE 4 Average values of the indirect effect in W m^{-2} estimated by different models for the listed aerosol species and for all aerosols, given as the difference between simulations with present-day aerosols and that with preindustrial aerosols

Reference	All	Sulfate	OC	BC
Ghan et al. (66)	—	−1.7 to −3.2	—	—
Jones et al. (67)	—	−0.5 to −1.5	—	—
Rotstayn (98)	—	−2.1	—	—
*Kiehl et al. (68)	—	−0.4 to −1.78	—	—
*Williams et al. (7)	—	−1.37	—	—
*Chuang et al. (65)	−1.85	−0.30	OC + BC = −1.51	—
Lohmann et al. (64)	−1.1 to −1.9	−0.4	OC + BC = −0.9 to −1.3	—
Menon (This work)	−2.29	−1.78	−1.87	−1.61

*models that simulate the first aerosol indirect effect only. OC and BC stand for organic and black carbon, respectively.

the basis of the nucleation and growth partitioning of sulfate mass. Another difference between model estimates of the indirect forcing arises due to the way the background aerosol burden is prescribed. Model estimates of the aerosol indirect effect are based on simulations that distinguish between preindustrial and present-day aerosol emissions. Although this serves as a useful indicator of the relative contribution of the aerosol-cloud effects to the total climate forcing since industrialization, comparison of the estimates with different climate models is difficult in view of the wide range used to represent the preindustrial aerosol concentrations that produce wide ranges in forcings (64–67, 69). For example, simulations with the GISS GCM for the first indirect effect (with sulfates, sea salt, and OC aerosols) with a minimum CDNC = 10 cm^{-3} was −2.1 W m^{-2}, whereas that for CDNC = 40 cm^{-3} was −1.1 W m^{-2}. This difference of 1 W m^{-2} is quite large and regionally can change the surface temperature response from a positive to a negative, as shown in Figure 3 (see color insert). At present, it is not possible to quantify what this background amount is, but observations can be used as a guideline to provide some constraints. During the second Aerosol Characterization Experiment (ACE-2), held in Tenerife in 1997, the minimum average CDNC values in adiabatic cloud parcels was ∼50 cm^{-3}, although values of ∼10 to 20 cm^{-3} have been measured in pure marine background air with no wind (J.-L. Brenguier, personal communication). Although this may apply to the ACE-2 region in the Atlantic Ocean, satellite retrievals of baseline aerosols (99) may also be used to infer background values for CDNC on a global scale.

In addition to these uncertainties that may arise due to the treatment of the coupling between aerosols and CDNC/precipitation, certain other process treatments also can contribute to the aerosol indirect effects. Boers & Mitchell (100) describe a mechanism whereby the albedo enhancement for thin clouds may be reduced, whereas that for an optically thick cloud can increase due to an absorption

CURRENT UNCERTAINTIES C-1

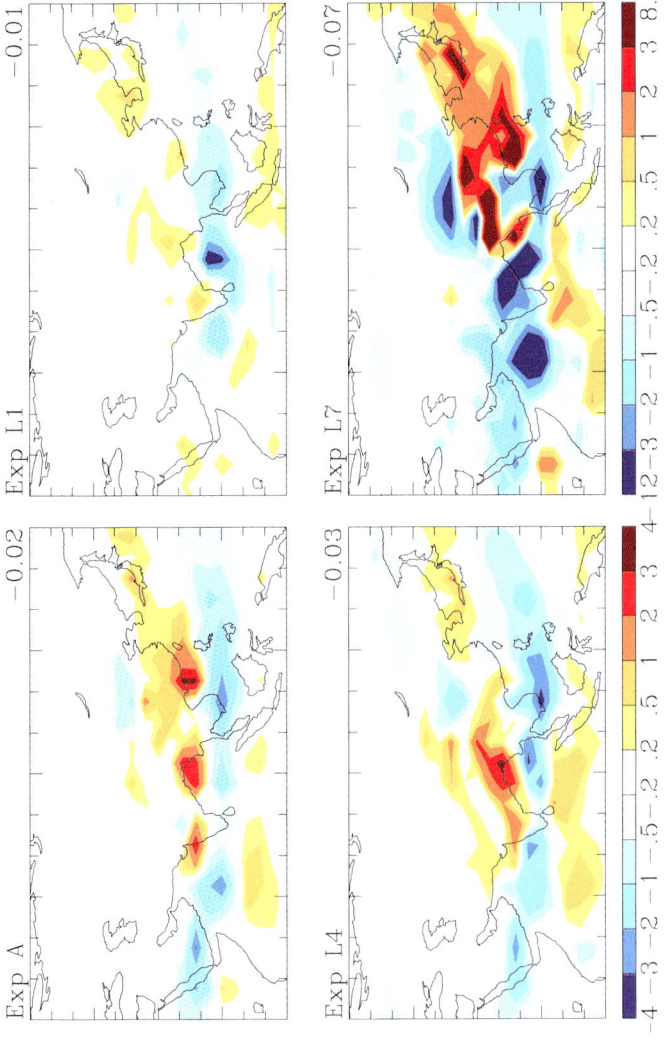

Figure 1 Simulated changes in precipitation fields (millimeter/day) for June-July-August for Exp A, L1, L4, and L7.

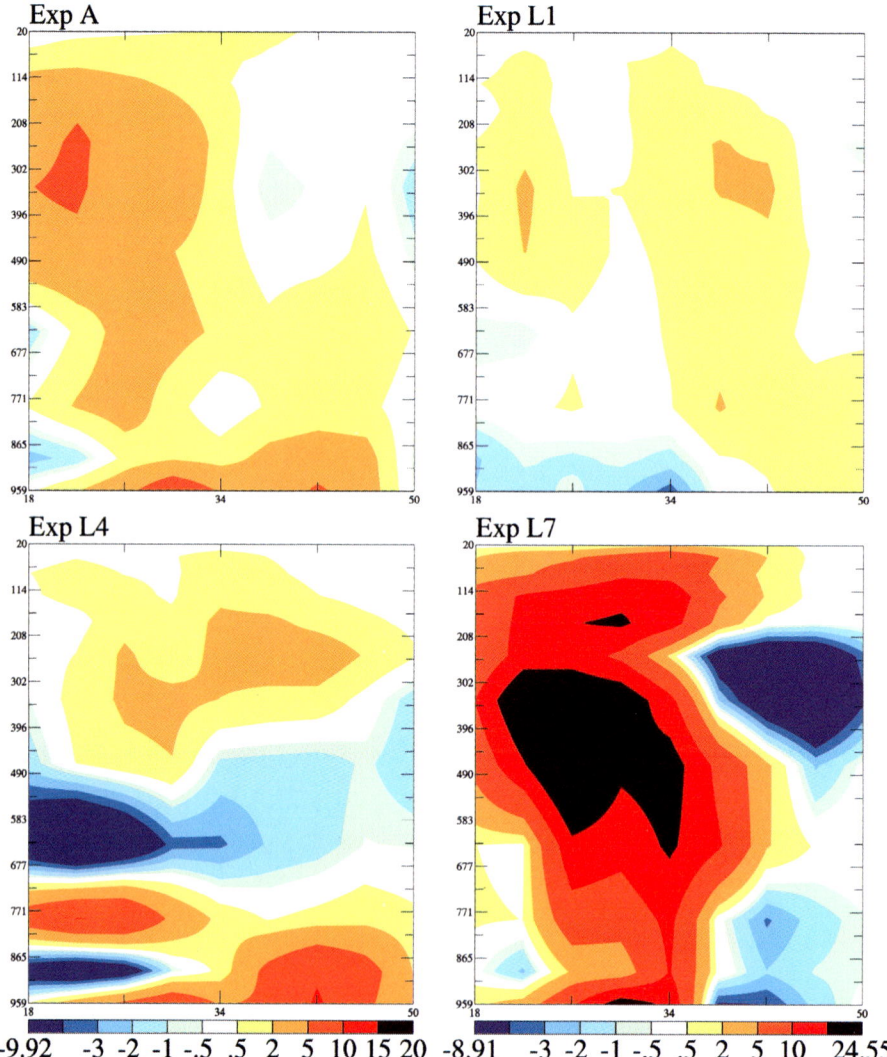

Figure 2 Similar to Figure 1 but for vertical profiles of total cloud cover change (%). Values extend from 2S to 62N and are averaged from 90 to 130E.

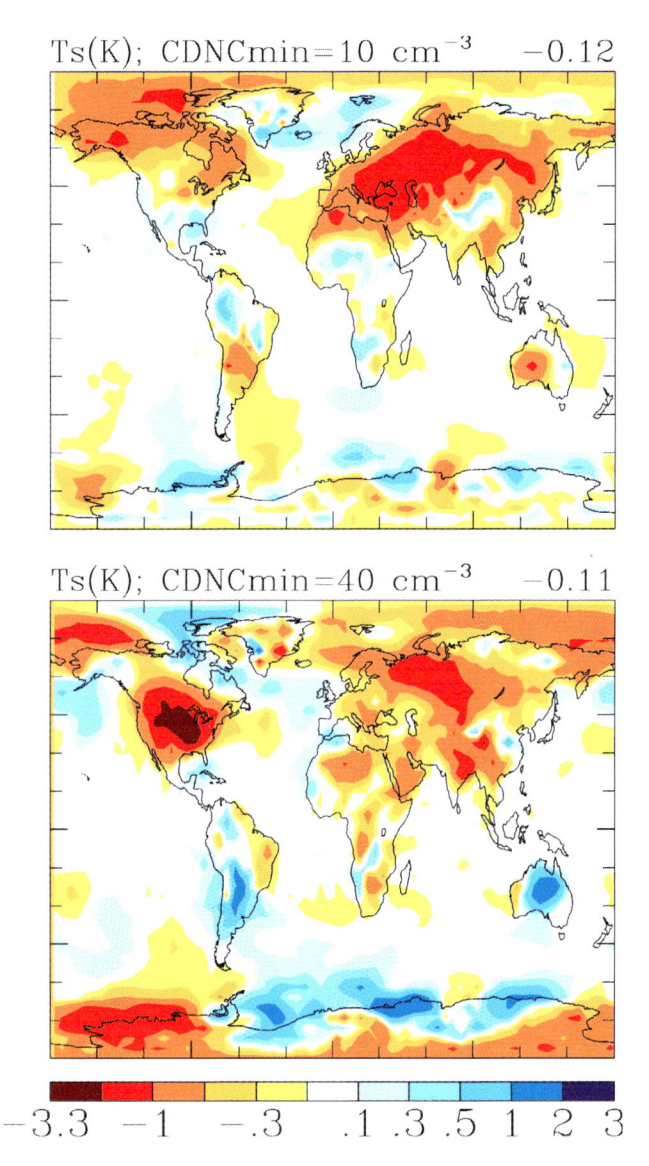

Figure 3 Changes in simulated surface temperature (Ts) for the first indirect effect for a minimum value of cloud droplet number concentration (CDNC) = 10 cm^{-3} and when CDNC = 40 cm^{-3}. Changes are for present-day versus preindustrial aerosol distributions. Global means are on the upper right-hand corner.

feedback effect that is based on the thermodynamic tendency of a cloud to stabilize itself against changes in absorption of solar radiation when cloud microphysics is affected through increased CDNC. This link between the convective and radiative nature of the cloud depends on the amount of convective mixing and the changes in the cloud thickness and therefore will depend on the extent to which the cloud thickness is diagnosed accurately. Most climate models diagnose a cloud thickness that is the same as the layer thickness of the model, i.e., the vertical extent of the cloud is assumed to be the same as the model layer height. For coarse resolution models this would be a drawback, as marine stratocumulus clouds, which cover a large portion of the Earth, are usually not as thick, with optical thickness ranging between 1 and 15 (100).

Most GCM estimates for the indirect effect are for warm nonconvective clouds. Parameterizations that represent aerosol effects on cold clouds are now being developed. The first such global results are from Lohmann et al. (101), who investigated volcanic aerosol effects on cirrus clouds and effects of soot on cirrus clouds (102). However, detailed observations of aerosol types that affect ice-cloud nucleation are still relatively rare, and mechanisms that promote homogeneous or heterogeneous freezing of ice nuclei are still being investigated.

The lack of schemes in GCMs that represent aerosol effects on all cloud types could also hamper comparison of model products with satellite products. As an example, Suzuki et al. (80) analyzed cloud $r_{\it eff}$ from a GCM and satellite and found that model results were closer to satellite retrievals over the ocean, but larger differences were evident over land locations and the tropics where deep and shallow convective clouds are more common. Because their treatment of the indirect effect was for warm nonconvective clouds, this difference over the tropics is not too surprising. So far, the only GCM estimate of the effect of aerosols on convection is that from Nober et al. (103), who investigated precipitation changes in convective clouds due to aerosol effects and found local changes in precipitation and latent heat release in areas where convective precipitation dominates (areas with strong biomass burning), which in turn affect convective heating, vertical temperature profiles, and global circulation.

Thus, omission of certain types of processes—aerosol effects on cold stratiform clouds and on all convective cloud types—and weakness in certain model diagnostics, such as updraft velocity and cloud thickness, can further exacerbate differences between various model aerosol indirect effect estimates, which makes it difficult to reconcile model cloud products with those from satellite retrievals.

5.3. Satellite Retrievals

Because aerosol-climate observations from field studies lack spatial detail, satellite retrieved observations over the past 20 years can be used to help reduce present uncertainties in aerosol climate effects. Once models and satellite data agree, extrapolating to the past or predicting the future should be less ambiguous.

Changes in cloud properties over land and ocean due to aerosol effects are implied by observations. These are usually reproduced in model simulations but may be a result of assumed differences in background conditions used in models. Differences also arise from the treatment of supersaturation, size distribution, and hygroscopicity of the aerosol particles that affect CDNCs (104). To identify mechanisms that may cause the implied changes in cloud properties over land versus ocean, assumptions used in satellite retrievals need to be analyzed carefully. Factors such as meteorology, cloud LWP variability, decoupling of the boundary layer, types of aerosols, and the type of clouds sampled by particular satellite sensors [e.g., AVHRR data misses optically thin and broken clouds over land, whereas POLDER is biased toward optically thin and less turbulent clouds (105)] have to be considered. This could help generate a more useful data set from the various satellite sensors that can then be used to draw inferences regarding aerosol effects on clouds.

6. PREDICTING FUTURE IMPACTS

When projecting future climate change based on IPCC emission scenarios or any other future emission projections, the range in climate sensitivity is important. Climate sensitivity refers to the temperature increase if CO_2 were to double and the climate allowed to reach equilibrium. The negative climate forcing due to reflective aerosols and the aerosol-cloud effects could act to mitigate the temperature increase. Most climate models report climate sensitivities between 2.1 to 4.6 K (1). Although it is more difficult to obtain accurate climate sensitivities for short time spans (for a century or so), Knutti et al. (72) obtain a climate sensitivity of ~4.6 K for surface temperature changes over the past century. Uncertainties of -1.5 to 1.5 K were attributed to model uncertainties and -1.3 to 2.6 K to uncertainties in the data. Additional uncertainties are thought to be present due to the uncertainties in radiative forcing. Knutti et al. (72) also find low estimates for climate sensitivity when ignoring the indirect aerosol effects and higher climate sensitivities when including a strong aerosol indirect effect. Using the 1906–1995 temperature records to constrain forcings during this time period, Forest et al. (106) estimate that the net forcing for aerosols whose forcing patterns are similar to that of sulfates (ozone, BC, OC, aerosol indirect effects) should be less than -0.95 W m^{-2}, much lower than IPCC (1) estimates. This net magnitude of -0.95 W m^{-2}, however, does not distinguish between positive and negative forcings, and thus does not provide sufficient constraints regarding the forcing efficacies for the various aerosols.

Key questions regarding the magnitude of future temperature or precipitation changes that affect climate and in turn influence policy changes are dependent on the certainty with which climate change due to certain aerosol species can be projected. Whereas the SO_2 emissions are expected to decline in the future, NO_x as well as carbonaceous emissions are expected to increase (1). Although these are mainly reflective aerosols, they could influence regional more than global climate because nitrates may be more prevalent in locations that do not have as much sulfate. Estimates of changes in radiative forcing for 2000–2050 based on the Hansen & Sato (107) trends in aerosol and greenhouse gas burdens versus IPCC estimates are in Figure 4. The figure indicates that the forcing from air pollutants can be greatly reduced (e.g., BC and ozone forcings) if BC and ozone emissions decline or do not exceed current levels, in contrast to the larger increases predicted by IPCC. This difference, coupled with the reduced forcing from CO_2 (flat CO_2 emissions in the "alternative scenario" of Hansen & Sato, versus, 4%/year growth estimated by IPCC) lead to a total forcing estimate of 0.85 W m^{-2} for the next 50 years (from 2000) if the Hansen & Sato scenario emerges. Every 1 W m^{-2} forcing can produce a 3/4°C change in temperature [based on the GISS GCM climate sensitivity (16)]. Every degree of warming is linked to a certain increase (subject to a large uncertainty) in sea-level rise [projected to be rising partly due to thermal expansion of the oceans due to warming and partly due to the melting of glaciers (1)]. This would imply that future projections of forcing estimates, which are used to predict changes in temperature, sea-level, etc., should be based on careful analysis of existing uncertainties and its range. Future aerosol-climate effect simulations should thus also include interactive feedbacks between aerosol processes that affect climate and the changing climate, which could in turn affect aerosol emissions.

7. POLICY NEEDS

Most integrated assessment models [e.g., the Mini-Climate Assessment Model of Edmonds et al. (108)] use only greenhouse gases and sulfate aerosols to obtain estimates of impacts of climate change on the economy or environment. This may be unrealistic (J. Sathaye, personal communication) in view of the larger projected impact of carbonaceous aerosols and the change in future ratios of reflective versus absorbing aerosols. The combined estimate and the uncertainty in the aerosol forcing effects implies that a more stringent analysis needs to be undertaken when making impact forecasts.

Jacobson (109) presents a quantitative analysis on controls of BC and OC versus greenhouse gases in controlling warming and the time period over which measures would be effective. He finds that reduction in emissions of fossil fuel BC and associated OC may slow warming more than any reductions in CO_2 and CH_4 for a specific period. To eliminate 20%–45% of net warming within 3–5 years, all fossil fuel BC and OC would have to be eliminated, and to achieve similar reductions in warming, approximately one third of CO_2 emissions would have to be eliminated, although the reduced warming would not come into effect for 50–200 years. Jacobson also calculates the warming due to gasoline versus diesel engines, and he finds that tax laws that promote diesel use may actually increase warming unless stringent emission controls are applied to diesel engines, which may shorten the warming period. Although this study provides useful measures on impacts of fossil fuel BC and OC versus greenhouse gases, the results and

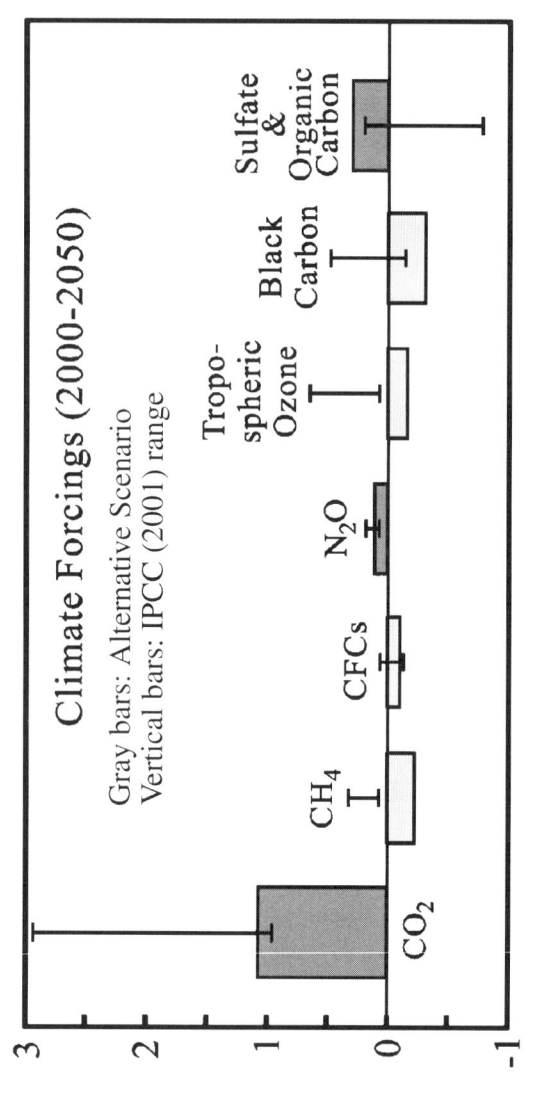

Figure 4 Climate forcings for 2000–2050 based on the "alternative scenario" of Hansen & Sato (107) and from the IPCC scenario (1). [Reprinted with permission of Hansen & Sato (107).]

assumptions used to derive the results need to be further quantified and assessed by other models so that appropriate measures may be taken to evaluate the impacts of diesel fuel use (110–112).

Diesel engine emissions should be quantified not only by weight but also by particle number and chemical content. Limitations of emissions by weight alone may make it relatively easy for engine manufactures to eliminate the largest and heaviest particles, whereas it is the smallest particles with the longest lifetimes that are more harmful to human health (113). Even though efficient particle traps for vehicles may reduce aerosol particles emitted, without fuel efficiency, controls on CO_2 will remain unchecked. Because effects from the unrealized warming [estimated to be approximately 0.5 K (3, 114)] of accumulated concentrations of long-lived greenhouse gases persist for several decades, attention should still be focused on CO_2 and other greenhouse gases. On the short term, benefits from reduction in aerosols—human health, visibility, acid rain, agriculture, etc.—may outweigh those from controls on CO_2. However, future temperatures may increase if aerosol levels are reduced and greenhouse gas levels remain unchanged.

To reduce harmful anthropogenic influences on climate, a global response on several different levels is needed. For example, incentives to coal manufacturers to help them reduce coal emissions and switch to cleaner-burning technologies may be a better alternative to costly litigations that may ensue once public concern with air pollution gains more prominence in the coming years. Issues related to air quality and health may thus be a primary motivating factor that may help reduce emissions.

8. SUMMARY

Although the quantification of the effect of anthropogenic activity on climate is uncertain, observational evidence related to aerosol effects on climate suggests that this aerosol effect is real. To avoid harmful impacts on the environment—melting of glaciers, sea-level rise, droughts, floods, change in growing season, reduction in visibility, air pollution, etc.—remedial action ought to be taken to control the human contribution to these impacts. These include application of appropriate standards in industrial activity; agricultural practices; coal, biofuel, and dung burning; and transportation. Because these are undoubtedly tied to economic activity, mitigation efforts to minimize human influence on climate have to be taken with great care. To guide policy experts on the range of steps that would be needed to reduce emissions, accurate climate change scenarios are needed.

To arrive at a reasonable consensus regarding the actual magnitude of anthropogenic influence on climate requires a more integrated understanding of how the processes that affect climate are connected to each other. This process is still under development in most climate models, as models are getting more and more sophisticated in their process treatments. For example, predictions on the effects of aerosols and greenhouse gases on the hydrological cycle were usually made through separate projections, and rarely were the two effects combined. Even when the effects of greenhouse gases and aerosols are combined, both aerosol indirect effects are usually not incorporated. Because the prediction of rain and LWP budgets by models remain challenging, adequate treatment of the precipitation process is necessary before we can make improved predictions on changes in water budgets (both atmospheric and surface). Also relevant is the aerosol-temperature feedback that results in lower aerosol burdens in a warmer climate due to the linkage between temperature changes and the hydrological cycle (115).

Present estimates of aerosol influence on climate—through the direct, semidirect, thermodynamical, indirect effects, and associated feedbacks—range from $+0.8$ to -2.4 W m^{-2}, with an implied value of -1.0 W m^{-2} (range from -0.5 to -2 W m^{-2}) for the aerosol indirect effect (107). Here, we use a value of -2.1 W m^{-2} as an upper bound to the indirect forcing estimate (based on the last two estimates given in Table 4 because they include most aerosol types and both the indirect effects). Combining the positive and negative forcings gives us values of -1.6 or -2.7 W m^{-2} (for implied values of -1.0 or -2.1 W m^{-2}, respectively, for the indirect effect) for the net aerosol effect. Placing these magnitudes in the context of other forcings, such as greenhouse gases, land use, solar activity, and volcanic aerosol effects, which add up to ~3.35 W m^{-2} (107), results in a contribution of $\sim50\%$ to 80% from the aerosol effect to the forcing from others.

However, as we have summarized in this review, this estimate can be uncertain (*a*) due to the various processes that affect aerosol distributions—both horizontal and vertical—and (*b*) due to the transformation of the emissions to particles that in turn affect the radiation and other climate diagnostics through the direct, semidirect, thermodynamcial, and indirect effect processes represented in models. In this regard, a multiplatform-based approach that makes use of satellite, meteorological, and process-based observations (field and laboratory) and the integration of these results in climate models are clearly needed to resolve various diagnostics used to decipher climate trends. Integrated assessments can then be reliably made regarding climate change impacts.

ACKNOWLEDGMENTS

The author thanks Jim Hansen for several insightful comments and guidance on the various aspects of this work, Tica Novakov for his valuable contribution in understanding and elucidating the role of carbonaceous aerosols on climate both historically and in this work, and Tony Del Genio for his thought provoking comments on the aerosol indirect effect. The author also thanks Larrisa Nazarenkov for contributions to the model simulations/results pertaining to the thermodynamical effects of aerosols. The author acknowledges support from the following NASA projects: Global Water and Energy Cycle Project under M. Jasinski and the Global Modeling and Analysis Program under T. Lee, and the Laboratory Directed Research and Development Program of Lawrence Berkeley National Laboratory.

The *Annual Review of Environment and Resources* is online at
http://environ.annualreviews.org

LITERATURE CITED

1. IPCC. 2001. In *Climate Change 2001: The Scientific Basis*, ed. TJ Houghton, Y Ding, DJ Griggs, M Noguer, pp. 289–348. Cambridge, UK: Cambridge Univ. Press
2. Hansen J, Ruedy R, Sato M, Lo K. 2002. Global warming continues. *Science* 295:275
3. Karl TR, Trenberth KE. 2003. Modern global climate change. *Science* 302:1719–23
4. Bauer E, Claussen M, Brovkin V, Huenerbein A. 2003. Assessing climate forcings of the Earth system for the past millennium. *Geophys. Res. Lett.* 30:1276
5. Rosenfeld D. 1999. TRMM observed first direct evidence of smoke from forest fires inhibiting rainfall. *Geophys. Res. Lett.* 26:3105–8
6. Ramanathan V, Crutzen PJ, Lelieveld J, Mitra AP, Althausen D, et al. 2001. The Indian Ocean Experiment: An integrated analysis of the climate forcing and effects of the great Indo-Asian haze. *J. Geophys. Res.* 104:2223–31
7. Williams KD, Jones A, Roberts DL, Senior CA, Woodage MJ. 2001. The response of the climate system to the indirect effects of anthropogenic sulfate aerosol. *Clim. Dyn.* 17:845–56
8. Rotstayn LD, Lohmann U. 2002. Tropical rainfall trends and the indirect aerosol effect. *J. Clim.* 15:2103–16
9. Chung CE, Ramanathan V, Kiehl JT. 2002. Effects of south Asian absorbing haze on the northeast monsoon and surface-air heat exchange. *J. Clim.* 15:2462–76
10. Menon S, Hansen J, Nazarenko L, Luo Y. 2002. Climate effects of black carbon aerosols in China and India. *Science* 297:2250–53
11. Haywood J, Boucher O. 2000. Estimates of the direct and indirect radiative forcing due to tropospheric aerosols: A review. *Rev. Geophys.* 38:513–43
12. Kirchstetter TW, Novakov T. 2004. Differences in the wavelength dependence of light absorption by aerosols emitted from urban sources and burning biomass. *Atmos. Environ.* In review
13. Haywood JM, Ramaswamy V. 1998. Global sensitivity studies of the direct radiative forcing due to anthropogenic sulfate and black carbon aerosols. *J. Geophys. Res.* 103:6043–58
14. Myhre G, Stordal F, Restad K, Isaksen I. 1998. Estimates of the direct radiative forcing due to sulfate and soot aerosols. *Tellus B* 50:463–77
15. Jacobson MZ. 2000. A physically-based treatment of elemental carbon optics: Implications for global direct forcing of aerosols. *Geophys. Res. Lett.* 27:217–20
16. Hansen J, Sato M, Nazarenko L, Ruedy R, Lacis A, et al. 2002. Climate forcings in GISS SI2000 simulations. *J. Geophys. Res.* 107(D18):4347
17. Hansen J, Nazarenko L. 2004. Soot climate forcing via snow and ice albedos. *Proc. Natl. Acad. Sci. USA* 101:423–28
18. Novakov T, Ramanathan V, Hansen JE, Kirchstetter TW, Sato M, et al. 2003. Large historical changes of fossil-fuel black carbon aerosols. *Geophys. Res. Lett.* 30(6):1324
19. Eck TF, Holben BN, Reid JS, O'Neill NT, Schafer JS, et al. 2003. High aerosol optical depth biomass burning events: A comparison of optical properties for different source regions. *Geophys. Res. Lett.* 30:2035
20. Kaufman YJ, Tanre D, Boucher O. 2002. A satellite view of aerosols in the climate system. *Nature* 419:215–23

21. Ramanthan V, Crutzen PJ, Kiehl JT, Rosenfeld D. 2001. Aerosols, climate and the hydrological cycle. *Science* 294:2119–24
22. Chylek P, Hallett J. 1992. Enhanced absorption of solar radiation by cloud droplets containing soot particles in their surface. *Q. J. R. Meteorol. Soc.* 118:167–72
23. Sato M, Hansen J, Koch D, Lacis A, Ruedy R, et al. 2003. Global atmospheric black carbon inferred from AERONET. *Proc. Nat. Acad. Sci. USA* 100:6319–24
24. Nakajima T, Sekiguchi M, Takemura T, Uno I, Higurashi A, et al. 2003. Significance of direct and indirect radiative forcings of aerosols in the East China Sea region. *J. Geophys. Res.* 108:8658
25. Douville H, Royer K-F, Polcher J, Cox P, Gedney N, et al. 2000. Impact of doubling CO_2 on the Asian summer monsoon: Robust versus model-dependent responses. *J. Meteor. Soc. Jpn.* 78:421–39
26. Roeckner EL, Bengtsson L, Feichter J, Lelieveld J, Rodhe H. 1999. Transient climate change simulations with a coupled atmosphere-ocean GCM including the tropospheric sulfur cycle. *J. Clim.* 12:3004–32
27. Xu Q. 2001. Abrupt change of the midsummer climate in central east China by the influence of atmospheric pollution. *Atmos. Environ* 35:5029–40
28. Meehl GA. 1994. Influence of the land surface in the Asian summer monsoon external conditions. *J. Clim.* 7:1033–49
29. Srinivasan J. 2001. A simple thermodynamic model for seasonal variation of monsoon rainfall. *Curr. Sci.* 80:73–77
30. Satheesh SK, Ramanathan V. 2000. Large differences in the tropical aerosol forcing at the top of the atmosphere and Earth's surface. *Nature* 405:60–63
31. Iwasaki T, Kitagawa H. 1998. A possible link of aerosol and cloud radiation to Asian summer monsoon and its implications in long-range numerical weather prediction. *J. Meteorol. Soc. Jpn.* 76:965–82
32. Koch D. 2001. The transport and direct radiative forcing of carbonaceous and sulfate aerosols in the GISS GCM. *J. Geophys. Res.* 106:20311–32
33. Anderson BE, Grant WB, Gregory GL, Browell EV, Collins JE, et al. 1996. Aerosols from biomass burning over the tropical South Atlantic region: Distribution and impacts. *J. Geophys. Res.* 101:24117–37
34. Hansen J, Sato M, Ruedy R. 1997. Radiative forcing and climate response. *J. Geophys Res.* 102:6831–64
35. Ackerman AS, Toon OB, Steven DE, Heymsfield AJ, Ramanathan V, Welton EJ. 2000. Reduction of tropical cloudiness by soot. *Science* 288:1042–48
36. Rudich Y, Sagi A, Rosenfeld D. 2003. Influence of the Kuwait oil fires plume (1991) on the microphysical development of clouds. *J. Geophys. Res.* 108:4478
37. Penner JE, Zhang SY, Chuang CC. 2003. Soot and smoke aerosol may not warm climate. *J. Geophys. Res.* 108:4657
38. Mader BT, Flagan RC, Seinfeld JH. 2002. Airborne measurements of atmospheric carbonaceous aerosols during ACE-Asia. *J. Geophys. Res.* 107:4704
39. Novakov T, Andreae MO, Gabriel R, Kirchstetter TW, Mayol-Bracero OL, Ramanathan V. 2000. Origin of carbonaceous aerosols over the Indian Ocean: Biomass burning or fossil fuels? *Geophys. Res. Lett.* 27:4061–64
40. Fromm MD, Servranckx R. 2003. Transport of forest fire smoke above the tropopause by supercell convection. *Geophys. Res. Lett.* 30:1542
41. Twomey S. 1977. The influence of pollution on the shortwave albedo of clouds. *J. Atmos. Sci.* 34:1149–52
42. Leaitch WR, Banic CM, Isaac GA, Couture MD, Liu PSK, et al. 1996. Physical and chemical observations in marine stratus during 1993 NARE: Factors

controlling cloud droplet number concentration. *J. Geophys. Res.* 101:29123–35
43. Borys RD, Lowenthal DH, Wetzel MA, Herrera F, Gonzalez A, Harris J. 1998. Chemical and microphysical properties of marine stratiform cloud in the north Atlantic. *J. Geophys. Res.* 103:22073–85
44. Brenguier J-L, Pawlowska H, Schuller L, Preusker R, Fischer J, Fouquart Y. 2000. Radiative properties of boundary layer clouds: Droplet effective radius versus number concentration. *J. Atmos. Sci.* 57:803–21
45. Menon S, Saxena VK. 1998. Role of sulfates in regional cloud-climate interactions. *Atmos. Res.* 4748:299–315
46. Menon S, Saxena VK, Durkee P, Wenny BN, Nielsen K. 2002. Role of sulfate aerosols in modifying the cloud albedo: A closure experiment. *Atmos. Res.* 61:169–87
47. Feingold G, Eberhard WL, Veron DE, Previdi M. 2003. First measurements of the Twomey aerosol indirect effect using ground-based remote sensors. *Geophys. Res. Lett.* 30(6):1287
48. Kaufman YJ, Fraser RS. 1997. Control of the effect of smoke particles on clouds and climate by water vapor. *Science* 277:1636–39
49. Han Q, Rossow WB, Chou J, Welch RM. 1998. Global survey of the relationships of cloud albedo and liquid water path with cloud droplet size using ISCCP data. *J. Clim.* 11:1516–28
50. Han Q, Rossow WB, Chou J, Welch RM. 2000. Near-global survey of cloud column susceptibility using ISCCP data. *Geophys. Res. Lett.* 27:3221–24
51. Coakley JA, Walsh CD. 2002. Limits to the aerosol indirect radiative effect derived from observations of ship tracks. *J. Atmos. Sci.* 59:668–80
52. Schwartz SE, Harshvardsan, SE, Benkovitz CM. 2002. Influence of anthropogenic aerosol on cloud optical depth and albedo shown by staellite measurements and chemical transport modeling. *Proc. Natl. Acad. Sci. USA* 99:1784–89
53. Albrecht BA. 1989. Aerosols, cloud microphysics, and fractional cloudiness. *Science* 245:1227–30
54. Nakajima T, Higurashi A, Kawamoto K, Penner JE. 2001. A study of correlation between satellite-derived cloud and aerosol microphysical parameters. *Geophys. Res. Lett.* 28:1171–74
55. Han Q, Rossow WB, Zeng J, Welch RM. 2002. Three different behaviors of liquid water path of water clouds in aerosol-cloud interactions. *J. Atmos. Sci.* 59:726–35
56. Ackerman AS, Toon OB, Steven DE, Coakley JA Jr. 2003. Enhancement of cloud cover and suppression of nocturnal drizzle in stratocumulus polluted by haze. *Geophys. Res. Lett.* 30:1381
57. Twomey S. 1991. Aerosols, clouds and radiation. *Atmos. Res.* 65:109–28
58. Brenguier J-L, Pawlowska H, Schuller L. 2002. Cloud microphysical and radiative properties for parameterization and satellite monitoring of the indirect effect of aerosol on climate. *J. Geophys. Res.* 108:8632
59. Rosenfeld D, Lahav R, Khain A, Pinsky M. 2002. The role of sea spray in cleansing air pollution over ocean via cloud processes. *Nature* 297:1667–70
60. Rudich Y, Khersonsky O, Rosenfeld D. 2002. Treating clouds with a grain of salt. *Geophys. Res. Lett.* 29:2060
61. Bréon F-M, Tanre D, Generoso S. 2002. Aerosol effect on cloud droplet size monitored from satellite. *Science* 295:834–38
62. Menon S, Brenguier J-L, Boucher O, Davison P, Del Genio AD, et al. 2003. Evaluating aerosol/cloud radiation process parameterizations with single-column models and ACE-2 cloudy column observations. *J. Geophys. Res.* 108:4762
63. Rotstayn LD, Penner JE. 2001. Indirect aerosol forcing, quasi forcing and climate response. *J. Clim.* 14:2960–74

64. Lohmann U, Feichter J, Penner J, Leaitch R. 2000. Indirect effect of sulfate and carbonaceous aerosols: A mechanistic treatment. *J. Geophys. Res.* 105:12193–206
65. Chuang CC, Penner JE, Prospero JM, Grant KE, Rau GH, Kawamoto K. 2002. Cloud susceptibility and the first aerosol indirect forcing: Sensitivity to black carbon and aerosol concentrations. *J. Geophys. Res.* 107:4564
66. Ghan S, Easter R, Hudson J, Bréon F-M. 2001. Evaluation of aerosol indirect forcing in MIRAGE. *J. Geophys. Res.* 106:5317–34
67. Jones A, Roberts DL, Woodage MJ, Johnson CE. 2001. Indirect sulphate aerosol forcing in a climate model with an interactive sulphur cycle. *J. Geophys. Res.* 106:20293–310
68. Kiehl JT, Schneider TL, Rasch PJ, Barth MC, Wong J. 2000. Radiative forcing due to sulfate aerosols from simulations with the National Center for Atmospheric Research Community Climate Model Version 3. *J. Geophys. Res.* 105:1441–57
69. Menon S, Del Genio AD, Koch D, Tselioudis G. 2002. An evaluation of the sulfate and carbonaceous aerosol indirect effect using the GISS coupled chemistry-climate model and satellite observations. *J. Atmos. Sci.* 59:692–713
70. Rotstayn LD. 2000. On the tuning of autoconversion parameterizations in climate models. *J. Geophys. Res.* 105:15495–507
71. Lohmann U, Lesins G. 2002. Stronger constraints on the anthropogenic indirect aerosol effect. *Science* 298:1012–15
72. Knutti R, Stocker TF, Joos F, Plattner G-K. 2002. Constraints on radiative forcing and future climate change from observations and climate model ensembles. *Nature* 416:719–23
73. Lohmann U, Lesins G. 2003. Comparing continental and oceanic cloud susceptibilities to aerosols. *Geophys. Res. Lett.* 30:1791
74. Chameides WL, Luo C, Saylor R, Streets D, Huang Y, et al. 2002. Correlation between model-calculated anthropogenic aerosols and satellite-derived cloud optical depths: Indication of indirect effect? *J. Geophys. Res.* 107:4085
75. Schuller L, Brenguier J-L, Pawlowska H. 2003. Retrieval of the microphysical, geometrical, and radiative properties of marine stratocumulus from remote sensing. *J. Geophys. Res.* 108:8631
76. Harshvardhan, H. Schwartz SE, Benkovitz CM, Guo G. 2002. Aerosol influence on cloud microphysics examined by satellite measurements and chemical transport modeling. *J. Atmos. Sci.* 59:714–25
77. Rosenfeld D. 2000. Suppression of rain and snow by industrial pollution. *Science* 287:1793–96
78. Liu GS, Shao HF, Coakley JA, Curry JA, Haggerty JA, Tschudi MA. 2003. Retrieval of cloud droplet size from visible and microwave radiometric measurements during INDOEX: Implication to aerosols' indirect effect. *J. Geophys. Res.* 108:4006
79. Sekiguchi M, Nakajima T, Suzuki K, Kawamoto K, Higurashi A, et al. 2003. A study of the direct and indirect effects of aerosols using global satellite data sets of aerosol and cloud parameters. *J. Geophys. Res.* 108:4699
80. Suzuki K, Nakajima T, Numaguti A, Takemura T, Kawamoto K, Higurashi A. 2004. A study of the aerosol effect on a cloud field with simultaneous use of GCM modeling and satellite observation. *J. Atmos. Sci.* 61:179–94
81. Penner JE, Zhang SY, Chin M, Chuang C, Feichter J, et al. 2002. A comparison of model and satellite derived aerosol optical depth and reflectivity. *J. Atmos. Sci.* 59:441–60
82. Mischenko MK, Geogdzhayev I, Cairns B, Rossow WB, Lacis AA. 1999. Aerosol retrievals over the ocean using channel 1 and 2 AVHRR data: A sensitivity analysis and preliminary results. *Appl. Opt.* 38:7325–41
83. Bréon F-M, Goloub P. 1998. Cloud

droplet effective radius from space-borne polarization measurements. *Geophys. Res. Lett.* 25:1879–82

84. Chowdhary J, Cairns B, Mishchenko M, Travis L. 2001. Retrieval of aerosol properties over the ocean using multispectral and multiangle photopolarimetric measurements from the Research Scanning Polarimeter. *Geophys. Res. Lett.* 28:243–46

85. Kaufman YJ, Holben BN, Tanre D, Slutsker I, Smirnov A, Eck TF. 2000. Will aerosol measurements from Terra and Aqua polar orbiting satellites represent the daily aerosol abundance and properties. *Geophys. Res. Lett.* 27:3861–64

86. Streets DG, Yarber KF, Woo J-H, Carmichael GR. 2003. Biomass burning in Asia: Annual and seasonal estimates and atmospheric emissions. *Glob. Biogeochem. Cycl.* 17:1099

87. Dickerson RR, Andreae MO, Campos T, Mayol-Bracero OL, Neusuess C, Streets DG. 2002. Analysis of black carbon and carbon monoxide observed over the Indian Ocean: Implications for emissions and photochemistry. *J. Geophys. Res.* 107:8017

88. Bond TC, Streets DG, Yarber KF, Nelson SM, Woo J-H, Klimont Z. 2004. A technology-based global inventory of black and orgnaic carbon emissions from combustion. *J. Geophys. Res.* 109:doi: 101029/2003JD003697

89. Cooke WF, Ramaswamy V, Kasibhatla P. 2002. A general circulation model study of carboncaeous aerosol distribution. *J. Geophys. Res.* 107:4279

90. Hansen JE, Bond T, Cairns B, Gaeggeler H, Liepert B, et al. 2004. Carbonaceous aerosols in the industrial era. *AGU EOS Newsl.* 85(25):1

91. Guazzotti SA, Suess DT, Coffee KR, Quinn PK, Bates TS, et al. 2003. Characterization of carbonaceous aerosols outflow from India and Arabia: Biomass/biofuel burning and fossil fuel combustion. *J. Geophys. Res.* 108:4485

92. Mayol-Bracero OL, Gabriel R, Andreae MO, Kirchstetter TW, Novakov T, et al. 2002. Carbonaceous aerosols over the Indian Ocean during the Indian Ocean Experiment (INDOEX): Chemical characterization, optical properties and probable sources. *J. Geophys. Res.* 107:8030

93. Salam A, Kassin K, Ullah SM, Puxbaum H. 2003. Aerosol chemical characteristics of an island site in the Bay of Bengal (Bhola-Bangladesh). *J. Environ. Monit.* 5: 1–9

94. Salam A, Bauer H, Kasisn K, Ullah SM, Puxbaum H. 2003. Aerosol chemical characteristics of a mega-city in Southeast Asia (Dhaka-Bangladesh). *Atmos. Environ.* 37:2517–28

95. Alfaro SC, Gaudichet A, Rajot JL, Gomes L, Maille M, Cachier H. 2003. Variability of aerosol size-resolved composition at an Indian coastal site during the INDOEX intensive field phase. *J. Geophys. Res.* 108:4235

96. Liu Y, Daum PH. 2002. Indirect warming effect from dispersion forcing. *Nature* 419:580–81

97. Chung CE, Ramanathan V. 2003. South Asian haze forcing: Remote impacts with implications to ENSO and AO. *J. Clim.* 16:1791–806

98. Rotstayn LD. 1999. Indirect forcing by anthropogenic aerosols: A global climate model calculation of the effective-radius and cloud-lifetime effects. *J. Geophys. Res.* 104:9369–80

99. Kaufman YJ, Smirnov A, Holben B, Dubovik O. 2001. Baseline maritime aerosols: Methology to derive the optical thickness and scattering properties. *Geophys. Res. Lett.* 28:3251–54

100. Boers R, Mitchell RM. 1994. Absorption feedback in stratocumulus clouds, influence on cloud top albedo. *Tellus A* 46:229–41

101. Lohmann U, Karcher B, Timmreck C. 2003. Impact of the Mt. Pinatubo eruption on cirrus clouds formed by homogenous freezing in the ECHAM4 GCM. *J. Geophys. Res.* 108:4568

102. Lohmann U. 2002. Possible aerosol effects on ice clouds via contact nucleation. *J. Atmos. Sci.* 59:647–56
103. Nober FJ, Graf H-F, Rosenfeld D. 2003. Sensitivity of the global circulation to the suppression of precipitation by anthropogenic aerosols. *Glob. Planet. Change* 37:57–80
104. Feingold G, Remer LA, Ramaprasad J, Kaufman YJ. 2001. Analysis of smoke impact on clouds in Brazilian biomass burning regions: An extension of Twomey's approach. *J. Geophys. Res.* 106:22907–22
105. Rosenfeld D, Feingold G. 2003. Explanation of discrepancies among satellite observations of the aerosol indirect effects. *Geophys. Res. Lett.* 30:1776
106. Forest CE, Stone PH, Sokolov AP, Allen MR, Webster MD. 2002. Quantifying uncertainties in climate system properties with the use of recent climate observations. *Science* 295:113–17
107. Hansen J, Sato M. 2001. Trends of measured climate forcing agents. *Proc. Natl. Acad. Sci. USA* 98:14778–82
108. Edmonds J, Wise M, Pitcher H, Richels R, Wigley T, MacCracken C. 1997. An integrated assessment of climate change and the accelerated introduction of advanced energy technologies. *Mitig. Adapt. Strateg. Glob. Change* 1:311–39
109. Jacobson MZ. 2002. Control of fossil-fuel particulate black carbon and organic matter, possibly the most effective method of slowing global warming. *J. Geophys. Res.* 107:4410
110. Chock DP, Song QY, Hass H, Schell B, Ackermann I. 2003. Comment on "Control of fossil-fuel particulate black carbon and organic matter, possibly the most effective method of slowing global warming" by M.Z. Jacobson. *J. Geophys. Res.* 108:4769
111. Feichter J, Sausen R, Grassl H, Fiebig M. 2003. Comment on "Control of fossil-fuel particulate black carbon and organic matter, possibly the most effective method of slowing global warming" by M.Z. Jacobson. *J. Geophys. Res.* 108:4767
112. Penner JE. 2003. Comment on "Control of fossil-fuel particulate black carbon and organic matter, possibly the most effective method of slowing global warming" by M.Z. Jacobson. *J. Geophys. Res.* 108:4771
113. Acid News. 2003. Stricter standards proposed. 4:18–19
114. Hansen JE. 2002. A brighter future. *Clim. Change* 52:435–40
115. Feichter J, Roeckner E, Lohmann U, Liepert B. 2004. Nonliner aspects of the climate response to greenhouse gas and aerosol forcing. *J. Clim.* 17(12):2384–98

MARINE RESERVES AND OCEAN NEIGHBORHOODS: The Spatial Scale of Marine Populations and Their Management

Stephen R. Palumbi

Department of Biological Sciences, Stanford University, Hopkins Marine Station, Pacific Grove, California 93950; email: spalumbi@stanford.edu

■ **Abstract** The movement of individuals defines a spatial neighborhood that can help determine marine management strategies. Here, I briefly review four fields of marine biology that each differentially illuminate the scale of marine neighborhoods: effects of marine reserves, tagging studies, microchemistry, and population genetics. These suggest adult neighborhood sizes for many demersal fish and invertebrates as small as kilometers and up to 10 to 100 km. Larval dispersal may be shorter than previously suspected: neighborhood sizes of 10 to 100 km for invertebrates and 50 to 200 km for fish are common in current compilations.

How can small reserves protect such species? One conceptual framework is to set reserve size based on adult neighborhood sizes of highly fished species and determine spacing of a reserve network based on larval neighborhoods. The multispecies nature of fisheries demands that network designs accommodate different life histories and take into account the way local human communities use marine resources.

CONTENTS

INTRODUCTION	31
RESULTS FROM MARINE RESERVE PROTECTION	33
MARINE RESERVES AS EXPERIMENTS IN OCEAN NEIGHBORHOODS	36
THE SPILLOVER CLOUD	39
TAGGING STUDIES OF ADULT MOVEMENT	43
CHEMICAL TAGS OF MOVEMENT IN OTOLITHS AND STATOLITHS	48
POPULATION GENETICS AND MEASURING DISPERSAL	53
WHAT DO SUCH DIFFERENT TYPES OF DATA TELL US?	56
NEIGHBORHOODS AND MANAGEMENT	58
CONCLUSIONS	60

INTRODUCTION

Effective management of marine ecosystems—either for fisheries or for conservation—must match the population biology and dispersal ability of target species.

Many commercially exploited fin fish, echinoderms, mollusks, and crustacea consist of populations of relatively sedentary adults spread across huge geographic ranges connected by larval dispersal. Other species, such as whales, tunas, and squid, have highly migratory adults that range over large distances. As a consequence of these life strategies, management approaches for commercial marine species typically emphasize control of fishing effort over large geographic scales.

Recently, a much smaller scale approach to marine environmental management has been suggested. Marine Protected Areas (MPAs), zones in which fisheries exploitation is spatially limited, have been used to protect critical habitats, such as spawning sites and nursery grounds. Fully protected MPAs, also called Marine Reserves, have been established to protect all the species of a marine ecosystem, and this has resulted in strong increases in biomass and density of species that are otherwise heavily exploited.

Most marine reserves are small—typically less than 1 km^2—yet many species with seemingly high dispersal respond to protection in reserves. Does this mean that most species have only small scale population movement? Or does an MPA protect only the subset of species that happens to have the right scale of dispersal for that particular MPA? Though there is no doubt that marine population movements can be wide over evolutionary time frames, the generation-to-generation range of dispersal for most marine species is poorly known. As a result, matching the spatial scale of management with the scale of dispersal is difficult, and our understanding the role of MPAs in ecosystem protection is incomplete.

Sewell Wright (1) suggested a framework for measuring and interpreting the scale of population spread by exploring the influence of neighborhood size on the geography of genetic differentiation. He defined a neighborhood, statistically, as the variance in dispersal distances from offspring to their parents. Although useful mathematically and heuristically, such formulations are unlikely to be strictly useful in marine systems. There are few situations in which offspring and parents can be tracked accurately (the best known exceptions may be benthic colonial ascidians and whales), and marine species differ widely in the distances that individuals move at various life stages.

Because of these complexities, neighborhoods for marine species must be defined differently. Here I use a general definition of neighborhoods as the area centered on a set of parents that is large enough to retain most of the offspring of those parents. If adults move widely, neighborhoods are large and diffuse. If adults are sessile and larvae are restricted in their dispersal, then a neighborhood might be small and distinct. Other species with sedentary adults and highly dispersed larvae may have large neighborhoods if long-distance dispersal is common or small neighborhoods if long-distance larval dispersal is rare.

The scale of ocean neighborhoods is fundamental to understanding how marine species make use of the seascape and is therefore fundamental to future management. Once known, the scale of ocean neighborhoods may be uniquely valuable. Species with vast ocean neighborhoods may require the type of large-scale management that is the hallmark of current fisheries. But for species in which ocean neighborhoods are small, then smaller-scale management in marine parks or reserves may be more appropriate. There are also species for which adult neighborhoods are probably small but larval neighborhoods are large. These species may require different types of spatial management, such as networks of marine reserves.

Although it is possible to immediately think of many practical difficulties in accurately measuring ocean neighborhood sizes, our current ignorance of the scale of marine dispersal from generation to generation of most species is so profound that we have little idea of even the order of magnitude of dispersal. Do most successful marine larvae drift 10 km, 100 km, or 1000 km before settling to their adult phase? Recently collected data from a variety of studies suggest the range of movements of adults and offspring in the sea. Small-scale marine reserves can be viewed as experiments in the functional application of spatial management to species with different ocean neighborhood sizes. By observing the impact of protecting species over small spatial scales, we can simultaneously gauge the importance of reserves and show which species have neighborhoods of the right size for particular sizes of reserves.

Other data are accumulating that also address the fundamental question of neighborhood size for different species. Tagging studies seem to relate most directly to efforts to define movement patterns of adults. These studies can distinguish species with highly vagile adults from those with sessile adults, but the results are very difficult to apply to larvae. Larval patterns of movement instead derive from data on the genetics of marine populations, from tracking invasive species, and on new information about chemical tags of fish otoliths and invertebrate statoliths.

Both the use of marine reserves to bolster coastal management and the measurement of ocean neighborhoods are in their infancy. However, progress on both these fronts encourages development of approaches that try to estimate the scale of population spread in marine species and incorporate this information into place-based management schemes. In this review, I highlight advances in marine reserve implementation and interpretation and place them in a framework that shows how scales of population spread and scales of marine management might be melded.

RESULTS FROM MARINE RESERVE PROTECTION

Fully protected marine reserves have been shown to generally produce striking increases in biomass of species that are heavily fished outside reserve boundaries (2, 3). Significant increases in population density and species diversity are also commonly reported. Overall, fish biomass increased 100% to 800% across 56 peer-reviewed published surveys of the effectiveness of reserves (4) based on data in Halpern (5). (Figure 1*A,B*). Among these 56 studies, density increases averaged between 60% and 150% across a wide range of countries in North America, in the tropical Pacific, and Africa. Lower values (increases of 20% to 35%) have been reported for the Mediterranean and the temperate South Pacific (Figure 1*B*). When

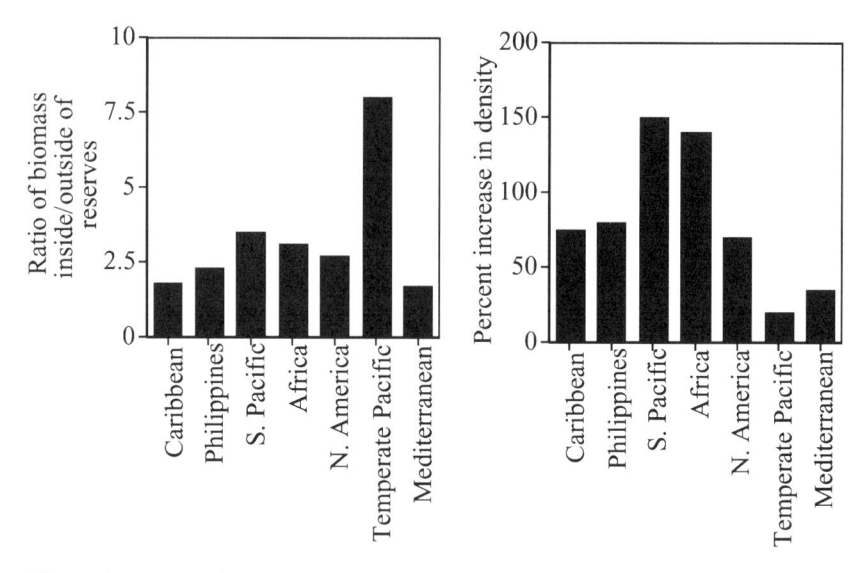

Figure 1 Increase in (*left*) biomass and (*right*) density of fish inside marine reserves from different parts of the world. Data are from studies summarized by Halpern (5) that were published in peer-reviewed journals.

multiple factors that might affect fish assemblages are examined, the presence of no-take reserves often outstrips other tested environmental effects, such as wave exposure, depth, or habitat complexity (6–8).

These broad compilations tend to average over multiple species and run the risk of obscuring declines in some species if other species increase markedly. However, some studies report results for individual species, and in these cases, patterns of response to protection are similar to those above. For example, on protected reefs in Belize, 16 of 30 species increased after protection compared to control reefs, whereas none decreased on these reefs (7). An earlier study in Belize showed 11 of 47 fish species had higher abundances inside areas with restricted fishing (3). In one of the first studies of reserve impacts, Bell (8) showed significant increases in 11 of 35 observed fish species and declines in a single species. Of eight fish families studied by McClanahan & Arthur (7) on protected reefs in eastern Africa, five showed significant increases in density, and seven showed significant increases in diversity. Few studies have examined a large number of invertebrate species inside reserves—typically such research emphasizes a few target species, such as limpets, lobsters, or abalone (9–11). However, in one study of 30 reef gastropods abundant enough for statistical analysis, McClanahan (12) showed increases of abundance in nine species and declines in three.

Despite overall increases in biomass, and despite increases in a larger number of species than decreases, some species in nearly every study do not benefit from a given reserve. In particular, species that are not exploited tend not to increase (13,

14). Such species actually serve as an additional control for the treatment effect of reserve protection. If, for example, reserves had larger biomass than control sites because they were all chosen in areas of high productivity, then we would expect nonexploited species to be higher inside than outside reserves. The generally poor response of nonexploited species suggests strongly that it is the protection from fishing that generates the strong differences between reserve and control sites—not some other invisible variable. This is important because studies of reserves do not generally have the same kind of rigorous before-and-after controls that carefully designed ecological experiments tend to include.

Species in different trophic groups also tend to respond differently to reserves. In a major metaanalysis of 20 studies of reserve effects, Micheli et al. (13) show that omnivores and detritivores respond poorly, if at all, to reserve protection. By contrast, species that consume algae, invertebrates, or plankton have moderate response. The strongest response comes from predatory fish, which nearly doubled in abundance across the 20 studies. These differences may be affected by fishing pressure. Predatory fishes, such as rockfish, groupers, and snappers, tend to be highly prized fishing targets and thus tend to respond to reserves because they are no longer heavily fished. Detritivores and herbivores may be less often fished and less likely to need protection. However, a second reason for the differences in response to reserves is that a higher abundance of predators may consume more prey, and if these prey are smaller species, then the middle trophic levels occupied by these smaller species may decline rather than increase. A strong example of this is the decline of sea urchins after creation of marine reserves in New Zealand (10). Experiments have shown that this decline results from an increased abundance of predatory lobsters inside reserves, which consume sea urchins and subsequently allow greater growth of kelp (15).

Micheli et al. (13) also show that there is a shift toward larger-sized individuals inside reserves. This trend is seen in most studies of reserve impact—the size of fish or invertebrates tends to increase markedly when protected from exploitation. Such protection is evident in areas heavily used by commercial as well as recreational fishermen. In the Hopkins Marine Life Refuge in central California, two species of rockfish caught almost exclusively by recreational fishing are larger inside the reserve than outside (16). Likewise, it is difficult to find a legal-sized rockfish or lingcod outside of the no-take reserves at the Edmunds Underwater Park in Puget Sound, Washington (17).

The larger size of individuals in reserves produces two of the most commonly cited benefits of reserve protection: increased biomass of fish and increased reproductive capacity (18). Reproductive capacity is particularly important because it tends to increase exponentially with adult size. Because biomass inside reserves is increased, and because this increase results from a larger proportion of larger fish, benefits of reserves for reproduction can be substantial. For example, a red snapper 62 cm long produces the same number of eggs as 212 individuals 41 cm long. Such huge differences can result in large increases in reproductive potential. Bohnsack (19) calculated that snappers inside tropical reef reserves produced

12 times more eggs than those outside. Likewise, ling cod in the Edmunds Underwater Park in the Puget Sound produce 20 times more eggs per hectare than do ling cod outside the reserve (17), implying that a reserve system encompassing 5% of the subtidal area would effectively double egg production. Manriquez & Castilla (11) showed a 1000-fold increase in egg production inside reserves for a heavily exploited Chilean limpet.

Unfortunately, there have been few demonstrations of the direct benefit of these increases in potential egg production to local reserves or to the number of larvae available to recruit into marine populations. Stoner & Ray (20) showed that the number of larvae of the heavily fished Queen conch was much higher inside a reserve in the Bahamas than elsewhere. Murawski et al. (21) reported increases in settlement of offshore scallops after adult populations increased inside trawler-exclusion zones near Cape Cod. An experiment by Tegner (22) in which local populations of abalone were experimentally increased by transplantation gave mixed results. There were some observations of increased local settlement, but in other areas, no such increase occurred before poaching reduced adult numbers. That there are few other examples may be because present-day reserves are so small that they contribute only a tiny fraction of the larvae available in a typical marine population. Alternatively, the extra larvae produced in some reserves may be lost to the overall population (e.g., by being swept offshore). Stock recruitment relationships in marine species are notoriously variable, and it may take long-term observations of recruitment in and near large reserves to confirm the general assumption that reserves will increase available settlers.

Increased fish populations have been noted within a few years of reserve implementation (23), and most reserves studied have generated substantial increases in fished species within five years of protection when the targeted species are short lived and fast growing (24). However, longer-term protection can lead to incremental increases in biomass and density (7, 25, 26). Especially for long-lived species, protection over the course of a full generation, which may require 20 to 50 years, may produce increasing benefits (7). Micheli et al. (13) show that this trend is strongest in predatory fish. Protection for 10 years or more resulted in a far greater increase in abundance compared to reserves that had been in existence for 10 years or less (13).

MARINE RESERVES AS EXPERIMENTS IN OCEAN NEIGHBORHOODS

The hallmark of marine reserve management is that resources are protected spatially. Individuals within the borders of the reserve are protected, and individuals outside are not. If all marine populations are highly vagile, then small marine reserves are not expected to have substantial impact (26). However, many marine invertebrates are sessile or sedentary, such as corals or sea urchins, respectively, and many adult fish appear to have small home ranges. As a result, small marine reserves have the potential to reduce fishing mortality in local populations—but only for those species whose neighborhood size is appropriate.

Simple mathematical models of marine reserves show that in order for the protection afforded within a reserve to create the optimal increase in population, the neighborhood size of a species should be less than about twice the size of the reserve (27, 28). Species with adult home ranges larger than a reserve's size will be protected for only part of the time. Furthermore, if the implementation of a reserve increases fishing pressure outside reserve boundaries, then a species that spends only part of its time in a reserve may have higher fishing mortality outside the reserve than before. In these cases, reserves may not afford much overall protection. If fishing effort is not displaced, then the impact of reserves on highly migratory species is similar to the effect of decreasing fishing effort by the same percentage as the percent area dedicated to reserves (29).

Highly migratory pelagic fish in general are thought not to respond well to reserves unless the size of the reserve is large. Of nine exploited pelagic species studied inside and outside reserves [reviewed by Micheli et al. (13)], only three showed substantial increases after reserve protection. By contrast, about 75% of non-pelagic species show increases inside reserves. Few reserves larger than 150 km^2 exist (5), and so far it has been impossible to document the size of reserve needed to protect highly migratory species. However, several such species have benefited from MPAs, such as in the large regions near Cape Cod, Massachusetts, that are closed to cod fishing. Over these areas, free-ranging fish seem to respond to protection and have nearly doubled in density in the 10 years since protection began.

If the poor response of pelagic fish to small reserves is the result of their high mobility, then what lessons are available from the large list of species that do respond well to protection in reserves? DeMartini (26) showed that the movement patterns of fish and invertebrates had a theoretical relationship to the ability of reserves to affect population size. The reduction in rate of fishing mortality that an individual experiences is related directly to the amount of time it spends in a reserve. For highly mobile fish, whose adult movements take them in and out of protected areas, this fraction is the same as the total fraction of a marine ecosystem that is protected by reserves. For most areas, this fraction is small—for example, the reserve system in the Florida Keys National Marine Sanctuary covers less than 1% of the sanctuary area. In such cases, highly mobile fish are unlikely to benefit from reserves. The small Caribbean island nation of St. Lucia has reserves in about 1/3 of the area along an 11-km stretch of reef, and in this case, it is possible that fish with neighborhood sizes of 11-km or less receive substantial protection. Fish with neighborhoods of several 100 km are much less likely to benefit. Roberts et al. (18) showed that fish densities outside reserves were higher after reserve protection than they were before, and they attributed this increase to the movement of fish from protected to unprotected areas. The species contributing most to the density increase outside tend to be in moderately mobile families (18).

For less mobile species, populations will increase inside reserves if the addition of new juveniles to the protected population is faster than the movement of adults from inside to outside the reserve boundaries. Thus, response to reserve protection is not merely scaled to adult movement; it is scaled to recruitment as well. As a result, species with low adult movement may show little reserve effect if their recruitment is low. A possible example may be the poor performance of fisheries in Jamaica, where reef overfishing has been so extreme that there are few adults left to provide recruits, and the buildup of fish populations is extremely slow (30). In such cases, only highly sedentary species may likely show a reserve response.

By contrast, even species with high adult movement may show a reserve increase if recruitment to reserve settings is high enough to balance loss. The variable reserve response of species with different recruitment strengths is poorly studied, but the possibility exists that recruitment levels and response to reserve protection are generally linked.

Additional traits that determine response to reserve protection may be difficult to discern for many fish species. Biological features beside the overall movement patterns may also be important determinants of impact. Micheli et al. (13) classified 544 species from 20 studies by level of mobility and response to reserve protection. Once pelagic species are removed, the proportion of species with low, medium, or high levels of movement are about the same among species that decrease in reserves compared to those that increase (Figure 2). In particular, the list of declining species is not dominated by those with high mobility, and the list of increasing species is not dominated by species with low mobility. The failure to see the predicted relationship between estimated mobility and reserve response suggests that our view of the important life history features of benthic fish is not yet complete enough to allow good prediction of which ones will respond to protection. Another possibility is that response to reserves is a combination of features of both the

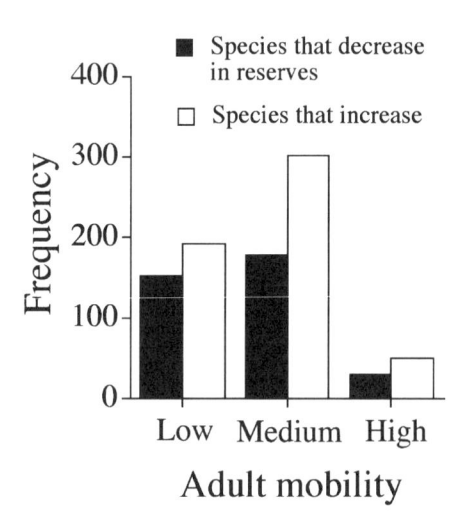

Figure 2 Number of species from different mobility classes for fish that increase inside marine reserves compared to those that decrease. From Micheli et al. (13).

targeted species and how humans use marine resources. For example, exploitation is generally higher for more mobile species (F. Micheli, personal communication), yet these are less likely to show a distinct reserve effect unless exploitation is very high and recruitment is consistent. Species with low movements, especially small reef fish such as butterflyfish and damselfish, may potentially show strong reserve effects. But because they are exploited only in severely overfished habitats, they will tend not to show a reserve effect except in extreme situations. Chapman & Kramer (31) estimated the effects of reserves on species of different potential mobilities. They concluded that low dispersal species did not show enhanced density or size in a reserve in Barbados.

THE SPILLOVER CLOUD

More poorly understood is the extent to which animals protected inside reserves move outside reserve boundaries and then enter local fisheries. This spillover effect is one of the key fisheries benefits of reserves, but this benefit has been well documented only a few times to date (18, 32, 33). From the standpoint of marine neighborhoods, measuring the spatial scale of spillover effects might tell us a great deal about how far populations tend to spread and the spatial scale of larval movement. Because the populations inside reserves are higher than outside, and because they potentially produce a large number of eggs and larvae, the existence of a successful reserve can be used as an experimental point source for tracking adult and larval movement, and thus it can provide a biological probe of neighborhood size. Unfortunately, current reserves are so small that larval clouds tend to be tiny, and most adult movement outside of reserves is monitored by the migration of fishing effort at reserve edges. As a result, we have little information about neighborhoods from these sources. However, a few preliminary data sets are available.

McClanahan & Mangi (32) monitored fish catch from the edge of a marine reserve in Kenya toward fished areas. Mass, size, and diversity of species dropped precipitously away from the reserve boundary. Higher fish abundance penetrates about 1 to 2 km into the fished areas on the south side of the reserve but only about 500 m on the north side. This difference may result from the prevalence of seine nets on the north side, suggesting the penetration of higher fish abundance depends on the intensity of fishing effort. If true, the extent of the spillover cloud can not be completely measured unless fishing is negligible, and if fishing is negligible, there will be no reserve effects and no spillover. In addition, the spillover effect appears variable across fish families even when mobility is similar. Rabbitfish, surgeonfish, and emperors decline significantly with distance from the African reserves, whereas goatfish, groupers, parrotfish, and snappers do not (32). Most of these families tend to be dominated by species with moderate to high rates of adult movement, and the differences in spillover pattern do not seem related simply to exploitation.

On Apo Island in the Philippines, Russ & Alcala have monitored the success of a small reserve since 1983 (34). Within a year or two of protection, large predatory fish showed a substantial increase in abundance within the reserve (35). Abundance of these species outside the reserve also increased, and 10–12 years after protection, mean adult density had increased severalfold (25, 34). Control sites that are 200–300 m from the reserve boundary showed nearly a 10-fold increase, whereas sites that are 400–500 m showed only about 50% increase. As in the case of Kenyan reefs, these data suggest that substantial spillover occurs over small distances.

Spillover from the set of marine reserves on the Caribbean island of St. Lucia has been suggested to have increased local fishing severalfold since the inception of the reserve system in 1995 (18). Along 11 km of coast, 4 to 5 reserves are interspersed with fished areas, and so the distance between fished areas and reserves is about 1 to 2 km. Spillover seems highest for moderately mobile fish families, such as parrotfish and grunts, groups that also showed movement across reserve boundaries during tagging studies (36).

Spillover from a reserve in Fiji derives from the movement of larvae. These reserves were established to allow regrowth of populations of clams (genus *Anadara*), which are heavily fished. Adult densities of clams are 14- to 18-fold higher in the locally managed Marine Area Network at the village of Uncunivanua, Fiji (37). Outside the area, within about a kilometer, densities of small postsettlement clams have increased about fivefold [see Tawake et al. in Gell & Roberts (38); Figure 3].

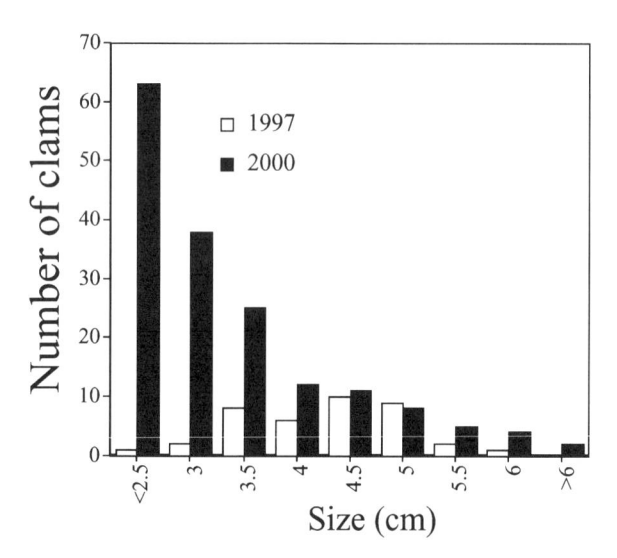

Figure 3 The number of clams (genus *Anadara*) outside marine reserves in Fiji in 1997 when the reserves were established and in 2000. Clams in fished areas outside of the reserves show an increase in postsettlement juveniles, probably as a result of spillover of larvae from large numbers of large adults inside adjacent reserve areas [redrawn from Tawake et al. (38)].

Because the adults are sedentary and the larvae are planktonic, this increase must be caused by export of larvae from the reserves. Other communities in Fiji have seen similar increases both inside and outside reserves. Although information about the magnitude of the larval spillover effect is available, the geographic scale of the effect is poorly known. Fished areas are interspersed with reserve zones, and measurements tend to compare fished and unfished populations over only small spatial scales. The shape and size of the larval cloud emanating from the reserves in Fiji is currently unknown, but this example suggests that it is now possible to use reserves as experimental sources of larvae to allow such measurements.

Similarly, Stoner & Ray (20) showed patterns of larval abundance for the commercially important Queen conch, *Strombus gigas*; these findings suggest spillover from a marine reserve in the Bahamas. Adults were 5–20 more numerous in the reserve compared to fished areas, and densities of early stage larvae were about 15 times greater. Offshore sampling about 1 to 2 km away from the reserve or fished areas showed approximately a 12-fold increase in abundance of larvae near the reserve, suggesting that larvae from the reserve were having an impact on larval abundance outside the reserve. However, the geographic extent of sampling was not high enough to show definitively that increased numbers of larvae are derived from reserve areas. As in the case of Fijian clams, no data showing the shape of the decline in larval abundance with distance from the reserve are available.

Larger-scale larval spillover has been reported for scallops in fishing closures on the Georges Bank in the Gulf of Maine. Since 1994, scallop (*Placopecten magellanicus*) densities have increased markedly in a series of zones closed to bottom trawling. Larger adults are available inside the trawl-free zone than outside. Though scallop fishing is now allowed in some of these previously closed areas, fishing has also intensified around the edges of zones that remain closed (21, 39). If this increased fishing effort is the result of spillover, then the geographic scale of spillover is at least 10 to 20 miles. Patterns of local current flow may dramatically affect the movement of larvae coming from protected populations, and it may be that oceanographic conditions on the Georges Bank favor larval retention near closed areas.

Though not derived from reserves, spillover clouds from marine restoration projects may provide some insight about neighborhoods. Peterson et al. (40) transplanted adult bay scallops (*Argopecten irradians*) into areas in North Carolina that had their previous populations destroyed by red tides. These restored populations sustained 10-fold increases in adult densities in a few transplant areas. Larval settlement and juvenile growth were also far higher near these restored populations than elsewhere in the region. Overall, larval settlement increased more than fivefold, but this increase was very local. One larval monitoring site within 2 to 5 km of several transplant areas (Emerald Island) showed large increases in settlement. A second site about 5 km from the closest transplant area showed no increase (40). Patterns of tidal inflow and outflow in the complex bay and estuary systems of North Carolina may constrain movement of larvae, and complicate patterns of larval dispersal. However, the clear increase in settlement after adult population restoration suggests that larval clouds can remain near adult populations and that local increases in adult densities can have a positive impact on recruitment to the next generation.

Few other clear examples of spillover clouds from reserves or restoration projects exist (41), possibly because reserves tend to be small and tend to have only a small effect on numbers of adults or larvae produced. In addition, data sets that suggest a spillover effect must be collected and analyzed carefully. For example, in St. Lucia, spillover was suggested by data that showed an increase in fish biomass outside reserves (18). However, there was no control for this experiment, and it is difficult to completely eliminate the possibility that fish biomass increased for reasons other than spillover. In such cases, monitoring biomass in a series of locations increasingly distant from reserve boundaries is an important component of an experimental design. Such studies of reserve spillover are becoming more common (23, 34). In the absence of such geographic sampling, the conclusion that spillover is occurring rests on the tacit assumption that no other changes have occurred that could significantly increase fish and invertebrate biomass. In the case of spillover of scallops from Cape Cod fishing closures, Murawski et al. (21) have pointed out that there were many changes in fishing regulations that could have increased scallop density outside reserves independently of a spillover effect. In the case of the St. Lucia reserves, no other fishing regulations were changed during the time of the study, and fishing elsewhere in the Caribbean was steadily declining (J. Hawkins personal communication) while fishing success in St. Lucia was increasing (18).

There are some cases in which spillover has been carefully investigated and is absent. Tewfik & Bene (42) showed that spillover of adult Queen conch from a protected area in the Turks and Caicos Islands is prevented by habitat barriers that surround the reserve. Similarly, a coral reef reserve in Barbados surrounded by sand patches 100s of meters wide shows little spillover (43). In other cases, some species showed spillover, but others did not. Spiny lobster in New Zealand (44) did not show a distinct spillover effect despite the fact that individuals are larger and more abundant in reserves (45). Long-distance movement of reproductively mature adults out of reserves may account for lack of spillover into adjacent habitats. In most cases, spillover from reserves is species specific: Although some species may move outside of reserves, others do not (46–48).

Because one quarter of the species inside a given reserve are not likely to show a reserve effect (13), and because only a fraction of the remaining three quarters of the species will have movement patterns appropriate to produce a spillover cloud (48, 49), it is perhaps not surprising that spillover is not universal. Spillover results that report summations of all species tend to show stronger positive effects than those that seek to understand patterns for just a few target species. Thus, it may be possible to document an overall spillover pattern across many target species without being able to pinpoint the way spillover is occurring for any single species. Such cases demand study of larger reserves but also suggest that statistical power of spillover investigations be carefully analyzed.

These problems have suggested the need for a different approach to understanding reserves, spillover, and the neighborhood size of fished species. As a result, the past few years has seen a marked increase in detailed studies of fish and invertebrate movement in natural and reserve settings. These studies complement investigations of biomass spillover and provide a very different view of the impact of reserves on fish and invertebrate populations.

TAGGING STUDIES OF ADULT MOVEMENT

Fish and invertebrates have been marked with a variety of methods that range from high-technology satellite transponders to low-technology colored thread (50). Physical tags are common for fish, crustacea, and mollusks (51), and range from coded archives that record environmental conditions after tagging to simple injected elastomer or tissue dyes that merely individualize an organism's appearance so that it can be recognized. More sophisticated devices record environmental variables while they are attached to an animal. Upon retrieval, these recorders can be read to estimate the geographic position of the tag while the host animal travels (52–56). Pop-up tags release themselves from the animal they were originally attached to and transmit geographic data via a satellite (57). Real-time data on geographic location have been gathered from triangulating audio receivers that pinpoint an individual's position or by detecting the sound of a unique sonic tag (58). Although this is not an exhaustive review of tagging approaches, I examined existing data from tagging studies to provide insight about movement patterns and adult neighborhood sizes.

There are few multispecies studies of movement based on tags. One long-term program has been the tagging of large pelagic billfish by recreational and commercial fishermen (59). Returns from 317,000 tagged animals over 50 years have established broad movement patterns and show that these large predators are truly ocean citizens. Moving over 1600 km in less than 6 months is a common result for black, blue, and white marlin, whereas sailfish and striped marlin tend to be found within 1000 km of their tagging site (59, 60).

Some fish are caught within 200 km of their release site even years after being tagged (59). However, proximity of release and capture sites may not necessarily translate to low rates of movement. For example, Takahashi et al. (61) fitted a swordfish with an archival tag off the eastern coast of Japan and recaptured the same animal 103 km away a year later. Archival tags collect data on environmental variables, such as temperature and day length. The combination of day length and date allows an estimate of latitude, and comparison of temperature data at that latitude with oceanic atlases allows an estimation of the longitude as well. Analysis of the archival data showed the fish tagged by Takahashi et al. (61) did not stay close to the tagging site but instead traveled 1000s of km to subtropical waters along the coast of New Zealand and then back to Japan. By contrast, bigeye tuna near Hawaii showed high levels of site fidelity, even using geolocation tags that record movements precisely (53).

Data on blue fin tuna show consistent seasonal returns to spawning grounds and a distribution among feeding grounds separated by 1000s of km (54, 56, 57, 62). Individuals in the Atlantic that are tagged off the coast of North America may spend several seasons in the western Atlantic, but then they move into the Mediterranean, possibly to spawn. Other individuals spawn in the Gulf of Mexico. A key insight of these data is that tuna move between eastern and western Atlantic stocks, suggesting that these management units are not a valid reflection of the basic biology of this species (11–14). Reconciling traditional delineations of stock structure with these new data is an important feature of future management.

It comes as no surprise that large pelagic fish in fact swim great distances and have ocean-scale neighborhoods (52). However, smaller pelagic fish may show more restricted movement. King George whiting (*Sillaginodes punctata*) showed movement patterns of up to 200 km, but even this level of movement seemed related to age. Younger fish did not travel far and tended to move long distances only when shifting habitats from shallow sea grass–dominated areas to deeper waters (63). Kingfish (*Seriola lalandi*) were recaptured typically within 50 km of point of tagging (64). Mackerel show a variety of movement patterns. School mackerel (*Scomberomorus queenslandicus*) moved small distances from their release point, on average 26 km (65). By contrast, the same study reported spotted mackerel (*Scomberomorus munroi*) moved 202 km on average.

Bottom-dwelling fish have less certain movement patterns, and even those that live in deep water can show remarkable site fidelity. Atlantic cod have been tracked by acoustic telemetry and show a complex pattern of seasonal migration. Acoustic tags emit an individually unique sound that can be monitored by a series of underwater receivers. By triangulating the directional signal collected by each receiver, the position of each tag can be estimated with great accuracy. Cod tagged off the Atlantic coast of Canada showed wide-ranging movements that took them to northern waters in two separate migrations (66). Fish overwintered in deep water but returned to coastal areas in spring. Some migrations were as short as 50 to 60 km, whereas others were over 200 km (66). Similarly, lingcod (*Ophiodon elongates*) in the northwest United States are resident in fairly small areas during part of the year but move seasonally to spawn (67). Red snappers in the Gulf of Mexico (*Lutjanus campechanus*) moved on average 29 km after an average 404 days at liberty before recapture (68), although hurricanes increase rates of movement considerably.

In the South African red steenbras (*Petrus rupetris*), tagging studies within the Tsitsikamma Marine Park have shown highly sedentary behavior of juveniles until about 70 cm length (Figure 4). Larger fish migrate 100s of km to the northeast, where they become resident and enter the fishery (69). Such ontogenetic shifts in mobility are a feature of many species (70–72). For example, deepwater Patagonian toothfish (*Dissostichus eleginoides*) have been tagged on fisheries' grounds and largely recaptured within about 25 km of their release point (73). One could interpret this to be a result of intense fishing that may make it more likely that a fish tagged on one fishing ground will be subsequently caught on the same ground. An alternative explanation suggests ontogenetic shift in mobility: These fish, similar to red steenbras, may be sedentary as juveniles on the banks that are heavily fished,

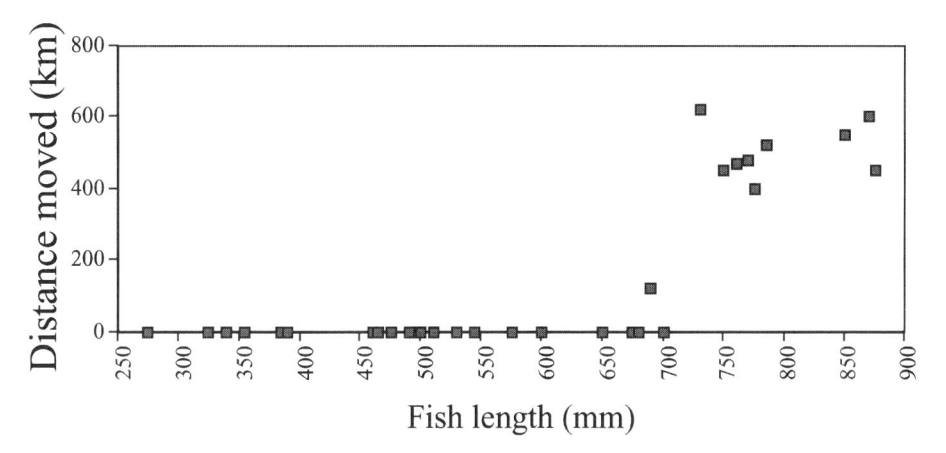

Figure 4 Ontogenetic changes in fish movement. Tag recoveries of red steenbras *Petrus rupestris* show low movement rates of juveniles. At the onset of sexual maturity, individuals migrate to adult habitats 500 km to the north. Redrawn from Brouwer (69).

but they may shift to a more mobile phase and thereafter become unavailable to the fishery.

Many benthic fish have been shown to be more sedentary as juveniles than adults (70–72). Yet, even adults can have remarkable small home ranges. Snappers in subtropical or temperate areas can have home ranges as small as a few 100 meters (74). The coral trout (*Plectropomus leopardus*) moved on average only about 2 km on Australian reefs. On temperate reefs amid kelp beds, three species of fish (*Chromis punctipinnis, Oxyjulis californica, Paralabrax clathratus*) showed no movement between adjacent but separated reefs (75). Perhaps the record for site fidelity goes to cardinalfishes, which over the course of more than a year consistently returned to within 1 m of their initially observed daytime resting positions (76).

Tagging studies of deepwater fish have been limited but Starr et al. (58) recorded movement patterns of two eastern Pacific rockfish using acoustic receivers deployed at about 100 m depth. Among greenspotted rockfish (*Sebastes chlorostictus*), 5 of 6 spent more than half their time within range of receivers dispersed over about 2 km. Among bocaccio (*Sebastes paucispinus*), 10 of 16 fish spent over 95% of their time within range of 5 receivers scattered along about 5 km of seafloor (Figure 5). However, in both species, some individuals moved outside of receiver detection, and in bocaccio, daily changes in depth caused animals to move short distances in areas of high vertical relief but move longer distances where the topography was more gentle (58).

Conclusions from these recapture surveys are limited. That some fish move more than others is no surprise. More detailed comparisons among species are hampered by vast differences in sampling effort between studies and by the largely descriptive nature of many tagging efforts. In addition, short-term movement patterns of an individual species tells us little about long-term residency. It is the combination of movement and timing that is likely to provide the most insight to neighborhood

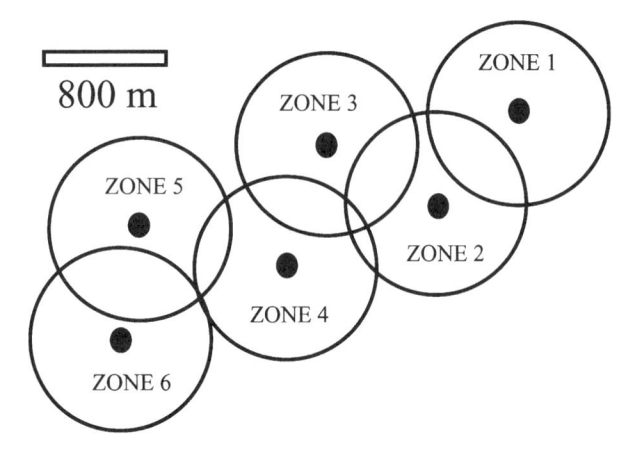

Figure 5 The geographic arrangement of acoustic sensors used by Starr et al. (58) to monitor movement of bocaccio (*Sebastes paucispinus*) on deep reefs off the coast of California. Most fish spent the majority of their time wholly within range of one of the sensors.

sizes. In this regard, data sets that show the relationship between time at liberty and overall movement are particularly useful (59, 68). From such plots, it might be possible to discern the area across which individuals tend to range over the course of a defined time period, such as a year. Nevertheless emerging patterns include the tendency of large pelagic fish to travel 100s to 1000s of km, and the tendency of smaller pelagics to have ranges more limited to 10s to 100s of km. Larger bottom-dwelling fish show movement patterns up to 100s of km, but some reef-associated species have home neighborhoods in the 10 km range. Finally, some benthic dwellers have such high site fidelity that they can be predictably found in an area for months to years (Table 1).

Across habitats, movement patterns seem to become larger from reefs to open bottom habitats to pelagics. Within habitats, movement tends to become more frequent with larger size, but such generalizations require larger comparative data sets than are usually available. For example, Kramer & Chapman (49) tagged a large number of species on reefs in Barbados and monitored resightings over time. On the basis of these data and a summary from the literature, they showed an exponential relationship between body size and movement pattern. In coral reef habitats, species with larger body size tend to have larger home ranges (Figure 6); species under 10 cm tended to have home ranges of 10 m or less.

In addition, Micheli et al. (13) documented a tendency of larger fish species to respond more positively to reserve protection—probably because they are more heavily exploited than smaller species and therefore show larger increases from even a low amount of protection inside reserves. The combination of these two trends is a pattern that seems counterintuitive: Species with greater tendency

TABLE 1 Some distances moved during tagging studies of benthic and pelagic fish

Species		Habitat	Scale	Evidence
Benthic or demersal				
Patagonian toothfish	*Dissostichus eleginoides*	Deep shelves	15 nm	Fishery recovery
Leafy sea dragons	*Phycodurus eques*	Kelp beds	5 ha	Acoustic
Snapper	*Pagrus auratus*	Kelp beds	500 m	Tag resighting
Red snapper	*Lutjanus campechanus*	Gulf of Mexico	29 km	Fishery recovery
Blue cod	*Parapercis colias*	New Zealand	100 m	Tag resighting
Atlantic cod	*Gadus morhua*	Northeast Atlantic	50–200 km	Acoustic
Coral trout	*Plectropomus leopardus*	Great Barrier Reef	2 km	Tag resighting
Cardinalfishes	Three species	Great Barrier Reef	<1 m	Tag resighting
King George whiting	*Sillaginodes punctata*		200 km	Fishery recovery
Small to medium pelagic				
Yellowtail kingfish	*Seriola lalandi*		50 km	Fishery recovery
School mackerel	*Scomberomorus queenslandicus*	Australia	26 km	Fishery recovery
Spotted mackerel	*Scomberomorus munroi*	Australia	202 km	Fishrey recovery
Large pelagic				
Black marlin	*Makaira indica*	Pacific	3–5000 km	Fishery recovery
Blue marlin	*Makaira nigricanus*	Global	2000 km	Fishery recovery
Sailfish	*Istiophorus platypterus*	Global	500–2000 km	Fishery recovery
Blue fin tuna	*Thunnus thynnus*	Atlantic	500–2000 km	Archival tags

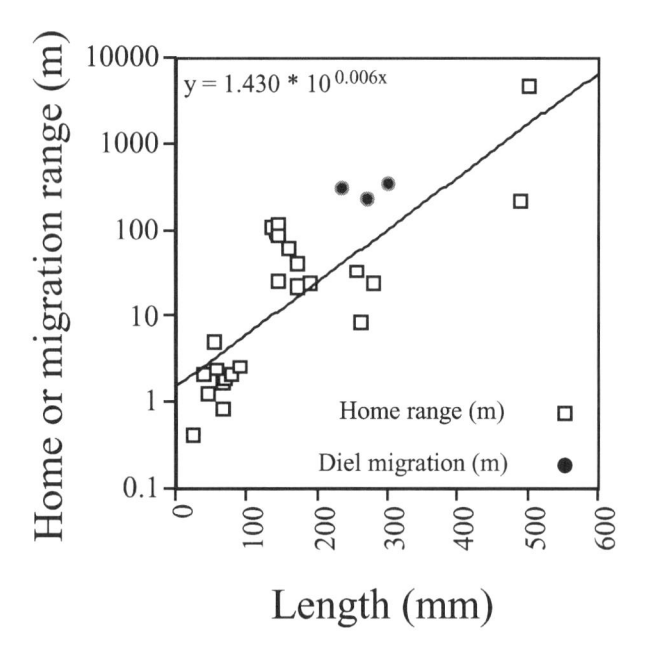

Figure 6 Relationship between home range size (or range of diel migration) and body size for coral reef fish. Data replotted from Appendix 1 of Kramer & Chapman (49).

to move outside reserves show a greater degree of reserve protection (Figure 7). Just the opposite prediction has usually been made: Sedentary species should be protected more completely (3, 26, 43). The emerging data, however, suggest that a combination of mobility, local fishing pressure, and reserve attributes are all critically important in determining response of a species to protection. Such complexities are very important to fold into expectations of the performance of marine reserves.

Other generalizations include the common observation that movement patterns shift over time in many species. Sometimes this seems associated with a shift from juvenile to adult phases (Figure 4). Other times, movement seems associated with seasonal migration of adults to spawning areas. In both cases, it becomes clear that a simple division of marine habitat use patterns into larval neighborhoods and adult neighborhoods is too simple.

CHEMICAL TAGS OF MOVEMENT IN OTOLITHS AND STATOLITHS

Tagging fish or invertebrates is generally limited to adults or larger juveniles, yet information about movements of smaller individuals is extremely valuable. Tags of larvae would be particularly useful in determining dispersal patterns (77).

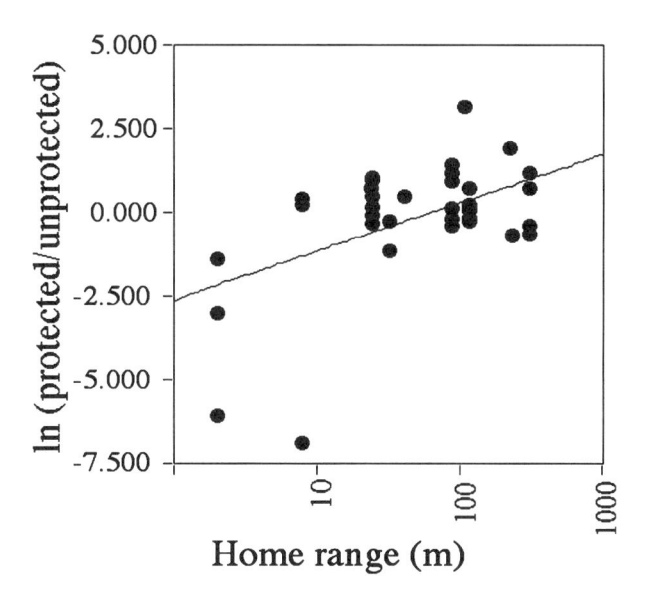

Figure 7 Response to reserve protection is higher in species with larger home range sizes. This counterintuitive pattern probably results from lower levels of exploitation in smaller fish that have low home range sizes (see Figure 6). Response is measured as the natural log of the ratio of abundance inside versus outside reserves [drawn from data in Micheli et al. (13)]. Home range sizes for these species were measured from movement patterns of tagged fish and are listed in Kramer & Chapman (49). All species are tropical reef fish, most of them from the Caribbean.

Movement of juveniles from nursery to adult habitats could be key to determining patterns of ecosystem use (78). To advance these capabilities, attention is increasingly focusing on the measurement of chemical signatures in calcified structures of fish and invertebrates. The tissues that form these structures incorporate elements such as barium, strontium, manganese, and magnesium into the calcium carbonate framework. Levels of incorporation vary with environmental availability of these various elements in sea water, and variation in the elemental signature can sometimes distinguish individuals that have lived in different water masses [see Campana (79) for review].

Most research focuses on the use of fish otolith microchemistry to identify distinct stocks of coastal fish (79–86). The simplest use of this technology is to completely dissolve the fish otolith (a small calcareous inclusion in fish ears) and measure the elemental signature in the resulting fluid. Such studies have shown that adult fish living in different estuaries or bays can have very different otolith signatures (82, 85, 87–92). For example, otolith chemistries (based on stable isotopes) inside hypersaline Shark Bay in western Australia are very distinctive compared to those from normal oceanic conditions. Individual pink snapper (*Pagrus auratus*) inside Shark Bay showed no sign of normal, oceanic otolith chemistries, and populations outside the bay never showed otolith chemistries characteristic of inside the bay. As a result, Edmonds et al. (90) concluded that adult pink snapper rarely moved and spent most of their lives either fully inside or outside Shark Bay (92). By contrast, the bluefish *Pomatomus saltatrix* showed individuals with both oceanic and bay signatures, and Edmonds et al. concluded they were more mobile. Similarly, Campana et al. (85) showed that otoliths of cod (*Gadus morhua*) differed between the southern and northern portions of the Gulf of St. Lawrence, and these otoliths could also be distinguished from those collected off the Nova Scotia shelf. They used different chemical tags to show how stocks mingled seasonally in the Gulf, a result similar to those reported for this species with acoustic tagging (66) [see also (79, 84)].

Otolith chemical signals often differ from place to place, but not all coastal areas differ in water chemistry. As a result, the spatial scale of discrimination for otolith studies can vary. Patterson et al. (91) showed that otoliths of Nassau grouper (*Epinephelus striatus*) were indistinguishable among localities in the Bahamas but were very different in Belize. Spatial discrimination among otolith studies seldom is less than 10 to 100 km, partly because differences among sites closer than this tend to shift over time. For example, chemical signatures in the Lessa and Lumpar rivers on the northwestern coast of Borneo were distinct in 1994 but not in 1995 (93). Similarly, discrimination of populations of shad (*Tenualosa ilisha*) was impossible over spatial scales of 100s of km in southeast India, largely because of strong differences in otolith chemistry from year to year (87). Discrimination in this species was successful in distant populations—Sumatra versus Kuwait versus India—which also showed genetic differences (87). By contrast, studies of spawning aggregations of cod in the northwest Atlantic showed otolith differences among most groups separated by as little as 50 km. These fine-scale results are associated with temporal stability of otolith chemical differences in cod. Over a period of two years, otolith signatures in cod remain largely consistent, although longer time periods showed substantial change (85).

In addition to studies on whole adult otoliths, increases in elemental discrimination allow the signatures of the central core of an otolith to be measured. This measurement allows the habitat of juveniles and adults to be compared and opens the possibility of measuring the retention of adults in natal spawning areas (94). Because it is not possible to predict the chemical signatures of otoliths from a knowledge of water chemistry (95), these signatures must be determined empirically for each fish species studied. Typically, whole otoliths from juveniles are compared among locations to generate a chemical atlas of signatures from different nursery areas. Then the cores of adult fish are assayed, and the juvenile atlas is used to estimate from which nursery area each adult is derived. These chemical assignment tests vary in power, but the tests can be assayed by asking how often they correctly assign juveniles to the nursery area from which they were collected (88, 96). Errors in assignments vary from 2% to 37% depending on the strength of spatial discrimination, but error rates of 5% to 10% appear typical (83, 88, 92, 96). Using these approaches, Thorrold et al. (96) showed significant differences in otolith chemical signatures among weakfish from estuaries separated by 100 to 200 km along the U.S. east coast. Error rates in assigning fish to their natal estuary were high in this study (29% to 37%) unless isotopic differences among estuaries were also included in the analysis. These authors also found significant differences among river systems within the Chesapeake Bay watershed, showing the potential for spatial discrimination over scales of about 50 km. When adult otolith signatures were compared to maps made from juveniles, Thorrold et al. (96) were able to show that adults tended to be found within the same estuary that they inhabited as juveniles (Figure 8). This homing of an estuarine fish back to nursery grounds shows spawning stock structure over scales of at least 100 km, with the possibility that finer-scale spatial structure may be found in the future.

Other juvenile-adult comparisons also show the degrees to which fish remain in the same region after recruitment or return to their natal nursery area to spawn. However, an unexpected complication is that the chemical atlas inferred from juvenile otoliths can shift significantly over time. For example, Gillanders & Kingsford (82) found marked spatial variation in otolith chemistries in a study of the trumpeter *Pelates sexlineatus*, but they also reported marked variation over time. Juvenile fish from the same estuaries showed significant differences in otoliths from year to year, and the ability to correctly predict the estuary from which a fish was collected actually decreased when data from two years were included in the analysis. Hamer

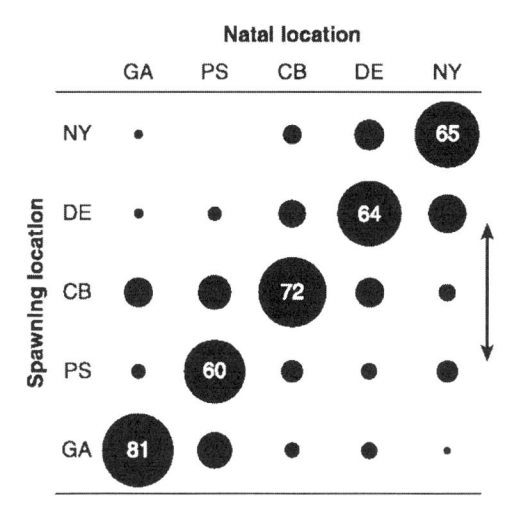

Figure 8 The degree of natal homing in weakfish as measured by chemical signatures in fish otoliths. Each circle represents the fraction of spawning fish that were juveniles in each of five estuaries along the U.S. east coast. Circle size is proportional to the fraction of juveniles from that locality. The abbreviations are GA, Georgia; PS, Pamlico Sound; CB, Chesapeake Bay; DE, Delaware; and NY, New York. Redrawn from Thorrold et al. (96a).

et al. (92, p. 261) provide parallel results for the snapper *Pagrus auratus* and conclude for this system: "Future classification of adults to nursery areas will require chemical tags characterised from juveniles of the same year classes as the adults being classified." Gillanders (78) used this approach and was able to show that a large fraction (89%) of the snappers caught on reefs near Sydney, Australia, settled as juveniles into adjacent estuaries.

Most of these studies to date have involved fish that use estuaries as either spawning or nursery habitats—fewer attempts have been made to apply these techniques to wholly oceanic species (97). In addition, these studies have tended to focus on habitat differences between juvenile and adult fish. Yet, the same techniques applied to distinguish the elemental signatures of the juvenile section of an otolith can be applied to the section of the otolith laid down in the larval fish as it develops in the plankton (84, 98). To date, attempts to use otolith chemistry to track larval movement have been limited by the technical difficulty of reading the signature of the tiny otolith core that was laid down during larval life, and the similarity in water chemistries in most open ocean settings where larval fish are found. However, both problems were solved by Swearer et al. (99) in a pioneering study of the movement of coral reef fish larvae. Taking advantage of the differences in water chemistry between the open ocean and coastal zones, Swearer et al. examined the otoliths of settling blue headed wrasses (*Thalassoma bifasciatum*) in St. Croix in the Caribbean. They asked the simple question—do settling larvae contain a signature of open ocean water? Or do they contain only a signature of coastal waters? If the latter were true, then the larvae could be assumed to have originated on St. Croix. Swearer et al. showed that 30% to 50% of the larvae settling in one area of St. Croix originated on the same island. This degree of larval retention was unexpected—conventional wisdom and current pattern diagrams suggested that larval wrasses would seldom complete development before being washed away from coastal zones. Further evidence suggested that periods of high settlement occurred when currents favored local retention.

A similar result derives from otolith studies on Lizard Island in the Great Barrier Reef, where the larvae of the damselfish *Pomacentrus amboinensis* were labeled with a fluorescent tag by Jones et al. (100). Collection of larvae returning to the same reef suggested that 30% to 60% of the settling larvae were retained around the island and, similar to the study of Caribbean wrasses, had much less demographic exchange among islands than previously thought.

So far, otolith studies do not identify the dispersal fate of larvae that are not retained on their natal island, and substantial long-distance dispersal may still occur. Recently a numerical model of ocean movements around Lizard Island suggested that this area acted as a major retention site within the Great Barrier Reef but also contributed substantially to regional larval pools (101). However, otolith investigations appear to have potential to map the movements of larvae, not just adults or juveniles. Furthermore, the basic approach of assaying elemental composition of larvae can be applied to larvae of mollusks and crustacea (98, 102, 103). Temporal shifts in chemical atlases, changes in the uptake of trace minerals from sea water depending on physiological condition or temperature, and the spatial resolution of significant differences in chemistry in nonestuarine settings (95) all complicate the interpretation of otolith data. Partly owing to these complexities, few measurements of larval dispersal patterns or distances are available yet from otolith studies. Further development of this technology may provide a new window into larval neighborhood sizes for a wide variety of species.

POPULATION GENETICS AND MEASURING DISPERSAL

Environmentally induced tags in larval fish and invertebrates have potential as markers of larval movement, but these environmental signatures can be difficult to find and use. Larvae and adults of all species also carry along with them a separate identity tag—their DNA—and this population or individual-level tag has been avidly investigated for several decades.

Most genetic studies of marine species emphasize patterns of genetic differentiation over evolutionary time frames, and many investigate genetics over spatial scales that range from 100s to 1000s to 10,000s of km (104–108). In general, patterns of marine genetic differentiation follow expectations based on larval life history. For species with relatively low potential for dispersal, genetic differentiation can occur over short spatial scales. Thus, animals or algae with crawl-away offspring tend to show genetic differences over scales of km (109–114), whereas species with larvae that are in the plankton for weeks or months generally show large genetic differences over only 100s or 1000s of km (106, 108, 115). Pelagic animals tend to have broadly dispersed population structure (116–118) except for species such as turtles (119–121) that have strong natal homing. Other animals with complex migration behaviors, such as whales, show strong genetic structure when offspring inherit their migration route preference or their spawning beach preference from their parents (122, 123).

Although the overall relationships between genetic structure and marine life histories seem to generally match, there are a growing number of exceptions that give us increased insight into marine populations. Working in the California Current, Bucklin et al. (124) showed that the euphaussid *Nematoscelis difficilis* differed genetically between inshore and offshore collections. Similar efforts in the Atlantic showed that the copepod *Calanus finmarchicus* had distinct genetic structure in different gyre systems (125). Morphospecies of planktonic foraminifera with global ranges have been shown to differ genetically between ocean basins and to sometimes consist of several sympatric cryptic species (126–129). Strong genetic differentiation in benthic species with extended larval durations have recently been reported, including stomatopods in Indonesia (130, 131) and gobies in the Caribbean (104). These data sets augment prior work showing genetic breaks at biogeographic boundaries in Atlantic (132), Indonesian (110, 133), and Mediterranean (134) marine species.

These cases in which an unexpected structure is observed provide powerful insights into the relationships between physical and biological oceanography (131,

132, 135). They imply that larvae are not moved like passive particles in ocean currents (130), that larvae may not survive the transit of deep water (104, 130, 136), or that the mixing of water in semidistinct ocean gyres does not significantly mix populations of plankton (126, 135). These genetic signatures of nominally high dispersal species are thus powerful allies in understanding the relationships between physical features of oceans and their biological populations.

Essentially, signals of strong genetic structure show regions across which gene flow is very low. A genetic signal is measured as the index F_{ST}, which is roughly the fraction of genetic variation that is distributed geographically. Values for F_{ST} in marine populations vary from very high (0.3–0.4) [e.g., Marko (112)] to vanishingly small (effectively zero), and a series of analytical methods and computer packages allow the calculation of F_{ST} from a wide variety of types of genetic data, including microsatellites, allozymes, restriction fragment length polymorphisms, and DNA sequences (137–139).

Interpreting the biological meaning of F_{ST} is more difficult than measuring it or testing it for statistical significance. Population genetic theory helps show how low gene flow must be before structure is observed, using a theoretical framework derived from work by Sewall Wright (1) and others on the Island Model of population structure (140, 141). A typical conclusion is that successful movement of even one migrant per generation is enough to prevent wholesale population divergence (142). Significant genetic differences can occur in cases of much higher rates of migration, but in these cases the populations are unlikely to evolve separately.

Some work has been done on different models of gene flow, including a stepping stone model in which populations exchange immigrants with populations only immediately adjacent to themselves (143, 144). Major advantages of these models are, for example, that they more realistically represent migration scenarios in the wild, especially of coastal marine species (4), and that they predict populations more geographically distant will show higher levels of genetic distinction at equilibrium (144). Furthermore, population arrays with lower gene flow show a greater accumulation of genetic distance over geographic distance (4, 143, 144), and therefore this signal of isolation by distance can be a powerful way to measure dispersal distances. In the past, these distances had been formally defined as genetic neighborhood size (1) and represented the variance of the geographic distribution of offspring relative to their parents. This is in effect the width of the dispersal cloud around reproducing adults, and it is a close approximation to the larval neighborhood size discussed in the Introduction.

For example, genetic differentiation of the coastal rockfish *Sebastes caurinus* builds up along the U.S. west coast so that F_{ST} increases by about 0.01 each 1500 km [(145), Figure 9]. Simulations of isolation by distance among 1000 populations each with 1000 reproductive individuals showed that this magnitude of geographic differentiation occurred when species had an average dispersal distance of about 50 to 100 km a generation (4), although this figure is sensitive to assumptions about the way larvae disperse, the overall population

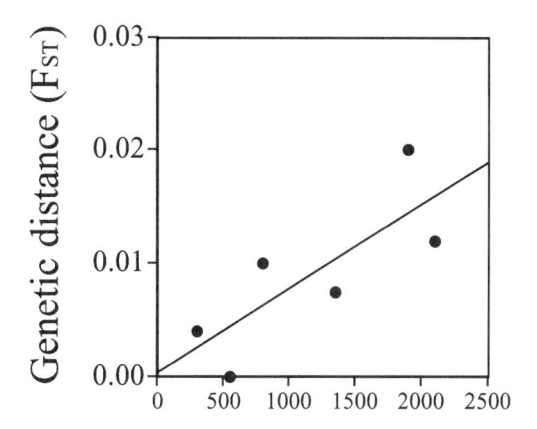

Distance between populations (km)

Figure 9 Genetic distance increases with geographic distance in populations of the copper rockfish (*Sebastes caurinus*) along the west coast of the United States. These signatures of genetic isolation by distance are consistent with limited gene flow between populations arrayed along a coastline and can be used to estimate average larval dispersal. Redrawn from Buonaccorsi et al. (145).

size, and the amount of time the population has had to reach drift-dispersal equilibrium.

Kinlan & Gaines (146) used this framework to estimate dispersal distances from a survey of genetic studies of marine plants and animals. They specifically excluded studies that showed no signal of isolation by distance and so excluded species that potentially have high enough dispersal to prevent genetic differentiation. However, the studies that did show isolation by distance reveal two interesting patterns of dispersal (Figure 10). First, taxa with generally low dispersal potential, such as algae, have low rates of dispersal—typically between 100 m and 1 km per generation. Second, taxa with generally high potential for dispersal, such as marine fish, have dispersal distances measured to be much higher—between 20 and 200 km. Marine invertebrates have a wide array of dispersal abilities (147) and show a correspondingly broad range of genetic dispersal distances (Figure 10).

Few of these dispersal estimates are above 200 km. The average for fish is about 100 km, and the average for invertebrates is about 10 km. These figures should be considered provisional for two reasons. First, they are calculated using a limited number of simulations, and the sensitivity of these estimates to changes in simulation conditions has not been fully explored. Second, taxa that did not show an isolation-by-distance signal are not included in this figure, so species with particularly high dispersal may have been eliminated from the analysis (S.D. Gaines, personal communication). Nevertheless, the relative ordering of results from these analyses are not sensitive to modeling conditions, and the relative ordering seems

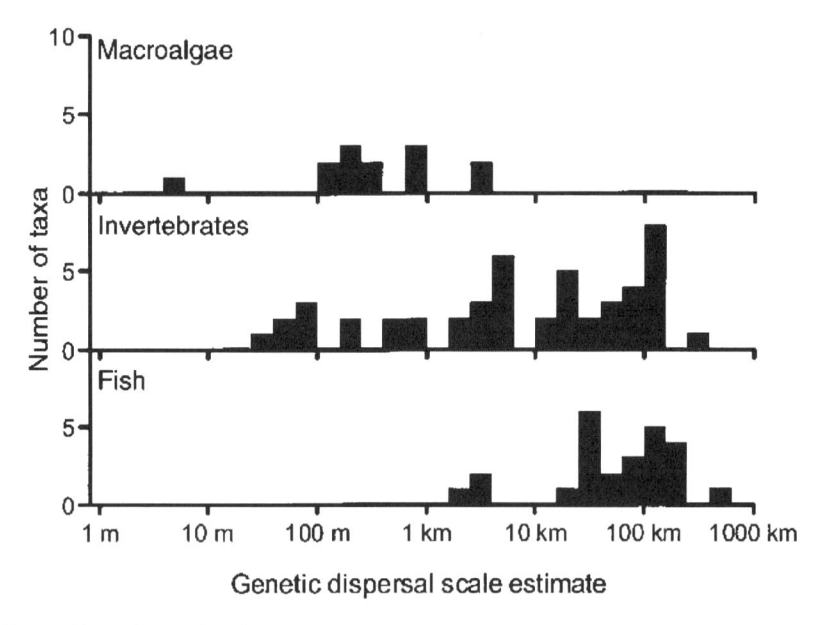

Figure 10 Dispersal estimates based on genetic isolation by distance for marine taxa summarized by Kinlan & Gaines (146), who used the methods of Palumbi (4). Taxa with dispersal high enough not to show an isolation-by-distance signal are not included in this analysis.

to make biological sense. In addition, the results are highly suggestive that genetic isolation patterns might be a powerful source of insight about larval dispersal profiles and that these profiles tend to cluster in the range of 10 to 100 km, not 100s to 1000s of km.

WHAT DO SUCH DIFFERENT TYPES OF DATA TELL US?

Movement patterns of marine species are highly variable, but emerging technologies allow a much more precise estimate of range occupation than ever before. Some approaches are designed to follow adult organisms over vast distances, some allow a continuous record of individual movement, and some can span life history stages to view the dispersal of planktonic eggs and larvae. Overall, emerging data show that the wide dispersion expected for mobile fish and larvae has many exceptions. Even some pelagic fish have more restricted movement patterns than thought previously, although as expected, this category of species appears to have the widest ranges. Across a variety of habitats, benthic fish appear often to have high site fidelities, pursue clear migration routes among habitats, or shift habitat use patterns in predictable ways with age. Individuals followed with acoustic monitoring may spend the majority of their time within a kilometer of a home site. Ranges of 10 to 20 km or above appear rare among nonmigratory benthic fish studied to date, although the number of careful studies is small, and species chosen for study may have low movement potential. Otolith chemistry and genetics have begun to delineate population boundaries in marine species, and these studies have been most successful at showing when and where adult populations do not mix. Between satellite responders, archival tags, acoustic surveys, chemical signatures of otoliths or other calcareous parts, and genetic analyses, methods now exist to follow virtually all individual marine organisms above about 10 cm. The potential to gain increased understanding of movement patterns in space and time is enormous, and it is possible to imagine high-resolution studies of marine species similar to those regularly conducted on terrestrial birds and mammals. Such detailed studies will contribute greatly to understanding the way species use habitats, the scales over which individual animals spend their lives, and the implications of protecting particular areas of the oceans from various types of human impact. Despite the ability to follow movement patterns of many species, there are very few comparative studies across taxa in the same environments. Such comparisons are essential if we are to build a picture of the way multiple marine species use habitats within the same ecosystem.

Larval movement patterns are vastly more difficult to discern than adult movement patterns, and the most promising approaches—otolith chemistry and genetics—require prodigious effort or a serious list of assumptions to turn raw data into discernable patterns. Yet, these methods have suggested an increasingly clear pattern of larval retention or evidence of restricted average dispersal. Summaries across many species for otolith microchemistry are not available, but a few studies have shown high levels of retention at the level of individual islands or along coastlines. Reviews of genetic differences based on stepping-stone models suggest larval movement of less than 100 km in the vast majority of cases in which genetic patterns are visible. These values are smaller than expected for highly dispersive marine larvae, and the values may reflect poor survival of larvae that move long distances, poor access to suitable settlement locations of larvae that are moved offshore, or the effect of large-scale environmental gradients on larval survival. The result of these overlayered processes of dispersal and mortality may be a small effective dispersal distance combined with occasional long-distance movement.

Data from marine reserves are far less valuable in determining patterns of movement—largely because fishing mortality changes the results dramatically. Spillover from reserves should measure fish movement rates, but the rate of fish removal outside reserves is the chief determinant of the extent of the spillover cloud. Even the expected pattern of decreased reserve protection for highly mobile fish is reversed in available data summaries (Figure 8). This is likely because highly mobile fish, which are protected less in small reserves, experience higher fishing pressure and thus show a greater benefit from even partial protection. Perhaps the clearest expected signal of dispersal from reserves will be the shape and size of the cloud of larvae released by adults within reserve borders. Monitoring the larval spillover cloud should provide one of the most direct views of the process of larval dispersal, but to date there are very few studies that have attempted these measurements.

NEIGHBORHOODS AND MANAGEMENT

Large migratory species have by far the largest neighborhood sizes. Baleen whales that migrate between polar feeding and subtropical breeding grounds, as well as marine turtles that move between feeding grounds and nesting beaches near different continents, can travel 10,000 km in a year. Ironically, these behaviorally complex species may often have a very fine scale population structure because individuals may return to the same areas year after year to breed. Thus, small scale spatial protection—particularly during breeding seasons—can be a powerful tool. However, the long-distance migration of these species requires at least low-level protection outside of breeding areas and times. Turtles and albatross, for example, are killed in great numbers by pelagic longliners when they forage far from breeding areas.

Similar patterns are seen in pelagic fish, many of which have migratory patterns that require movement over 1000s of km. For blue fin tuna, migrations between oceans are rare, but movement across ocean basins appears common (56, 57, 62). Whether tuna return to their natal spawning areas to breed is currently unknown, but this could be discovered through a combination of tagging and genetic surveys. Smaller pelagic fish can show much more restricted ranges—50 to 200 km for some mackerel or kingfish (9, 52)—and similar species may have different range sizes. Despite this potential for movement, moderately sized pelagic fish have been shown to respond well to protection in relatively small reserves (85), though this is likely a reflection of high fishing mortality.

Many benthic fish seem to fall into the same range of movement as small pelagic fish, moving 10s to 100s of km, although temperate and tropical reef fish may have home ranges of 1 km or less. These species may be as sedentary as many terrestrial mammals and nonmigratory birds, and they may be well protected by reserves that are just a few times larger than average home ranges. Even if individuals roam outside reserve boundaries (58), they may still receive significant protection from fishing mortality. Small benthic fish can have very small home ranges but are probably not often a target of strong fishing pressure unless overall fishing pressure is very high. In such cases, small reserves function well to protect populations. Likewise, many mobile benthic invertebrates probably have low range sizes, unless they engage in spawning migrations (148), although much less attention has been paid to understanding their movement patterns. In summary (Table 2), spatial management of marine populations over scales of 10 to 100 km may well cover the adult neighborhood sizes of a large fraction of species important in commercial harvest and ecosystem dynamics. Species not well covered by such management scales are species with spawning migrations or ontogenetic habitat shifts, or medium-to-large pelagic fish, turtles, and mammals.

Larval neighborhood sizes are likely far higher than these adult neighborhoods. For many marine species with planktonic larvae, gene flow across large distances

TABLE 2 Approximate adult and larval neighborhood sizes for a variety of marine life history groups[a]

Scale (km)	Adult	Larval
>1000s	Large migratory species	Intermittent gene flow, many species
100s–1000s	Large pelagic fish	Some fish
10s–100s	Most benthic fish Smaller pelagic fish	Most fish Most invertebrates
1–10s	Small benthic fish Many benthic invertebrates	Algal spores Planktonic direct developers
<1	Sessile species Species with highly specialized habitat needs	Benthic direct developers

[a]Values are based on emerging data from the variety of studies discussed here, contain significant exceptions, and require continued validation.

occurs commonly over evolutionary time frames (108, 149). These long-distance events may have only minor impact on population growth, except when they seed new habitats with species that typically did not occur there. Long-distance dispersal over ecological time frames has been difficult to document rigorously. One summary of patterns of genetic differentiation over distance suggests that larval dispersal clouds for fish are often in the range of 50 to 200 km. Invertebrates can have a wider distribution of dispersal distances due to their wider range of larval life histories and show buildup of genetic differentiation consistent with dispersal of 10 to 100 km in most cases studied. Both genetic and microchemical surveys of larval spread suggest cases in which local retention of larvae is surprisingly high, leading to the possibility that marine populations are not universally open over large geographic scales.

However, even these indications of lower-than-expected dispersal still tend to yield neighborhood sizes that are larger than most present-day marine reserves. In such cases, single, small reserves are unlikely to provide the best balance of conservation and fisheries' benefits (27), and networks of marine reserves are likely to be necessary. One approach to the design of reserve networks is to set the size of reserves on the basis of adult neighborhood scales and to set the spacing of reserves on the basis of larval neighborhood scales. Yet, the variety of these scales among species and the need for reserves to protect all species in a habitat make such simple rules quite complicated to implement. A second principle suggested by the data reviewed here is that species that are not overfished, and do not depend on fished species for shelter or food, have little response to reserves. Thus life history traits of unfished species may be less important in setting the scales of reserves than the species that differ strongly inside and outside reserves. A third principle is that even species with large adult neighborhoods benefit from reserves if the fishing pressure on them is severe. Reserve networks built using the variety of neighborhood sizes demanded by fished species and species otherwise affected by fishing may be the most practical way to proceed.

CONCLUSIONS

Information about marine neighborhood size can be gleaned from a large variety of sources. For example, marine reserves can be considered spatial experiments that may tell us a great deal about neighborhood size. Species that respond well to reserve protection may have neighborhood sizes that are the same as the scale of the reserve. A review of the reserve literature shows several nonintuitive patterns, especially that species with the largest adult neighborhoods show the strongest protection in small reserves. This results most likely from the overarching importance of fishing pressure on larger species that tend to move greater distances. Fishing pressure also dramatically affects the width of the spillover cloud of adults from reserves. One of the best uses of reserves as ecological experiments will be to measure the dispersal of larvae from these sources of highly fecund adults.

Numerous other methods, in addition to reserve experiments, have been developed to track movement patterns of marine species, and one or more will probably be appropriate for virtually all species over 10 cm in length. Data from physical tags, archival tags that send data via satellite, and acoustic tags supply information about movement on different scales of time and space, and in general tagging has shown the range of motion for pelagic and dermersal fish. Demersal fish can have surprisingly small home ranges, and even small pelagic fish have been shown to have limited neighborhood sizes. Not surprisingly, large pelagic fish can range over thousands of kilometers. Tagging data are limited by their tendency to be descriptive and by the difficulty in comparing results from one study to the next. The most informative data sets compare movement over time, but in some cases such detailed data are not available.

Larval dispersal patterns have been examined with microchemistry and genetics. Recent results hint at much smaller larval dispersal ranges than previously suspected but need corroboration among taxa. Chemical signals from otoliths have great potential to trace movement patterns of larvae and adults, but these studies are hampered by the need to document a detailed physical map of chemical availabilities before otolith data can be interpreted. Genetic results do not have this limitation but are impeded by small amounts of migration that may lead to very similar genetic signatures from place to place. This problem has been solved lately through use of models that use the geographic scale of genetic differentiation to measure average dispersal distances, but the link between genetic change and dispersal measured in kilometers requires a series of poorly tested assumptions.

Current data suggest the overall scale of neighborhood sizes for different species commonly studied in a variety of marine communities but provide incomplete guidance for reserve networks. This is largely because so few comparative surveys of larval dispersal patterns and adult movement patterns have been made for the wide variety of species currently used as fishing targets. For example, the National Marine Fisheries Service lists the following species as the most important to the commercial fishery of California (in order of declining revenues in 2000): squid, crab, sea urchin, swordfish, salmon, sardines, sablefish, and lobster. Recreational fishing is highest on ling cod, halibut, barracuda, rockfish, and tuna. Of these species qualitative data on adult neighborhoods are available for ling cod, rockfish, tuna, crab, sea urchin, swordfish, and salmon, with patterns being similar to those in Table 2. However, little information is available for larval neighborhoods except for indications of low dispersal potential for at least one species of rockfish (145) and high dispersal in squid and sea urchins (150, 151). Obtaining more detailed information about adult neighborhoods is now possible through a combination of the tagging methods described above. Obtaining more information about larval neighborhoods awaits refinement of microchemical approaches and application of more intense genetic sampling.

ACKNOWLEDGMENTS

I thank E. Sotka, Liz Alter, and T. Oliver for comments and S. Belliveau for technical and production assistance. Work on marine reserves and genetics is supported by the Pew Charitable Trusts and the Andrew Mellon Foundation.

The *Annual Review of Environment and Resources* is online at
http://environ.annualreviews.org

LITERATURE CITED

1. Wright S. 1978. *Variability Within and Among Natural Populations.* Vol. 4. Chicago: Univ. Chicago Press. 565 pp.
2. Alcala AC, Russ GR. 1990. A direct test of the effects of protective management on abundance and yield of tropical marine resources. *J. Cons.* 46:40–47
3. Polunin N, Roberts CM. 1993. Greater biomass and value of target coral-reef fishes in two small Caribbean marine reserves. *Mar. Ecol. Prog. Ser.* 100:167–76
4. Palumbi SR. 2003. Population genetics, demographic connectivity, and the design of marine reserves. *Ecol. Appl.* 13:S146–58
5. Halpern B. 2003. The impact of marine reserves: Do reserves work and does reserve size matter? *Ecol. Appl.* 13:S117–37
6. Friedlander AM, Brown EK, Jokiel PL, Smith WR, Rodgers KS. 2003. Effects of habitat, wave exposure, and marine protected area status on coral reef fish assemblages in the Hawaiian archipelago. *Coral Reefs* 22:291–305
7. McClanahan TR, Arthur R. 2001. The effect of marine reserves and habitat on populations of East African coral reef fishes. *Ecol. Appl.* 11:559–69
8. Bell JD. 1983. Effects of depth and marine reserve fishing restrictions on the structure of a rocky reef fish assemblage in the northwestern Mediterranean Sea. *J. Appl. Ecol.* 20:357–69
9. Davis D, Banks S, Cuthill M. 1997. Whale sharks in Ningaloo Marine Park: managing tourism in an Australian marine protected area. *Tour. Manag.* 18:259
10. Babcock RC, Kelly S, Shears NT, Walker JW, Willis TJ. 1999. Changes in community structure in temperate marine reserves. *Mar. Ecol. Prog. Ser.* 189:125–34
11. Manriquez P, Castilla J. 2001. Significance of marine protected areas in central

Chile as seeding grounds for the gastropod *Concholepas concholepas. Mar. Ecol. Prog. Ser.* 215:201–11
12. McClanahan T. 1989. Kenyan coral reef-associated gastropod fauna—a comparison between protected and unprotected reefs. *Mar. Ecol. Prog. Ser.* 53:11–20
13. Micheli F, Halpern BS, Botsford L, Warner RR. 2004. Community changes in marine reserves. *Ecol. Appl.* In press
14. Roberts CM. 1995. Rapid build-up of fish biomass in a Caribbean marine reserve. *Conserv. Biol.* 9:815–26
15. Shears NT, Babcock RC. 2002. Marine reserves demonstrate top-down control of community structure on temperate reefs. *Oecologia* 132:131–42
16. Paddack M, Estes J. 2000. Kelp forest fish populations in marine reserves and adjacent exploited areas of central California. *Ecol. Appl.* 10:855–70
17. Fujita RM, Willingham V, Freitas J. 1998. *A Review of the Performance of Some U.S. West Coast Marine Reserves.* Environ. Def., Oakland, CA
18. Roberts CM, Bohnsack JA, Gell F, Hawkins JP, Goodridge R. 2001. Effects of marine reserves on adjacent fisheries. *Science* 294:1920–23
19. Bohnsack JA. 1994. How marine fishery reserves can improve reef fisheries. *Proc. Gulf Caribb. Fish. Inst.* 43:217–41
20. Stoner AW, Ray M. 1996. Queen conch, *Strombus gigas*, in fished and unfished locations of the Bahamas: effects of a marine fishery reserve on adults, juveniles, and larval production. *Fish. Bull.* 94:551–65
21. Murawski SA, Brown R, Lai HL, Rago PJ, Hendrickson L. 2000. Large-scale closed areas as a fishery-management tool in temperate marine systems: the Georges Bank experience. *Bull. Mar. Sci.* 66:775–98
22. Tegner MJ. 1992. Brood-stock transplants as a approach to abalone stock enhancement. In *Abalone of the World: Their Biology, Fisheries and Culture,* ed. SA Shepherd, MJ Tegner, SA Guzman del Proo, pp. 461–73. Oxford, UK: Blackwell Sci.
23. Russ GR, Alcala AC. 1996. Do marine reserves export adult fish biomass? Evidence from Apo Island, central Philippines. *Mar. Ecol. Prog. Ser.* 132:1–9
24. Halpern BS, Warner RR. 2002. Marine reserves have rapid and lasting effects. *Ecol. Lett.* 5:361–66
25. Russ GR, Alcala AC. 1996. Marine reserves: Rates and patterns of recovery and decline of large predatory fish. *Ecol. Appl.* 6:947–61
26. DeMartini EE. 1993. Modeling the potential of fishery reserves for managing Pacific coral reef fishes. *Fish. Bull.* 91:414–27
27. Botsford LW, Hastings A, Gaines SD. 2001. Dependence of sustainability on the configuration of marine reserves and larval dispersal distance. *Ecol. Lett.* 4:144–50
28. Botsford LW, Micheli F, Hastings A. 2003. Principles for the design of marine reserves. *Ecol. Appl.* 13:S25–31
29. Hastings A, Botsford LW. 1999. Equivalence in yield from marine reserves and traditional fisheries management. *Science* 284:1537–41
30. Gobert B. 2000. Comparative assessment of multispecies reef fish resources in the Lesser Antilles. *Fish. Res.* 44:247–60
31. Chapman MR, Kramer DL. 1999. Gradients in coral feef fish density and size across the Barbados Marine Reserve boundary: effects of reserve protection and habitat characteristics. *Mar. Ecol. Prog. Ser.* 181:81–96
32. McClanahan T, Mangi S. 2000. Spillover of exploitable fishes from a marine park and its effect on the adjacent fishery. *Ecol. Appl.* 10:1792–805
33. Russ GR, Alcala AC. 1999. Management histories of Sumilon and Apo Marine Reserves, Philippines, and their influence on National Marine Resource Policy. *Coral Reefs* 18:307–19

34. Russ GR, Alcala AC. 2003. Marine reserves: rates and patterns of recovery and decline of predatory fish, 1983–2000. *Ecol. Appl.* 13:1553–65
35. Russ GR, Alcala AC. 1989. Effects of intense fishing pressure on an assemblage of coral reef fishes. *Mar. Ecol. Prog. Ser.* 56:13–28
36. Corless M, Hatcher B, Hunte W, Scott S. 1997. Assessing the potential for fish migration from marine reserves to adjacent fished areas in the Soufriere Marine Management Area, St. Lucia. *Proc. Gulf Caribb. Fish Inst.* 49:71–98
37. Tawake A, Parks J, Radikedike P, Aalbersberg B, Vuki V, Salafsky N. 2001. Harvesting clams and data: involving local communities in monitoring: a case in Fiji. *Conserv. Biol. Pract.* 2:32–35
38. Tawake A, Gell F, Roberts C. 2002. Community-based closed areas in Fiji. In *The Fishery Effects of Marine Reserves and Fishery Closures*, ed. F Gell, C Roberts, pp. 59–62. Washington, DC: WWF-US
39. Rago PJ, McSherry M. 2002. *Spatial distribution of fishing effort for sea scallops: 1998–2000*. Presented at Northeast Reg. Essent. Fish Habitat Steer. Comm., Workshop Eff. Fish. Gear Mar. Habitats Northeast. United States, Boston, Mass.
40. Peterson CH, Summerson HC, Luettich RA. 1996. Response of bay scallops to spawner transplants: a test of recruitment limitation. *Mar. Ecol. Prog. Ser.* 132:93–107
41. Knowlton N, Keller B. 1986. Larvae which fall short of their potential-highly localized recruitment in an alpheid shrimp with extended larval development. *Bull. Mar. Sci.* 39:213–23
42. Tewfik A, Bene C. 2003. Effects of natural barriers on the spillover of a marine mollusc: implications for fisheries reserves. *Aquat. Conserv.: Mar. Freshw. Ecosyst.* 13:473–88
43. Chapman MR, Kramer DL. 2000. Movements of fishes within and among fringing coral reefs in Barbados. *Environ. Biol. Fish.* 57:11–24
44. Kelly S, Scott D, MacDiarmid A. 2002. The value of a spillover fishery for spiny lobsters around a marine reserve in northern New Zealand. *Coast. Manag.* 30:153–66
45. Davidson R, Villouta E, Cole R, Barrier R. 2002. Effects of marine reserve protection on spiny lobster (*Jasus edwardsii*) abundance and size at Tonga Island Marine Reserve, New Zealand. *Aquat. Conserv. Mar. Freshw. Ecosyst.* 12:213–27
46. Tupper M, Rudd MA. 2002. Species-specific impacts of a small marine reserve on reef fish production and fishing productivity in the Turks and Caicos Islands. *Environ. Conserv.* 29:484–92
47. Russ GR. 2002. Yet another review of marine reserves as reef fisheries management tools. In *Coral Reef Fishes: Dynamics and Diversity in a Complex Ecosystem*, ed. PF Sale, pp. 421–43. San Diego: Academic
48. Zeller D, Stoute SL, Russ GR. 2003. Movements of reef fishes across marine reserve boundaries: effects of manipulating a density gradient. *Mar. Ecol. Prog. Ser.* 254:269–80
49. Kramer DL, Chapman MR. 1999. Implications of fish home range size and relocation for marine reserve function. *Environ. Biol. Fish.* 55:65–79
50. Hastein T, Hill BJ, Berthe F, Lightner DV. 2001. Traceability of aquatic animals. *Rev. Sci. Tech.* 20:564–83
51. Kelly S, MacDiarmid A. 2003. Movement patterns of mature spiny lobsters, *Jasus edwardsii*, from a marine reserve. *N. Z. J. Mar. Freshw. Res.* 37:149–58
52. Gunn JS, Patterson TA, Pepperell JG. 2003. Short-term movement and behaviour of black marlin *Makaira indica* in the Coral Sea as determined through a pop-up satellite archival tagging experiment. *Mar. Freshw. Res.* 54:515–25
53. Sibert J, Musyl M, Brill R. 2003. Horizontal movements of bigeye tuna (*Thunnus*

obesus) near Hawaii determined by Kalman filter analysis of archival tagging data. *Fish. Oceanogr.* 12:141–51

54. Block BA, Costa DP, Boehlert GW, Kochevar RE. 2002. Revealing pelagic habitat use: the tagging of Pacific pelagics program. *Oceanol. Acta* 25:255–66

55. Boustany AM, Davis SF, Pyle P, Anderson SD, Le Boeuf BJ, Block BA. 2002. Satellite tagging—expanded niche for white sharks. *Nature* 415:35–36

56. Block BA, Dewar H, Williams T, Prince ED, Farwell C, Fudge D. 1998. A new satellite technology for tracking the movements of Atlantic bluefin tuna. *Proc. Natl. Acad. Sci. USA* 95:9384–89

57. Block BA, Dewar H, Blackwell SB, Williams TD, Prince ED, et al. 2001. Migratory movements, depth preferences, and thermal biology of Atlantic bluefin tuna. *Science* 293:1310–14

58. Starr R, Heine J, Felton J, Cailliet G. 2002. Movements of bocaccio (*Sebastes paucispinis*) and greenspotted (*S. chlorostictus*) rockfishes in a Monterey submarine canyon: implications for the design of marine reserves. *Fish. Bull.* 100:324–37

59. Ortiz M, Prince ED, Serafy JE, Holts DB, Davy KB, et al. 2003. Global overview of the major constituent-based billfish tagging programs and their results since 1954. *Mar. Freshw. Res.* 54:489–507

60. Hoolihan J. 2003. Sailfish movement in the Arabian Gulf: a summary of tagging efforts. *Mar. Freshw. Res.* 54:509–13

61. Takahashi M, Okamura H, Yokawa K, Okazaki M. 2003. Swimming behaviour and migration of a swordfish recorded by an archival tag. *Mar. Freshw. Res.* 54:527–34

62. Block BA, Dewar H, Williams T, Prince E, Farwell C. 1998. Archival tagging of Atlantic bluefin tuna (*Thunnus thynnus*). *Mar. Technol. Soc. J.* 32:37–46

63. Fowler AJ, Jones GK, McGarvey R. 2002. Characteristics and consequences of movement patterns of King George whiting (Perciformes: *Sillaginodes punctata*) in South Australia. *Mar. Freshw. Res.* 53:1055–69

64. Gillanders BM, Ferrell DJ, Andrew NL. 2001. Estimates of movement and life-history parameters of yellowtail kingfish (*Seriola lalandi*): How useful are data from a cooperative tagging programme? *Mar. Freshw. Res.* 52:179–92

65. Begg G, Cameron D, Sawynok W. 1997. Movements and stock structure of school mackerel (*Scomberomorus queenslandicus*) and spotted mackerel (*S. munroi*) in Australian East-Coast waters. *Mar. Freshw. Res.* 48:295–301

66. Comeau LA, Campana SE, Castonguay M. 2002. Automated monitoring of a large-scale cod (*Gadus morhua*) migration in the open sea. *Can. J. Fish. Aquat. Sci.* 59:1845–50

67. Martell SJD, Walters CJ, Wallace SS. 2000. The use of marine protected areas for conservation of lingcod (*Ophiodon elongatus*). *Bull. Mar. Sci.* 66:729–43

68. Patterson WF, Watterson JC, Shipp RL, Cowan JH. 2001. Movement of tagged red snapper in the northern Gulf of Mexico. *Trans. Am. Fish. Soc.* 130:533–45

69. Brouwer S. 2002. Movement patterns of red steenbras *Petrus rupestris* tagged and released in the Tsitsikamma National Park, South Africa. *S. Afr. J. Mar. Sci.-Suid-Afr. Tydskr. Seewetenskap* 24:375–78

70. Miller MJ, Able KW. 2002. Movements and growth of tagged young-of-the-year Atlantic croaker (*Micropogonias undulatus* L.) in restored and reference marsh creeks in Delaware Bay, USA. *J. Exp. Mar. Biol. Ecol.* 267:15–33

71. Ross SW, Lancaster JE. 2002. Movements and site fidelity of two juvenile fish species using surf zone nursery habitats along the southeastern North Carolina coast. *Environ. Biol. Fish.* 63:161–72

72. Watson M, Munro JL, Gell FR. 2002. Settlement, movement and early juvenile mortality of the yellowtail snapper

Ocyurus chrysurus. Mar. Ecol. Prog. Ser. 237:247–56

73. Williams R, Tuck GN, Constable AJ, Lamb T. 2002. Movement, growth and available abundance to the fishery of *Dissostichus eleginoides* Smitt,1898 at Heard Island, derived from tagging experiments. *CCAMLR Sci.* 9:33–48

74. Willis TJ, Parsons DM, Babcock RC. 2001. Evidence for long-term site fidelity of snapper (*Pagrus auratus*) within a marine reserve. *N. Z. J. Mar. Freshw. Res.* 35:581–90

75. Hartney K. 1996. Site fidelity and homing behaviour of some kelp-bed fishes. *J. Fish Biol.* 49:1062–69

76. Marnane MJ. 2000. Site fidelity and homing behaviour in coral reef cardinalfishes. *J. Fish Biol.* 57:1590–600

77. Levin LA, Huggett D, Myers P, Bridges T, Weaver J. 1993. Rare-earth tagging methods for the study of larval dispersal by marine-invertebrates. *Limnol. Oceanogr.* 38:246–360

78. Gillanders BM. 2002. Connectivity between juvenile and adult fish populations: Do adults remain near their recruitment estuaries? *Mar. Ecol. Prog. Ser.* 240:215–23

79. Campana SE. 1999. Chemistry and composition of fish otoliths: pathways, mechanisms and applications. *Mar. Ecol. Prog. Ser.* 188:263–97

80. Bath GE, Thorrold SR, Jones CM, Campana SE, McLaren JW, Lam JWH. 2000. Strontium and barium uptake in aragonitic otoliths of marine fish. *Geochim. Cosmochim. Acta* 64:1705–14

81. Gillanders BM. 2001. Trace metals in four structures of fish and their use for estimates of stock structure. *Fish. Bull.* 99:410–19

82. Gillanders BM, Kingsford MJ. 2000. Elemental fingerprints of otoliths of fish may distinguish estuarine 'nursery' habitats. *Mar. Ecol. Prog. Ser.* 201:273–86

83. Gillanders BM. 2002. Temporal and spatial variability in elemental composition of otoliths: implications for determining stock identity and connectivity of populations. *Can. J. Fish. Aquat. Sci.* 59:669–79

84. Thorrold SR, Jones GP, Hellberg ME, Burton RS, Swearer SE, et al. 2002. Quantifying larval retention and connectivity in marine populations with artificial and natural markers. *Bull. Mar. Sci.* 70:291–308

85. Campana SE, Chouinard GA, Hanson JM, Frechet A, Brattey J. 2000. Otolith elemental fingerprints as biological tracers of fish stocks. *Fish. Res.* 46:343–57

86. Campana SE, Thorrold SR. 2001. Otoliths, increments, and elements: keys to a comprehensive understanding of fish populations? *Can. J. Fish. Aquat. Sci.* 58:30–38

87. Milton DA, Chenery SR. 2001. Can otolith chemistry detect the population structure of the shad hilsa *Tenualosa ilisha*? Comparison with the results of genetic and morphological studies. *Mar. Ecol. Prog. Ser.* 222:239–51

88. Morris JA, Rulifson RA, Toburen LH. 2003. Life history strategies of striped bass, *Morone saxatilis*, populations inferred from otolith microchemistry. *Fish. Res.* 62:53–63

89. Edmonds J, Caputi N, Morita M. 1991. Stock discrimination by trace-element analysis of otoliths of orange roughy (*Hoplostethus atlanticus*), a deep-water marine teleost. *Aust. J. Mar. Freshw. Res.* 42:383–89

90. Edmonds J, Steckis R, Moran M, Caputi N, Morita M. 1999. Stock delineation of pink snapper and tailor from western Australia by analysis of stable isotope and strontium/calcium ratios in otolith carbonate. *J. Fish Biol.* 55:243–59

91. Patterson HM, Thorrold SR, Shenker JM. 1999. Analysis of otolith chemistry in Nassau grouper (*Epinephelus striatus*) from the Bahamas and Belize using solution based Icp Ms. *Coral Reefs* 18:171–78

92. Hamer PA, Jenkins GP, Gillanders BM. 2003. Otolith chemistry of juvenile

snapper *Pagrus auratus* in Victorian waters: natural chemical tags and their temporal variation. *Mar. Ecol. Prog. Ser.* 263: 261–73

93. Milton D, Chenery S, Farmer M, Blaber S. 1997. Identifying the spawning estuaries of the tropical shad, *Terubok tenualosa toli*, using otolith microchemistry. *Mar. Ecol. Prog. Ser.* 153:283–91

94. Latkoczy C, Strasse WP, Thorrold S, Swart PK, Gunther D. 2003. Fish ear bones hold clues to migration—implications for fisheries models and design of marine protected areas. *Forensic Sci. Int.* 136:384–85

95. Campana SE, Jones C. 1998. Radiocarbon from nuclear testing applied to age validation of black drum, *Pogonias cromis*. *Fish. Bull.* 96:185–92

96. Thorrold S, Jones C, Swart P, Targett T. 1998. Accurate classification of juvenile weakfish *Cynoscion regalis* to estuarine nursery areas based on chemical signatures in otoliths. *Mar. Ecol. Prog. Ser.* 173:253–65

96a. Thorrold S, Latkoczy C, Swart P, Jones C. 2001. Natal homing in a marine fish metapopulation. *Science* 291:297–99

97. Campana S, Joyce W, Marks L, Natanson L, Kohler N, et al. 2002. Population dynamics of the porbeagle in the Northwest Atlantic Ocean. *N. Am. J. Fish. Manag.* 22:106–21

98. Zacherl DC, Manriquez PH, Paradis G, Day RW, Castilla JC, et al. 2003. Trace elemental fingerprinting of gastropod statoliths to study larval dispersal trajectories. *Mar. Ecol. Prog. Ser.* 248:297–303

99. Swearer SE, Caselle JE, Lea DW, Warner RR. 1999. Larval retention and recruitment in an island population of a coral-reef fish. *Nature* 402:799–802

100. Jones GP, Milicich MJ, Emslie MJ, Lunow C. 1999. Self-recruitment in a coral reef fish population. *Nature* 402:802–4

101. James MK, Armsworth PR, Mason LB, Bode L. 2002. The structure of reef fish metapopulations: modelling larval dispersal and retention pattern. *Proc. R. Soc. London Ser. B* 269:2079–86

102. Dibacco C, Levin L. 2000. Development and application of elemental fingerprinting to track the dispersal of marine invertebrate larvae. *Limnol. Oceanogr.* 45:871–80

103. Zacherl DC, Paradis G, Lea DW. 2003. Barium and strontium uptake into larval protoconchs and statoliths of the marine neogastropod *Kelletia kelledi*. *Geochim. Cosmochim. Acta* 67:4091–99

104. Taylor MS, Hellberg ME. 2003. Genetic evidence for local retention of pelagic larvae in a Caribbean reef fish. *Science* 299:107–9

105. Waples RS. 1998. Separating the wheat from the chaff: patterns of genetic differentiation in high gene flow species. *J. Hered.* 89:438–50

106. Palumbi SR. 1992. Marine speciation on a small planet. *Trends Ecol. Evol.* 7:114–18

107. Palumbi SR. 1996. What can molecular genetics contribute to marine biogeography? An urchin's tale. *J. Exp. Mar. Biol. Ecol.* 203:75–92

108. Grosberg RK, Cunningham CW. 2001. Genetic structure in the sea: from populations to communities. In *Marine Community Ecology*, ed. MD Bertness, S Gaines, ME Hay, pp. 61–84. Sunderland, MA: Sinauer

109. Grosberg R, Levitan D, Cameron B. 1996. Evolutionary genetics of allorecognition in the colonial hydroid *Hydractinia symbiolongicarpus*. *Evolution* 50:2221–40

110. McMillan W, Palumbi SR. 1995. Concordant evolutionary patterns among Indo-West Pacific butterflyfishes. *Proc. R. Soc. London Ser. B* 260:229–36

111. McFadden CS. 1997. Contributions of sexual and asexual reproduction to population structure in the clonal soft coral, *Alcyonium rudyi*. *Evolution* 51:112–26

112. Marko PB. 1998. Historical allopatry and the biogeography of speciation in the prosobranch snail genus *Nucella*. *Evolution* 52:757–74
113. Hellberg ME. 1994. Relationships between inferred levels of gene flow and geographic distance in a philopatric coral, *Balanophyllia elegans*. *Evolution* 48:1829–54
114. Hellberg ME. 1998. Sympatric sea shells along the sea's shore: the geography of speciation in the marine gastropod *Tegula*. *Evolution* 52:1311–24
115. Bohonak AJ. 1999. Dispersal, gene flow, and population structure. *Q. Rev. Biol.* 74:21–45
116. Waples RS, Rosenblatt RH. 1987. Patterns of larval drift in Southern California USA marine shore fishes inferred from allozyme data. *US Natl. Mar. Fish. Serv. Fish. Bull.* 85:1–12
117. Bowen BW, Bass AL, Rocha LA, Grant WS, Robertson DR. 2001. Phylogeography of the trumpetfishes *(Aulostomus)*: ring species complex on a global scale. *Evolution* 55:1029–39
118. Hedgecock D. 1994. Temporal and spatial genetic-structure of marine animal populations in the California current. *Calif. Coop. Ocean. Fish. Investig. Rep.* 35:73–81
119. Bowen BW, Clark AM, Abreugrobois FA, Chaves A, Reichart HA, Ferl RJ. 1997. Global phylogeography of the ridley sea turtles *(Lepidochelys* Spp.) as inferred from mitochondrial DNA sequences. *Genetica* 101:179–89
120. Bowen B, Kamezaki N, Limpus C, Hughes G, Meylan A, Avise J. 1994. Global phylogeography of the loggerhead turtle *(Caretta caretta)* as indicated by mitochondrial-DNA haplotypes. *Evolution* 48:1820–28
121. Bowen B, Meylan A, Avise J. 1991. Evolutionary distinctiveness of the endangered Kemps ridley sea-turtle. *Nature* 352:709–11
122. Bowen B, Abreugrobois F, Balazs G, Kamezaki N, Limpus C, Ferl R. 1995. Trans-Pacific migrations of the loggerhead turtle *(Caretta caretta)* demonstrated with mitochondrial-DNA markers. *Proc. Natl. Acad. Sci. USA* 92:3731–34
123. Baker C, Perry A, Bannister J, Weinrich M, Abernethy R, et al. 1993. Abundant mitochondrial-DNA variation and worldwide population-structure in humpback whales. *Proc. Natl. Acad. Sci. USA* 90:8239–43
124. Bucklin A, Wiebe PH, Smolenack SB, Copley NJ, Clarke ME. 2002. Integrated biochemical, molecular genetic, and bioacoustical analysis of mesoscale variability of the euphausiid *Nematoscelis difficilis* in the California current. *Deep-Sea Res. I* 49:437–62
125. Bucklin A, Astthorsson OS, Gislason A, Allen LD, Smolenack SB, Wiebe PH. 2000. Population genetic variation of *Calanus finmarchicus* in Icelandic waters: preliminary evidence of genetic differences between Atlantic and Arctic populations. *ICES J. Mar. Sci.* 57:1592–1604
126. de Vargas C, Norris R, Zaninetti L, Gibb SW, Pawlowski J. 1999. Molecular evidence of cryptic speciation in planktonic foraminifers and their relation to oceanic provinces. *Proc. Natl. Acad. Sci. USA* 96:2864–68
127. de Vargas C, Bonzon M, Rees NW, Pawlowski J, Zaninetti L. 2002. A molecular approach to biodiversity and biogeography in the planktonic foraminifer *Globigerinella siphonifera* (D'orbigny). *Mar. Micropaleontol.* 45:101–16
128. Darling KF, Wade CM, Stewart IA, Kroon D, Dingle R, Brown AJL. 2000. Molecular evidence for genetic mixing of Arctic and Antarctic subpolar populations of planktonic foraminifers. *Nature* 405:43–47
129. Norris RD. 2000. Pelagic species diversity, biogeography, and evolution. *Paleobiology* 26:236–58
130. Barber PH, Palumbi SR, Erdmann MV, Moosa MK. 2002. Sharp genetic breaks

among populations of *Haptosquilla pulchella* (Stomatopoda) indicate limits to larval transport: patterns, causes, and consequences. *Mol. Ecol.* 11:659–74

131. Barber PH, Palumbi SR, Erdmann MV, Moosa MK. 2000. Biogeography—a marine Wallace's line? *Nature* 406:692–93

132. Avise JC. 1994. *Molecular Markers, Natural History and Evolution*. New York: Chapman & Hall. 511 pp.

133. Williams ST, Jara J, Gomez E, Knowlton N. 2002. The marine Indo-West Pacific break: contrasting the resolving power of mitochondrial and nuclear genes. *Integr. Comp. Biol.* 42:941–52

134. Pannacciulli F, Bishop J, Sj H. 1997. Genetic structure of populations of two species of *Cthamalus* (Crustacea: Cirripedia) in the North-East Atlantic and Mediterranean. *Mar. Biol.* 128:73–82

135. Bucklin A, Frost BW, Bradford-Grieve J, Allen LD, Copley NJ. 2003. Molecular systematic and phylogenetic assessment of 34 calanoid copepod species of the Calanidae and Clausocalanidae. *Mar. Biol.* 142:333–43

136. Cowen RK, Lwiza KMM, Sponaugle S, Paris CB, Olson DB. 2000. Connectivity of marine populations: open or closed? *Science* 287:857–59

137. Raymond M, Rousset F. 2004. *Genepop on the Web*. Montpellier, FR: Lab. Genet. Environ.

138. Excoffier L, Smouse P, Quattro J. 1992. Analysis of molecular variance inferred from metric distances among DNA haplotypes—application to human mitochondrial-DNA restriction data. *Genetics* 131:479–91

139. Schneider S, Roessli D, Excoffier L. 2000. Arlequin: a software for population genetics data analysis. Ver 2. *Genet. Biometry Lab., Dep. Anthropol., Univ. Geneva*

140. Slatkin M, Barton H. 1989. A comparison of 3 indirect methods for estimating average levels of gene flow. *Evolution* 43:1349–68

141. Niegel JE. 1997. Population genetics and demography of marine species. In *Marine Biodiversity: Patterns and Processes*, ed. RFG Ormond, JD Gage, MU Angel, pp. 274–92. Cambridge: Cambridge Univ. Press

142. Slatkin M. 1987. Gene flow and the geographic structure of natural populations. *Science* 236:787–92

143. Rousset F. 1997. Genetic differentiation and estimation of gene flow from F-statistics under isolation by distance. *Genetics* 145:1219–28

144. Slatkin M. 1993. Isolation by distance in equilibrium and nonequilibrium populations. *Evolution* 47:264–79

145. Buonaccorsi VP, Kimbrell CA, Lynn EA, Vetter RD. 2002. Population structure of copper rockfish (*Sebastes caurinus*) reflects postglacial colonization and contemporary patterns of larval dispersal. *Can. J. Fish. Aqua. Sci.* 59:1374–84

146. Kinlan B, Gaines S. 2003. Propagule dispersal in marine and terrestrial environments: a community perspective. *Ecology* 84:2007–20

147. Shanks A, Grantham B, Carr M. 2003. Propagule dispersal distance and the size and spacing of marine reserves. *Ecol. Appl.* 13:S159–69

148. Kelly S, Scott D, MacDiarmid A, Babcock R. 2000. Spiny lobster, *Jasus edwardsii*, recovery in New Zealand marine reserves. *Biol. Conserv.* 92:359–69

149. Palumbi SR. 1994. Genetic divergence, reproductive isolation, and marine speciation. *Annu. Rev. Ecol. Syst.* 25:547–72

150. Reichow D, Smith MJ. 2001. Microsatellites reveal high levels of gene flow among populations of the California squid *Loligo opalescens*. *Mol. Ecol.* 10:1101–9

151. Flowers JM, Schroeter SC, Burton RS. 2002. The recruitment sweepstakes has many winners: genetic evidence from the sea urchin *Strongylocentrotus purpuratus*. *Evolution* 56:1445–53

ELEMENTAL CYCLES: A Status Report on Human or Natural Dominance

R.J. Klee and T.E. Graedel

Center for Industrial Ecology, School of Forestry and Environmental Studies, Yale University, New Haven, Connecticut 06511; email: robert.klee@yale.edu, thomas.graedel@yale.edu

Key Words biogeochemical cycles, industrial ecology, mobilization, periodic table, trace elements

■ **Abstract** The modern technological society mobilizes and uses a very large number of materials. These substances are derived from rocks, sediments, and other natural repositories, and most undergo transformation prior to use. A large fraction of the materials is eventually returned to the environment. Natural processes do the same but not necessarily with the same suite of materials. For purposes of better understanding industrial development and potential environmental impact, it is important to know, even approximately, the elemental cycles of all materials potentially useful for modern technology. In this review, we examine and summarize cycle information for 77 of the first 92 elements in the periodic table. Mobilization calculations demonstrate that human activities likely dominate or strongly perturb the cycles of most of the elements other than the alkalis, alkali earths, and halogens. We propose that this pattern is ultimately related to the aqueous solubilities of the predominant chemical forms of the elements as they occur in nature: Human action dominates the cycles of the elements whose usual forms are highly insoluble, nature those that are highly soluble. Examples of the utility of anthropogenically dominated cycle determinations for resource supply analyses, environmental impact assessment, and public policy are presented and discussed. If the rapid rise in the use of materials by the technological society in the twentieth century continues into the next century, anthropogenic dominance of the cycling of a majority of the elements of the periodic table will only increase.

CONTENTS

INTRODUCTION 70
COMPONENTS OF CYCLES 71
SURVEY OF ELEMENTAL CYCLE INFORMATION 73
ESTIMATING RELATIVE ANTHROPOGENIC DOMINANCE
  OF ELEMENTAL CYCLES 74
CYCLES OVER SPACE AND TIME 93
THE PRACTICAL UTILITY OF CYCLES 101
DISCUSSION 103

INTRODUCTION

The characterization of cycles has a rich history in biogeochemistry. The obvious example, among many others, is the global carbon cycle. Knowledge of this cycle has evolved over several decades as new sources and sinks have been discovered, flows quantified, missing flows identified, and the relatively small but climatically important human influence monitored in detail. Two goals have driven this effort: (*a*) to establish a firm scientific understanding and (*b*) to do so with sufficient reliability and in enough detail that policy options related to human perturbations might be reasonably discussed. The utility of this approach has given rise to similar efforts related to other chemical cycles of nature, including nitrogen, sulfur, and phosphorus. The job is not yet complete, but good progress is being made.

In contrast to these vigorous efforts related to Earth's natural cycles, little effort has been expended on the cycles of materials dominated by human action, such as the engineering metals. There have been suggestions that human action has an effect on the global cycles of the crust-forming elements and metals—Bertine & Goldberg (1) discussed this issue from the perspective of rock weathering; Martin & Meybeck (2) for riverine systems; and Lantzy & Mackenzie (3) for the atmosphere—but those efforts made only a very preliminary attempt to quantify the human-initiated flow magnitudes. Perhaps the most noteworthy work in this area (but work that is now outdated) is the estimation of global metal flows from natural and anthropogenic sources by Nriagu, Pacyna, and their colleagues (see for example, References 4, 5). Clearly, if we have a good quantitative understanding of cycles dominated by human action, we will be much better able to assess the long-term availability of resources, the potential for accumulative toxicity to ecosystems, and the potential for "mining" the landfills and other nonvirgin resource reservoirs, among a host of other issues that currently cannot be reliably addressed.

Despite the potential utility of technological material cycles, there are surprisingly few available. In an effort to provide a status report, we have collected and summarized anthropogenically related cycle information. We have chosen, for tractability, to restrict our scope to the first 92 elements of the periodic table (or most of them). We thus do not treat aggregates, such as stone or sand, products synthesized wholly or virtually so by human technology [chlorofluorocarbons (CFCs), plastics, composites, and others], or renewables, such as forest products. The cycles of the elements themselves prove to be subjects of great breadth and interest, and serve as a guide toward approaches suitable for the groups of materials we have omitted.

Because there are so few complete, global, elemental cycles available, we have attempted here a preliminary calculation of the total global mobilization of 77 elements (all but the noble gases and short-lived radioactive elements) from both anthropogenic and natural processes. Accordingly, herein we attempt to address the following questions:

- How well do we know the cycles of the naturally occurring elements? Although both nature and humans sequester and/or mobilize essentially all of the elements, are all of the cycles of interest?
- Which of these cycles are dominated by human activity? Some cycles are without question dominated by nature, at least so far as total fluxes are concerned. Some are not. The degree of human dominance has thus far been addressed only in special cases, not universally.
- What are the implications of human dominance? Three areas might well be addressed in this connection: resource depletion, the functioning of natural systems, and biological toxicity.

COMPONENTS OF CYCLES

Cycles of technological and natural materials provide perspectives difficult to achieve by other techniques. A well-done analysis begins with an overview of the more important and less important inputs and outputs, identifies gaps in knowledge, and stimulates additional efforts to identify and quantify poorly known cycle elements (6). Unlike biogeochemical cycles, where some of the most important input and output processes may be unknown (such as the current scientific debate surrounding the forest, soil, and/or ocean sinks in the global carbon cycle), technological cycles, in principle, have no components that cannot be determined by studying the activities of industries, governments, and customers. In practice, however, issues of national sovereignty, corporate proprietary information, or absent measurement and monitoring systems to collect the desired information represent challenges to the analyst.

An overview of cycle analysis can be demonstrated with the aid of the two-reservoir model shown in Figure 1*a*. *Reservoirs* are compartments in which a material can be stored, and the amount of a particular material in a reservoir constitutes the *stock*. Reservoirs may be ensemble entities difficult to assess with great accuracy (e.g., an ocean) or small, easily quantifiable ones (e.g., a warehouse). Flows into and out of reservoirs are termed *fluxes*. An analysis treating fluxes into and out of only a single reservoir (a personal bank account or an organism, for example) is termed a *budget*. We refer to the reservoir or reservoirs within which nature stores the majority of a given element as *sequestration reservoirs*. Residence times in these reservoirs are typically long. Analogously, the reservoir or reservoirs into which this material is transferred, typically for much shorter periods of time, are termed *mobilization reservoirs*. Flows from the former are termed *mobilization flows*, and those from the latter *sequestration flows*. Because material that is transferred from a sequestration reservoir is eventually returned to it, the cycle of Figure 1*a* is termed *closed*. A somewhat more complicated anthropogenic system is pictured in Figure 1*b*. In this system, the first reservoir (Earth's crust) continually supplies material, and the fourth reservoir (the landfill)

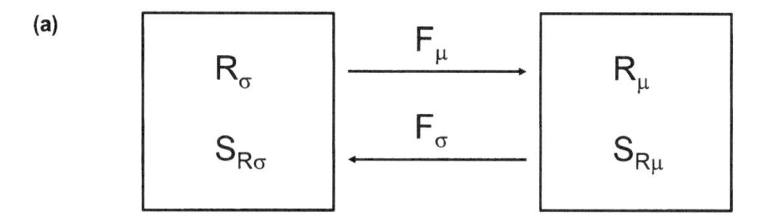

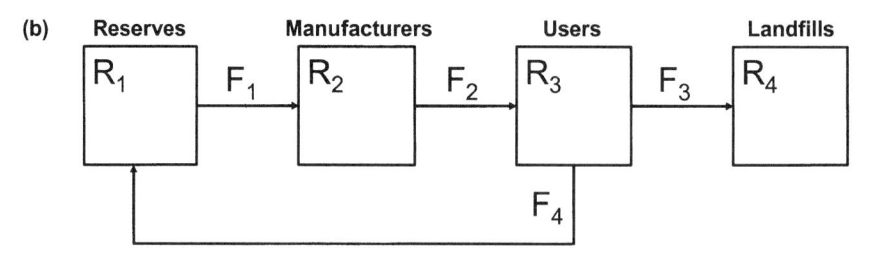

Figure 1 (a) A two-reservoir model of a closed cycle. The notation is R, reservoir; S, stock; F, flow; μ, mobilization; and σ, sequestration. (b) A four-reservoir model of an anthropogenic open cycle, where raw material resources are mobilized from geologic reserves, transformed during manufacturing and use, and then discarded to a landfill or recycled.

continually receives it. (The term *landfill* implies a generic final repository for anthropogenic material, which, in addition to actual landfills, would also include terrestrial sediments, ocean sediments, and seawater, among others.) As a result, even though the diagram contains cyclic elements, the cyclicity is not complete, and the cycle is not in balance. In the terminology of cycling, the landfill is an *accumulative* reservoir, and the system is *open*.

Cycle analysis becomes more complicated when the amount of time that a material spends in a specific reservoir (which need not be the same as the time spent in other reservoirs) is factored in. In Figure 1b, for example, we expect that material will flow rapidly through a manufacturing facility and much more slowly through the cycle of use. This characteristic is determined by dividing the pool size of a reservoir by the total flux from it; the result is the *turnover time*, which can be thought of as the time necessary to empty the reservoir if the sinks remained constant and the sources were removed. Cycle analyses can become much more intricate than suggested by the simple example above, particularly if nonlinearities and coupled cycles are involved (6). For the present purposes, however, the rudimentary approach of Figures 1a and 1b represents a level of sophistication that is quite sufficient to produce interesting and useful results.

SURVEY OF ELEMENTAL CYCLE INFORMATION

To derive an assessment of the current state of elemental cycle understanding, we searched for existing cycles or partial cycles that met the following criteria:

- Encompass at least several of the flows and/or stocks of the generic Figure 1a, not merely a single one, such as gaseous emissions;
- Use what appears to be reliable data, not conjectures; and
- Are directed to a geographical region, country, or the planet, not merely a localized system, such as a factory.

The complete results of our survey are shown in the Supplemental Table: Follow the Supplemental Material link from the Annual Reviews home page at http://www.annualreviews.org. In this Supplemental Table, we provide information on the major anthropogenic uses, the type of cycle analysis available in the literature (flows only, or stocks and flows; we found none dealing with stocks only), the year or years for which the cycle was developed, the geographical scope, and relevant citations for each of the elements. In some cases, the cycles include both anthropogenic and natural components. Where they do not, we provide a citation to the natural flows.

One unsurprising result from our survey is the number of elements for which little or no global cycle information is available (21 of 92, or slightly over 20%). Most of these elements are inert gases, rare earths, or actinides. Only two groups have tended to receive extensive study: (a) the grand nutrient and halogen cycles of nature [e.g., carbon (7), nitrogen (8), phosphorus (9), and chlorine (10)], of interest because of the degree to which those natural cycles are being perturbed by human action, and (b) the toxic metals, of interest because of their human health hazards [e.g., lead (11, 12), mercury (13, 14), cadmium (12, 15, 16), and arsenic (17, 18)]. There are pieces of information for many of the common engineering metals [e.g., iron (19), nickel (20), and copper (21, 22)], but few broad-scale cycles, and there is essentially no information for materials with comparatively low flows but critical uses (e.g., gallium, germanium, and indium). A few of the elements have extensive country-scale information but little on a broader scale [e.g., cobalt (23), silver (24), tungsten (25), and vanadium (26)].

Even where cycles have been characterized, they tend to lack a number of desirable attributes. Most deal only with flows, not with stocks. Most also were derived for only a single point in time; they are thus merely snapshots of transport between reservoirs. This characteristic effectively decouples flows from stocks, because the stocks in the various reservoirs cannot generally be measured and because the absence of flow information as a function of time prevents the stocks from being derived. Although some measures of geologic stocks vary over time according to the price of the resource, extraction technology, and new discoveries, geologists customarily estimate the *reserve base* (the quantity of identified resources regardless of their current economic viability) or *resources* (the total quantity of a resource thought to exist regardless of its location or concentration) (27).

A final inadequacy of nearly all the cycles is a lack of spatial distribution of the flows, the stocks, or both. The only exceptions are carbon, nitrogen, and sulfur, for which anthropogenic influences are treated as perturbations to the natural cycles. It is clear from even casual assessment that a signal characteristic of human materials use is the spatial transfer of materials from their geological source reservoirs (typically in remote areas) to human reception reservoirs (typically in urban and peri-urban areas). Very little quantitative information on such spatial transfers is thus far available.

ESTIMATING RELATIVE ANTHROPOGENIC DOMINANCE OF ELEMENTAL CYCLES

One item of particular interest for the elemental cycles is the degree to which they reflect anthropogenic activity. The relevant data are not the stocks, which nature always dominates, but the mobilization flows from the geological reservoirs. These flows are the F_μ flows of Figure 1a. If all relevant flows and their magnitudes are known, anthropogenic cycle dominance exists if

$$\sum F_\mu(a) > \sum F_\mu(n),$$

where a and n refer to anthropogenic and natural, respectively.

As stated above, there are only a handful of complete, global elemental cycles that incorporate both natural and anthropogenic mobilization flows (including carbon, nitrogen, sulfur, phosphorous, and mercury). For purposes of preliminary investigation (and to stimulate thought, debate, and further research), we have devised a system to approximate anthropogenic and natural mobilization flows for over 70 other elements on the basis of three anthropogenic mobilization factors and three natural mobilization factors. The former are (a) the amount of element mobilized through mining; (b) the amount of element mobilized through fossil-fuel combustion; and (c) the amount of element mobilized through human-initiated biomass burning (such as deforestation, biofuel burning, charcoal making, charcoal burning, and combustion of agricultural residues). The latter factors are (a) the amount of element mobilized through weathering of continental crust into rivers; (b) the amount of element mobilized through sea spray; and (c) the amount of element mobilized through net primary production. These mobilization factors are graphically depicted, using sample data for the mobilization of magnesium, in the cartoon in Figure 2.

First and foremost, the simplified method used herein to estimate the relative anthropogenic dominance of elemental cycles has been designed for standardized comparison across the breadth of the periodic table. Therefore, the calculations derived in this review will not necessarily exactly match (nor even measure) the exact same fluxes of existing biogeochemical cycle analyses [such as the work of

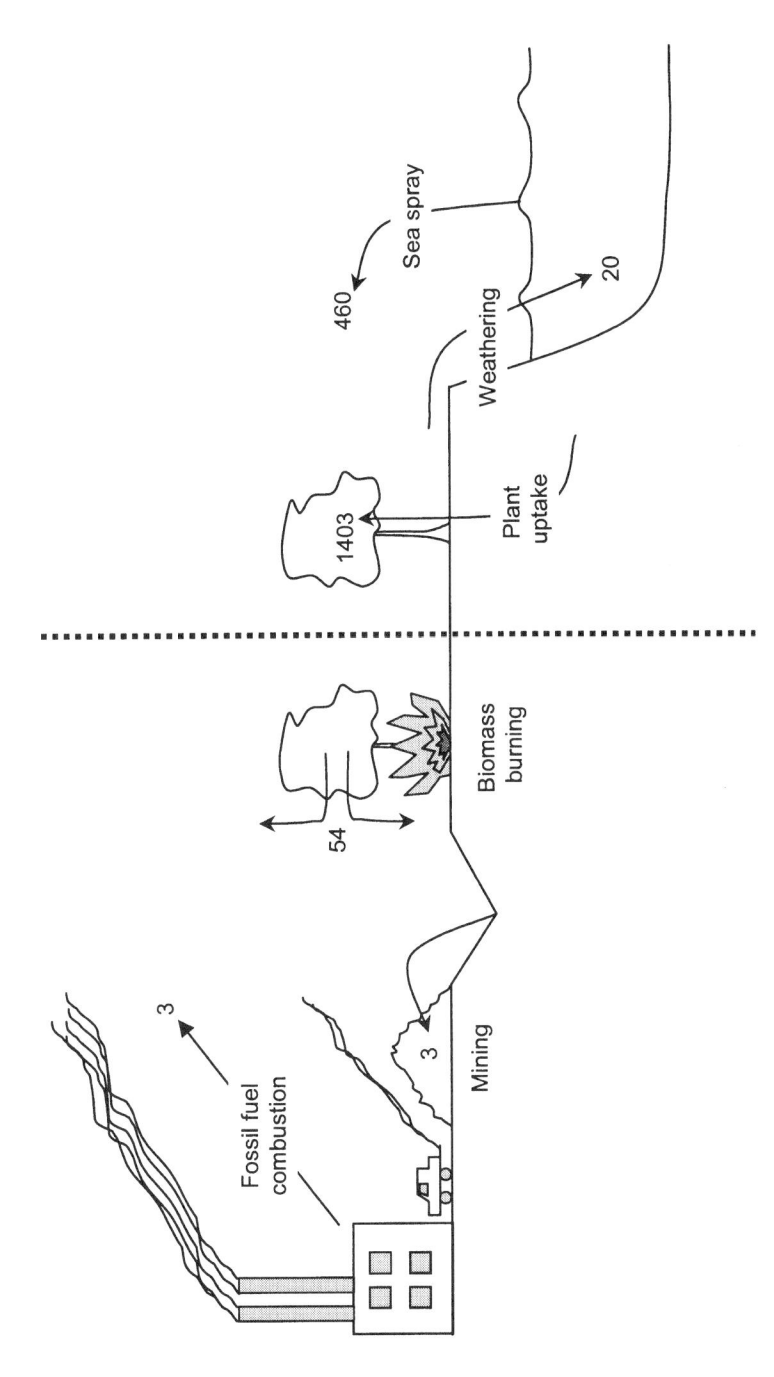

Figure 2 (*left*) Cartoon depicting anthropogenic mobilization (mining, fossil-fuel combustion, and biomass burning) and (*right*) natural mobilization (crustal weathering, sea spray, and plant primary production). Sample data (calculated in this review) on the relative anthropogenic and natural mobilization of magnesium is provided in terragrams per year.

Schlesinger (28), among others]. For instance, gaseous volcanic emissions are not included in this analysis; they are sporadic, poorly quantified, and almost certainly not dominant for the timescales we address [for example, for aluminum and iron, gaseous volcanic mobilization appears to be less than 10% of natural mobilization (3)]. Submarine hydrothermal emissions are also not included. As with gaseous volcanic emissions, they are currently poorly quantified on a global scale for the breadth of elements addressed herein. Mobilization of material through sea-spray processes is also poorly quantified, but it is included here because it is a perpetual and significant movement of material. Most of it, but not all, quickly returns to the sea surface, so this mobilization is more transient and involves less change over time than the other processes. Sea-spray mobilization is important for only a handful of elements (e.g., sodium, chlorine, bromine, sulfur, and a few others), but these deserve at least a preliminary estimate. We also make the logical assumption that nature mobilizes the majority of hydrogen and oxygen (obviously through the hydrologic cycle).

Definitions of mobilization are open to considerable discussion, largely because different definitions serve different uses. Our aim is to reflect the average rate at which the state of a material is transformed from passive (e.g., in rock or soil) to potentially interactive (e.g., in industrial products or in vegetation), with a focus on the pedosphere (where humans literally and figuratively leave their footprints) and the near-surface ocean. Although measuring the amount of these potentially interactive elements that are actually bioavailable but not yet bioincorporated would also be important and interesting, such detailed analysis is not currently possible for the breadth of elements we address in this analysis. We do not address very short-term processes, such as the uptake of carbon by plant photosynthesis during the day and its release by respiration at night. Our inclusion of sea spray might be contested on this basis but seems worth including because of its importance for addressing the cycles of a few elements. Overall, as a rough approximation, we believe that this method would capture over 80% of the actual total mobilization.

This method borrows from the work of Park & Schlesinger (29) on the geochemical cycle of boron, although with a key distinction. We do not partition the mobilization of material into the different recipient reservoirs (the atmosphere, oceans, or land) as is done by Park & Schlesinger. Therefore, the entire mass that has been mobilized is counted as mobilized with our method, regardless of the final destination of the element. For instance, our biomass burning mobilization estimates consider the entire bulk of combusted plant matter as mobilized for the purpose of our calculations. Unlike recent analyses that estimate the gaseous flux of various elements into the atmosphere (see, for example, References 29, 30), we do not differentiate between the amount of the plant matter that becomes a gas or an airborne particulate or that is left behind as ash. Park & Schlesinger's added level of detail would be an improvement for future analyses and would begin to more closely link human perturbation with sensitive natural processes, but this would only be possible with intimate knowledge of the behavior of each individual element. Our method sacrifices this detail to enable a broad comparison of a large number of elements. Also, we believe that our method is an improvement over that of Azar et al. (31), which limited natural mobilization to only weathering and volcanic processes (disregarding the considerable mobilization for a small number of elements from sea spray and biological production).

Table 1 provides the basic concentration factors used in the calculation of anthropogenic and natural mobilization. Specifically, the average elemental compositions of coal, petroleum, continental crust, seawater, and dry plant matter are given. Table 2 uses the basic concentration factors in Table 1, annual mine production statistics from Reference 55 (unless otherwise noted), and values for the annual consumption of fossil fuels (4741 Tg/yr coal, 3268 Tg/yr petroleum) (32), biomass burning (8600 Tg/yr) (30), suspended sediment flow in rivers (1500 Tg/yr) (33), sea-salt aerosol formation (3800 Tg/yr, see derivation below), and net primary production (224,500 Tg/yr) (34).

Sea-spray estimations for the suite of elements are computed using the method employed by Park & Schlesinger (29), except for chlorine, sodium, sulfur, and nitrogen, which have independently calculated values from Graedel & Keene (10) (for chlorine and sodium) and Schlesinger (28) (for sulfur and nitrogen). Specifically, the annual production of sea-salt aerosols has been estimated at 10×10^{15} g/yr (35) to 11.7×10^{15} g/yr (36). The average seawater salinity is 0.035% (29). Multiplying the estimated production of aerosols by the average seawater salinity and by the average concentration of each element in Table 1 [from Stumm & Morgan (37)], we yield two estimates of sea-spray flux. A third estimate is obtained using a similar calculation that takes the calculated sea-spray flux of chlorine estimated by Graedel & Keene (10) (6000 Tg/yr) and multiplies this value by the "chlorinity ratio" of each element in seawater—that is the ratio of the average concentration of each element in seawater to the concentration of chlorine in seawater, again from Table 1. We use the mean of these three estimates in the final estimate of sea-spray flux in Table 2.

Although the magnitudes of the mobilization flows may be known only approximately, such information is often sufficiently quantitative to permit us to explore the relationship between anthropogenic and natural mobilizations. The final three columns of Table 2 offer summary statistics on total element mobilization from its geological reservoirs, the ratio of anthropogenic to natural mobilization, and the percent of total flow of the element that is attributable to anthropogenic activity.

These summary statistics are used to create Figure 3, which depicts the logarithm of anthropogenic mobilization divided by natural mobilization for all of the elemental mobilization flows calculated herein. The elements where human activity dominates mobilization are on the left-hand (positive) side of the graph, and the elements for which nature dominates mobilization are on the right-hand (negative) side of the graph. Of the 77 elements depicted in this graph, human activities dominate 54 elements, and nature dominates 23 elements. Recall that nature also dominates the mobilization of hydrogen and oxygen, although these are not included in Figure 3. Figure 4*a–f* displays this information in more detail, showing bar graphs of the various elements and their relative mobilization from

TABLE 1 Concentration factors used in mobilization calculations

Element		Average concentration in coal in g/Mg[a]	Average concentration in petroleum in g/Mg[b]	Average concentration in crust in g/Mg[c]	Average concentration in seawater in g/Mg[d]	Average concentration in dry plant matter in g/Mg[e]
2	He	—	—	0.003[f]	0.00001	—
3	Li	20	—	22	0.2	—
4	Be	2.0	0.0004[g]	3.1		—
5	B	50	0.2[h]	17	4.5	58
6	C	890,000[i]	855,000[i]	3,240	28	478,000[k]
7	N	5,850[i]	10,500[j]	83	150	25,000
9	F	150	—	611	1.3	—
11	Na	400[l]	12	25,670	10,770	1,100
12	Mg	700[l]	0.1[g]	13,510	1,290	6,250
13	Al	11,000[l]	0.5[g]	77,440	0.002	500[m]
14	Si	—	—	303,480	2.2	—
15	P	150	—	665	0.1	2,250
16	S	13,500[i]	10,300[j]	953	905	2,000
17	Cl	1,000	10	640	19,354	550
19	K	1,000[l]	4.9	28,650	399	32,500
20	Ca	2,300[l]	5.0[g]	29,450	412	30,000
21	Sc	4.0	0.004	7.0	—	—
22	Ti	600	0.1	3,117	—	1.0[m]
23	V	40	279	53	0.003	1.6[m]
24	Cr	20	2.7[n]	35	0.0003	0.2[m]
25	Mn	70	0.6	527	0.0002	138
26	Fe	7,500[l]	20	30,890	0.002	175
27	Co	5.0	3.4	12	0.00005	15
28	Ni	20	66	19	0.001	3.0[m]
29	Cu	15	0.4[n]	14	0.001	10
30	Zn	50	0.8[n]	52	0.8	45
31	Ga	5.0	0.2	14	—	—
32	Ge	5.0	0.001[g]	1.4	—	—
33	As	10	0.2[n]	2.0	0.004	0.2[m]
34	Se	1.0	0.5	0.08	—	0.2[m]
35	Br	20	0.6	1.6	67	—
37	Rb	15	—	110	0.1	—
38	Sr	200	0.1[g]	316	8	—
39	Y	15	0.001[g]	21	—	—

(*Continued*)

TABLE 1 (*Continued*)

Element		Average concentration in coal in g/Mg[a]	Average concentration in petroleum in g/Mg[b]	Average concentration in crust in g/Mg[c]	Average concentration in seawater in g/Mg[d]	Average concentration in dry plant matter in g/Mg[e]
40	Zr	50	—	237	—	—
41	Nb	5.0	—	26	—	—
42	Mo	3.0	7.9	1.4	0.01	2.8
44	Ru	0.1[o]	—	0.001	—	—
45	Rh	0.1[o]	—	0.0006	—	—
46	Pd	0.1[o]	—	0.004	—	—
47	Ag	0.1	0.0001[g]	0.055	0.00004	0.06[m]
48	Cd	0.5	0.002[n]	0.102	0.0001	0.6[m]
49	In	0.1[o]	—	0.06	—	—
50	Sn	2.0	0.01[g]	2.5	0.00001	0.3[m]
51	Sb	1.0	0.1	0.3	0.0002	0.06[m]
52	Te	0.1[o]	—	0.005	—	—
53	I	5.0	1.4	1.4	0.1	—
55	Cs	1.0	—	5.8	0.0004	—
56	Ba	200	0.1[g]	668	0.02	—
57	La	10	0.005[g]	32	—	—
58	Ce	20	0.01[g]	66	—	—
59	Pr	3.0	—	6.3	—	—
60	Nd	10	—	26	—	—
62	Sm	2.0	—	4.7	—	0.01[m]
63	Eu	0.5	—	1.0	—	—
64	Gd	1.0	—	2.8	—	—
65	Tb	0.2	—	0.5	—	—
66	Dy	3.0	—	2.9	—	—
67	Ho	1.0	—	0.6	—	—
68	Er	1.0	0.001[g]	2.1	—	—
69	Tm	0.1[o]	—	0.3	—	—
70	Yb	1.0	—	1.5	—	—
71	Lu	0.2	—	0.3	—	—
72	Hf	1.0	—	5.8	—	—
73	Ta	0.2	—	1.5	—	—
74	W	1.0	—	1.4	0.0001	—
75	Re	0.1[o]	—	0.0004	—	—

(*Continued*)

TABLE 1 (*Continued*)

Element	Average concentration in coal in g/Mg[a]	Average concentration in petroleum in g/Mg[b]	Average concentration in crust in g/Mg[c]	Average concentration in seawater in g/Mg[d]	Average concentration in dry plant matter in g/Mg[e]
76 Os	0.1[o]	—	0.00005	—	—
77 Ir	0.1[o]	—	0.00005	—	—
78 Pt	0.1[o]	—	0.0004	—	—
79 Au	0.01[o]	—	0.003	0.000004	—
80 Hg	0.1	7.7	0.06	0.00003	0.02[m]
81 Tl	0.1[o]	—	0.8	—	—
82 Pb	40	0.3[g]	17	0.00004	2.7[m]
83 Bi	0.1[o]	—	0.1	—	—
90 Th	4.0	—	10	0.00001	—
92 U	2.0	0.02	2.5	0.003	—

[a]From Reference 45 unless otherwise noted.
[b]From Reference 46 unless otherwise noted.
[c]From Reference 47 unless otherwise noted.
[d]From Reference 37 unless otherwise noted.
[e]From Reference 48.
[f]From Reference 53.
[g]From Reference 50.
[h]From Reference 29.
[i]Major element concentrations derived from empirical formulas of bituminous ($C_{137}H_{97}O_9NS$) and anthracite ($C_{240}H_{90}O_4NS$) coal.
[j]From Reference 51.
[k]Average plant carbon concentration estimated from the Biomass Feedstock Composition and Properties Database (54).
[l]From Reference 49, on the basis of mean concentration in U.S. coal.
[n]From Reference 52.
[m]From Reference 3.
[n]From Reference 52.
[o]Maximum concentration (element concentration at or below detection limit).

anthropogenic and natural processes. These diagrams are organized according to the total calculated mobilization flow. For ease of graphing, we only include those elements whose total mobilization is greater than 0.01 Tg/year; therefore only 56 of the 77 elements from Table 2 are depicted. As is apparent from these figures, nature generally dominates the high total flow elements (Figure 4*a–c*), whereas human activities generally dominate the low total flow elements (Figure 4*d–f*). This relationship is graphically displayed in Figure 4*g*, which shows the anthropogenic dominance of elements with low total mobilization.

An important caveat with respect to our dominance determinations is that they apply only to flows, not to impacts. The environmental impact of CFCs is very

TABLE 2 Calculation of mobilization rates and dominance

	Element		Anthropogenic mobilization				Natural mobilization				Mobilization summary		
			From mining in Gg/year[a]	From fossil fuels in Gg/year[b]	From biomass burning in Gg/year[c]	Total in Tg/year	From crustal weathering in Gg/year[d]	From seaspray in Gg/year[e]	From plant primary production in Gg/year[f]	Total in Tg/year	Total in Tg/year	Anthropogenic vs. natural ratio	Anthropogenic as % of total
2	He		19	—	—	0.02	0.005	0.002	—	0.00001	0.02	2,879	100
3	Li		5.6[g]	95	—	0.1	33	62	—	0.10	0.2	1.1	51
4	Be		0.3	9.5	—	0.01	4.7	—	—	0.005	0.01	2.1	68
5	B		1,360	238	495	2.1	26	1,604	12,909	15	17	0.1	13
6	C		—	7,013,630	4,110,800	11,124	4,860	9,991	107,311,000	107,326	118,450	0.1	9
7	N		109,000	100,000[h]	215,000	424	125	30,000[h]	5,612,500	5643	6,067	0.1	7
9	F		2,320	711	—	3.0	917	463	—	1.4	4.4	2.2	69
11	Na		90,771	1,937	9,460	102	38,505	390,0000[i]	246,950	4,185	4,288	0.02	2
12	Mg		3,458	3,319	53,750	61	20,265	459,891	1,403,125	1,883	1,944	0.03	3
13	Al		24,000	52,153	4,300	80	116,160	0.8	112,250	228	309	0.4	26
14	Si		100,500	—	—	101	455,220	795	—	456	557	0.2	18
15	P		12,000[h]	711	19,350	32	998[h]	22	505,125	506	538	0.06	6
16	S		57,200	97,664	17,200	172	1,430	144,000[h]	449,000	594	766	0.3	22
17	Cl		129,812	4,772	4,730	139	960	6,000,000[i]	123,475	6,124	6,264	0.02	2
19	K		21,002	4,757	279,500	305	42,975	142,245	7,296,250	7,481	7,787	0.04	4
20	Ca		54,000[g]	10,921	258,000	323	44,175	146,915	6,735,000	6,926	7,249	0.05	4
21	Sc		0.3[j]	19	—	0.02	11	—	—	0.01	0.03	1.8	65
22	Ti		2,817	2,845	8.6	5.7	4,676	—	225	4.9	11	1.2	54
23	V		43	1,102	14	1.2	80	0.9	359	0.4	1.6	2.6	72
24	Cr		14,400	103	2.0	15	53	0.1	52	0.1	15	139	99
25	Mn		7,280	334	1,183	8.8	791	0.08	30,869	32	40	0.3	22
26	Fe		725,000[g]	35,622	1,505	762	46,335	0.6	39,288	86	848	8.9	90
27	Co		33	35	126	0.2	17	0.02	3,278	3.3	3.5	0.1	6

(*Continued*)

TABLE 2 (*Continued*)

	Element	Anthropogenic mobilization				Natural mobilization				Mobilization summary		
		From mining in Gg/year[a]	From fossil fuels in Gg/year[b]	From biomass burning in Gg/year[c]	Total in Tg/year	From crustal weathering in Gg/year[d]	From seaspray in Gg/year[e]	From plant primary production in Gg/year[f]	Total in Tg/year	Total in Tg/year	Anthropogenic vs. natural ratio	Anthropogenic as % of total
28	Ni	1,250	311	26	1.6	28	0.5	673.5	0.7	2.3	2.3	69
29	Cu	13,200	72	86	13	21	0.2	2,245	2.3	16	5.9	85
30	Zn	8,730	240	387	9.4	78	293	10,103	10	20	0.9	47
31	Ga	0.1	24	—	0.02	21	—	—	0.02	0.05	1.2	54
32	Ge	0.1	24	—	0.02	2.1	—	—	0.002	0.03	11	92
33	As	34	48	1.7	0.08	3.0	1.3	45	0.05	0.1	1.7	63
34	Se	1.4	6.2	1.7	0.01	0.1	—	45	0.05	0.05	0.2	17
35	Br	542	97	—	0.6	2.4	23,993	—	24	25	0.03	3
37	Rb	0.001	71	—	0.07	165	43	—	0.2	0.3	0.3	25
38	Sr	520	949	—	1	474	2816	—	3.3	4.8	0.4	31
39	Y	1.9	71	—	0.07	31	—	—	0.03	0.1	2.4	70
40	Zr	1,040	237	—	1	356	—	—	0.4	1.6	3.6	78
41	Nb	33	24	—	0.1	39	—	—	0.04	0.1	1.4	59
42	Mo	129	40	24	0.2	2.1	3.4	617	0.6	0.8	0.3	24
44	Ru	0.01[k]	0.5	—	0.0005	0.002	—	—	0.000002	0.0005	325	100
45	Rh	0.03[l]	0.5	—	0.0005	0.001	—	—	0.000001	0.001	555	100
46	Pd	0.2	0.5	—	0.0006	0.01	—	—	0.00001	0.001	108	99
47	Ag	18	0.5	0.5	0.02	0.1	0.02	13	0.01	0.03	1.4	58
48	Cd	20	2.4	5.2	0.03	0.2	0.04	135	0.1	0.16	0.2	17
49	In	0.3	0.5	—	0.0008	0.1	—	—	0.0001	0.001	8.8	90
50	Sn	238	10	2.6	0.3	3.8	0.004	67	0.07	0.3	3.5	78
51	Sb	118	5.2	0.5	0.1	0.5	0.09	13	0.01	0.1	8.8	90
52	Te	0.1	0.5	—	0.0006	0.008	—	—	0.000008	0.0006	80	99

DOMINANCE OF ELEMENTAL CYCLES

53	I	19	28	—	0.05	2.1	23	—	0.02	0.07	1.9	66
55	Cs	100	4.7	—	0.1	8.7	0.1	—	0.009	0.1	12	92
56	Ba	3,060	949	—	4	1002	8	—	1.0	5.0	4.0	80
57	La	20ʲ	47	—	0.1	48	—	—	0.05	0.1	1.4	58
58	Ce	33ʲ	95	—	0.1	99	—	—	0.1	0.2	1.3	56
59	Pr	0.3ʲ	14	—	0.01	9.5	—	—	0.01	0.02	1.5	61
60	Nd	11ʲ	47	—	0.06	39	—	—	0.04	0.10	1.5	60
62	Sm	0.3ʲ	9.5	0.05	0.01	7.1	—	1.2	0.01	0.02	1.2	54
63	Eu	0.3ʲ	2.4	—	0.003	1.4	—	—	0.001	0.004	1.9	65
64	Gd	0.3ʲ	4.7	—	0.005	4.2	—	—	0.004	0.01	1.2	55
65	Tb	0.3ʲ	0.9	—	0.001	0.8	—	—	0.001	0.002	1.7	63
66	Dy	0.3ʲ	14	—	0.01	4.4	—	—	0.004	0.02	3.3	77
67	Ho	0.3ʲ	4.7	—	0.005	0.9	—	—	0.001	0.006	5.5	85
68	Er	0.3ʲ	4.7	—	0.005	3.2	—	—	0.003	0.01	1.6	62
69	Tm	0.3ʲ	0.5	—	0.001	0.5	—	—	0.0005	0.001	1.8	64
70	Yb	0.3ʲ	4.7	—	0.005	2.3	—	—	0.002	0.01	2.3	69
71	Lu	0.3ʲ	0.9	—	0.001	0.4	—	—	0.000	0.002	3.2	76
72	Hf	21ᵐ	4.7	—	0.03	8.7	—	—	0.01	0.03	2.9	75
73	Ta	0.8	0.9	—	0.002	2.3	—	—	0.002	0.004	0.8	44
74	W	37	4.7	—	0.04	2.1	0.03	—	0.002	0.04	20	95
75	Re	0.03	0.5	—	0.001	0.001	—	—	0.000001	0.001	838	100
76	Os	0.0002ⁿ	0.5	—	0.0005	0.0001	—	—	0.0000001	0.0005	6323	100
77	Ir	0.004ᵏ	0.5	—	0.0005	0.0001	—	—	0.0000001	0.0005	6373	100
78	Pt	0.2	0.5	—	0.001	0.001	—	—	0.000001	0.001	1049	100
79	Au	2.6	0.05	—	0.003	0.004	0.001	—	0.0000005	0.003	504	100
80	Hg	1.4	26	37	0.06	0.08	0.01	3.4	0.003	0.07	18.5	95
81	Tl	0.02	0.5	—	0.0005	1.1	—	—	0.001	0.002	0.4	30

(*Continued*)

TABLE 2 (Continued)

Element		From mining in Gg/year[a]	From fossil fuels in Gg/year[b]	From biomass burning in Gg/year[c]	Total in Tg/year	From crustal weathering in Gg/year[d]	From seaspray in Gg/year[e]	From plant primary production in Gg/year[f]	Total in Tg/year	Total in Tg/year	Anthropogenic vs. natural ratio	Anthropogenic as % of total
82	Pb	3,100	191	23	3.3	26	0.01	606	0.6	3.9	5.2	84
83	Bi	5.9	0.5	—	0.01	0.2	—	—	0.0002	0.01	34	97
90	Th	1.5[o]	19	—	0.02	15	0.003	—	0.02	0.04	1.3	57
92	U	35[g]	10	—	0.04	3.8	1.1	—	0.005	0.05	9.2	90

Anthropogenic mobilization — Natural mobilization — Mobilization summary

[a]From Reference 55 unless otherwise noted. Some elemental values were calculated from their common mineral ore compounds.
[b]Assuming worldwide consumption of 4741 Tg/yr (32) and concentration factors from Table 1.
[c]Assuming worldwide biomass burning of 8600 Tg/yr (30) and concentration factors from Table 1.
[d]Assuming suspended sediment flux of 1500 Tg/yr (33) and concentration factors from Table 1.
[e]Assuming 2×10^{11} Mg/yr seawater becomes sea spray, using the method from Park & Schlesinger (29).
[f]Assuming worldwide net primary production of 224,500 Tg/yr (34).
[g]Reference 27.
[h]Independently calculated values (28).
[i]Independently calculated values (10).
[j]Rare-earth mining estimated using average ratio of rare-earth elements in common mineral ores (56) and bulk rare-earth mining statistics (55).
[k]Reference 57.
[l]Reference 58.
[m]Hafnium mining estimated from average ration between zirconium and hafnium in common mineral ores of 50:1 (55).
[n]Estimate from Christie & Challis (59).
[o]Estimate from Roskill (60), using thorium content of total monzanite produced for its rare-earth element content (thorium is an unwanted by-product).

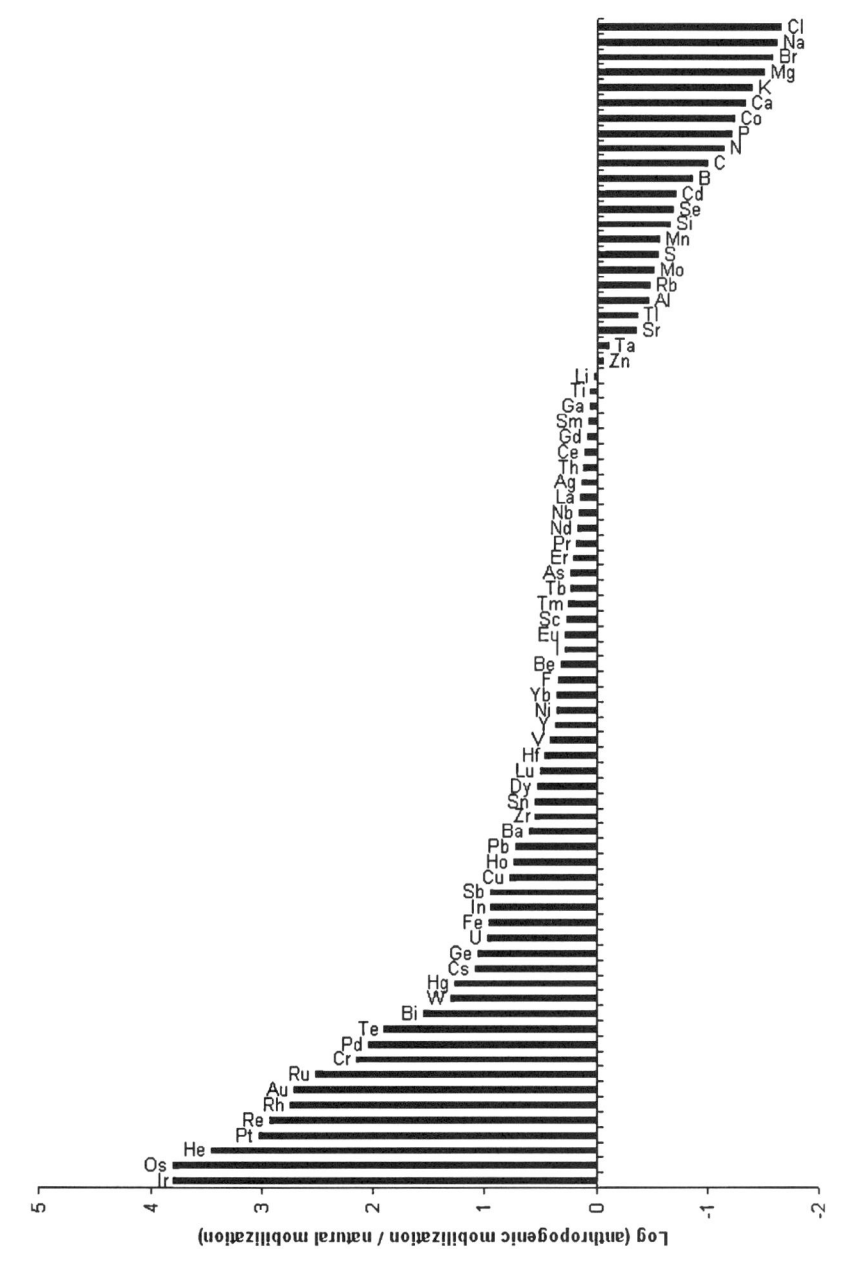

Figure 3 Graphic comparison of the ratio of anthropogenic and natural mobilization flows. Human activities mobilize more of each element on the left side of the diagram; natural processes mobilize more of each element on the right side of the diagram.

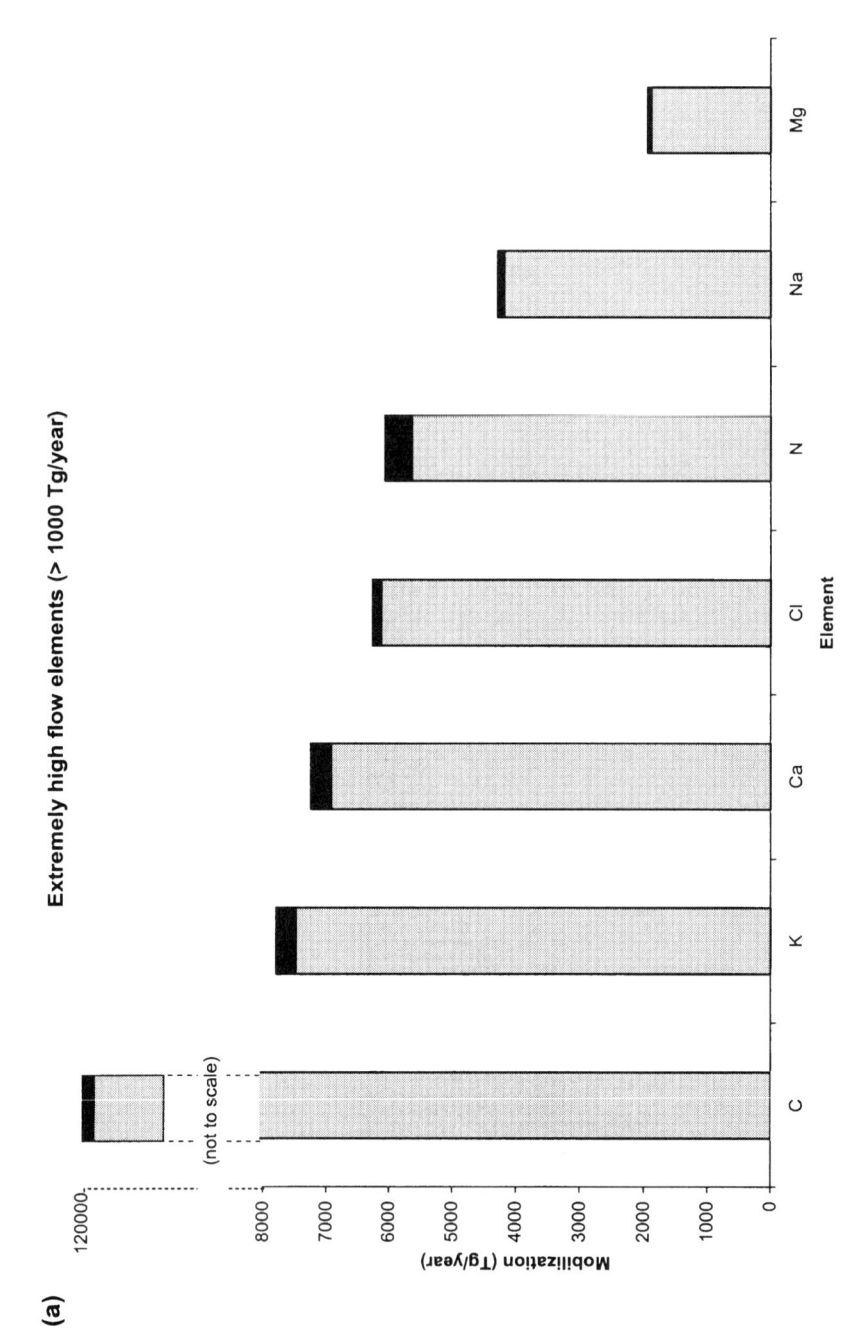

Figure 4 Charts depicting anthropogenic (*black* regions) and natural (*gray* regions) mobilization of selected elements, organized according to descending magnitude of total mobilization. Elements with total mobilization below 0.01 Tg/year are not shown.

DOMINANCE OF ELEMENTAL CYCLES 87

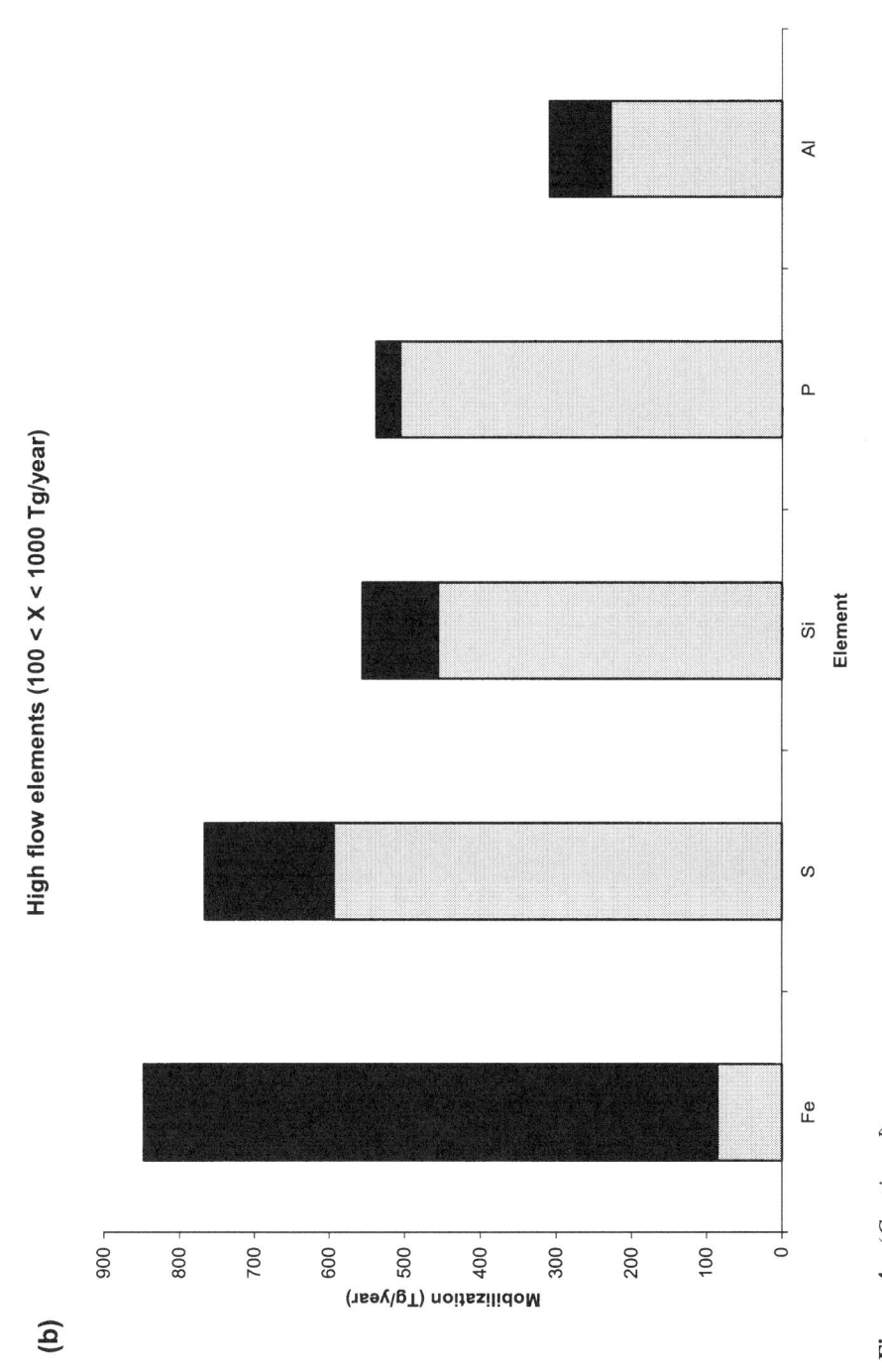

Figure 4 (*Continued*)

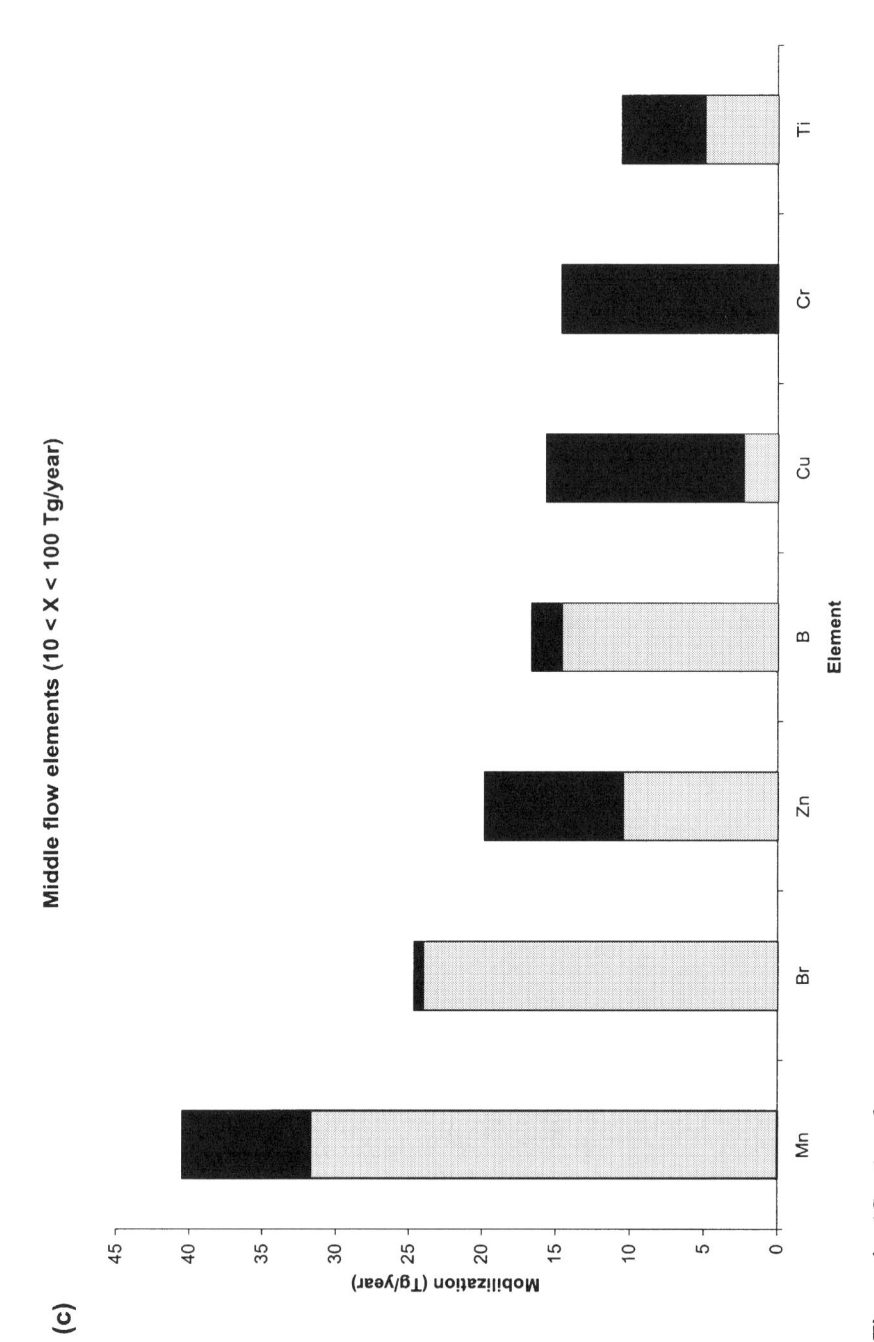

Figure 4 (*Continued*)

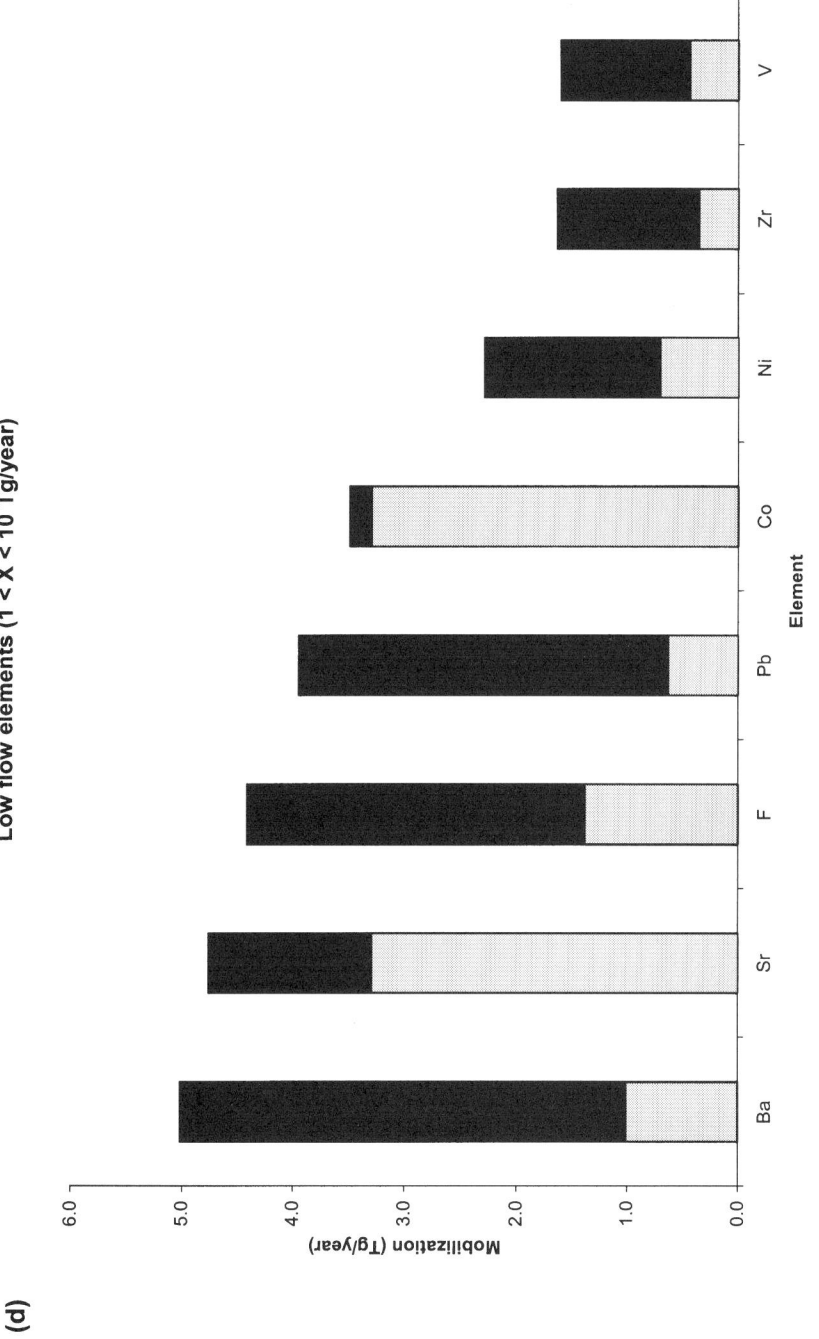

Figure 4 (*Continued*)

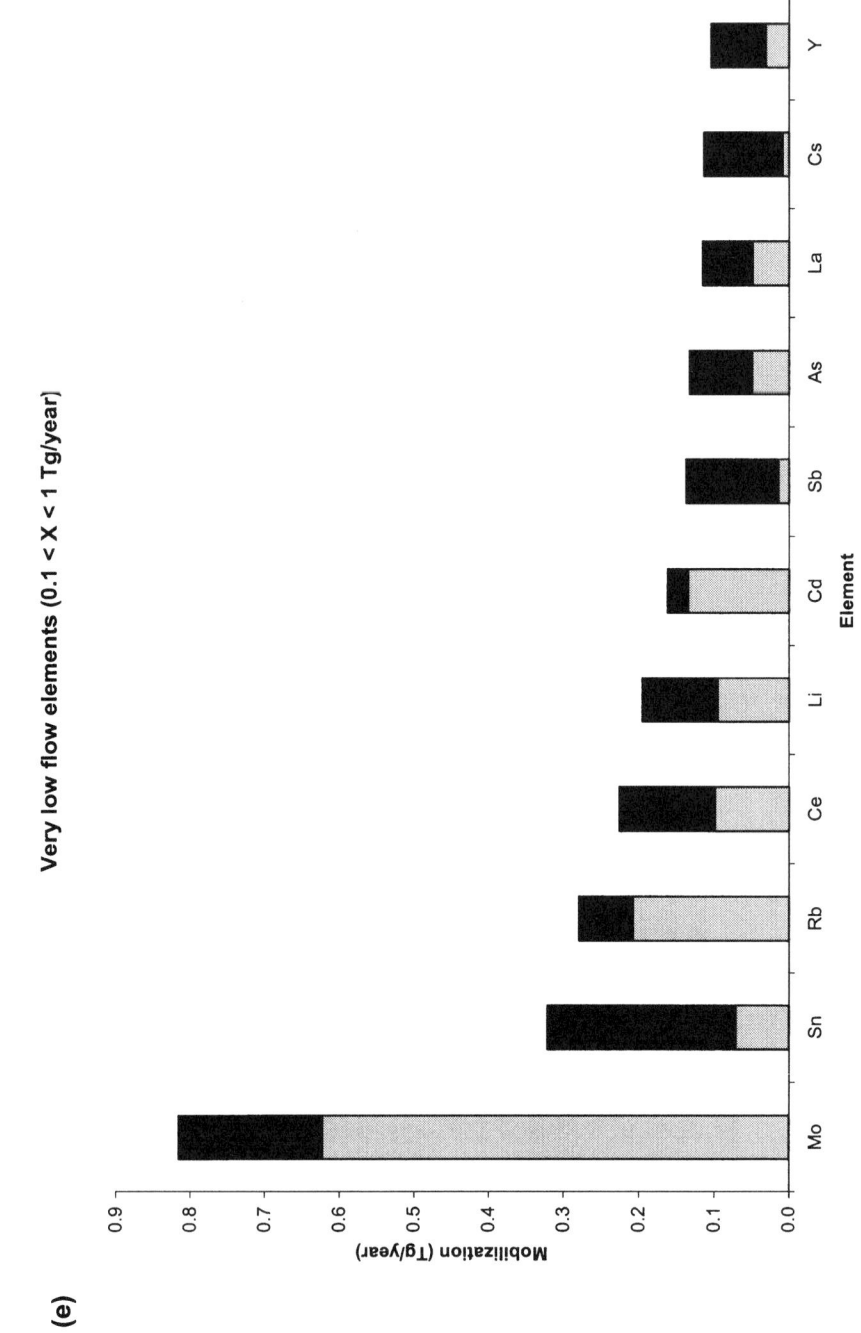

Figure 4 (*Continued*)

DOMINANCE OF ELEMENTAL CYCLES 91

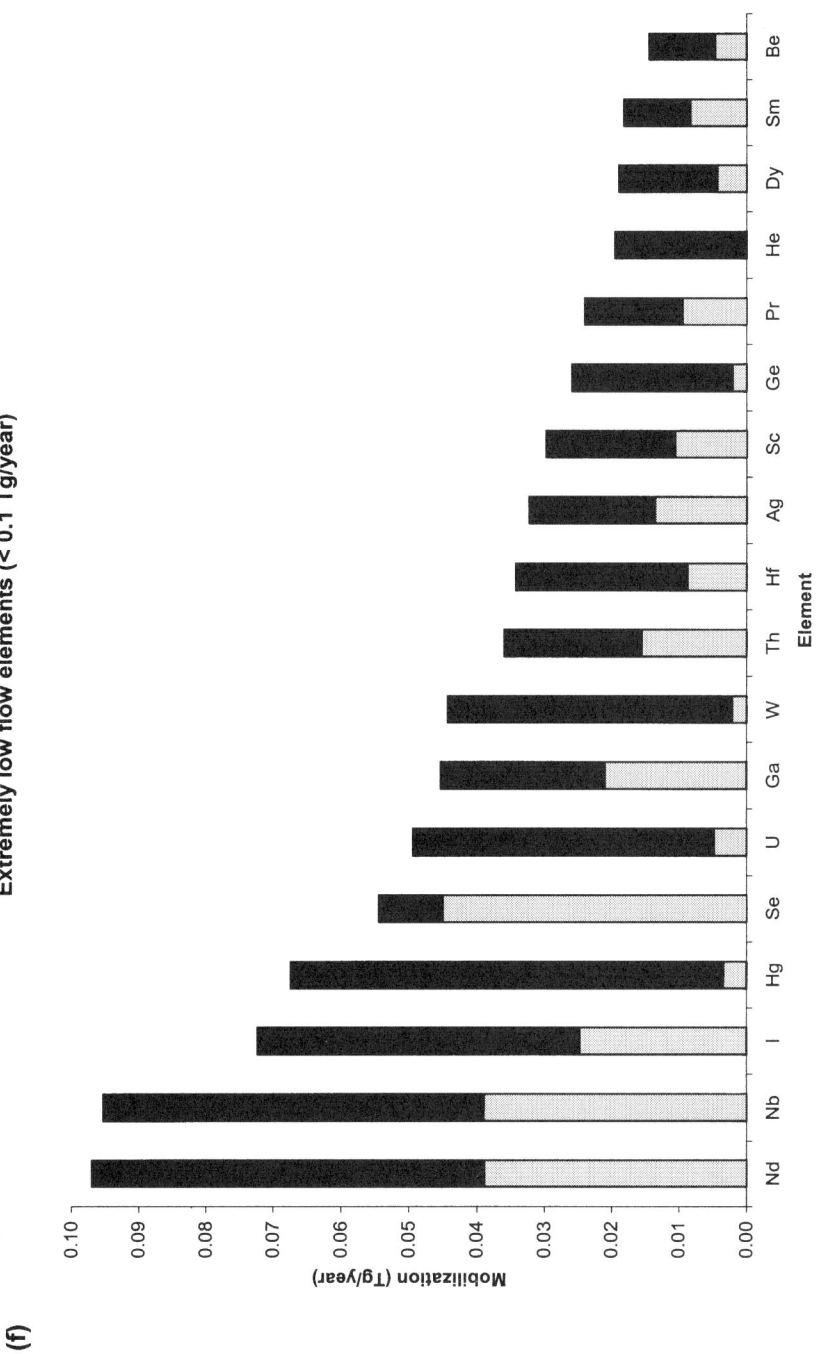

Figure 4 (*Continued*)

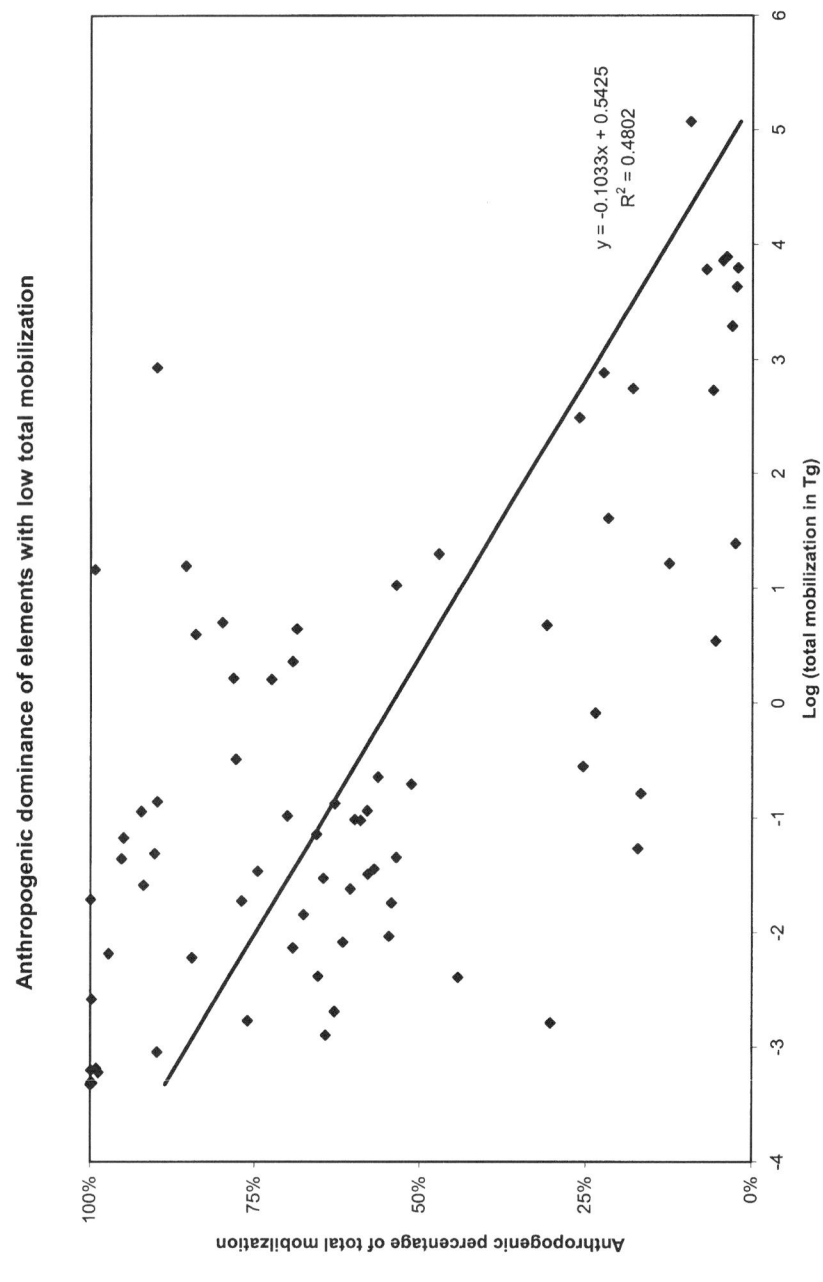

Figure 4 (*Continued*)

great, for example, but the CFC flows are only tiny parts of the flows of carbon and the halogens. In many cases, environmental impacts are better studied using cycles of particular molecules rather than those of the elements that make up the molecules. For tractability, however, this paper restricts itself to the elements.

Again we stress that the precise ratio calculated herein is simply an initial measure until more detailed determinations are undertaken. Acknowledging the large uncertainties in our method for estimating anthropogenic and natural mobilization in elemental cycles, it may be more useful to group our estimates of anthropogenic influence on elemental mobilization on a three-level scale: unperturbed (<15%), perturbed (15% to 50%), and dominant (>50%). In some cases, these evaluations can be quite accurate; in others, the information is sketchy at best. In Figure 5, indications of the degree of anthropogenic dominance are shown on a periodic table. Figure 5 demonstrates dramatically the dominance of nature for many of the elements in Groups IA, IIB, and VIIA of the periodic table, and of human action for most of the elements in Groups IB, IIIB, IVB, VB, VIB, and VIIIB. Groups IIB, IIIA, IVA, VA, and VIIB show mixed dominance. However, it is clear from this figure that humanity places a considerable footprint on the entire periodic table.

We propose that the reason for this pattern of dominance is related principally to the solubility in water of the predominant natural forms of the elements. Calcium carbonate is relatively water soluble, for example, and nature dominates the calcium cycle. The oxides and sulfides of copper are very poorly soluble in water, and human action dominates the copper cycle. The way the elements are used reflects their water solubility. Those that are water soluble include the nutrients transported to and taken in by plants and animals, whereas the water-insoluble structural metals provide humans with long-lasting structures. This potential correlation is demonstrated in Figure 6 by plotting the anthropogenic cycle dominance against the aqueous solubility of common naturally occurring compounds for a selection of elements.

The outliers of Figure 5—manganese, cobalt, zinc, cadmium, selenium, and molybdenum—do not follow the proposed pattern of human dominance of most of the metals and heavier elements. As the underlying data show (see Table 2), the natural mobilization from plant uptake during primary production tilts the mobilization dominance of these elements toward nature. Closer inspection of Table 2 shows that plant uptake also accounts for considerable mobilizations of iron, arsenic, tin, antimony, and lead, even though human activity still dominates total mobilization.

CYCLES OVER SPACE AND TIME

Only since the industrial revolution (i.e., since about 1750) have human beings conducted technological activities on a scale broad enough to be noticeable in planetary materials' cycles. As shown in Figure 7a, virtually the entire historical production of copper and zinc, for example, occurred within the years 1800–2000, and some 90% occurred within the twentieth century alone. Trends in coal

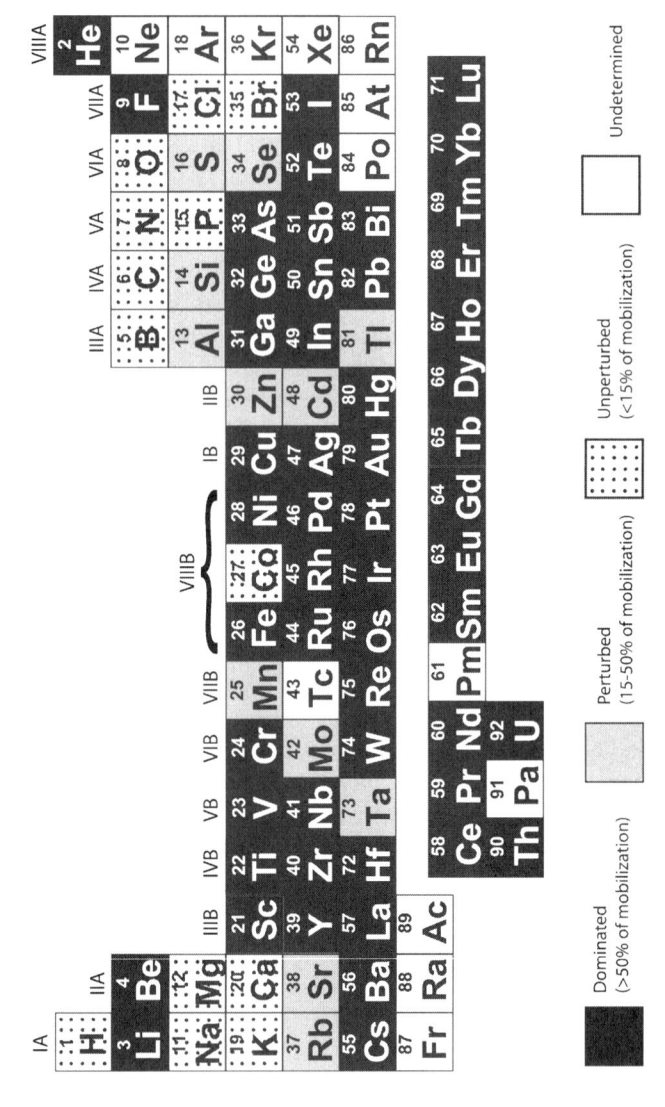

Figure 5 A periodic chart of the relative anthropogenic dominance of the mobilization flows of the elements. Unfilled boxes indicate elements for which dominance is undetermined.

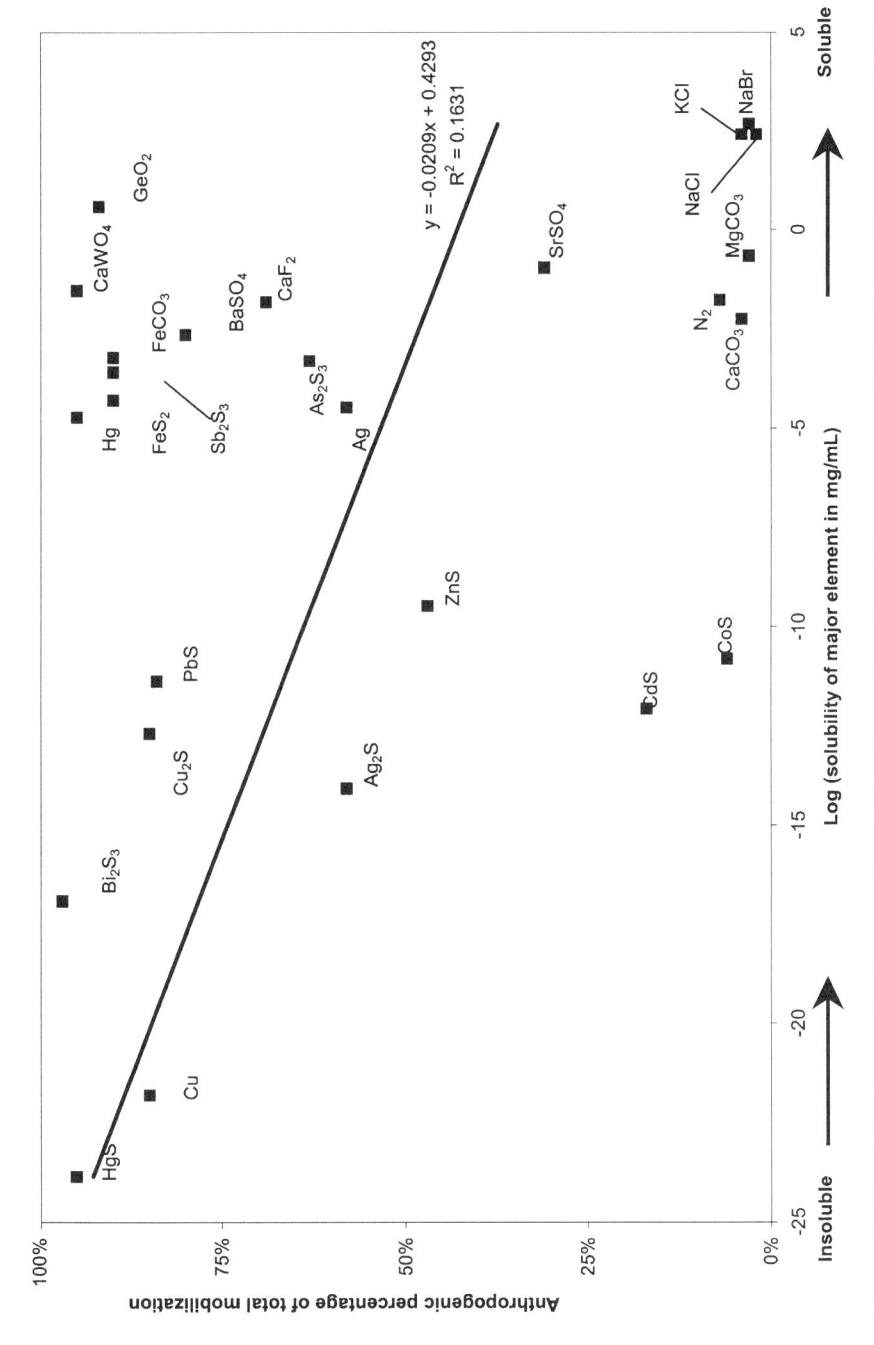

Figure 6 Plot of the degree of anthropogenic cycle dominance for selected elements versus the logarithm of the aqueous solubility of common chemical forms of the element in nature. Aqueous solubility data from References 61–64.

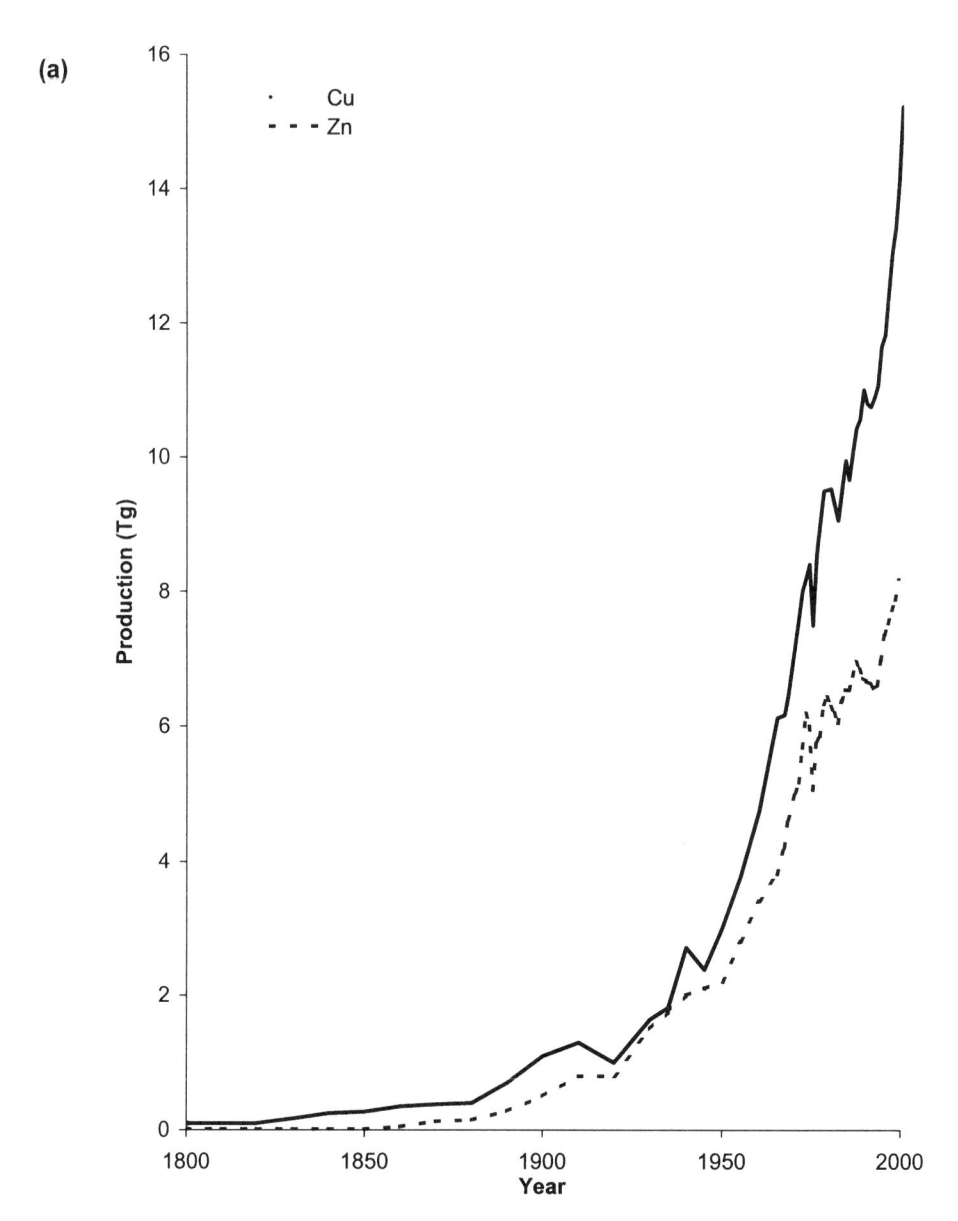

Figure 7 Trends in material production (i.e., mining and extraction statistics) from 1800 to 2000 for (*a*) copper and zinc (adapted from References 65–68); and (*b*) coal and oil (adapted from References 69–70).

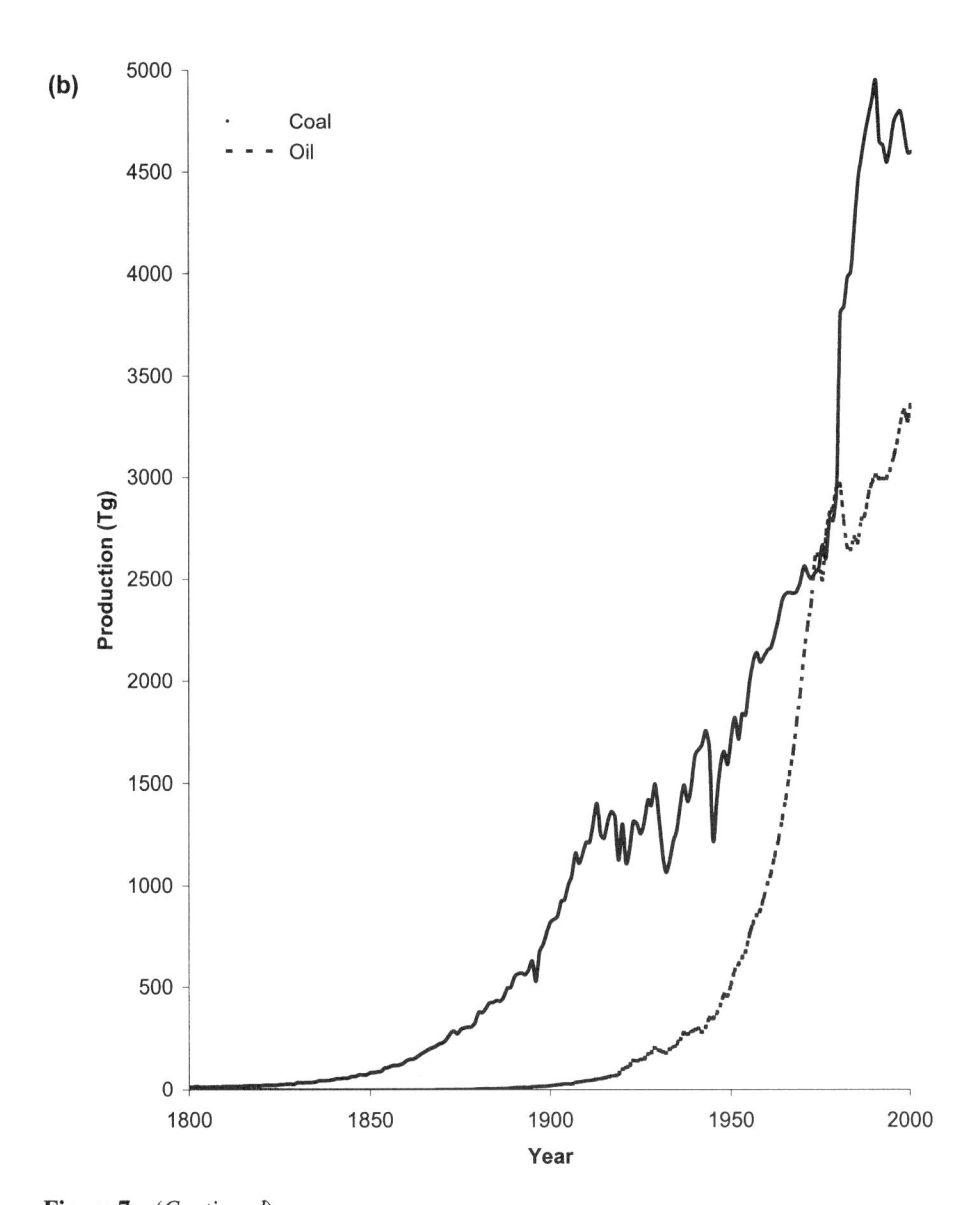

Figure 7 (*Continued*)

and crude oil production, shown in Figure 7b, are similar. Accordingly, relatively accessible commercial and industrial information should, in principle, be sufficient to prepare at least an approximate analysis of human influence.

Such cycles are potentially of great value to environmental scientists and to resource specialists. Cycles developed by Socolow & Thomas and the United States Interagency Working Group on Industrial Ecololgy, Material and Energy Flows (11, 38) for lead in the United States for 1970 and 1993 (Figure 8a and b, respectively) suggest the benefits that may accrue from technological cycle analysis. As shown in Figure 8, there are some very interesting differences between the cycles for the two years, including the following:

- Total lead consumption in 1993 was about 17% higher than in 1970.
- The 1993 lead recycling percentage is much higher: 64% vs 37%.
- Mine production in 1993 was down by 40% relative to 1970 because of recycling.
- The loss of lead to gasoline exhaust emissions was about 30% of total emissions in 1970; by 1993, there was none.
- Lead paint use was down by more than 30% in 1993 vs 1970 (one cannot tell exactly how much because the category includes lead in glass, which has increased with high rates of computer screen manufacture).

Note how environmental and human health issues (including the hazards from lead releases to the environment, especially from auto emissions; the hazards of using leaded paints in indoor situations, where paint chips may be ingested by children; and the efforts to recycle batteries) drove these changes. Also note that neither of these cycles attempted to quantify any of the reservoir contents, so they are partial (though very illuminating) assessments.

Although the lead-cycling work in Figure 8 is a significant step forward, the fact that it is limited to only two years, and to only anthropogenic flows, prevents the preparation of a time-integrated, comprehensive cycle. It also prevents the analyst from deriving information about pool size for the various reservoirs. In theory, integrated industrial materials cycles should be relatively straightforward to construct, once the cycle for a single year is available to serve as guidance. As seen in Figure 8, the first part of those cycles—the extractions from the natural reservoirs—are reasonably well quantified. However, the uses and fates of the materials over time are not well quantified. Additionally, the uptake of lead from soil by plants, about 15% of the total mobilization (Table 2), is not included. Such integrated cycles are likely to be of great value, but they will require substantial effort to construct with any accuracy. However, the lead-cycling work is still very useful because of the strong human dominance of the lead cycle.

Another type of cycle analysis with the potential to produce extremely useful results is the spatially resolved cycle. In such a cycle, the extraction, use, and deposition of the subject material are specified within a discrete spatial scale. Several possible uses for such a cycle are (*a*) potential environmental impacts to sensitive

DOMINANCE OF ELEMENTAL CYCLES 99

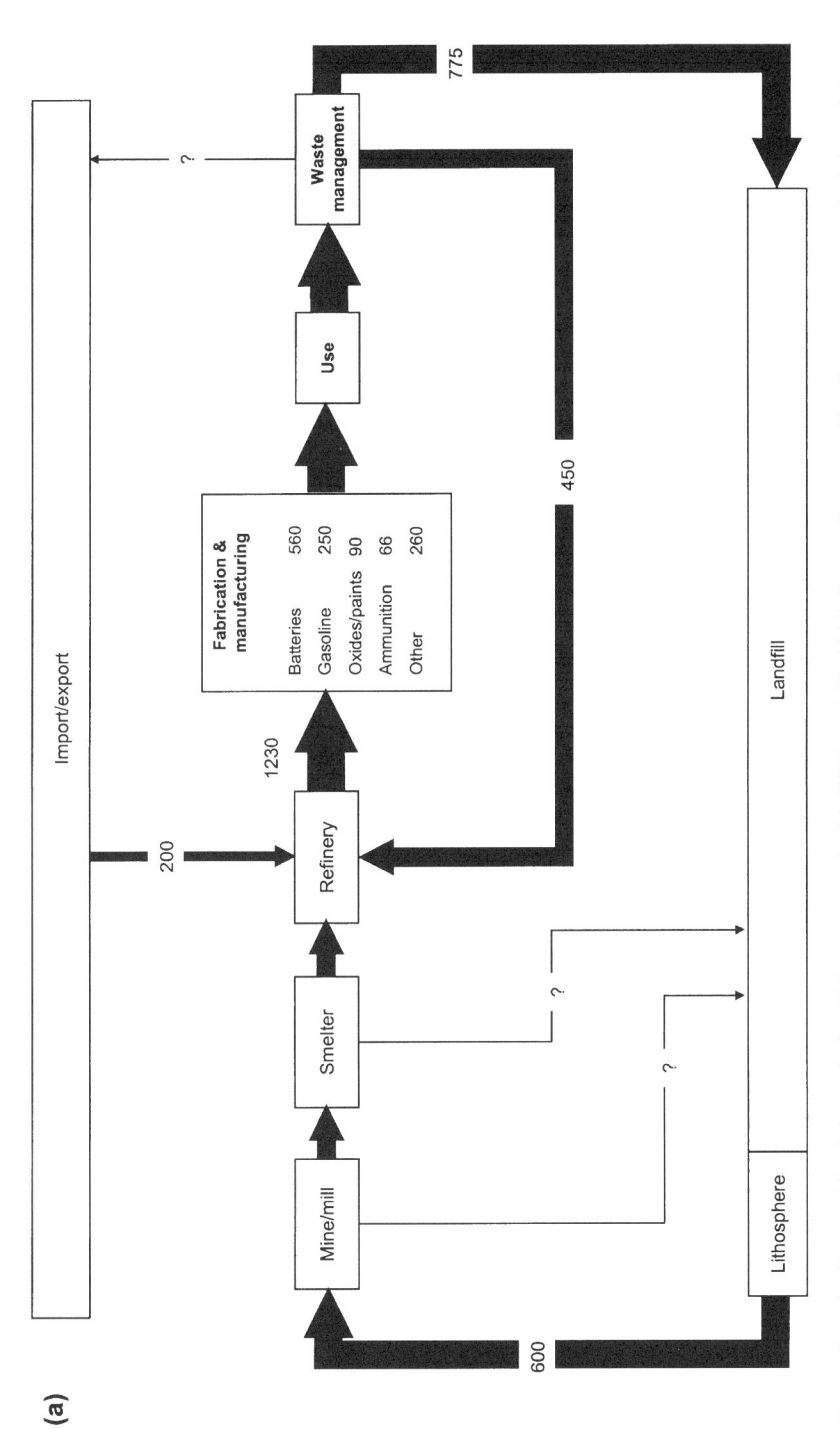

Figure 8 The flows of lead through the U.S. economy in (*a*) 1970 and (*b*) 1993 (in metric tons of lead content per year). Adapted from Reference 38.

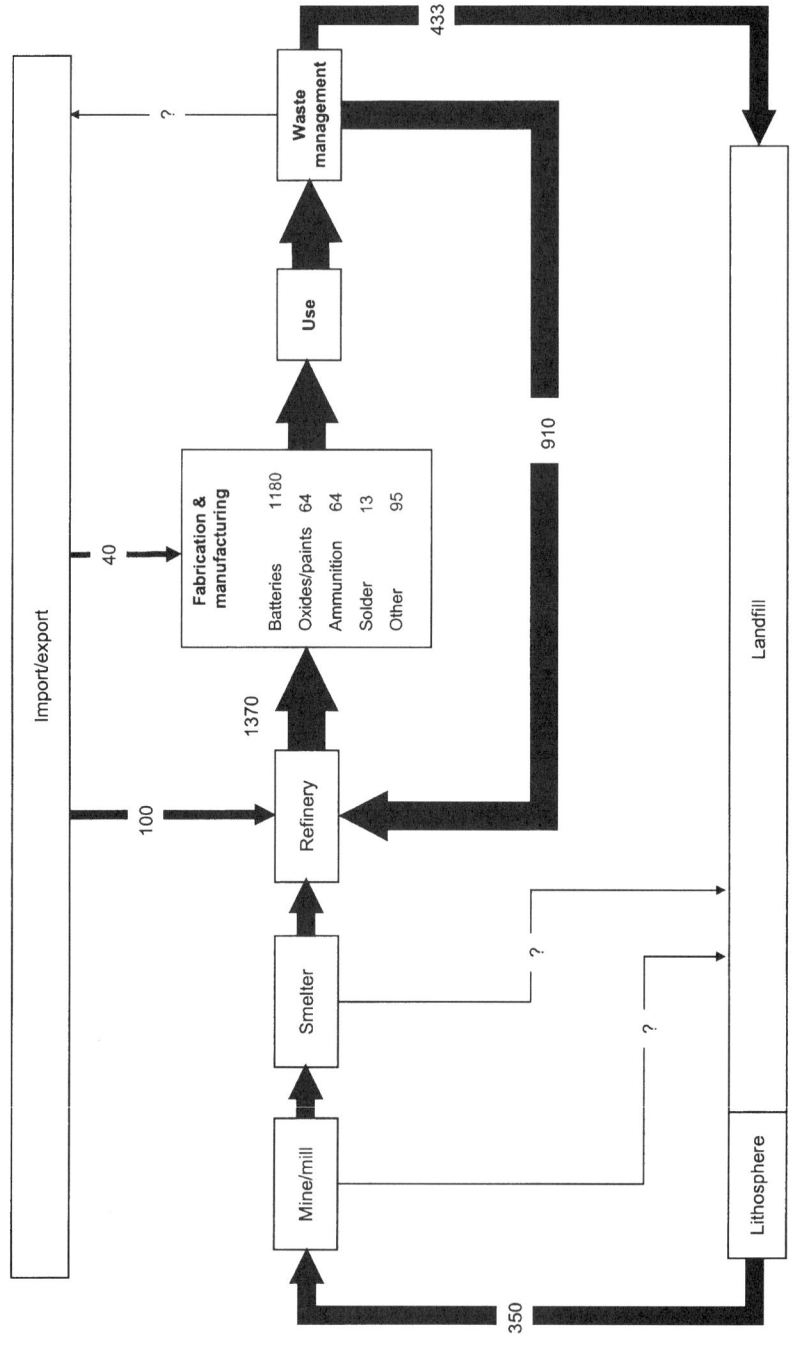

Figure 8 (*Continued*)

ecosystems could be better anticipated; (*b*) reservoirs of materials in use or deposited in specific locations could be of use in future recycling activities; and (*c*) the economics of materials use could be followed in more detail. To our knowledge, no comprehensive spatially resolved industrial cycles have been produced. The closest to that goal may be the cycle for the emissions of carbon dioxide derived by Andres et al. (39). In that work, the emissions (i.e., the source term) were presented globally on a 1° × 1° grid. Because all emissions were to the atmosphere, where carbon dioxide is well mixed and essentially unreactive, the work dealt with sources that were spatially resolved and sinks that were not. Benkovitz et al. (40) developed gridded emissions for sulfur and nitrogen. Comprehensive spatially resolved cycles for copper or zinc, for example, present a more difficult challenge. Spatially diverse reservoirs (e.g., rural mine tailings piles, urban apartment buildings, or suburban landfills), transformations (e.g., refining, milling, or alloying), and alternative uses (e.g., automobile parts, electronics, or plumbing fixtures) need to be considered, and these stocks and flows are not yet very well characterized. However, a spatially discrete determination of stocks of copper in Cape Town, South Africa (41), showed that because of high population densities in poor areas, the copper per square kilometer in those areas was higher than in the wealthy areas. This nonintuitive result hints at the potential value of spatially discrete cycles.

THE PRACTICAL UTILITY OF CYCLES

An example of an industrial materials cycle analysis that demonstrated its usefulness is one for silver in the United States. Kimbrough and coworkers (42) began this cycle study after observing unexpectedly high levels of silver in the sediments of San Francisco Bay. Its origins were not understood until a detailed analysis showed that 15% of the silver supply to the region was being used for X-ray photography in doctor and dentist offices. Individually, these users employed too little silver to justify economic recovery, and so any silver lost to the photographic fluids was being sent to sewage treatment plants and ultimately into the Bay. Once this source was determined, new regulations were written to require pickup and recycling of developing fluids.

The second part of this story was supplied by Ortiz, a student at Harvard, (43) who studied the flow of silver in photographic applications in more detail. His analysis, reproduced in Figure 9, contained a startling result: About 20% of the silver used in photography (i.e., 10% of the total silver flow) was retained on X-ray films in the medical offices. Over time, those offices became rich lodes of silver. Furthermore, modern technology was on the verge of offering a way to make that silver available, namely scanning the X-ray films into some form of digital storage so that the films themselves were no longer needed. As of this writing, neither the value of the silver nor the information transfer technology has reached the point where the silver in the film is being mined, but the potential is obvious.

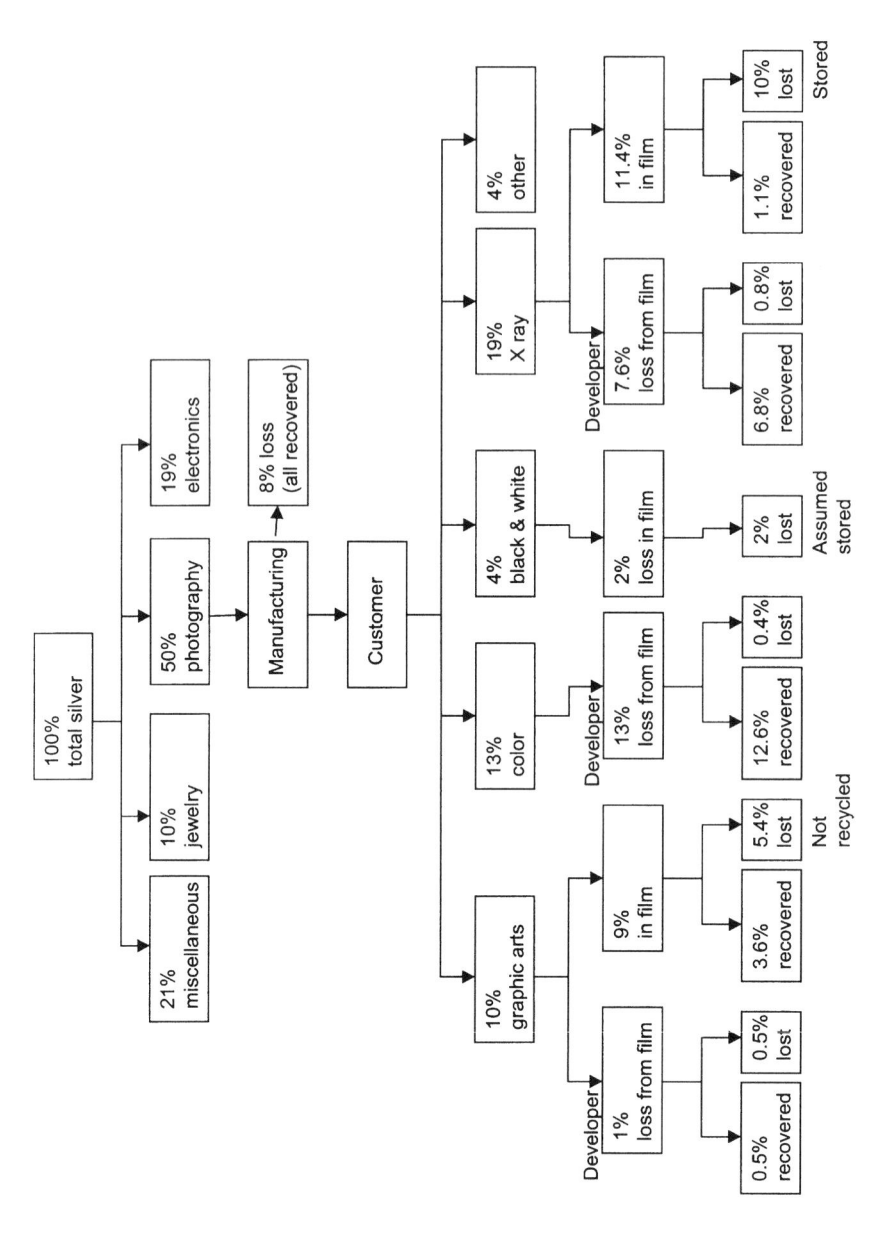

Figure 9 A cycle for the use of silver in photographic applications in the United States. All percentages are the amount of total silver consumed, for example, X rays use 19% of total silver. Adapted from (43).

As with the lead example above, this silver analysis has utility because human mobilization of silver exceeds natural mobilization (Table 2) and because most natural mobilization is by vegetation, which does not tend to generate fluxes of silver to surface waters. In contrast, a similar analysis for aluminum, with only about 25% of the mobilization being anthropogenic, is much more problematic and much less useful.

DISCUSSION

The results and conclusions of this paper rest in large part on our definition of mobilization. Most people would probably not contest our inclusion of mining, fossil-fuel combustion, weathering, or sea spray. Mobilization by plants, however, takes up from the soil elements that are already to some extent nonpassive in that they are periodically recycled. The same reservation may apply to mobilization by biomass burning. In each case, however, the elements involved in such processes are much more available for interaction with humans and the environment than was the situation before the mobilization processes occurred; this is the basis for their inclusion in our methodology. In any case, because the flux from each process is broken out in Table 2, individuals can apply whatever mix of mobilization processes they deem appropriate for their purposes.

Few existing elemental cycles are well enough established to justify decision making on the basis of the perspectives in this review. It is worth contemplating the uses to which such cycles could be put, however, when they are sufficiently validated. Resource analysts will find these cycles useful for coupling information on reserves vis-à-vis resources held in in-use reservoirs, stockpiles, the environment, and landfills, which could hypothetically be the mines of the future. Environmental scientists could use such information to examine sources and flows of hazardous materials to ecosystems, historical environmental impacts in space and time, and potential future inputs and outputs to natural reservoirs. These data will be useful to begin the process of actually measuring our progress toward environmental sustainability, when we can measure whether or not the extraction of nonrenewable resources exceeds the ability to find renewable substitutes and whether or not the flows of materials from the technological society will overwhelm the natural assimilative capacity of the environment (44).

At the industrial facility level, analysis of elemental cycling also has a role to play. Managers find that tracking product or process constituent flows within a facility can help to identify portions of materials that were purchased but discarded, avoidable burdens on waste-treatment or air-handling systems, and potential regulatory and liability concerns. The result is more efficient operation as well as an improved interaction with government agencies and with the environment.

Finally, accurate cycles have roles to play in the environmental policy arena. They can identify opportunities for the avoidance or minimization of resource imports, for national stockpile determinations, and for modifications in policy to balance technology and the environment as we make the journey toward environmental sustainability. Furthermore, our findings are not likely to be stable over time, as indicated by the dramatic trends in material consumption shown in Figure 7. Although natural mobilization rates likely remain relatively constant over time, anthropogenic mobilization has clearly increased over the past century, and if trends continue, it will continue to increase in this century. Environmental policy directed toward increasing the cycling of technological materials once extracted from natural reservoirs and promoting renewable energy sources can play a role in controlling future anthropogenic mobilization rates, thereby reducing the anthropogenic footprint on the periodic table of elements.

As the examples above demonstrate, the characterization and analysis of cycles for the materials used in our technological society provide substantial insight into the flows of resources, the ways in which industry utilizes materials, and the magnitude of interaction of those materials with the environment. The present state of cycles is, however, insufficient for firm guidance in many of these areas. Much more effort is needed to characterize and validate detailed cycles on regional, national, and global scales to take full advantage of the opportunities that these tools can provide.

ACKNOWLEDGMENTS

This research was funded by the U.S. National Science Foundation under grant BES-9818788. R.J.K. thanks the Environmental Research and Education Foundation for graduate student support.

The *Annual Review of Environment and Resources* is online at
http://environ.annualreviews.org

LITERATURE CITED

1. Bertine KK, Goldberg ED. 1971. Fossil fuel combustion and the major sedimentary cycle. *Science* 173:233–35
2. Martin JM, Meybeck M. 1979. Elemental mass-balance of material carried by major world rivers. *Mar. Chem.* 7:173–206
3. Lantzy RJ, Mackenzie FT. 1979. Atmospheric trace metals: global cycles and assessment of man's impact. *Geochim. Cosmochim. Acta* 43:511–25
4. Nriagu JO, Pacyna JM. 1988. Quantitative assessment of worldwide contamination of air, water and soils by trace metals. *Nature* 333:134–39
5. Pacyna JM, Scholtz MT, Li YF. 1995. Global budget of trace metal sources. *Environ. Rev.* 3:145–59
6. Rodhe H. 1992. Modeling biogeochemical cycles. In *Global Biogeochemical Cycles*, ed. SS Butcher, RJ Charlson, GH Orians, GV Wolfe, pp. 55–72. London: Academic
7. IPCC Working Group I. 2001. *Climate Change 2001 Summary for Policymakers: The Scientific Basis.* http://www.ipcc.ch/pub/spm22-01.pdf
8. Ayres RU, Schlesinger WH, Socolow RH. 1994. Human impacts on the carbon and nitrogen cycles. See Ref. 71, pp. 121–55

9. Smil V. 2000. Phosphorous in the environment: natural flows and human interferences. *Annu. Rev. Energy Environ.* 25:53–88
10. Graedel TE, Keene WC. 1996. The budget and cycle of Earth's natural chlorine. *Pure Appl. Chem.* 68:1689–97
11. Socolow RH, Thomas V. 1997. The industrial ecology of lead and electric vehicles. *J. Ind. Ecol.* 1(1):13–36
12. Thomas V, Spiro T. 1994. Emissions and exposure to metals: cadmium and lead. See Ref. 71, pp. 297–318
13. Mason RP, Fitzgerald WF, Morel F. M. 1994. The biogeochemical cycling of elemental mercury: Anthropogenic influences. *Geochim. Cosmochim. Acta* 58:3191–98
14. Jasinski SM. 1995. The materials flow of mercury in the United States. *Resourc. Conserv. Recycl.* 15:145–79
15. Brunner PH, Rechberger H. 2001. Anthropogenic metabolism and environmental legacies. In *Encyclopedia of Global Environmental Change. Vol. III: Causes and Consequences of Global Environmental Change*, ed. T. Munn, pp. 54–72, Chichester, UK: Wiley
16. Llewleyn TO. 1994. *Cadmium (materials flow). US Bureau Mines Inf. Circ. 9380*, Washington, DC: US Dep. Inter. 17 pp.
17. Ayres RU, Ayres LW. 1996. *Industrial Ecology: Toward Closing the Materials Cycle*. Cheltenham, UK: Elgar. 379 pp.
18. Loebenstein JR. 1999. *The material flow of arsenic in the United States. US Bureau Mines Inf. Circ. 9382*, Washington, DC: US Dep. Inter. 12 pp.
19. Baccini P, Brunner PH. 1991. *Metabolism of the Anthroposphere*. Berlin: Springer-Verlag. 157 pp.
20. Nriagu JO. 1980. Global cycle and properties of nickel. In *Nickel in the Environment*, ed. JO Nriagu, pp. 1–26. New York: Wiley
21. Graedel TE, Bertram M, Fuse K, Gordon RB, Lifset R, et al. 2002. The characterization of technological copper cycles. *Ecol. Econ.* 42:9–26
22. Spatari S, Bertram M, Fuse K, Graedel TE, Rechberger H. 2002. The contemporary European copper cycle: 1 year stocks and flows. *Ecol. Econ.* 42:27–42
23. Shedd KB. 1993. *The materials flows of cobalt in the United States. US Bureau Mines Inf. Circ. 9350*. Washington, DC: US Dep. Inter. 26 pp.
24. Kimbrough DE, Wong PW, Biscoe J, Kim J. 1996. A critical review of photographic and radiographic silver recycling. *J. Solid Waste Technol. Manag.* 23:197–207
25. Smith GR. 1994. *Materials flow of tungsten in the United States. US Bureau Mines Inf. Circ. 9388*. Washington, DC: US Dep. Inter. 23 pp.
26. Hilliard HE. 1994. *The materials flow of vanadium in the United States. US Bureau Mines Inf. Circ. 9409*. Washington, DC: US Dep. Inter. 18 pp.
27. Kesler SE. 1994. *Mineral Resources, Economics, and the Environment*. New York: Macmillan. 391 pp.
28. Schlesinger WH. 1997. *Biogeochemistry: An Analysis of Global Change*. San Diego: Academic. 588 pp.
29. Park H, Schlesinger WH. 2002. The global biogeochemical cycle of boron. *Glob. Biogeochem. Cycles* 16:1072;10.1029/2001GB001766
30. Andreae MO, Merlet P. 2001. Emission of trace gasses and aerosols from biomass burning. *Glob. Biogeochem. Cycles* 15:955–66
31. Azar C, Holmberg J, Lindgren K. 1996. Socio-ecological indicators for sustainability. *Ecol. Econ.* 18:89–112
32. US Dep. Energy-Energy Inf. Adm. (DOE-EIA). 2000. *International Energy Annual 2000*. http://www.eia.doe.gov/emeu/iea/wec.html
33. Nriagu JO. 1990. Human influence on the global cycling of trace metals. *Paleogeogr. Palaeoclimatol. Palaeoecol.* 82:113–20
34. Vitousek PM, Ehrlich PR, Ehrlich AH, Matson PA. 1986. Human appropriation of

the products of photosynthesis. *BioScience* 36:368–73
35. Möller D. 1990. The Na/Cl ratio in rainwater and the seasalt chloride cycle. *Tellus B.* 42:254–62
36. Gong SL, Barrie LA, Prospero JM, Savoie DL, Ayers GP, et al. 1997. Modeling seasalt aerosols in the atmosphere. *J. Geophys. Res.* 61:3819–30
37. Stumm W, Morgan JJ. 1981. *Aquatic Chemistry: An Introduction Emphasizing Chemical Equilibria in Natural Waters.* New York: Wiley. 780 pp.
38. US Interag. Work. Group Ind. Ecol. Mater. Energy Flows. 1998. *Materials.* Washington, DC: Counc. Environ. Qual. 29 pp.
39. Andres RJ, Marland G, Fung I, Matthews E. 1996. A $1° \times 1°$ distribution of carbon dioxide emissions from fossil fuel combustion and cement manufacture, 1950–1990. *Glob. Biogeochem. Cycles* 10:419–29
40. Benkovitz CM, Scholtz MT, Pacyna J, Tarrasón L, Dignon J, et al. 1996. Global gridded inventories of anthropogenic emissions of sulfur and nitrogen. *J. Geophys. Res.* 101:29,239–53
41. van Beers R, Graedel TE. 2003. The magnitude and spatial distribution of in-use copper stocks in Cape Town, South Africa. *S. Afr. J. Sci.* 99:61–69
42. Kimbrough DE, Wong PW, Biscoe J, Kim J. 1996. A critical review of photographic and radiographic silver recycling. *J. Solid Waste Technol. Manag.* 23:197–207
43. Ortiz L. 1995. *Uses of silver in the United States.* MS thesis. JF Kennedy Sch. Gov. Harvard Univ.
44. Graedel TE, Klee RJ. 2002. Getting serious about sustainability. *Environ. Sci. Technol.* 36:523–29
45. Clarke LB, Sloss LL. 1992. *Trace Elements—Emissions from Coal Combustion and Gasification.* London: Int. Energy Agency Coal Research. 111 pp.
46. Filby RH, Shah KR. 1975. Neutron activation methods for trace elements in crude oils. In *The Role of Trace Metals in Petroleum*, ed. TF Yen, pp. 89–110. Ann Arbor, MI: Ann Arbor Sci.
47. Wedepohl KH. 1995. The composition of the continental crust. *Geochim. Cosmochim. Acta* 59:1217–32
48. Hewitt EJ, Smith TA. 1974. *Plant Mineral Nutrition.* New York: Wiley
49. Finkelman R. 1999. Trace elements in coal: Environmental and health significance. *Biol. Trace Elem. Res.* 67:197–204
50. Bertine KK, Goldberg ED. 1971. Fossil fuel combustion and the major sedimentary cycle. *Science* 173:233–35
51. Kinghorn RRF. 1983. *An Introduction to the Physics and Chemistry of Petroleum.* Chichester, UK: Wiley. 420 pp.
52. Stigter JB, de Haan HPM, Guicherit R, Dekkers CPA, Daane ML. 2000. Determination of cadmium, zinc, copper, chromium and arsenic in crude oil cargoes. *Environ. Pollut.* 107:451–64
53. Graedel TE. 1978. *Chemical Compounds in the Atmosphere.* New York: Academic
54. Biomass Feedstock Composition and Properties Database. Accessed Jan. 11, 2002. http://www.ott.doe.gov/biofuels/properties_database.html#biomass
55. US Geol. Surv. 2002. *Mineral Commodity Summary.* Reston, VA: Miner. Inf. Cent. http://minerals.usgs.gov/minerals/pubs/mcs/
56. Molycorp, Inc. 1992. *Cerium: A Guide to its Role in Chemical Technology.* Mountain Pass, CA: Molycorp. www.molycorp.com/cerium_ book.pdf
57. Johnson Matthey, PLC. 2002. *Platinum 2002.* London: Johnson Matthey, PLC. http://www.platinum.matthey.com/publications/pdf2002/Pt_ 2002. pdf
58. Johnson Matthey. 2002. *Platinum Today—Market Data.* London: Johnson Matthey, http://www.platinum.matthey.com/data/rh_ 92-02.pdf
59. Christie J, Challis A. 1994. *Mineral Commodity Report 5—Platinum Group Metals.* Wellington, NZ: NZ Minist. Econ. Dev. Crown Miner. http://www.med.govt.

nz/crown_minerals/minerals/docs/comrepo rts/report05_pgm.pdf
60. Roskill Consult. Group. 1985. *The Economics of Thorium.* London: Roskill Inf. Serv. http://www.roskill.co.uk/thorium.html
61. Stephen H, Stephen T, eds. 1963. *Solubilities of Inorganic and Organic Compounds.* Vol. I: *Binary Systems*, pp. 5–79. New York: Pergamon
62. Linke WF. 1965. *Solubilities of Inorganic and Metal-Organic Compounds.* Vol. I & II. Washington, DC: Am. Chem. Soc. 1914 pp. 4th ed.
63. Weast RC, Astle MJ, eds. 1980. *CRC Handbook of Chemistry and Physics.* Boca Raton, FL: CRC Press. 2454 pp. 61st ed.
64. Lide DR, ed. 2000. *CRC Handbook of Chemistry and Physics.* Boca Raton, FL: CRC Press. 2540 pp. 81st ed.
65. Craig J. 1998. *Scarcity and abundance* Presented at Workshop Mater. Flows, Natl. Acad. Eng. Washington, DC
66. World Bureau Stat. 1996. *Metal Statistics.* Ware, UK: World Bureau Metal Stat.
67. Int. Copper Study Group. 2001. *Focus on Copper.* http://www.icsg.org
68. Int. Zinc Assoc. Accessed Sept. 7, 2001. *Zinc Production and Consumption: Annual World Totals 1970–1999*, http://www.zincworld.org/zwo_org/zwo00-index.htm
69. Etemad B, Luciani J. 1991. *World Energy Production 1800–1985.* Geneva: Libr. Droz. 272 pp.
70. US Dep. Energy—Energy Inf. Adm. 2000. *International Energy Annual—2000.* http://www.eia.doe.gov/emeu/iea/contents.html
71. Socolow R, Andrews C, Berkhout F, Thomas V, eds. 1994. *Industrial Ecology and Global Change.* Cambridge, UK: Cambridge Univ. Press

PROSPECTS FOR CARBON CAPTURE AND STORAGE TECHNOLOGIES

Soren Anderson[1] and Richard Newell[2]

[1]Department of Economics, University of Michigan, Ann Arbor, Michigan 48109; email: sorenta@umich.edu
[2]Energy and Natural Resources Division, Resources for the Future, Washington, District of Columbia 20036; email: newell@rff.org

Key Words climate change, sequestration, carbon dioxide, fossil fuel

■ **Abstract** Carbon capture and storage (CCS) technologies remove carbon dioxide from flue gases for storage in geologic formations or the ocean. We find that CCS is technically feasible, with current costs of about $200 to $250 per ton of carbon. Although currently a relatively expensive mitigation option, CCS could be attractive if we have a stringent carbon policy, if CCS turns out unexpectedly inexpensive relative to other options, or if it is otherwise desired to retain fossil fuels as part of the energy mix while reducing carbon emissions. Near-term prospects favor CCS for electric power plants and certain industrial sources with storage in depleted oil and gas reservoirs as opposed to aquifers. Deep aquifers may provide an attractive longer-term-storage option, whereas ocean storage poses greater technical and environmental uncertainty. CCS should be seriously considered for addressing climate change, alongside energy efficiency and carbon-free energy, although significant environmental, technical, and political uncertainties and obstacles remain.

CONTENTS

INTRODUCTION	110
The Potential Role of Carbon Capture and Storage	111
Importance of the Energy Penalty, Reference Technology, and Model Assumptions for Carbon Capture and Storage Costs	113
OPPORTUNITIES FOR CO_2 CAPTURE	115
Electric Power Generation	115
Industry	119
CO_2 TRANSPORTATION AND STORAGE	121
Transportation	122
Geologic Storage	123
Ocean Storage	127
Other Options	128
CARBON CAPTURE AND STORAGE COST MODELING FOR ELECTRICITY GENERATION	130

Plant-Level Modeling of Carbon Capture and Storage 130
Integrated Modeling of Carbon Capture and Storage 133
SUMMARY AND CONCLUSION 136

INTRODUCTION

Global climate change is one of the most prominent environmental and energy policy issues of our age. Although scientific and economic uncertainties remain, there is little doubt: Human beings are altering the Earth's climate (1–4). Through the burning of fossil fuels, certain industrial processes, and various land use practices, we are contributing greatly to the accumulation of so-called greenhouse gases (GHGs) in the atmosphere, which trap heat and block outward radiation. By far the most prevalent of these GHGs is carbon dioxide (CO_2), accounting for 82% of total U.S. GHG emissions from 1991 to 2000 (4). About 96% of these carbon emissions resulted from using fossil fuels for energy (5). For these reasons, climate change discussions have tended to focus on the reduction of CO_2.

Energy efficiency improvements and switching from high-carbon fossil fuels, such as coal, toward less carbon-intensive energy sources, such as natural gas, were once seen as the only realistic means of reducing CO_2 emissions. In recent years, however, analysts and policy makers have begun to recognize a third option—the development of "end-of-pipe" technologies that would allow for the continued utilization of fossil-fuel energy sources while significantly reducing carbon emissions. These technologies have collectively come to be known as "carbon capture and storage" (CCS) technologies. Using these technologies, CO_2 would be captured from large, stationary sources (e.g., power plant flue gases), preventing its release to the atmosphere. This is analogous to the removal of sulfur dioxide from emissions using end-of-pipe scrubbers. This CO_2 would be compressed and transported to a location where it would be stored (in an aquifer, depleted oil field, or deep ocean). Unlike indirect forms of sequestration (afforestation or enhanced ocean uptake of CO_2), which rely on removing CO_2 from the atmosphere, CCS intends to avoid atmospheric emissions altogether. Besides CO_2, other significant climate forcing agents derived from fossil-fuel usage include black carbon (soot), tropospheric ozone, aerosols, and nitrogen oxides (6–8). Some methods of removing CO_2 from flue gases involve first the removal or catalytic reduction of some of these other agents, such as soot and nitrogen oxides, thereby increasing the value of CCS technology to mitigating climate change (9).

One sign of the increased seriousness with which policy makers view the potential for CCS is the budget devoted by the U.S. Department of Energy to researching it: $1 million in 1998, $40 million in 2003, and a 2004 budget request of $62 million. Another sign is that the Intergovernmental Panel on Climate Change (IPCC) recently convened a group of policy makers and experts to outline the structure of a future report on CCS technologies (10). Corporations, such as BP, Chevron Texaco, ExxonMobil, Shell International, and Ford Motor Company, have also been investing tens of millions of dollars into CCS research, through private institutes (e.g., Electric Power Research Institute), university initiatives (e.g., Princeton's Carbon Mitigation Initiative and Stanford's Global Climate and Energy Project), and international initiatives (e.g., International Energy Agency Greenhouse Gas R&D Programme).

In this review, we synthesize the existing literature to examine the CCS prospects for technical feasibility, cost, timing, ancillary environmental effects, and potential contribution to overall climate policy. These issues have been addressed in several academic, international, and U.S. governmental reports (11–17) and in articles in the popular economic and scientific press (18–21). In addition to discussing these materials, we make a number of important new contributions.

We systematically present both the carbon reduction potential and the estimated mitigation cost associated with CCS technologies as applied to electric power generation and various industrial emissions sources. In addition to reporting capture costs, we systematically include transport and storage costs in our estimates. Moreover, we present a careful discussion of CCS costs that helps clarify some of the differences among estimates reported in the literature, drawing particular attention to the critical role of natural gas prices. Finally, we discuss and interpret the most recent integrated modeling results, synthesizing insight from these studies regarding the potential role of CCS technologies under future climate policies.

The Potential Role of Carbon Capture and Storage

Some suggest that the carbon problem could be solved through the increased use of renewable energy sources. Even if renewables become cost competitive, however, the time it will take them to become widespread will necessitate significant continued use of fossil fuels. Others see a built-in solution to the problem of fossil-fuel combustion in the limited supply of fossil fuels and believe they will become too expensive, forcing a switch to alternative energy sources (22, 23). Following this reasoning, the policy should be to wait until the fossil-fuel supply is depleted and allow rising fossil-fuel prices to induce the development of renewable energy sources. But this argument assumes that fossil fuels will become scarce before the effect of gradual atmospheric buildup of GHGs becomes too costly. We believe this is likely to be incorrect.

The carbon content of proven fossil-fuel reserves exceeds cumulative historic carbon emissions from 1860 through 1998 by a factor of five (17). Moreover, future years will likely bring the development of even more reserves, as undeveloped fossil-fuel resources become technically and economically recoverable. Thus, at current rates of extraction, it could well be hundreds of years before the current supply is exhausted. Add to this the fact that rapidly developing countries, such as China and India, show little interest in abandoning the use of their relatively inexpensive coal reserves, which constitute 20% of the global total (24).

Putting this in perspective, people often speak of limiting CO_2 to double the preindustrial concentration of atmospheric carbon (to 450 ppm by volume), which could result in global temperature increases of almost 2°C above 1990 levels by 2100 (25, p. 101). Stabilization at this level of approximately 400 gigatons (billion metric tons) of carbon (GtC) of additional emissions assumes we would leave about 70% of the carbon held in current proven reserves untouched (17). The optimal target for atmospheric CO_2 concentrations, however, as well as the optimal transitional trajectory, will of course vary depending on the levels of ecological modification and uncertainty deemed tolerable (26, 27). Regardless, the huge stock of wealth invested in fossil fuels, nearly $150 billion in 2000 alone (1, 4), stands as a large obstacle to any policy that would significantly curtail their continued use. The history of failed attempts to raise U.S. energy taxes attests to this. These reasons suggest a likely reliance on fossil fuels in the foreseeable future, and policy makers are looking for alternative ways to reduce carbon emissions.

Many view CCS as a promising third alternative to relying solely on increasing energy efficiency and switching to less carbon-intensive energy sources. Carbon capture technologies themselves are not new. Specialized chemical solvents were developed more than 60 years ago to remove CO_2 from impure natural gas. These solvents are still in use. Several industries, such as food-processing and power plants, use the same or similar solvents to recover CO_2 from their flue gases. Finally, a variety of alternative methods are used to separate CO_2 from gas mixtures during the production of hydrogen for petroleum refining, ammonia production, and other industries (28). Although capture technologies are considered relatively mature, some believe that substantial technical improvements and cost reductions could be realized if applied on a large scale (15).

Oil producers have significant experience with some carbon storage technologies. As prices rose in the late 1970s and early 1980s, U.S. producers found it profitable to extract oil from previously depleted fields by means of enhanced oil recovery (EOR) methods. These methods involve injecting liquefied CO_2 to repressurize the field, which facilitates the extraction of additional oil but can also store the injected CO_2. Falling energy prices caused these particular capture operations to shut down, but the use of EOR methods continues. It accounts for 9 million (metric) tons of carbon (MtC), about 80% of the CO_2 used by U.S. industry every year (14, 29). Most injected CO_2 is currently extracted from natural formations, however, and does not represent a net reduction in emissions.

Worldwide, the only known industrial operation engaged in CCS for the explicit purpose of avoiding carbon emissions is Statoil's natural gas mining operation off the shore of Norway. Rather than pay Norway's hefty carbon emissions tax of $140/tC in 2000 (20), Statoil has been compressing and injecting the captured CO_2 into an aquifer below the ocean floor since 1996, at a cost of approximately $55/tC (30). The project incurred an incremental investment cost of $80 million dollars, with an annual tax savings of $55 million dollars. Scientific monitoring of the site indicates that the aquifer is indeed holding the injected CO_2, though continuing observation will provide a better indication of storage stability (31).

Although CCS technologies are currently not widely used as a way to avoid carbon emissions, we have already seen that it is technically feasible to capture

CO$_2$ from flue gases and store it in geologic formations. In this review, we examine opportunities for applying CCS technologies on a much larger scale, considering issues of cost and timing. We also describe remaining environmental uncertainties and risks, particularly in the section on transportation and storage.

Importance of the Energy Penalty, Reference Technology, and Model Assumptions for Carbon Capture and Storage Costs

We now clarify how several important considerations influence the variety of CCS cost measures that appear in the literature. First, the carbon capture process has a parasitic effect on electricity production. It imposes a so-called energy penalty by increasing the fossil-fuel energy needed to generate a fixed output of electricity. Hence, the quantity of carbon captured and stored will be greater than the quantity of carbon actually avoided. For electricity production, average capture costs in $/tC avoided are given by $(c_{cap} - c_{nocap})/(e_{nocap} - e_{cap})$, where c is the cost in kilowatt-hours ($/kWh), e is the rate of carbon emissions (tC/kWh), and the subscripts denote these variables with and without capture. Similar nomenclature can be used to tabulate costs in other industries. These calculations often ignore CO$_2$ transportation and storage costs, however, which are generally reported in $/tC stored and must be adjusted upward to reflect the fact that the ratio of carbon captured to carbon avoided is greater than 1. This can be done by multiplying transport and storage costs in $/tC stored by the ratio of total carbon captured to total tons avoided (and assuming that the process of transportation and storage itself contributes negligibly to carbon emissions). All cost estimates in this review are given in average $/tC avoided, including transport and storage, unless otherwise noted. Electricity production costs refer to bus bar, ignoring transmission and distribution, unless otherwise noted.

Second, when making judgments about the competitiveness of CCS, the choice of the comparison plant (i.e., the c_0 and e_0 above) is also important. As demonstrated in Table 1, assumptions about the reference plant can have a dramatic effect on CCS costs. One approach is to calculate the incremental cost of applying CCS to a particular generation technology (e.g., a pulverized-coal plant with CCS compared with the same plant without CCS), as given by the bold figures in Table 1.

Nonetheless, the true cost competitiveness of CCS is best measured by comparing the marginal costs of a CCS plant with its closest competitor, which can only be determined in context. This is the economically relevant cost concept for gauging the attractiveness of CCS relative to other mitigation options, such as fuel switching and energy-efficiency improvements. For example, the relevant point of comparison for a new integrated gasification combined-cycle (IGCC) coal plant with CCS may not be a new IGCC plant without CCS, but rather a new natural gas combined-cycle (NGCC) plant. Using our IGCC example, Table 1 illustrates that if new NGCC is the relevant reference case, a new IGCC plant with CCS entails costs of about $542/tC—not the smaller $138/tC relative to an IGCC reference plant.

TABLE 1 Sensitivity of carbon capture costs to reference plant ($3/MBtu gas price)

Reference plant	Carbon capture and storage (CCS) costs ($/tC avoided)		
	New PC, CCS[a]	New NGCC, CCS[b]	New IGCC, CCS[c]
New PC	**229**[d]	47	162
New NGCC	741	**224**	542
New IGCC	208	18	**138**

[a]PC, pulverized coal.
[b]NGCC, natural gas combined cycle.
[c]IGCC, integrated gasification combined cycle.
[d]Bold figures show incremental CCS costs where the same generation technology is used in the reference and the CCS case. Figures are calculated on the basis of estimates and assumptions in David & Herzog (36) for new PC, NGCC, and IGCC plants, except that the numbers have been adjusted to include the same gas price ($3/MBtu) and transport and storage costs ($37/tC stored).

Finally, most cost calculations are sensitive to various modeling assumptions, especially with regard to natural gas prices, which may change significantly. Average gas prices may not only be relatively volatile—for example, the 300% spike from about $3 per million Btu (MBtu) in early 2000 to $9/MBtu in early 2001 (32)—they may also increase significantly over this century. Although the Department of Energy does not forecast significantly rising prices over the next two decades (33), gas supplies are in relatively short supply compared with coal. Hence, most CCS modeling studies assume rising gas prices, resulting in part from the imposition of climate policies that encourage greater natural gas use (see Integrated Modeling of CCS below).

Table 1 assumes gas prices of $3/MBtu, the average price over the past decade (32). If gas prices are twice as high as this, the reference technology for new plants switches from an NGCC to a pulverized-coal (PC) plant. As shown in Table 2, this change in reference plant significantly decreases the carbon price at which new PC, NGCC, and IGCC plants with CCS become competitive, because a reference coal

TABLE 2 Sensitivity of carbon capture costs to reference plant ($6/MBtu gas price)[a]

Reference plant	Carbon capture and storage (CCS) costs ($/tC avoided)		
	New PC, CCS	New NGCC, CCS	New IGCC, CCS
New PC	**229**	152	162
New NGCC	482	**256**	298
New IGCC	208	129	**138**

[a]This table is identical to Table 1 (i.e., sources and assumptions) except that it assumes a 100% higher gas price of $6/MBtu. At this gas price, a new NGCC plant without capture produces electricity at a bus bar cost of $0.052/kWh and ceases to be the lowest-cost reference technology for new power plants. For new plants, a PC plant without capture produces the cheapest electricity at $0.044/kWh, followed by IGCC without capture at $0.050/tC.

plant without CCS has a higher rate of emissions than an NGCC plant. Different assumptions regarding technological advance and future cost reductions can also dramatically affect results.

OPPORTUNITIES FOR CO_2 CAPTURE

As shown in Table 3, the United States emitted nearly 1.6 GtC in 2000. About 97% of these emissions came from the use of fossil fuels, virtually all through combustion (4). About 40% of direct carbon emissions came from the generation of electricity. The transportation and industrial sectors also accounted for a significant portion of direct emissions, at 32% and 15%, respectively. Finally, commercial and residential sectors accounted for a combined 11% of CO_2 emissions from fossil fuels (4).

Not all of these sectors are amenable to CCS. Because of their high capital costs and economies of scale, CCS technologies are particularly well suited to large, stationary sources of CO_2 emissions; power plants are the clearest contenders. But energy-intensive industries, such as oil refining, iron and steel manufacturing, and cement production, also combust large quantities of fossil fuels and have significant carbon emissions. The cost of capture from these sources depends primarily on the properties of their flue gas streams: Costs generally fall with higher concentrations of CO_2 and lower temperatures (see Table 3).

In addition to those combustion sources, natural gas operations produce concentrated CO_2 by-products for which the incremental cost of capture and compression is relatively low. Similarly, most of the hydrogen used in ammonia manufacture, oil refining, and other industries is derived from the decarbonization of fossil fuels, which also generates a by-product stream of CO_2 and presents low-cost opportunities for CCS. If hydrogen production from fossil fuels increases substantially, then low-cost opportunities for CCS would be even greater. Should hydrogen use increase substantially, CCS could play an important role in the generation of hydrogen through fossil-fuel decarbonization. In that event, the environmental consequences of increased hydrogen production and use must be considered, but these consequences are beyond the scope of this review [see Tromp et al. (34) and Schultz et al. (35)].

Electric Power Generation

The U.S. power generation sector produced more than 17.5 trillion kWh of electricity between 1995 and 1999, resulting in 3.1 GtC of emissions. About 78% of these emissions came from coal-fired and 14% from natural gas-fired power plants. As large, stationary sources of CO_2 emissions, these types of plants represent the foremost opportunity for CCS. Given current technology and gas prices of $3/MBtu, recent estimates suggest that the incremental cost of applying CCS to new conventional coal or natural gas plants would be about $225/tC to $230/tC (36). Although

TABLE 3 U.S. CO_2 emissions and cost of capture and storage in 2000

Emissions source	Carbon emissions (MtC)[a]	Percentage of total emissions	Capture and storage cost ($/tC avoided)[b]
Primary energy use	1556.8	97.4	
Electricity generation	641.6	40.2	200–250
Coal	522.4	32.7	
Natural gas	93.2	5.8	
Petroleum	26.0	1.6	
Transportation	513.9	32.2	
Industrial[c]	234.1	14.7	
Petroleum refining (combustion, 57.8 MtC = 4.1% of total in 1994)			≈electricity?
Petroleum refining (noncombustion, 16.5 MtC = 1.1% of total in 1994)			50–90
Chemicals (combustion, 40.6 MtC = 2.8% of total in 1994)			245
Chemicals (noncombustion, 12.0 MtC = 0.8% of total in 1994)			≈hydrogen?
Iron and steel (32.6 MtC = 2.3% of total in 1994)			195
Cement (6.3 MtC = 0.4% of total in 1994)			180–915
Lime (1.7 MtC = 0.1% of total in 1994)			≈cement?
Hydrogen production (noncombustion, 17.8 MtC = 1.3% of total in 1990)[d]			50–75
Residential	101.9	6.4	
Commercial	65.3	4.1	
Industrial process emissions	40.9	2.6	
Cement manufacture	11.3	0.7	180–915
Lime manufacture	4.3	0.3	≈cement?
Carbon dioxide in natural gas	5.0	0.3	55 (Sleipner)
Ammonia manufacture (i.e., hydrogen production)[e]	4.9	0.3	70 (fertilizer)
Waste combustion	7.1	0.4	
Natural gas flaring	4.5	0.3	
Other industrial	3.8	0.2	
Total (sum of primary energy use and industrial process emissions)	1597.7	100.0	

[a]Emissions for 2000 are from the Energy Information Administration (4).

[b]Costs include our addition of a transport and storage cost of $37/tC stored, except where authors already included such costs. Sources for capture costs are cited in text; see Opportunities for CO_2 Capture.

[c]No breakdown of industrial energy use emissions is available for 2000; we include older numbers in parentheses for a rough sense of scale (14, 44).

[d]There is overlap among nonfuel emissions in petroleum refining (e.g., hydrogen production), chemicals (e.g., hydrogen production in ammonia manufacture), ammonia manufacture (e.g., hydrogen production) under industrial processes (below), and all hydrogen production.

[e]Figures for ammonia manufacture are from the Environmental Protection Agency (5) and have been subtracted from industrial energy use emissions to avoid double counting.

retrofits of existing facilities may be technically feasible, costs would likely be much higher. To put these costs in perspective, studies typically show a wide range of carbon reductions available at costs well below this level. These lower-cost mitigation options include fuel switching to natural gas and renewables, energy efficiency improvements, and carbon sequestration in forests (37).

Note that when necessary, we converted all cost figures to the year 2000 U.S. dollars, using the annual Producer Price Index and average annual exchange rates (the exceptions being figures from studies that were published during or after 2000). These costs also include our addition of transport and storage costs of $37/tC. When possible, we have also adjusted previous estimates to use comparable gas prices (38).

CONVENTIONAL POWER PLANTS WITH CHEMICAL ABSORPTION OF CO_2 Most coal-burning power plants use simple, steam-driven turbines to produce electricity, whereas most new natural gas plants employ a gas turbine and use excess heat to power a second, steam-driven turbine. For flue gas streams with low or moderate concentrations of CO_2, typically found in these plants, the best existing capture method is absorption using a chemical solvent, such as monoethanol amine (MEA). Because CO_2 is an acid gas, MEA and other alkaline solvents form chemical bonds with CO_2 and can absorb it from a flue gas stream. Once the CO_2 is absorbed, these solvents are regenerated by applying heat, releasing a stream of CO_2, and allowing the solvent to be recycled. These techniques have been used to recover by-product CO_2 or directly manufacture CO_2 from fossil-fuel combustion for decades.

Although chemical absorption can remove CO_2 at low concentrations, breaking the chemical bond between the CO_2 and the chemical solvent is energy intensive (e.g., steam removal requires 3900–4200 kJ/kg CO_2). Moreover, contaminants typically found in flue gases (e.g., SO_2, NO_X, hydrocarbons, and particulates) usually must be removed prior to capture because they inhibit the ability of solvents to absorb CO_2. Note, therefore, that the CCS cost estimates cited typically assume that these pollutants have already been controlled, and thus the cost of their removal is not included.

Postcombustion chemical absorption imposes an energy penalty of about 15% to 30% for natural gas plants and 30% to 60% for coal plants (15, 36, 39). Pilot studies aimed at improving the absorption process show that the use of new solvent technologies and better integration of capture technologies can lower energy penalties to about 20% for conventional coal and about 10% for natural gas (15, 36). Reduced thermal efficiencies and significant capital costs for capture increase the bus bar cost of electricity by about 80% for coal and by 50% for natural gas (39). With present technologies, the incremental cost of applying CCS by means of chemical absorption to new conventional coal and gas plants is about $225/tC to $230/tC, but near-term technical improvements could reduce these costs to about $160/tC to $190/tC (36). Retrofitting existing coal plants with chemical capture currently costs about $190/tC (40), including transport and storage costs of $37/tC stored.

IGCC PLANTS WITH PHYSICAL ABSORPTION OF CO_2 The "decarbonization" of fossil fuels and potential movement toward a hydrogen-based energy system may provide unique opportunities for CCS. In the IGCC process, coal is gasified to form a mixture of carbon monoxide (CO) and hydrogen (H_2) known as synthesis gas (syngas). In IGCC without capture, syngas is combusted directly in gas turbines. In IGCC with capture, syngas undergoes an additional reaction with steam in the presence of catalysts to form a mixture of H_2 and CO_2. The H_2 is separated, generating a pure stream of CO_2 that can be directly compressed and stored. The U.S. Department of Energy recently completed two IGCC demonstration projects in Florida and Indiana and are partially funding a third in Tennessee. Several companies have announced plans to use coal gasification technologies in future power plants. Researchers at various Department of Energy laboratories and industry sites are also looking into improved technologies for CO_2 and H_2 separation (41).

For source streams with high concentrations of CO_2, physical absorption using solvents, such as Selexol (dimethylether of polyethylene glycol) or Rectisol (cold methanol), represents a less costly alternative. The absorptive capacity of these solvents increases with external gas pressure and decreases with temperature, so applying heat or easing external pressure will release the CO_2. This type of absorption would be done at an IGCC plant, with energy penalties of about 15% (36). Thus, the incremental cost of applying capture is lower for IGCC plants—currently about $140/tC and with near-term technical improvements about $100/tC (36)—than for conventional natural gas and coal plants. Nonetheless, conventional gas plants beat both coal technologies when gas prices are sufficiently low (36).

The cost of replacing an existing conventional coal plant facility with IGCC and CCS (at the same site) is currently about $150/tC (40), including transport and storage costs. Recall from Table 1 and the discussion above, however, that although these costs are lower than for CCS applied to conventional coal and gas plants, the true cost of carbon mitigation through IGCC with CCS is likely to be much greater. This is because IGCC without CCS is unlikely to be the relevant reference technology for comparison. Goldthorpe & Davison (42) find that physical absorption processes by means of a specialized solvent (i.e., Selexol) and plain seawater combined with ocean storage have similar mitigation costs for a plant near the ocean. Seawater scrubbing has low capture efficiency, however, and so the quantity of carbon avoided is less.

PURE OXYGEN COMBUSTION   A potential alternative to these technologies would be to combust fossil fuels in pure oxygen instead of air, which contains approximately 78% nitrogen by volume. If nitrogen were removed from the process, flue gas streams would have a much higher concentration of CO_2, reducing or eliminating the need for costly CO_2 capture. Moreover, NO_X emissions (a source of acid rain and an ozone precursor) and the subsequent need for scrubbing would be reduced significantly. Finally, trace pollutants, such as NO_X and SO_2, could potentially be compressed and stored along with CO_2, allowing control costs to be shared among pollutants and resulting in a zero-emissions power plant—assuming, of course, that the environmental effects of jointly storing these other pollutants are acceptable. The obvious drawback to this technique is that production of oxygen in an air separation unit is quite costly (15), and thus, capture costs are higher than for other techniques (43). Therefore, application of this process seems very unlikely, even before considering issues of managing oxygen atmosphere combustion, which involves additional handling risks.

Industry

Industrial manufacturing alone accounts for about 81% of energy-related carbon emissions (4, 44, 45), especially those that are energy intensive, such as petroleum refining, petrochemicals, and iron and steel manufacturing. In principle, it is possible to capture CO_2 from the flue gases of these industries. In practice, however, opportunities for carbon capture vary. In some cases, it may be straightforward to build or retrofit a manufacturing plant to accommodate carbon capture; in other cases, these changes may not be compatible with particular manufacturing processes.

In addition to emissions from fossil-fuel combustion, industries, such as natural gas and hydrogen production, currently employ capture technologies to separate CO_2 from gas mixtures. Although there are some commercial uses for this CO_2, most is simply vented to the atmosphere. These industries represent relatively inexpensive first options for CCS because incremental costs would include only transportation and storage. The total estimated cost of CCS is 55% to 80% lower for these industries than for electric power generation, about $50 to $90/tC.

PETROLEUM REFINING Within the manufacturing sector, the single largest source of carbon emissions is the petroleum refining industry. About 78% of these emissions come from the combustion of waste products (e.g., petroleum coke and still gas), petroleum fuels, and natural gas (44, 45). CCS applied to these emissions may incur comparable or slightly greater costs than for electric power plants (15, 46), with chemical absorption being the most promising method for CO_2 removal. The remaining 22% of refinery emissions result from the noncombustion use of fossil fuels, such as the gasification of petroleum residues and waste products. Incremental mitigation costs for CCS applied to these processes are significantly lower because they already generate relatively pure streams of CO_2. CCS costs for Dutch residue gasification plants are estimated at $90/tC (38, 47).

CHEMICALS The chemical industry is the second-largest source of manufacturing emissions, with about 77% coming from the combustion of fossil fuels (44, 45) and 23% coming from the nonfuel use of fossil-fuel resources, such as hydrogen production from natural gas during ammonia manufacture. CCS costs for Dutch petrochemical industries using MEA are estimated at about $245/tC (38, 47).

IRON AND STEEL MANUFACTURE Iron and steel production is the third-largest source of manufacturing emissions. Most flue gas emissions result from the direct combustion of fossil fuels; a small fraction comes from the oxidization of metallurgical coke in blast furnaces. In steel plants that use a basic oxygen furnace to convert pig iron to steel, approximately 80% of carbon emissions is contained in flue gas from blast furnaces (47). About 15% of the carbon introduced into the process ends up incorporated into steel, slag, or other by-products and is thus sequestered from the atmosphere. Estimates suggest that 71% of Dutch iron and steel emissions could be avoided through CCS at a cost of about $195/tC (38, 47).

CEMENT MANUFACTURE   In cement manufacture, limestone is heated (calcined) in a cement kiln to produce lime, which is then combined with other materials to produce clinker, an intermediate product in the manufacture of cement. Roughly one half of cement industry emissions comes from this process, releasing a concentrated CO_2 by-product that amounted to 11 MtC in the United States in 2000 (4). Flue gas concentrations of CO_2 are relatively high in cement manufacture, ranging from 14% to 33% (48). Preliminary calculations suggest that the application of CCS technologies in cement production could reduce carbon emissions by as much as 65% to 70%. If feasible, capture and storage costs would likely be $180/tC to $915/tC (48, 49). Similarly, the calcination of limestone in commercial lime production generated 4.3 MtC of process-related emissions in 2000 (4). Mitigation costs for CCS would likely be similar to those for cement manufacture.

NATURAL GAS PRODUCTION   Natural gas contains up to 20% CO_2 by volume. Most of it must be removed to produce pipeline-quality gas, and MEA solvents were developed some 60 years ago specifically for this purpose. Some of this CO_2 is used for industrial applications—20% of the CO_2 used in EOR operations, for example, comes from the purification of natural gas (50). Most is simply released to the atmosphere; these operations vented 5 MtC in 2000 (4). This CO_2 could, however, be compressed and stored in various geological formations, as demonstrated by Statoil's gas production operation at Sleipner, offshore Norway. Compression and injection of CO_2 at Sleipner raised total commercial gas production costs by about 1% (51, 52), with mitigation costs of about $55/tC to store the CO_2 that was already being captured (30). Nearly 3 MtC has been stored to date (53).

HYDROGEN PRODUCTION FROM NATURAL GAS FOR INDUSTRIAL USES   Nine megatons of hydrogen were used by industry in 1990—about 30% during the manufacture of ammonia and about 60% for petroleum refining (14). Approximately 98% of the hydrogen used in ammonia production comes from the catalytic steam reforming of natural gas, which releases a stream of pure CO_2 representing 5.2 MtC in 2000 (5). Approximately 40% of the hydrogen used in petroleum refining is produced in dedicated facilities, most of which also use steam reforming of natural gas (14).

Many of these processes rely on adsorption technologies to separate CO_2 from hydrogen. Adsorption refers to the capture of CO_2 on the surface of a high-surface-area solid. In contrast, absorption, described in Electric Power Generation above, refers to the capture of CO_2 in a liquid chemical solvent (e.g., MEA for PC plant flue gas) or liquid physical solvent (e.g., Selexol for separation of CO_2 from hydrogen in an IGCC plant). See the Appendix in Reference 38 for more information.

Because hydrogen production in these industries already involves the capture and separation of CO_2, the incremental cost of applying CCS technologies (for cleanup, compression, transportation, and injection) is among the lowest for all CCS opportunities. Chargin & Socolow (14) estimate that CCS would add only 10% to the cost of hydrogen production in a large facility. Adding transportation and storage, this implies a mitigation cost of about $75/tC (38). Others have estimated the cost to be about $50/tC to $70/tC (54). Note, however, that recent reports indicate that such opportunities for low-cost capture and storage of CO_2 may be diminishing because of retrofits, which have reduced exhaust stream concentrations of CO_2, of many hydrogen production facilities (P. Freund, personal conversation).

FUTURE HYDROGEN PRODUCTION   Most sources of CO_2 emissions from primary fossil-fuel combustion in the residential, commercial, and transportation sectors are not currently amenable to CCS technologies. Many researchers believe, however, that hydrogen has the potential to replace gasoline and other petroleum-based fuels for use in hydrogen fuel cells. This use of hydrogen would eliminate direct carbon emissions from these sectors. Hydrogen would most likely come from syngas derived from steam-reformed natural gas or gasified coal (described above), unconventional hydrocarbon fuels, municipal wastes, or biomass. Although it is also possible to produce hydrogen through the electrolysis of water, this is the most costly method. Electrolysis incurs no direct carbon emissions, but it could generate them indirectly if the necessary electricity is derived from fossil-fuel combustion.

Hydrogen production from carbon-based sources would release a pure stream of CO_2, creating a relatively low-cost opportunity for the large-scale application of CCS technologies (56). Capture costs would likely be similar to those for hydrogen and ammonia production (see above). Still, the widespread use of hydrogen-powered vehicles will depend on the development of an infrastructure for hydrogen supply and distribution that, if it occurs, would likely occur only after significant delay (50).

CO_2 TRANSPORTATION AND STORAGE

Once CO_2 has been captured, cleaned, and compressed, it must be transported and stored in a suitable location. Several options, including depleted oil and natural gas fields, deep coal beds, saline aquifers, and the ocean, have been suggested. Although estimated storage costs are small relative to capture, the capacity, storage integrity, technological feasibility, and potential environmental impacts of these storage options are uncertain. Moreover, transport costs often depend on a fortuitous matching of CO_2 sources and storage locations, generating considerable variations in cost. The combined costs of transport and storage are typically estimated to range from about $20/tC to $55/tC stored (15). There may be limited

TABLE 4 U.S. transportation and storage capacities, costs, and risks

Storage option	Capacity (GtC)[a]	Transport and storage costs ($/tC stored)[b,c]	Storage integrity[d]	Environmental risk[d]
Depleted oil and gas fields	25–30	5–70	High	Low
Active oil wells (EOR)	Low	(30)–(15)	High	Low
Enhanced coal-bed methane	5–10	(95)–70	Medium	Medium
Deep aquifers	1–150	5–45	Medium	Medium
Ocean (global)[e]	1,000–10,000	10–50	Medium	High
Carbonate storage (no transport)[f]	Very high	110–370	Highest	High

[a] Capacity sources: oil and gas (63, 66); coal beds (14, 15, 58); aquifers (68); and the ocean (14).

[b] Cost sources: enhanced oil recovery (EOR) (63); depleted oil and gas, enhanced coal-bed methane, aquifers, and ocean storage via pipeline (64); carbonate storage (15, 80); and transport (15). Costs of transport alone are based on estimates of $5/tC to $10/tC per 100 km (15).

[c] Negative cost values (i.e., net benefits to storage) are given in parentheses. All storage cost numbers are given on a $/tC stored basis and do not consider the additional emissions generated by the transportation and storage process itself.

[d] Storage integrity and risks are from Herzog et al. (15) and the subjective judgment of the authors.

[e] The capacity of the ocean is given on a global scale. One can get a rough sense of the magnitude of the storage capacity estimates by dividing by the current U.S. emissions rate of 1.6 GtC/year for geologic storage options and the current global emissions rate of 6.1 GtC/year for ocean storage.

[f] Carbonate storage cost numbers do not include transport. Further, this process is likely to be highly energy intensive, implying that the cost figures above may significantly understate costs in $/tC avoided.

opportunities for net benefits of $15/tC to $30/tC stored, however, in the case of EOR and enhanced coal-bed methane recovery operations that generate revenue in excess of storage costs (57, 58). We discuss these issues below, with summary information in Table 4, and discussion of environmental risks in each subsection.

Transportation

Transport in dedicated pipelines is the most promising method for delivering captured CO_2 to storage locations, although other methods, such as barges and ships, have been suggested (12, 15). The oil-and-gas industry has years of experience with pipelines, transporting CO_2 hundreds of kilometers for use in EOR operations. Large-scale transport would undoubtedly require the development of additional infrastructure, though there may be limited opportunities to use existing oil and gas pipelines when the fields they serve are retired and converted to storage sites (12).

Transport costs are dominated by the investment in pipeline infrastructure. Operation and maintenance costs are small in comparison, and the average cost of transporting CO_2 falls dramatically with scale. Transport costs are also reduced significantly when CO_2 has been pressurized to its liquid form and are estimated to be about $5/tC to $10/tC per 100 km when matched to a coal plant of typical size (15).

Although transport of concentrated CO_2 presents some concerns for human health—CO_2 is denser than air and could cause suffocation in the event of a pipeline break and mass release—the avoidance of low-lying and densely populated areas would mitigate the harm from possible pipeline breaks (12). In 1986, for example, a sudden release of CO_2 gas was emitted from the volcanic Lake Nyos in Cameroon, suffocating 1700 people and hospitalizing 845 others. Although concentrated releases of CO_2 on this massive scale would be highly unlikely, this freak occurrence illustrates concerns regarding CO_2 storage. Further, experience with pipeline transport in the oil-and-gas industry suggests that the risk of a major pipeline break is very low. Still, the general public's perceptions of risk could pose potential obstacles to the siting of CO_2 pipelines.

Geologic Storage

Storage of CO_2 in geologic formations, particularly in depleted oil and gas reservoirs, represents the best near-term option for application of CCS technologies. Ignoring transportation, the cost of geologic storage is about $5/tC to $30/tC stored (15). Costs, including transportation, are roughly comparable with ocean storage options, but use of geologic formations is considerably better understood. Whereas the environmental risks, discussed below, are uncertain, they appear much lower for geologic than ocean storage and lower for geologic storage in depleted wells compared to saline aquifers (59). Thus, although some environmental groups have become more receptive to carbon capture and geologic storage (including geologic storage beneath the ocean floor), they remain strongly against storage in ocean water (60, 61). Leakage is also a concern; we discuss leakage further in Regulatory Issues and Leakage below.

DEPLETED OIL AND GAS RESERVOIRS   Storage of CO_2 in depleted oil and gas reservoirs may represent the best near-term option. EOR operations currently pipe CO_2 hundreds of kilometers for injection into depleted oil fields, facilitating the extraction of oil that would otherwise be too costly or impossible to recover. About 9 MtC of CO_2 was pumped into the ground for EOR in 2000 (29). In September 2000, Pan Canadian Resources Ltd. began injecting CO_2 into the Weyburn oil field in southeastern Saskatchewan using by-product CO_2 piped 320 km from a coal gasification plant in North Dakota. It is expected that about 5 MtC will be stored over the Weyburn project's 25-year lifetime (62). Most EOR operations, however, currently obtain their CO_2 from natural formations and do not contribute to the reduction of carbon emissions.

The price paid for CO_2 by EOR operations is about $40/tC to $65/tC (14, 57). Thus, for limited amounts of CO_2 used in EOR, storage could generate net benefits ranging from $15/tC to $30/tC stored (63). In recent work, Bock et al. (64) estimate that EOR storage of CO_2 would generate average net benefits of about $45/tC stored. Opportunities for EOR would be insufficient, however, for larger amounts of CO_2 storage. Further, if CCS technologies were applied widely, the market price paid by EOR operations for CO_2 would almost certainly plummet, implying little or no economic value for captured CO_2. Storage of CO_2 in gas reservoirs would also be unlikely to generate many opportunities for positive economic value, because up to 95% of natural gas can be recovered using conventional extraction techniques. This is in contrast to conventional oil recovery, which leaves a significantly higher percentage of oil in the ground. (65). Where feasible, however, there is limited evidence that enhanced natural gas recovery through injection of CO_2 could generate a positive economic value of about $30/tC stored (54).

There is an estimated 1 GtC of storage capacity in currently abandoned U.S. oil and gas fields and an eventual capacity of about 25–30 GtC (63, 66). To get a rough sense of this magnitude, if 100% of U.S. carbon emissions were captured and stored in these reservoirs, about 15 to 20 years of emissions could be stored at the current U.S. emissions rate of 1.6 GtC per year. Effective capacities could be lower, however, if water from other nearby formations intrudes into depleted reservoirs. Storage costs in these reservoirs could range from $5/tC to $70/tC stored, with a base case estimate of about $15/tC (64).

Finally, current knowledge suggests that storage of CO_2 in depleted oil and gas reservoirs carries the least potential environmental risk. These formations have already demonstrated their ability to store pressurized fluids for millions of years, and knowledge gained during exploration for oil and gas has led to a relatively good understanding of them. Environmental risks do exist. One is potential leakage of CO_2 through natural pathways or fractures caused by injection into geologic formations with possible contamination of groundwater. Leakage from surface installations and wells is also possible, although experience from EOR demonstrated that these risks can be mitigated through quality construction and operation of storage facilities (12). The reservoir-monitoring project at the Weyburn EOR facility will provide further information regarding the long-term storage capacity and integrity of these locations (67).

AQUIFERS Although depleted oil and gas reservoirs represent the best near-term storage option, deep aquifers may represent a better option in the longer term, as shown in Table 3. Deep aquifers, whose locations are mapped in Figure 1, are generally better matched to sources of emissions than oil and gas reservoirs, implying lower transport costs. Whereas the specific properties of oil and gas reservoirs are better understood, the potential U.S. storage capacity of aquifers is much larger, ranging from 1 GtC to 150 GtC (68) and providing storage for up to 100 years of emissions. Estimated costs are about $5/tC to $45/tC stored, with a base case estimate of about $10/tC (64).

Although there is uncertainty regarding the environmental effects of CO_2 storage in aquifers, most studies suggest that adverse effects can be mitigated by choosing suitable locations (69). Suitable aquifers will have an impermeable cap, prohibiting the release of injected CO_2, and high permeability and porosity below, allowing large quantities of injected CO_2 to be distributed uniformly (15). Most such aquifers are saline and separated geologically from shallower freshwater

CARBON CAPTURE AND STORAGE   125

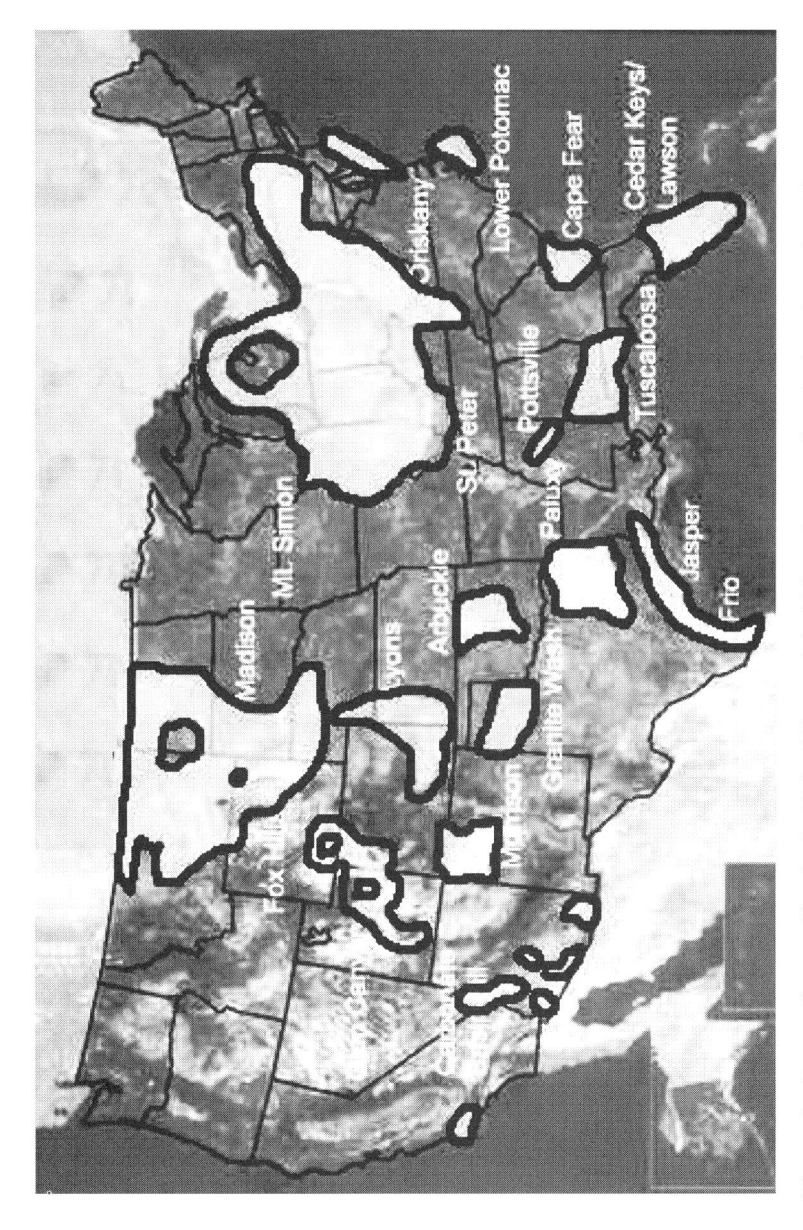

Figure 1 Deep saline aquifers in the United States. A bold line circumscribes the locations of aquifers. The map is from Reference 70.

aquifers and surface water supplies used by humans. Theoretically, there is the potential for leakage into groundwater drinking supplies, but the risk is small. Several states have in fact permitted the limited storage of various liquid and gaseous wastes in deep aquifers. Injected CO_2 would likely displace formation water at first but would eventually dissolve into pore fluids. Under ideal circumstances, chemical reactions between absorbed CO_2 and surrounding rock would lead to the formation of highly stable carbonates, which may result in longer storage times (52).

Still, given the uncertainty of these processes, better scientific information is needed regarding how long CO_2 can remain stored in aquifers and the means by which this process occurs. Toward this end, the U.S. Department of Energy is funding a research team headed by American Electric Power and Battelle to study potential aquifer sites in the Ohio River Valley, the heart of the largest concentration of fossil-fuel power plants in the United States, notably the massive Mount Simon sandstone saline formation (70).

Statoil's natural gas mining and CO_2 injection operation offshore of Norway also provides an excellent opportunity to obtain more information (71). To date, nearly 3 MtC has been stored in the Utsira aquifer (53). Statoil is taking core samples from it and will use seismic methods to follow the movement of the injected bubble of CO_2; release of the data from these measurements is expected shortly. Exxon, Mobil, and Pertamina are planning a similar but much larger project at Indonesia's Natuna natural gas field off the shore of Borneo. Carbon contained in this natural gas will be brought to the surface at a rate of 30 MtC per year, or 100 times the rate at Sleipner. The plan involves capturing 90% of this CO_2 and injecting it into a nearby deep aquifer (14). Project sponsors reasoned that by the time of peak production, they would likely face political and economic difficulties if they vented the CO_2 to the atmosphere; such a release would create a massive point source equal to about 0.5% of the current global CO_2 emissions from fossil fuels.

ENHANCED COAL-BED METHANE   Deep coal beds may provide additional opportunities for CO_2 storage. As with EOR, storage of CO_2 in coal deposits has the potential to generate economic benefits. Under certain conditions, CO_2 injected into a coal seam can displace fossil-fuel methane that is adsorbed on coal surfaces, allowing the methane to be recovered and put to economic use. This technology is in its early stages of development. Burlington Resources' Allison Unit pilot project in the San Juan basin in New Mexico is the only commercial recovery operation (58). The Alberta Research Council is leading a multinational group to explore opportunities for enhanced coal-bed methane recovery and is conducting field tests in Fenn Big Valley, Alberta (72). Opportunities for coal-bed methane in the United States could provide an estimated 5–10 GtC of storage capacity (14, 15, 58), assuming the coal is not mined at a later date. This amounts to about three to six years of emissions storage if 100% of the current U.S. carbon emissions were captured and stored in these reservoirs. Enhanced coal-bed methane storage of CO_2 could generate net benefits as high as $95/tC stored, or cost as much as $70/tC stored, with a base case net benefit of about $20/tC (64).

Ocean Storage

Oceans have by far the largest potential capacity for storage of captured CO_2. They already contain some 40,000 GtC of carbon, mainly as stable carbonate ions, and have a virtually unlimited capacity to absorb even more (14). Natural ocean uptake of CO_2 is a slow process that works over millennia to balance atmospheric and oceanic concentrations. Anthropogenic emissions of carbon have upset this balance, and there is currently an estimated net flow of 2 GtC per year from the atmosphere to ocean surface waters, which are eventually transferred to the deeper ocean. Indeed, roughly 90% of present-day emissions will eventually end up in the ocean, but we know little about the effect on marine organisms and ecosystems (14).

Direct injection of captured CO_2 into the ocean would greatly accelerate the process, bypassing the potentially damaging atmospheric concentrations of CO_2 but generating certain new risks. As with natural absorption, direct injection of CO_2 increases the acidity of the ocean—but at a rate that may not give marine organisms time to adapt. By applying what they deem an acceptable increase in average ocean-water acidity, scientists have estimated the storage capacity of the ocean at roughly 1000 to 10,000 GtC (14). If 100% of global carbon emissions were captured and stored in the ocean, this would imply roughly 200 to 2000 years of emissions storage at the current global emissions rate of 6.1 GtC per year. Storage times of up to 500 years for two thirds of the CO_2 may be possible, provided it is injected initially at depths of 1000 meters or more (15, 73).

There are several potential methods for ensuring that injected CO_2 reaches these depths (12, 15, 74). The most practical near-term option appears to be injection at depths of 1000 to 1500 meters by a pipeline or towed pipeline, which would create a rising stream of CO_2 that would be absorbed into surrounding waters. Alternatively, a carefully controlled shallow release of dense seawater and absorbed CO_2 would sink to the deeper ocean, especially if aided by a natural sinking current—where salty Mediterranean enters the Atlantic Ocean. Other experiments show that CO_2 exceeds the density of seawater at 3000 meters and deeper (29).

If CO_2 is injected at these depths, it would, in theory, sink to the ocean floor to form a stable, isolated lake. Finally, solid CO_2, or "dry ice," is 1.5 times as dense as surface-level seawater and blocks of it could be dropped into the ocean and sink to depths sufficient for long-term storage (12, 15, 29). Unfortunately, refrigeration and compression of CO_2 are quite costly.

The cost and technical feasibility for ocean storage depend on the transport distance and the depth of injection. Shorter transport distances favor pipeline injection, and the oil-and-gas industry has experience with underwater pipelines to depths of 850 meters (12). Pipeline transportation and storage would incur costs of about $10/tC to $50/tC, with a base case estimate of $20/tC (64). The success of a shallow release of a dense CO_2 and seawater mixture depends on having a good location with the proper slope, as well as on designing a device that will sufficiently concentrate CO_2 to get negative buoyancy. Currently, the only proven technology is injection from the bottom of a pipe.

Despite the large potential capacity, the negative environmental effects of ocean storage are the most uncertain of the storage options and seem likely to be the highest. The primary issue would be the increased acidity of the ocean, with potential effects such as corrosion of organisms with calcium carbonate shells or skeletal structures. One should keep in mind, however, that the ocean will eventually absorb about 90% of present-day atmospheric emissions anyway, also leading to increased acidity. But direct injection would also lead to more rapid and localized effects. If injected CO_2 is sufficiently dispersed, as could occur from a deeply towed pipeline, then mortality of marine organisms could, in principle, be largely avoided. The high concentrations of CO_2 needed for shallow-water injection could lead to significant increases in acidity over several kilometers (12) and could have serious adverse impacts on marine organisms. For most methods, however, acidity would increase primarily at depths of 1000 meters or greater, with potentially less serious environmental effects if the CO_2 remains in the deep ocean where there is a lower abundance of marine organisms. Nonetheless, Siebel & Walsh (75) find evidence that deep-sea organisms are highly sensitive to even modest pH changes, indicating that small perturbations in CO_2 or pH may have important consequences for the ecology of the deep sea and for the global biogeochemical cycles dependent on deep-sea ecosystems.

Brewer et al. (76) suggest that deep-ocean sequestration may be a solution with long residence time, but not permanent and not without ecological consequences of hydrate volume expansion and dissolution. Caldeira (77) and Johnston & Santillo (60) identify two primary concerns with ocean sequestration: leakage of stored carbon into the atmosphere; and unknown consequences on marine organisms of elevated CO_2 concentrations, reduced ocean pH, and trace pollutants injected along with industrial CO_2. Huessemann et al. (78) evaluate the potential effects of ocean CO_2 storage on marine nitrogen chemistry, suggesting that lower pH would inhibit nitrification and ammonia oxidation, which would cause accumulation of ammonia that could change phytoplankton abundance and community structure and cause unpredictable eutrophication.

Other Options

DIRECT USE   In addition to storage options, there may be some limited opportunities for direct economic use of captured CO_2. Industry uses approximately 10 MtC per year, 80% of it for EOR, as described above. The use of captured CO_2 in these industries would displace CO_2 that currently comes from natural formations, resulting in a net reduction in carbon emissions. Further, CO_2 could be used as a feedstock for plastics or inorganic carbonates, and new discoveries in chemistry and bioprocessing could lead to additional uses. Still, the market for these uses seems likely to remain small relative to the large quantities of CO_2 that would become available upon the widespread application of CCS. Moreover, chemical conversion of CO_2 is often energy intensive and, in many (if not most) cases, would generate more net CO_2 emissions than would be released absent conversion (79).

CONVERSION TO CARBONATES   A weathering process occurs, whereby CO_2 reacts with alkaline rocks to form highly stable, environmentally benign, and nonhazardous carbonate compounds. Left to nature, this process can take millennia, but it takes just minutes in an industrial setting. The concept of conversion is to accelerate this process by reacting CO_2 with carbonate materials prior to injection so that it enters the environment in a more stable form to begin with—thereby greatly reducing or eliminating concerns about increased ocean acidity, leakage from geologic reservoirs to human water supplies or the atmosphere, and safety (80).

The techniques, however, involve processing large quantities of calcium- or magnesium-rich rock—several times the weight of CO_2 sequestered—and handling large quantities of intermediate chemicals, such as hydrochloric acid (81). Hence, mineral conversion presents significant potential for adverse environmental impacts, comparable to issues caused by quarrying and mining operations of similar size (80). Overall, the operation would be slightly smaller than present-day U.S. coal mining. The incremental increase in energy needed for pulverization and handling of rock would be about 1% to 15% of the total energy needed for storage (15). Estimated costs for this process are about $220/tC to $360/tC stored, ignoring capture and transportation; costs per ton avoided would be higher, given that the process itself would consume energy and contribute to carbon emissions (80). Capture and transport costs would be roughly an additional $180/tC to $220tC avoided (80).

BIOLOGICAL CONVERSION TO FUELS   Flue gases from industrial processes could be fed directly into ponds containing high concentrations of microalgae, which can convert solar energy to biomass at about 1% to 3% efficiency, although bioengineering and other technological improvements promise higher efficiencies (15). This biomass could be harvested and converted to fuels, displacing some fossil-fuel consumption. Unfortunately, the process would have high water, natural solar energy, and land requirements—a 500 MW power plant would need 50 to 100 square km of pond area—and these resources are not generally found in the same locations as power plants. Further, only about 54% of a power plant's annual CO_2 production could be captured (82). With typical solar radiation levels and current technology, costs have been estimated at $350/tC, although they could potentially fall to $150/tC under ideal conditions (82).

REGULATORY ISSUES AND LEAKAGE   Most CCS research to date has focused on the costs and technical feasibility of CO_2 capture and storage. Recently, researchers have begun to consider other related issues. Wilson & Keith (83) conclude that the future of CO_2 storage regulation is unclear. The myriad of existing regulations makes it difficult to include geologic storage of CO_2 in the existing regulatory structure, and a separate approach may be required. A review of the U.S. Environmental Protection Agency's (EPA's) Underground Injection Control program (84) suggests that the EPA Class I injection well is most relevant for CO_2 injections into brine formations, requiring among other conditions, injection below the deepest underground sources of drinking water, separated by at least one thick and relatively impermeable stratum. Reiner & Herzog (85) conclude that legitimate political opposition to the siting of storage facilities, although often strong, could be overcome through transparency, compensation, monitoring, and enforcement.

Researchers have also begun to treat the issue of CO_2 leakage more explicitly. As Hawkins (86) points out, if one assumes that 100% of carbon reductions come through CCS, a long-term, system-wide annual leakage rate of 0.1% would still result in a global emissions source of 1 to 2 GtC per year in 2200. Leakage of this magnitude would account for 20% to 100% of total annual allowable emissions. Although geologic storage would likely be capable of much lower rates (P. Freund, personal conversation), a potential problem of CO_2 leakage exists. Wildenborg & van der Meer (87) identify the potential for leakage to occur because of poor well integrity, overpressured aquifers, unintended stress, faulting, or fracturing of the reservoir seal. Benson & Myer (88) review methods for monitoring for CO_2 leakage in surface and subsurface environments and suggest that groundwater monitoring wells be monitored periodically to ensure CO_2 storage is not harming groundwater quality.

As Herzog et al. (89) observe, however, even temporary storage associated with a leaky reservoir has value in providing a delay in the onset of climate change and additional time to develop other, low-cost options. In this view, establishing nonpermanent CO_2 sequestration reservoirs would be, in effect, comparable to other climate change mitigation strategies that involve some level of continued long-term emissions. As such, the choice to employ temporary storage would depend on how the value of such delay compares to CCS costs, and how the resultant net benefits compare to those of other strategies. The results of such an analysis are beyond the scope of this review. Still, many analysts and environmental advocates argue that caution is required, given the significant uncertainty in our knowledge regarding the storage time of injected CO_2, the potential for a catastrophic leak, the precise environmental consequences of CCS, and the challenge of developing alternative mitigation options if CCS fails (90).

CARBON CAPTURE AND STORAGE COST MODELING FOR ELECTRICITY GENERATION

In this section, we discuss and interpret recent climate policy modeling results, synthesizing insight from these studies regarding the potential role of CCS technologies in electricity generation under future climate policies.

Plant-Level Modeling of Carbon Capture and Storage

To assess the competitiveness of CCS versus other carbon mitigation options, some measure of the cost using CCS technologies is needed. Unfortunately, thus far the literature has struggled to provide clear answers. Given cost and performance data for two new power plants (i.e., a plant with CCS and its non-CCS counterpart), a number of studies have calculated average plant-level cost ($/tC) by dividing the difference in the cost of electricity generation ($/kWh) by the difference in carbon emissions (tC/kWh), as described above in Model Assumptions for Carbon Capture and Storage Costs. A number of studies also compare energy penalties, although they only reflect differences in thermal efficiencies and are clearly an inadequate measure of costs. As shown in Table 1, recent estimates put current CCS costs at about $229/tC for new pulverized-coal plants, $224/tC for new natural gas combined-cycle plants (NGCC), and $138/tC for new integrated gasification combined-cycle (IGCC) coal plants, relative to those technologies without CCS (36). These costs all assume a natural gas price of $3/MBtu and transport and storage costs of $37/tC stored.

Using the Integrated Environmental Control Model (IECM), researchers at Carnegie Mellon University have conducted more advanced plant-level analyses of CCS in the electricity generation sector. About 30 independent model parameters were examined, including both plant and CCS performance parameters, as well as cost parameters (91, 92). They found that costs would range from $115/tC to $270/tC (95% confidence interval), with a probability-weighted mean value of $185/tC. These results suggest that estimates discussed above may misstate mean costs while failing to reflect the true range of potential costs.

As researchers have been quick to point out, however, plant-level cost estimates are sensitive to the reference plant chosen, and the appropriate base case is the closest competitor at the margin. One way of visualizing this margin is to compare the cost of electricity for competing options at different carbon prices (93), as demonstrated, for example, by Figure 2. When the price of carbon emissions is zero, plants without CCS produce electricity at a lower cost than their CCS counterparts. As the price of carbon rises, however, adding CCS becomes increasingly attractive by virtue of its lower rate of emissions. Eventually, the price of carbon is such that the cost of electricity generation with and without CCS is equivalent, as indicated by the circles in Figure 2. Note that these prices are identical to the costs from above, about $224/tC for NGCC and $190/tC for PC retrofits, because they are based on the same underlying estimates (36, 40). As discussed above, however, these numbers can be both misleading and irrelevant. In this example, we see that existing coal plants produce the cheapest electricity for all carbon prices up to about $125/tC. Then new NGCC plants produce the cheapest electricity until carbon prices reach $224/tC, at which point NGCC with capture produces the cheapest electricity. PC plants retrofitted with CCS are uneconomic at any carbon price under the assumptions of the figure, even though the CCS costs for coal retrofits are only $190/tC, whereas the incremental cost of adding CCS to a new NGCC plant is $224/tC.

However useful that analysis, its embedded assumptions are subject to uncertainty and change. If gas prices are higher, for example, the NGCC lines would both be shifted upward, implying that replacement of an existing PC with a new NGCC plant would be economical only at a higher carbon price. Still, with or without

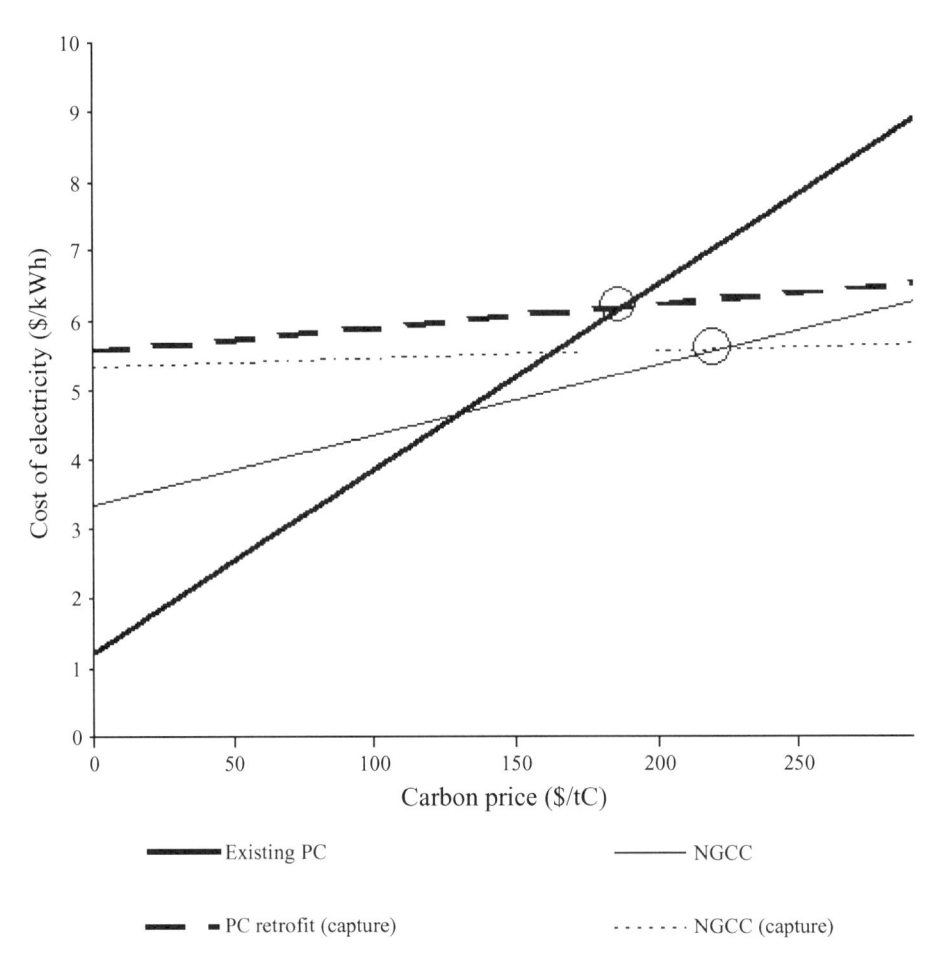

Figure 2 Cost of electricity with and without carbon capture and storage (CCS) versus hypothetical price of carbon emissions. Note: Costs for natural gas combined-cycle (NGCC) plants are from David & Herzog (36) and for existing pulverized-coal (PC) plants and retrofits from Simbeck (40). These costs include a transport and storage cost of $37/tC stored, which we converted to $/tC avoided based on estimates of the ratio of carbon captured to carbon avoided (38). The figure assumes a natural gas price of $3/MBtu. See Conventional Power Plants with Chemical Absorption of CO_2 above.

uncertainty, these plant-level analyses are unable to provide us with a clear understanding of how CCS technologies affect the overall shape of the marginal abatement cost curve for carbon emissions. Such an analysis would consider other factors including: dispatch among existing technologies; fuel switching and plant retirement; retrofitting existing plants with CCS technologies; and future cost reductions, energy efficiency improvements, and technological innovations. Several

TABLE 5 Key results for CCS costs in electricity sector from integrated modeling studies

Study, scenario, and time frame	CCS technology	CCS entry price ($/tC)	CCS entry year	Maximum percentage share of electricity production in year
EPPA, global price of $50/tC in 2010, rising to $200/tC by 2040, 1995–2095[a]	NGCC IGCC	100 100	2020 2020	16 in 2040 50 in 2100
CMU, $150/tC applied across MAAC region, 2000–2040[b]	NGCC IGCC PC retrofit	175[c] 75 50	— Immediate Immediate	— 35 in 2040 10 in 2040
MiniCam, stabilization at 550 ppmv, 1995–2095[d]	NGCC New PC	90 90	2020–2035 2020–2035	15 in 2095 6 in 2095

[a]MIT Emissions Prediction and Policy Analysis (EPPA) results are from McFarland et al. (94).
[b]Carnegie Mellon University (CMU) results are from Johnson & Keith (93).
[c]The $175/tC entry price for NGCC plants in the CMU results represents the level at which NGCC would penetrate, if the 2000–2040 tax is higher than $150/tC.
[d]Pacific Northwest National Laboratory MiniCAM results are from Edmonds et al. (95).

studies, discussed below, have incorporated such effects into integrated modeling frameworks.

Integrated Modeling of Carbon Capture and Storage

Researchers at Massachusetts Institute of Technology (MIT) (94), Carnegie Mellon University (93), and Pacific Northwest National Laboratory (95) have examined the role of CCS technologies under various carbon policies. Although their models differ significantly in methodology and geographic scope, the CCS results are fairly consistent, as shown in Table 5. CCS technologies are typically found to start being adopted after about 20 to 35 years at carbon prices of $50/tC to $100/tC. The competitiveness of CCS relative to other mitigation options depends, of course, on a number of hotly debated assumptions regarding future fuel prices and future technology costs for both CCS and alternative mitigation options (37). Also notable is the finding that IGCC plants with CCS appear surprisingly competitive in these models, eventually surpassing NGCC as the dominant fossil-fuel technology. These results appear to differ markedly from the results presented above, which indicate that NGCC plants without CCS are the relevant reference technology and, consequently, that the carbon price at which new plants with CCS become competitive is at least $200/tC.

There are two primary sources for these apparent inconsistencies. First, these models all make assumptions regarding future technology that could lower the cost of CCS by about one third compared with our estimates above (36). Second, and more importantly, these models all predict that natural gas prices will rise significantly in this century. Gas price increases lead to a reduction in the carbon price at which plants with CCS become competitive relative to an NGCC plant without capture. This is demonstrated by the differences between Table 1 (relatively low 2000 gas prices) and Table 2 (high gas prices). If gas prices rise sufficiently, the relevant reference technology actually shifts from NGCC plants without capture to IGCC and PC plants without capture. Because IGCC plants and PC plants without capture both have relatively high carbon emissions compared with NGCC plants, this shift leads to a discontinuous drop in the carbon price at which CCS technologies for IGCC and PC plants become competitive. We briefly describe the models below and give their key results.

MIT EMISSIONS PREDICTION AND POLICY ANALYSIS WORLD ECONOMY MODEL
The Emissions Prediction and Policy Analysis (EPPA) model at MIT is the only general equilibrium framework in which CCS technologies for carbon mitigation in the United States have been studied (94, 96–99). The model encompasses 12 world regions linked by international trade, 9 sectors of production, and a representative consumer in each region. In recent applications (94, 98, 99), the model, which generates results in five-year intervals between 1995 and 2100, explicitly incorporates new NGCC and IGCC plants with CCS, as well as new NGCC plants without CCS. CCS cost parameters come from David & Herzog (36) and represent moderate technical improvements on current technology. The rest of the electricity sector comprises nuclear power and a mix of all other generation technologies (i.e., conventional coal, oil, natural gas, and hydroelectric power). The model does not include the possibility of CCS retrofits. Electricity and energy prices are determined endogenously, and technological improvements in energy efficiency are exogenous to the analysis.

Recent EPPA modeling efforts examine the role of CCS in multiple world regions in response to a carbon tax that grows from $50/tC in 2010 to a maximum of $200/tC in 2040 (94). The imposition of a price on carbon emissions initially leads to increased electricity production from NGCC and a corresponding increase in gas prices. NGCC and IGCC with CCS enter in 2020 at a carbon price of $100/tC, which implies that gas prices have by this time increased sufficiently to shift the reference technology from NGCC to IGCC without capture.

Overall, the results of the EPPA studies show that presence of CCS technologies leads to a smaller reduction in the demand for coal, oil, and gas while making electricity generation from coal more attractive than gas. The benefits of CCS technologies include a reduction in electricity prices over time and greater economic welfare (94). In earlier studies, the model predicts that up to 38 GtC of carbon would be captured in the United States, which would be unlikely to exceed estimated geologic storage capacity, as shown in Table 4 (98). McFarland et al. (98) highlight a number of uncertainties in these estimates, including the rate of technological change, fuel prices, economic growth, and baseline emissions.

CARNEGIE MELLON ELECTRICITY SECTOR MODEL Researchers at Carnegie Mellon University have examined CCS technologies in an electricity sector model of the Mid-Atlantic Area Council (MAAC) of the North American Electricity Reliability Council (93, 100). The model assumes a centrally controlled utility that minimizes capital and operating costs to meet electricity demand over the 40-year planning horizon from 2000 to 2040. Generic plant categories are specified by cost and performance parameters designed to model the MAAC region in each of the model's five-year intervals from 2000 to 2040. CO_2 capture parameters remain static over time and reflect the judgment of researchers regarding the probable state of technology in 2015; a fixed cost of $25/tC is assumed for CO_2 transport and storage. Given exogenous fuel prices and plant parameters, the model dispatches installed capacity to meet peak and off-peak electricity demand in each interval.

Johnson & Keith (93) find that CCS retrofits of existing PC plants could be competitive at $50/tC, that a mix of new IGCC with CCS and PC CCS retrofits makes sense at $75/tC, and that NGCC with CCS is not competitive until the price of carbon exceeds $175/tC. These results, which imply different CCS costs than those discussed above, partially reflect the assumption of less costly 2015 technology.

For moderate reductions in CO_2 emissions (93), fuel switching from coal to natural gas and reordering of plant dispatch are the least costly options. Without CCS, reductions above 50% come only at high carbon prices, as renewable energy sources become economically competitive. CCS technologies play a significant role in reducing mitigation costs for reductions above 50% and carbon prices above $75/tC. For example, a $200/tC charge on emissions would yield a 50% reduction in emissions without CCS but an 80% reduction in emissions with CCS. These results demonstrate the potential role of CCS in the electricity supply sector. The overall results are sensitive to changes in assumptions regarding gas prices, the initial distribution of capacity, electricity demand, and the cost of CCS technologies. For instance, new coal CCS enters earlier in scenarios where gas prices or electricity demand are higher. Further, mitigation costs are uniformly higher if one considers that the electricity supply sector is already becoming less carbon intensive as coal plants are replaced with less costly natural gas.

PACIFIC NORTHWEST NATIONAL LABORATORY WORLD ECONOMY MODEL The Mini Climate Change Assessment Model (MiniCAM) of Pacific Northwest National Laboratory is a partial equilibrium model of the world economy that simulates interactions between various drivers of energy use to project greenhouse emissions in 14 regions. The electricity generation sector in the model includes fossil-fuel, renewable, and nuclear generation technologies, which are specified by costs of fuel, operating and maintenance, and capital (101). Edmonds et al. (95), assuming moderate technological advance and cost reductions, use this model to examine the role of CCS technologies for coal and natural gas. CCS is assumed to impose a 25% energy penalty and an 88% capital cost penalty for coal in 1990; by 2100, these figures fall to 15% and 63%, respectively. CCS imposes a 15% energy penalty and an 89% capital cost penalty for natural gas in 1990; by 2100, these penalties fall to 10% and 72%, respectively. These and other technological improvements are exogenous to the analysis, but fuel prices and energy demand are determined endogenously. The model runs in 15-year increments from 1990 through 2095, with a uniform carbon price applied across all sectors.

After the imposition of carbon constraints that achieve atmospheric stabilization of 550 parts per million by volume (ppmv), Edmonds et al. (95) find that natural gas with CCS and coal with CCS enter between 2020 and 2035 at a carbon price of $90/tC. In 2100, natural gas with CCS and coal with CCS account for 15% and 6% of total global electricity production, respectively.

Kim & Edmonds (101) find that highly optimistic assumptions regarding future cost reductions in CCS, combined with atmospheric stabilization at a stringent 450 ppmv, would result in approximately 850 GtC captured worldwide. This estimate can be thought of as an upper bound on the ultimate storage capacity needed for about 100 years of CO_2 capture and storage, given twenty-first century population levels and energy demand. This figure is toward the bottom of the current estimated range of total worldwide geologic storage capacity of 370 GtC to 3000 GtC (102) and is well below the estimated storage capacity of the ocean.

SUMMARY AND CONCLUSION

Human beings are greatly contributing to the accumulation of CO_2 and other GHGs in the atmosphere, primarily through the unchecked combustion of fossil fuels. CCS technologies could provide a partial solution to this dilemma by facilitating reductions in carbon emissions along with the continued use of fossil fuels. Experience with these technologies in the oil, gas, and other niche industries shows that their application to carbon mitigation is technically feasible.

The existing evidence also suggests that these technologies, although typically more expensive than many energy-efficient and fuel-switching opportunities, could be economically attractive given sufficiently stringent climate policies. Natural gas and hydrogen production already produce pure streams of CO_2, which could be compressed and diverted to storage sites at relatively low costs (under $50/tC). Such opportunities are, however, quite small. Recent estimates suggest that the application of CCS in the electric power and industrial sectors could significantly reduce total U.S. emissions at a current cost of about $200/tC to $250/tC, and many expect that these costs could fall substantially with time and technological development. In addition, a rise in natural gas prices—as is likely to occur with the onset of a price on carbon emissions—could also lower the carbon price at which CCS technologies become competitive.

A number of technical, environmental, and political issues arise with regard to transportation and storage of captured CO_2. Despite significant experience with storage of CO_2 and other substances in underground reservoirs, there is substantial uncertainty regarding how much CO_2 such reservoirs can hold, how long injected

CO_2 would remain trapped, and whether injected CO_2 would escape from storage reservoirs. The effects of ocean storage raise additional environmental concerns and are more likely to generate controversy. Storage of CO_2 as carbonates could lessen many of these concerns but would generate others and would entail substantially higher costs. Although the safety hazards of storage leakage are likely minimal, public perceptions of risk could pose potential obstacles to the siting of storage and transportation facilities, and it is unclear whether and how current underground storage regulations would apply to CCS. Finally, leakage from storage facilities would weaken CCS as a source of permanent emissions reduction, though CCS could still provide valuable temporary storage while less costly permanent means of mitigation are being developed (e.g., renewable energy sources).

Several modeling studies suggest that CCS could play an important role in mitigating carbon emissions, conditional on policies that place a significant price on carbon. Fuel switching from coal to natural gas and energy efficiency improvements would appear to be the least costly options for moderate reductions in emissions. For larger reductions and higher carbon prices, however, CCS substantially lowers mitigation costs. Assuming no barriers to implementation other than cost (i.e., ignoring political and environmental issues) and given certain assumptions (e.g., regarding fuel prices and energy demand), these studies suggest that a significant number of new plants with CCS will enter the power supply sector within the next few decades, though CCS retrofits can enter in just a few years. The availability and use of CCS technologies would decrease reliance on renewable energy sources while encouraging electricity production to shift from natural gas to coal power. CCS would significantly reduce the present value of the cost of mitigation over time. Finally, CCS would result in the capture of significant quantities of CO_2 without exceeding most current storage capacity estimates.

At the present time, prospects appear to be most promising for carbon capture from electric power generation and some industrial sources, with storage in geologic formations, such as depleted oil and gas reservoirs and deep aquifers. It would, therefore, seem prudent to seriously consider carbon capture and storage in the portfolio of options for addressing global climate change, alongside energy efficiency and fuel switching to less carbon-intensive energy sources. Further efforts are needed, however, in demonstrating the economic and technical feasibility of large-scale CCS, assessing the environmental risks, and considering the constraints and opportunities provided by legislation, regulation, and public opinion on widespread application of CCS.

ACKNOWLEDGMENTS

We thank Jeffrey Chow for research assistance, Howard Herzog, Jake Jacoby, Dan Kammen, and Ed Rubin for comments on a previous version of this review, and we acknowledge financial support from U. S. Department of Energy grant DE-FG02-98ER62702. The views expressed do not necessarily reflect those of Department of Energy or these individuals. Please address correspondence to Richard Newell.

The *Annual Review of Environment and Resources* is online at
http://environ.annualreviews.org

LITERATURE CITED

1. Crowley TJ. 2000. Causes of climate change over the past 100 years. *Science* 289:270–77
2. Alley RB, Marotzke J, Nordhaus WD, Overpeck JT, Peteet DM, et al. 2003. Abrupt climate change. *Science* 299:2005–10
3. Karl TR, Trenberth KE. 2003. Modern global climate change. *Science* 302:1719–23
4. Energy Inf. Adm. 2001. Annual energy review 2000. *Rep. DOE/EIA-03842001*, US Dep. Energy, Washington, DC
5. US Environ. Prot. Agency. 2002. Inventory of U.S. greenhouse gas emissions and sinks: 1990–2000. *Rep. EPA 430-R-02-003*, Off. Atmos. Programs, Washington, DC
6. Hansen J. 2002. A brighter future. *Clim. Change* 52:435–40
7. Hansen J. 2003. Can we defuse the global warming time bomb? *Nat. Sci.* http://naturalscience.com/ns/articles/01-16/ns_jeh.html
8. Hansen J. 2004. Defusing the global warming time bomb. *Sci. Am.* 290:68–77
9. Chapel DG, Mariz CL, Ernest J. 1999. *Recovery of CO_2 from flue gases: commercial trends.* Presented at the Can. Soc. Chem. Eng. Annu. Meet. October 4–6, Saskatoon, Sask., Can.
10. Intergov. Panel Clim. Change. 2002. *IPCC Workshop on Carbon Capture and Storage Proceedings*, Regina, Can. Petten, Neth.: Energy Research Cent. Neth.
11. Riemer P, Audus H, Smith A. 1993. Carbon dioxide capture from power stations. *Report SR2P*, Int. Energy Agency Greenh. Gas Res. Dev. Program, Cheltenham, UK
12. Adams D, Ormerod W, Riemer P, Smith A. 1994. Carbon dioxide disposal from power stations. *Report SR3P*, Int. Energy Agency Greenh. Gas Res. Dev. Program, Cheltenham, UK
13. Ishitani H, Johansson TB. 1996. Energy supply mitigation options. In *Climate Change 1995: Impacts, Adaptations and Mitigation of Climate Change. Work. Group III, Second Assess. Rep. Intergov. Panel Clim. Change*, ed. RT Watson, MC Zinyowera, RH Moss, pp. 587–647. Cambridge, UK: Cambridge Univ. Press
14. Chargin A, Socolow R. 1997. Fuels decarbonization and carbon sequestration: report of a workshop. *Rep. PU/CEES 302*, Princeton Univ. Cent. Energy Environ. Stud., Princeton, NJ
15. Herzog HJ, Drake E, Adams E. 1997. *CO_2 Capture, Reuse, and Storage Technologies for Mitigating Global Climate Change*, Mass. Inst. Technol. Energy Lab., White Pap., Cambridge, MA
16. US Dep. Energy. 1999. Carbon sequestration research and development. *Rep. DOE/SC/FE-1*, Off. Sci./Off. Fossil Energy, Washington, DC
17. Moomaw WR, Moreira JR. 2001. Technological and economic potential of greenhouse gas emissions reduction. See Ref. 103, pp. 167–299
18. Parson EA, Keith DW. 1998. Fossil fuels without CO_2 emissions. *Science* 282:1053–54
19. Herzog HJ. 2000. Capturing greenhouse gases. *Sci. Am.* 282:72–79
20. Herzog HJ. 2001. What future for carbon capture and sequestration? *Environ. Sci. Technol.* 37:A148–53
21. Anonymous. 2002. Fired up with ideas. *Economist* 364 (8280):78–79
22. Krautkraemer J, Toman M. 2003. Fundamental economics of depletable energy supply. *Rep. 03–01*, Resour. Future, Washington, DC

23. Tahvonen O. 1997. Fossil fuels, stock externalities, and backstop technology. *Can. J. Econ.* 30:855–74
24. Energy Inf. Adm. 2002. International energy annual 2000. *Rep. DOE/EIA-02192000*, US Dep. Energy, Washington, DC
25. Watson RT. 2001. *Climate Change 2001: Synthesis Report. Assess. Rep.* Intergov. Panel Clim. Change. Cambridge, UK/New York: Cambridge Univ. Press
26. Caldeira K, Jain AK, Hoffert MI. 2003. Climate sensitivity uncertainty and the need for energy without CO_2 emission. *Science* 299:2052–54
27. O'Neill BC, Oppenheimer M. 2002. Dangerous climate impacts and the Kyoto Protocol. *Science* 296:1971–72
28. Herzog HJ. 1999. *An Introduction to CO_2 Separation and Capture Technologies*, Work. Pap., Mass. Inst. Technol. Energy Lab.
29. Natl. Energy Technol. Lab., US Dep. Energy. 2003. *Carbon sequestration*. http://www.netl.doe.gov/coalpower/sequestration/
30. Herzog HJ. 2000. The economics of CO_2 separation and capture. *Technology* 7:13–23
31. Torp TA. 2000. Saline aquifer CO_2 storage: final technical rep. *Contract OG/306/98/NO*. Statoil/Int. Energy Agency, Cheltenham, UK
32. Energy Inf. Adm., US Dep. Energy. 2002. *Natural gas prices by sector.* http://www.eia.doe.gov/oil_gas/natural_gas/info_glance/prices.html
33. Energy Inf. Adm. 2003. Annual energy outlook 2003. *Rep. DOE/EIA-03832003*, US Dep. Energy, Washington, DC
34. Tromp TK, Shia R-L, Allen M, Eiler JM, Yung Y. 2003. Potential environmental impact of a hydrogen economy on the stratosphere. *Science* 300:1740–42
35. Schultz MG, Diehl T, Brasseur GP, Zittel W. 2003. Air pollution and climate-forcing impacts of a global hydrogen economy. *Science* 302:624–27
36. David J, Herzog HJ. 2000. The cost of carbon capture. See Ref. 104, pp. 985–90
37. Hourcade J-C, Shukla P. 2001. Global, regional, and national costs and ancillary benefits of mitigation. See Ref. 103, pp. 499–559
38. Anderson ST, Newell RG. 2003. Prospects for carbon capture and storage technologies. *Resour. Future Discuss. Pap. 02–68*. Washington, DC
39. Turkenburg WC, Hendriks CA. 1999. Fossil fuels in a sustainable energy supply: the signficance of CO_2 removal. *Rep. NW&S-99032*, Minist. Econ. Aff., The Hague, Utrecht, Neth.
40. Simbeck DR. 2001. *CO_2 mitigation economics for existing coal-fired power plants*. Presented at Pittsburgh Coal Conf., Newcastle, NSW, Aust.
41. Off. Fossil Energy., US Dep. Energy. 2003. *Gasification technologies*. http://www.fe.doe.gov/programs/powersystems/gasification/
42. Goldthorpe S, Davison J. 2000. Capture of CO_2 using water scrubbing. See Ref. 104, pp. 155–60
43. Göttlicher G, Pruschek R. 1997. Comparison of CO_2 removal systems for fossil-fuelled power plant processes. *Energy Convers. Manag.* 38:S173–78
44. Energy Inf. Adm. 2000. *Energy-Related Carbon Emissions in Manufacturing 1994*. Washington, DC: US Dep. Energy
45. US Environ. Prot. Agency. 1998. Inventory of U.S. greenhouse gas emissions and sinks: 1990–1996. *Rep. EPA 236-R-98-006*, Off. Policy Plan. Eval., Washington, DC
46. Thambimuthu KV, Davison J, Gupta M. 2002. CO_2 capture and storage. See Ref. 105, pp. 31–52
47. Farla CM, Hendriks CA, Blok K. 1995. Carbon dioxide recovery from industrial processes. *Energy Convers. Manag.* 36:827–30
48. Hendriks CA, Worrell E, de Jager D, Blok K, Riemer P. 1998. *Emission*

reduction of greenhouse gases from the cement industry. Presented at 4th Int. Conf. Greenh. Gas Control Technol., Aug. 30–Sept. 2, Interlaken, Switz. http://www.ieagreen.org.uk/prghgt42.htm
49. Gale J, Freund P. 2000. Greenhouse gas abatement in energy intensive industries. See Ref. 104, pp. 1211–16
50. Simbeck DR. 2002. *CO_2 capture and storage: the essential bridge to the hydrogen economy.* Presented at 6th Int. Conf. Greenh. Gas Control Technol., Oct. 1–4, Kyoto, Jpn
51. Hanisch C. 1998. The pros and cons of carbon dioxide dumping. *Environ. Sci. Technol.* 32:A20–24
52. Johnson JW. 2000. A solution for carbon dioxide overload. *Sci. Technol. Rev.* http://www.llnl.gov/str/Johnson.html
53. Arts R, Elsayed R, van der Meer L, Eiken O, Østmo S, et al. 2002. *Estimation of the mass of injected CO_2 at Sleipner using time-lapse seismic data.* Presented at Eur. Assoc. Geosci. Eng. Annu. Conf. Exhib., Florence, Italy
54. Blok K, Williams RH, Katofsky RE, Hendriks CA. 1997. Hydrogen production from natural gas, sequestration of recovered CO_2 in depleted gas wells and enhanced natural gas recovery. *Energy* 22:161–68
55. Deleted in proof
56. Audus H, Kaarstad O, Kowal M. 1996. *Decarbonisation of fossil fuels: hydrogen as an energy carrier.* Presented at World Hydrog. Energy Conf., Stuttgart, Ger.
57. Stevens SH, Gale J. 2000. Geologic CO_2 sequestration may benefit upstream industry. *Oil Gas J.* 98:40–46
58. Stevens SH, Kuuskraa VA, Spector D, Riemer P. 1998. *CO_2 sequestration in deep coal seams: pilot results and worldwide potential.* Presented at 4th Int. Conf. Greenh. Gas Control Technol., Aug. 30-Sept. 2, Interlaken, Switz
59. Benson SM, Hepple R, Apps J, Tsang CF, Lippman M. 2002. Lessons learned from natural and industrial analogues for storage of carbon dioxide in deep geological formations. *Rep. LBNL-51170*, Earth Sci. Div., E.O. Lawrence Berkeley Natl. Lab., Berkeley, CA
60. Johnston P, Santillo D. 2002. Carbon capture and sequestration: potential environmental impacts. See Ref. 105, pp. 95–110
61. Johnston P, Santillo D, Stringer R, Parmentier R, Hare B, Krueger M. 1999. Ocean disposal/sequestration of carbon dioxide from fossil fuel production and use: an overview of rationale, techniques and implications. *Rep. Tech. Note 01/99*, Greenpeace Res. Lab., Amsterdam, Neth.
62. Moberg R, Stewart DB, Stachniak D. 2002. *The IEA Weyburn CO_2 monitoring and storage project.* Presented at 6th Int. Conf. Greenh. Gas Control Technol., Oct. 1–4, Kyoto, Jpn
63. Stevens SH, Kuuskraa VA, Gale J. 2000. Sequestration of CO_2 in depleted oil and gas fields; global capacity, costs and barriers. See Ref. 104, pp. 278–83
64. Bock B, Rhudy R, Herzog H, Klett M, Davison J, et al. 2002. Economic evaluation of CO_2 storage and sink enhancement options. *Rep. DE-FC26-00NT40937*, US Dep. Energy/Tenn. Valley Auth. Public Power Inst., Washington, DC
65. van der Meer LGH. 2002. *CO_2 storage in the subsurface.* Presented at 6th Int. Conf. Greenh. Gas Control Technol., Oct. 1–4, Kyoto, Jpn
66. Winter EM, Bergman PD. 1996. *Potential for terrestrial disposal of carbon dioxide in the US.* Presented at US/Jpn. Jt. Tech. Workshop, State College, PA
67. Brown K, Jazrawi W, Moberg R, Wilson M. 2001. *Role of enhanced oil recovery in carbon sequestration: the Weyburn Monitoring Project, a case study.* Presented at 1st Natl. Conf. Carbon Sequestration, Washington, DC
68. Bergman PD, Winter EM. 1996. *Disposal of carbon dioxide in deep saline aquifers in the US.* Presented at US/Jpn. Jt. Tech. Workshop, State College, PA

69. Davis LA, Graham AL, Parker HW, Ingber MS, Mammoli AA, et al. 2001. *Maximizing storage rate and capacity and insuring the environmental integrity of carbon dioxide sequestration in geologic reservoirs.* Presented at 1st Natl. Conf. Carbon Sequestration, Washington, DC
70. Off. Fossil Energy, US Dep. Energy. 2002. *A climate change solution beneath our feet?* http://www.netl.doe.gov/publications/press/2002/tl_sequestration_aep.html
71. Karstad O. 2002. Geologic storage, including costs and risks, in saline aquifers. See Ref. 105, pp. 53–60
72. Int. Energy Agency Greenh. Gas Res. Dev. Program. 2003. *CO_2-enhanced coal bed methane recovery.* http://www.ieagreen.org.uk/ecbm.htm
73. Orr JR, Aumont O, Yool A, Plattner K, Joos F, et al. 2000. Ocean CO_2 sequestration efficiency from a 3-D ocean model comparison. See Ref. 104, pp. 469–74
74. Int. Energy Agency Greenh. Gas Res. Dev. Program. 2003. *Capture and storage of CO_2.* http://www.ieagreen.org.uk/capture.htm
75. Siebel BA, Walsh PJ. 2001. Potential impacts of CO_2 injection on deep-sea biota. *Science* 294:319–20
76. Brewer PG, Friederich G, Peltzer ET, Orr FM Jr. 1999. Direct experiments on the ocean disposal of fossil fuel CO_2. *Science* 284:943–45
77. Caldeira K. 2002. Monitoring ocean storage projects. See Ref. 105, pp. 153–60
78. Huessemann MH, Skillman AD, Crecelius EA. 2001. *The effects of CO_2 disposal on marine nitrification processes.* Presented at 1st Natl. Conf. Carbon Sequestration, Washington, DC
79. Audus H, Oonk H. 1997. An assessment procedure for chemical utilisation schemes intended to reduce CO_2 emissions to atmosphere. *Energy Convers. Manag.* 38:S409–14
80. Herzog HJ. 2002. Carbon sequestration via mineral carbonation: overview and assessment. *Carbon Sequestration Initiat. Rep.* Mass. Inst. Technol., Lab. Energy Environ., Cambridge, MA. http://sequestration.mit.edu/pdf/carbonates.pdf
81. Freund P. 2000. Progress in understanding the potential role of CO_2 storage. See Ref. 104, pp. 272–77
82. Ormerod W, Riemer P, Smith A. 1995. Carbon dioxide utilisation. *IEA GHG Public Summ. Rep.* Int. Energy Agency Greenh. Gas Res. Dev. Program, Cheltenham, UK
83. Wilson EJ, Keith DW. 2002. *Geologic carbon storage: understanding the rules of the underground.* Presented at 6th Int. Conf. Greenh. Gas Control Technol., Oct. 1–4, Kyoto, Jpn
84. Tsang CF, Benson SM, Kobelski B, Smith R. 2001. *Scientific considerations related to regulation development for CO_2 sequestration in brine formations.* Presented at 1st Natl. Conf. Carbon Sequestration, Washington, DC
85. Reiner DM, Herzog HJ. 2002. *A search for regulatory analogs to carbon sequestration.* Presented at 6th Int. Conf. Greenh. Gas Control Technol., Oct. 1–4, Kyoto, Jpn
86. Hawkins DG. 2002. *Passing gas: policy implications of leakage from geologic carbon storage sites.* Presented at 6th Int. Conf. Greenh. Gas Control Technol., Oct. 1–4, Kyoto, Jpn
87. Wildenborg AFB, van der Meer LGH. 2002. The use of oil, gas and coal fields as CO_2 sinks. See Ref. 105, pp. 61–67
88. Benson SM, Myer L. 2002. Monitoring to ensure safe and effective geologic sequestration of carbon dioxide. See Ref. 105, pp. 137–51
89. Herzog HJ, Caldeira K, Reilly J. 2003. An issue of permanence: assessing the effectiveness of temporary carbon storage. *Clim. Change* 59:293–310
90. Muttitt G, Diss B. 2001. Carbon injection: an addict's response to climate change. *Ecologist.* http://www.theecologist.org/archive_article.html?article=279

91. Rao AB, Rubin ES. 2002. A technical, economic, and environmental assessment of amine-based CO_2 capture technology for power plant greenhouse gas control. *Environ. Sci. Technol.* 36:4467–75

92. Rubin ES, Rao AB, Berkenpas MB. 2001. *A multi-pollutant framework for evaluating CO_2 control options for fossil fuel power plants.* Presented at 1st Natl. Conf. Carbon Sequestration, Washington, DC

93. Johnson TL, Keith DW. 2001. *Fossil electricity and CO_2 sequestration: How natural gas prices, initial conditions and retrofits determine the cost of controlling CO_2 emissions.* Carnegie Mellon Ind. Electr. Cent. Work. Pap. CEIC-03-01. Carnegie Mellon Univ., Pittsburgh, PA

94. McFarland J, Reilly J, Herzog H. 2002. Representing energy technologies in top-down economic models using bottom-up information. *Rep. 89.* Mass. Inst. Technol. Jt. Program Sci. Policy Glob. Change, Cambridge, MA

95. Edmonds JA, Clarke J, Dooley JJ, Kim SH, Smith SJ. 2002. *Modeling greenhouse gas energy technology responses to climate change.* Presented at 6th Int. Conf. Greenh. Gas Control Technol., Oct. 1–4, Kyoto, Jpn

96. Biggs SD. 2000. *Sequestering carbon from power plants: The jury is still out.* MS thesis. Mass. Inst. Technol., Cambridge, MA

97. Biggs SD, Herzog H, Reilly J, Jacoby H. 2000. Economic modeling of CO_2 capture and sequestration. See Ref. 104, pp. 973–78

98. McFarland J, Herzog HJ, Reilly J, Jacoby H. 2001. *Economic modeling of carbon capture and sequestration technologies.* Presented at 1st Natl. Conf. Carbon Sequestration, Washington, DC

99. McFarland J, Herzog H, Reilly J. 2002. *Economic modeling of the global adoption of carbon capture and sequestration technologies.* Presented at 6th Int. Conf. Greenh. Gas Control Technol., Oct. 1–4, Kyoto, Jpn

100. Johnson TL, Keith DW. 2001. Electricity from fossil fuels without CO_2 emissions: assessing the costs of carbon dioxide capture and sequestration in US electricity markets. *J. Air Waste Manag. Assoc.* 51:1452–59

101. Kim SH, Edmonds JA. 2000. Potential for advanced carbon capture and sequestration technologies in a climate constrained world. *Rep. PNNL-13095*, Pac. Northwest Natl. Lab., Washington, DC

102. Gale J. 2002. *Geological storage of CO_2: what's known, where are the gaps and what more needs to be done.* Presented at 6th Int. Conf. Greenh. Gas Control Technol., Oct. 1–4, Kyoto, Jpn

103. Metz B, Davidson O, Swart R, Pan J, eds. Climate change 2001: mitigation. *Working Group III, Third Assess. Rep.* Intergovern. Panel Clim. Change. Cambridge, UK: Cambridge Univ. Press

104. Williams D, Durie B, McMullan P, Paulson D, Smith A, eds. 2000. *Proc. 5th Int. Conf. Greenh. Gas Control Technol., Cairns, Aust.* North Ryde, N. S. W.: Commonw. Sci. Ind. Res. Organ.

105. Intergov. Panel Clim. Change 2002. Workshop carbon capture storage. *Proc. Intergov. Panel Clim. Change. Regina, Can.* Petten, Neth.: Energy Res. Cent. Neth.

PLANT GENETIC RESOURCES FOR FOOD AND AGRICULTURE: Assessing Global Availability[1]

Cary Fowler[1] and Toby Hodgkin[2]

[1]*Center for International Environment and Development Studies, Agricultural University of Norway, N-1432 Aas, Norway; email: cary.fowler@noragric.nlh.no*
[2]*International Plant Genetic Resources Institute, 00057 Maccarese, Rome, Italy; email: t.hodgkin@cgiar.org*

Key Words genebanks, conservation, crops, plant breeding, germplasm

■ **Abstract** Plant genetic resources provide the biological underpinning for agriculture and food production. No nation is independent in terms of these resources. Interdependence levels are high among countries. Policy impediments to access may subside, increasing already substantial germplasm flows. Serious questions exist, however, about the health and availability of the actual resources. Genebank collections contain many unintended duplicates, making aggregate numbers seem larger than they really are. Information about individual accessions, particularly those found in situ, is often poor, reducing frequency and efficiency of use and ultimate benefits. Although not firmly established today, the link between conservation and use must be strengthened.

CONTENTS

INTRODUCTION	144
HISTORICAL BACKGROUND	145
INTERDEPENDENCE AND PGRFA TRANSFERS	147
EX SITU AND IN SITU PGRFA COLLECTIONS	148
Genebanks and PGRFA Collections	150
Genebanks Today	152
Germplasm Flows	156
Obstacles to Availability from Genebanks Users' Perceptions	159
Problems of Supply	160
Availability of Germplasm Maintained In Situ	163

---

[1]The acronyms used are CGIAR, Consultative Group on International Agricultural Research; CIMMYT, International Maize and Wheat Improvement Center; FAO, Food and Agriculture Organization of the United Nations; IBPGR, International Board for Plant Genetic Resources (now IPGRI); ICARDA, International Center for Agricultural Research in the Dry Areas; IPGRI, International Plant Genetic Resources Institute; IRRI, International Rice Research Institute; and PGRFA, plant genetic resources for food and agriculture.

POLICY, LAW, AND ACCESS 166
DISCUSSION 168

INTRODUCTION

When it comes to food security, all countries share something important and fundamental. All depend on crops domesticated in distant lands during the Neolithic era. As crops, the maize grown in Africa, the wheat that blankets the Canadian prairies, and the potatoes cultivated on more than 10 million acres in China are botanical immigrants, and old ones at that. None are native to those lands (1). Directly or indirectly, therefore, the world's six billion people depend on crops and, thus, on genetic resources that would not normally be found in and are not part of the indigenous flora of their country. The questions of farmer and breeder access to and of availability of genetic resources—seeds, plants, and plant parts useful in crop breeding, research, or conservation for their genetic attributes—are of tremendous importance.

The definition of genetic resources offered here is a slightly condensed version of that used by the National Research Council (2). The International Board for Plant Genetic Resources defined the term as the genetic variability in crop plants and their wild relatives that is potentially useful in agronomy, a somewhat broader definition, perhaps, as it employs the term agronomy (3). The Convention on Biological Diversity simply says that they are genetic materials of actual or potential value, an even broader approach (4). Callicott et al. (5) have addressed the complexity involved in defining many normative conservation concepts, such as biological diversity, biological integrity, indigenous, and nonindigenous. The term genetic resources employed in both scientific and legal contexts is certainly no less problematic.

Regardless of definitions, one thing is certain: genetic resources underpin plant breeding and agricultural production and are thus essential to food security, livelihoods, and the development aspirations of every country on Earth.

In recent years much noise and controversy has surrounded the political issue of access to plant genetic resources for food and agriculture (PGRFA). New and colorful words have entered the lexicon; "biopiracy" from 1993 (6) is one of the most evocative. Amid this considerable turmoil, governments have been negotiating formal agreements to clarify the status of genetic resources and establish frameworks for conservation and rules for access and benefit sharing. In 1993, the Convention on Biological Diversity came into force, the product of years and some would say centuries of conflict over the status of biological diversity and how the benefits from this resource would be divided. In 2004, the International Treaty on Plant Genetic Resources for Food and Agriculture (7) is likely to come into force, establishing rules for access and benefit sharing to PGRFA of certain specified crops, a matter left outstanding when the Convention was finalized.

These international agreements are insufficiently comprehensive or robust to resolve completely or forever the larger historical disputes. Nevertheless, they provide a legal framework for access to PGRFA, a framework that until now never existed. This development, therefore, provides the opportunity to return to the object of the struggles, to the genetic resources themselves, and to the question of their availability. We distinguish between access and availability in this way: "Access" has to do with whether one has permission to or is legally entitled to obtain PGRFA, whereas "availability" relates to whether the genetic material exists in a usable form, can be identified, and potentially obtained.

As the political dust settles, at least momentarily, what, we might ask, do we really know about these genetic resources: the ways in which they have been and are valued, and used; the modes of acquiring them, past and present; the extent of interdependence on them at the international level; and the nature of current flows of materials? A brief look at such questions prepares us, and indeed leads us, to examine a second set of questions: Where are the resources, how many are there, what are the conditions of their conservation, and how might these affect access, availability, and use? Our review covers the state of knowledge of such subjects, building in particular on the foundation laid by United Nations Food and Agriculture Organization's (FAO's) first global assessment, *The State of the World's Plant Genetic Resources for Food and Agriculture* (8). In part, because this review looks at international aspects of PGRFA, our primary focus is on genetic resources stored as seed in genebanks, a more common source of materials for plant improvement today than in situ sources, which are addressed in less depth here.

HISTORICAL BACKGROUND

Agricultural crops and their associated genetic resources have been spreading about the globe from the earliest Neolithic times (9). In large part, the movement of food crops out of their ancient native habitats can be explained as a by-product of human movements, with the occasional assist from birds, winds, and ocean currents. Gradually, the ad hoc spread of seeds and planting materials has yielded to more deliberate, organized, and formalized systems of acquisition.

The qualities for which PGRFA are desired or valued, what kinds of biological materials are collected, and the ways in which they are exploited, developed, and commercialized are all a reflection of the times and, in particular, a reflection of the capacity of people and institutions to use the materials, the technology available for this purpose, and the nature of the markets for which the crops are produced. The earliest accounts of organized plant exploration and acquisition are those of the ancient Sumarians and Egyptians (10). Later, royal and monastic gardens featured exotic species. As far as we know, rulers in these ancient times sought spices, ornamentals, and medicinal plants for the most part, although examples of acquisition of food crops can be found (11).

As the colonial period arrived, several European powers had the maritime and military technology to locate, acquire, and move plants around the world in a very deliberate and organized manner (12, 13). They also had the capacity to test and develop them and to supply them to distant production sites through networks of botanic gardens established for this purpose (10, 12, 14). The "Columbian Exchange" marked the beginning of the wholesale transfer of crops between the New World and the Old (15), but the primary object of organized transfer efforts was high-value plantation crops, such as rubber, cinchona (for quinine), coffee, tea, and oil palm (12). And the object was species—it was not until later that intraspecies diversity would be sought on any scale to supply plant breeding programs (14).

The commercialization of agriculture, the establishment of plant breeding programs, and the rediscovery of Mendel's laws of heredity served to shift focus to the genetic variability within agricultural crops. The United States, for example, was extremely interested in acquiring different landraces of major crops in order to establish agriculture in all its diverse environments. How did agriculture become established from "sea to shining sea" in the United States? The government acquired thousands of landraces of wheat, barley, oats, and other crops and then produced catalogs describing them and provided seed samples to farmers for testing and adaptation (14). By the end of the 1800s, the U.S. government was mailing as many as 20 million packets of seed per annum to farmers for such purposes (16).

Today, breeders search not so much for new species as for specific characteristics. The new biotechnologies, including marker-assisted selection, have turned the attention of breeders even more to the genetic components of a sample. Institutions have also changed. The genebank has replaced the botanic garden as the principal source of materials, and collecting from the wild, while still important, is never the first option breeders consider when sourcing PGRFA (17).

Breeders, even before 1900, began to assemble working collections of genetic resources. As commercial agriculture spread, concern with the loss of traditional landraces led to calls for conservation (18–20).

In the former Soviet Union, N.I. Vavilov began to examine the geographic distribution of crop diversity and map out what he described as their "Centers of Origin," or more properly centers of genetic diversity (21). Vavilov's work (22), which included the establishment of a major germplasm collection in St. Petersburg, not only served to highlight the economic importance of diversity and of genebank collections, but it also gave a practical tool to collectors by pointing to areas where diversity of particular crops was likely to be concentrated. Later, work by other scientists added greatly to the knowledge of specific crops, their history, diffusion, and areas of diversity (1, 23, 24).

By the 1940s, both the United States and the Soviet Union had reasonably large collections encompassing numerous crops (10, 25). Few restrictions existed to the collection or to the subsequent transfer of genetic resources. Farmers were happy, even proud, to offer them, and scientists exchanged them freely, treating genetic resources as a common heritage rather than as a commodity (26).

As scientific advancements have dramatically increased the powers of plant breeders, and as agriculture and food processing have become big business, governments have come to change their views about plant genetic resources. The concept of these resources as the "common heritage of mankind" was undermined by the introduction and application of intellectual property rights in developed countries, followed by assertions of national sovereignty and restrictions on access to PGRFA in developing countries. Almost as soon as governments assembled basic collections of farmer landraces for use by their plant breeders, unfettered international access to the remaining plant genetic diversity ended.

INTERDEPENDENCE AND PGRFA TRANSFERS

Today, most people from Copenhagen to Kampala eat foods that would have been unfamiliar to the inhabitants of their country not so long ago. This is the result of a kind of botanical chess game that has been played out over millennia, changing the agricultural and food systems of virtually every land. Relying only on native crops, the American hamburger would have to come without a wheat-based bun, without the ketchup, mustard, lettuce, tomato, onion, and pickle. (There also would be no beef.) Pasta sauce in Italy could not be tomato based, but there would not be any pasta anyway, nor any wine made from grapes. There would be no French-fries in France and no maize in Africa (1, 23).

Various assertions and estimates have been made about the nature and degree of interdependence of countries on PGRFA (27–29). Definitive quantifications are beyond anyone's grasp. Production and consumption figures cannot be precise. In addition, contributions to nutrition are hard to disentangle and quantify (30, 31). Micronutrients are essential, of course, but there is no accepted formula for quantifying the importance of a particular food to overall nutrition and well-being. Thus, dietary dependency can be measured in different ways, all somewhat subjective. Palacios (29) uses the criterion of "food energy supply" and examines the extent to which the crops that supply it are indigenous or not. In calculating the percentage of dependence of a nation on nonindigenous crops, she provides a range in order to address the gap caused by consumption of unknown foods (such as those from home gardens). The more conservative, and we would argue generally unrealistic, lower figure assumes that all unspecified food consumption (in data assembled by FAO) is of foods that are native. The higher figure for dependency assumes that all such consumption is of nonnative foods, also not likely but much closer to reality in most cases.

Palacios (29) found that most countries are heavily dependent on nonindigenous crops. For example, China is 46% to 55% dependent, Colombia 84% to 94%, Republic of Congo 82% to 94%, Cuba 87% to 97%, Germany 83% to 98%, India 35% to 47%, Iraq 83% to 89%, Nicaragua 62% to 75%, Nigeria 46% to 61%, Papua New Guinea 76% to 100%, the Philippines 28% to 38%, Rwanda 80% to 94%, and the United States 84% to 99% dependent. Interestingly, many of the poorest and most food-insecure countries are those relying the most on native crops. Thus, Ethiopia, for example, is 28% to 56% dependent, and Niger is just 13% to 27% dependent.

Most countries and their farmers are now also dependent on modern, improved varieties of rice, wheat, maize, and other crops (32). For example, in Asia, 67% of the rice, 88% of the wheat, and 45% of the maize area is planted in modern varieties, and in Latin America, 58% of the rice, 68% of the wheat, and 46% of the maize area is planted in modern varieties (33). At one time, a single rice variety, IR36, accounted for 10% of the world's rice area, occupying more than 11 million hectares in its heyday (34), and selections from a single wheat cross at the International Maize and Wheat Improvement Center (CIMMYT) accounted for one seventh of the area sown to wheat in developing countries (34). Such varieties are typically developed using genetic resources sourced from numerous countries, demonstrating again the reality of interdependence and the importance of access and availability of PGFRA to agriculture and food security. The Sonalika wheat cultivar provides a good example. This cultivar, after its development by the CIMMYT and release in 1966, came to be planted widely and is still important primarily as a parent used in breeding programs for new cultivars. The Sonalika pedigree (Figure 1)—what is known of it—runs six meters long on normal paper and amply demonstrates how many landraces can contribute to the production of a single cultivar and how many different countries may provide material for such a cultivar, which is then both planted in many countries and used in breeding programs around the world.

Gollin (35) examined the complete pedigrees of 1709 modern rice varieties released since the early 1960s and found that only 145 of the varieties were developed entirely from own country parents, grandparents, and other ancestors. Table 1, drawn from Gollin (35, p. 241), shows the extent to which released varieties drew on material from other countries.

Finally, countries are also increasingly interdependent in PGRFA conservation efforts (36). Materials held in genebanks eventually require regeneration (37), ideally in the same environment in which they were collected in order to avoid changes in the genetic composition of the sample, and even loss of some genes or alleles. Because most collections contain materials from many countries, cooperation is needed if high conservation standards are desired (36). In Europe, there is increasing collaboration. In some cases, different genebanks concentrate on maintaining different crops, and for a number of crops, common information resources have been developed (38).

Even in the best situations, genetic resources will sometimes be lost through, for example, accident, negligence, or replacement in farmers' fields by modern cultivars. When this occurs, repatriation from other—often foreign—sources can help restore diversity to collections and farming systems (39).

EX SITU AND IN SITU PGRFA COLLECTIONS

Plant genetic resources are typically obtained by breeders, researchers, and other institutional users from ex situ conditions, in other words from outside the plant's natural habitat whether that is on-farm or in less-managed ecosystems. Ex situ sources include genebanks (cold storage facilities where genetic resources are kept typically under low temperature and reduced humidity conditions), field

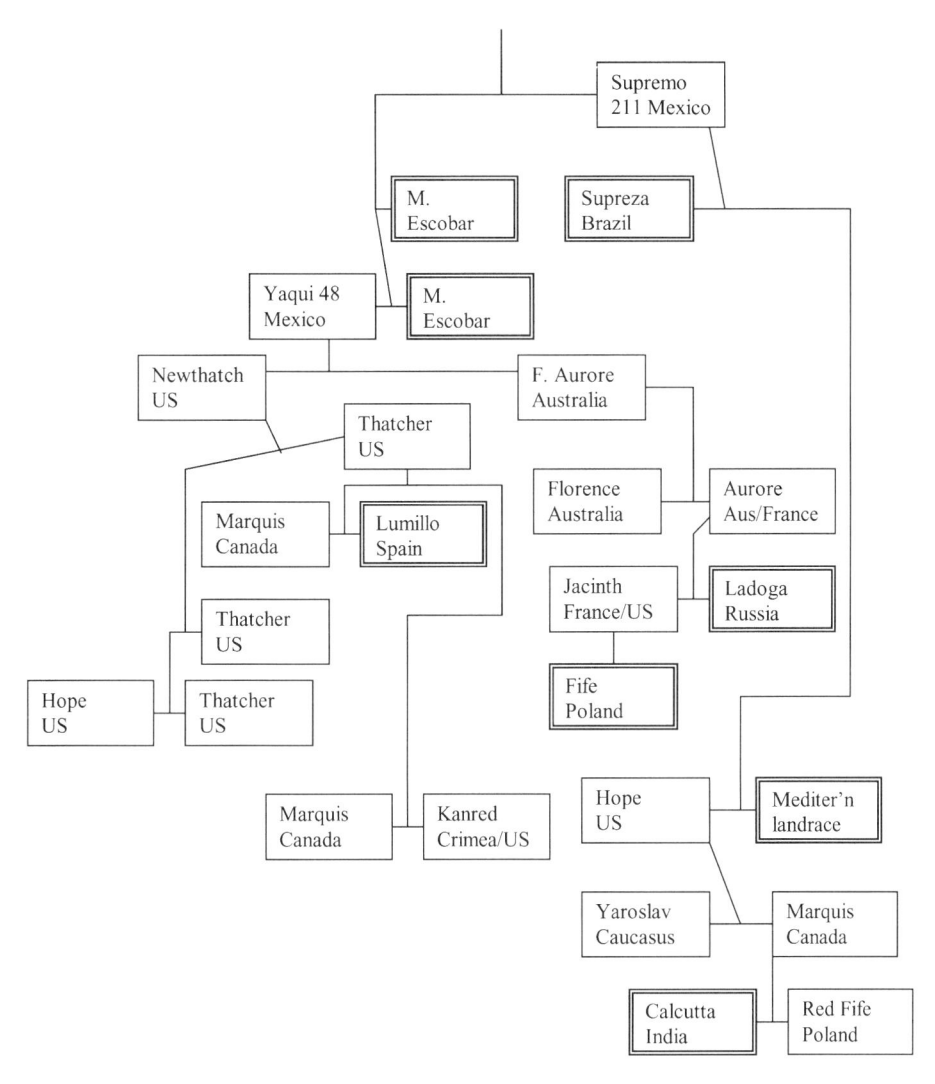

Figure 1 A small segment of the bread wheat (cv. Sonalika) pedigree. Landraces are in a double box.

genebanks, which contain living specimens usually of species whose seed is difficult to maintain in genebanks, and botanic gardens.

Genebank collections are composed of genetic materials originally sourced from in situ conditions and from breeding/research programs. Many of these materials can no longer be found in situ for a variety of reasons (40), because they have fallen out of use or been replaced by modern cultivars, for example. For most institutional users, genebanks provide a convenient source of material; they contain large numbers of accessions coming from many different places, often

TABLE 1 Summary of international flows of rice landrace ancestors in selected countries (35)

Country	Total landrace progenitors in all released varieties	Own landraces	Borrowed landraces
Bangladesh	233	4	229
Brazil	460	80	380
Burma	442	31	411
China	888	157	731
India	3917	1559	2358
Indonesia	463	43	420
Nepal	142	2	140
Nigeria	195	15	180
Pakistan	195	0	195
Philippines	518	34	484
Sri Lanka	386	64	322
Taiwan	20	3	17
Thailand	154	27	127
United States	325	219	106
Vietnam	517	20	497

with at least some information on characteristics and performance. For this and other reasons, breeders and researchers prefer to source materials from genebanks, if possible (17).

Genetic resources may be maintained in situ by virtue of their use in production or their continued existence in natural or semimanaged ecosystems. Sometimes they occur in areas that are part of planned conservation programs, such as national parks or biosphere reserves. However, deliberately planned in situ conservation of plant genetic resources is uncommon, although it does occur for some wild crop relatives, such as teosinte in Mexico or citrus in North India (41). Jarvis et al. (42) analyzed the origins of 2175 geo-referenced observations of wild *Arachis* species and found that only 48 came from populations found in national parks. Deliberate conservation of crop landraces on more than a local or experimental scale is even more uncommon (43). In considering the availability of in situ material, one needs to take into account whether material forms part of a deliberate conservation program or whether its maintenance is dependent on production or ecosystem factors.

Genebanks and PGRFA Collections

International efforts to conserve and make available PGRFA are young, at least when viewed against the backdrop of agricultural history. Discussions began in the FAO in the late 1940s, spurred in part by a plea from the chair of the U.S. National Research Council to the director general of the FAO to take steps to assemble and maintain breeding materials that he realized were being lost with the introduction of improved varieties (2). The FAO established a Panel of Experts on Plant Exploration and Introduction in 1962 (44) and convened international technical conferences on the topic in 1967, 1973, 1981, and 1996. The first two conferences recommended the establishment of a global network of genebanks. The International Board for Plant Genetic Resources (now the International Plant Genetic Resources Institute), established in 1974 and originally housed in the FAO, assumed the mandate for catalyzing and coordinating a global initiative to collect and conserve PGRFA.

The International Board for Plant Genetic Resources (IBPGR) began its work in an atmosphere of crisis. The very success of the "green revolution" meant that many traditional farmer landraces were being taken out of production and being replaced with fewer, higher-yielding cultivars. There was a general belief that substantial amounts of genetic diversity were being lost (19, 20, 45–49). Some of the most knowledgeable and respected scientists of the day were penning articles with alarming titles, such as "Plant Introduction and Genetic Conservation: Genecological Aspects of an Urgent World Problem" (50), "Genetics of Disaster" (51), and "Our Vanishing Genetic Resources" (46). In such an atmosphere, the small band of scientists at the IBPGR, only eight in number in 1983 (25), and elsewhere had little time and less capacity to address and solve all the legal, institutional, and practical problems associated with collecting and safeguarding massive amounts of endangered biological materials. As a consequence, both political and technical problems soon emerged, some of which persist today.

The first national cold storage facility for seed crops, the National Seed Storage Laboratory, was established by the U.S. Department of Agriculture in 1958 (52), prior to the concerted international efforts to conserve germplasm. Participants at the FAO-convened conferences in 1967 and 1973 originally advocated the establishment of a small number of international genebanks to safeguard the world's PGRFA (25). As the work progressed, the IBPGR began planning for 50 base collections—comprehensive and freely accessible designated collections held in long-term storage—associated with 60 active collections (53). Table 2, constructed from a number of sources (8, 10, 25, 53–59), shows the growth in numbers of genebanks and conserved collections from the early days of international action, when few facilities existed, to today, when more than 75 are operating. The data are incomplete and in some cases contradictory, but the big picture is clear. By the mid-1980s, the IBPGR's scientifically based target of 50 long-term facilities was reached. When the next comprehensive survey of genebanks was undertaken by FAO in the mid-1990s, the IBPGR's goal was exceeded by 50%. There were more than 75 (8). Meanwhile, the total number of germplasm collections (whether under long-, medium-, or short-term storage conditions) and, thus, the number of genebanks reached 1300, although the lack of reliable data makes it impossible to estimate just how much of an increase this represents over the situation that existed in the early 1970s.

TABLE 2 Growth in genebanks and number of accessions

	Number of countries with genebanks	Number of long-term facilities	Number of accessions
1974	—	5 or 6	—
1976	—	5 or 6; less than 5	—
1979	—	25	—
1982	—	33	—
1984	—	55	2 million
1985	72	52	2.5 million
1989	—	80	—
1992	—	—	3.6 million
1996	137	76	6.2 million

It should be noted that definitions of what constitutes long-term storage change over time. For example, in 1979, the definition required storage at 0°C. Only nine had −18°C or better. In 1994, the FAO and the International Plant Genetic Resources Institute (IPGRI) published standards for genebanks specifying preferred conditions for long-term storage (60).

Genebanks Today

The FAO's World Information and Early Warning System database currently lists more than 1300 germplasm collections, ranging in size from the U.S. National Seed Storage Laboratory with more than 500,000 accessions, to a collection in the United States with a single accession (S. Diulgheroff, FAO, personal communication). The median size of the collections is 650 accessions, indicating that many, perhaps most, collections are part of research or breeding programs, maintained by those actively involved in using them. Table 3 provides figures on number of genebanks and accessions, by region, assembled by the FAO (8), and reveals both the magnitude of collections and their wide geographic spread.

By size, the top 10% of genebanks include all those with more than 7438 accessions and the top 25%, 2325 accessions. The lower figure is the approximate size of the national collections of countries such as Cameroon, Trinidad, Tobago, and Libya, yet they are far smaller than the national collections of Kenya and Ethiopia, which conserve more than 50,000 accessions each (8).

Some genebanks, such as those of international agricultural research centers, specialize in one or a few specific crops, whereas others, including most national genebanks, attempt to conserve germplasm associated with virtually all crops grown in a particular country. No optimal size (in terms of numbers of accessions) has been identified for genebanks, although capturing a wide range of diversity of a particular crop can require a rather large number of accessions (2, 45). Some

TABLE 3 Genebanks and accessions in ex situ collections by region (8)

Region	Accessions Number	%	Genebanks Number	%
Africa	353,523	6	124	10
Latin America & the Caribbean	642,405	12	227	17
North America	762,061	14	101	8
Asia	1,533,979	28	293	22
Europe	1,934,574	35	496	38
Near East	327,963	6	67	5
Total	5,554,505	100	1,308	100
CGIAR	593,191	—	12	—

economies of scale certainly exist. The institutional costs of the Tanzanian and the Kenyan genebanks are approximately the same according to Virchow (61), though Kenya maintains 20 times more accessions.

Various authors have identified problems, particularly shortage of funding and the lack of trained curators and professional management, that one might consider to be associated particularly with small genebanks (8, 62). Professional curation is essential if a collection is to be assembled, managed, and made available in a way that is conducive to effective use. A good curator should, for instance, have a considerable depth of understanding of the given taxon, be familiar with the current commercial situation in, as well as institutions and individuals associated with, a particular crop, and be adept at working cooperatively with this community (63)—quite a challenge for a single scientist at a small facility housing materials of 20 or more crops. Because of these and other constraints, Africa, for instance, has been reported as having relatively few genebanks that function effectively (64).

Padulosi et al. (65) have described the representation of "minor crops" in genebanks. Bearing in mind that some 150 crops historically have entered into world commerce and that many others are important locally, it is interesting to note that in the case of only 72 crops are there genebank collections containing a thousand or more accessions (65). For most crops, albeit many minor ones, there is not a single collection containing as many as a thousand accessions. This might be considered a poor foundation upon which to begin or sustain breeding programs. There are, by contrast, only 16 crops that have individual collections containing more than 5000 accessions (65).

By any measure, a huge amount of material has been collected and placed in genebanks during the past thirty years. Today, more than 6 million accessions are held in genebanks, an increase of approximately 4 million from 1985 (57) and 2.5 million from 1992 (58). If one is comforted by numbers, the numbers, which clearly show big increases in genebanks and conserved accessions in a relatively short period of time, paint a rosy picture. But, it is not a numbers game. The reality is complex because accession numbers are not a reliable proxy for how much diversity is conserved, how well it is conserved, or the extent to which it is currently available to breeders and researchers. Nevertheless, the numbers are a good place to start when looking at the questions raised in the Introduction to this review.

It is not possible to catalog a crop's genepool and its genetic diversity with any precision. The concept of genepools was first elaborated by Harlan & de Wet (66). The primary genepool consists of the taxa of a crop within which gene transfer is straightforward, i.e., there are no sterility problems. The secondary genepool consists of taxa that will cross with the crop, albeit with difficulty. The tertiary genepool is comprised of taxa that exhibit strong sterility barriers, making gene transfer extremely difficult.

No "head count" of diversity or a crop's genepool could ever be complete. In some cases, estimates of varietal diversity have been made. For example, the International Rice Research Institute (IRRI) estimates that 120,000 varieties of rice may exist. But varietal diversity is not the same as genetic diversity. A group of distinct rice varieties—varieties containing different combinations of genes and alleles—may contain little genetic diversity. For various reasons, including the purpose of setting priorities for collecting, surveys of crop experts have been undertaken at least three times in an effort to estimate, subjectively, how much of crop genepools remain to be collected (8, 53, 68). The results of these surveys are shown in Table 4. Estimates of cultivars remaining to be collected also fall within the ranges provided in Table 4 (69).

Questions could be raised, of course, about the reliability of the survey results. The striking thing, however, is that the results are rather similar (except in the case of cassava)—even though in the 10-year period that elapsed between the first

TABLE 4 Percentage of genepool remaining to be collected (8, 53, 68)

Crop	Estimated, mid-1980s percentage	Estimated 1986 percentage	Estimated, mid-1990s percentage
Wheat	10	5	5
Rice	8–15	30	5
Maize	2	10	5
Sorghum	25	20	20
Pearl millet	<30	—	20
Potato	10–20	5	5
Sweet potato	>50	40	50
Cassava	25–33	—	65
Soybean	30	—	40
Common bean	<50	50	35

and the last survey—the number of accessions held by genebanks almost tripled. Whereas some of the increased numbers are attributable to collecting activities, a far larger portion may come from the exchange between genebanks of existing accessions, which thus circle around genebanks as duplicates, artificially swelling the aggregate figures.

Some duplication is needed for safety purposes. But even in the early days of assembling genebank collections, possible overduplication was recognized as a management problem at the global level. In 1984, Holden (57) noted that estimates of inadvertent duplication of genotypes in two or more collections, while varying with crops, were as high as 60%. Lyman (68) asserted that at least half of the combined collections of most crop species are duplicates.She considered that three quarters of the 400,000 wheat accessions found in major genebanks were duplicates. More recently, the International Center for Agricultural Research in the Dry Areas (ICARDA) estimated that well over half of its barley collection consisted of accessions acquired knowingly as duplicates from other genebanks, principally in the United States, China, and Germany (70).

Observations about the extent of duplication in early collections are relevant here because they shed light on the question of what and how much PGRFA are actually available. Are there many unique accessions or simply many copies of the same handful of accessions? There are a number of complex interacting aspects to be considered. Apparently similar accessions with identical names and common phenotypic characteristics may possess differences detectable using molecular methods (71), i.e., in a number of cases duplication is only partial, reflecting a genetic drift or shift that has occurred as a result of maintenance of the same accession in different genebanks (72). Because of the circulation of accessions, some genebanks may have almost no unique accessions themselves in the sense that all of their accessions may be duplicated one or more times, albeit in different genebanks. However, they still posses a good collection providing a constant supply of material to their own national users, as in the case of the Centre for Genetic Resources, Netherlands, barley collection (72, 73). There is also rather little information with respect to numbers of accessions duplicated and to the numbers of times they are duplicated. Hodgkin et al. (74) found that most wild Triticeae accessions were in fact unique in that they occurred in only one genebank. However, a small proportion was duplicated many times, occurring in almost every collection that had wild Triticeae accessions.

Early estimates of the extent of duplications, made when the total number of accessions was between 2 and 2.5 million accessions, indicate that genebanks contained about 1 million unique accessions in the mid-1980s. Ten years later, the FAO (8) estimated that of the 6.2 million accessions in genebanks, 1 to 2 million were unique. The implication of such figures is that the growth in the number of accessions being conserved by genebanks may not indicate a similar increase in the amount of diversity conserved. It may reveal a combination—some additional increase in diversity collected and conserved combined with a great deal of intended and unintended duplication.

The cost of maintaining a collection is influenced by the size of the collection. Fixed costs may not increase dramatically each time an accession is added to a collection, but regeneration costs are directly related to the number of accessions conserved. Eventually, even under optimum storage conditions, germination rates of any sample will fall below acceptable levels. In order to minimize genetic drift, international standards call for seed to be regenerated and fresh seed returned to the genebank when viability drops to 85% of the initial value (60). Regeneration costs vary substantially between crops and are substantial for some crops (75). Regeneration of 6 million accessions—the amount currently held ex situ today—will therefore not be a trivial expense, even when spread out over a number of years.

Data from centers of the Consultative Group on International Agricultural Research (CGIAR), which according to the FAO (8) may hold as much as 40% of the conserved diversity of major crops in their 11 genebanks, indicate a dramatic decrease—a 94% drop—in numbers of accessions acquired or collected annually from 1985 to 1999 (S. Gaiji, IPGRI, unpublished information). This drop may be the result of a number of factors: the success of previous collecting and consequently the lessening need to acquire more germplasm, changes in institutional priorities away from collecting, and increased political and legal barriers to acquisition.

Historic data on germplasm collections are not extensive, completely precise, or reliable. When one compares data on the amount of collecting and transfers against related data on the growth of collections, the numbers do not agree. Nevertheless, some generalizations can be drawn from the data concerning the PGRFA themselves and their availability. The bulk of the growth in genebank holdings, particularly from the mid-1980s onwards, cannot be accounted for by collecting, i.e., by increases in unique accessions being conserved. Most of it must have been the result of intended (safety) duplications as well as a considerable amount of other duplications: a growth that was a consequence of existing accessions circulating around the system, as exemplified in the barley example noted above.

Germplasm Flows

Virtually all of the world's healthy and productive agricultural systems have been built on a foundation of access to and availability of both local and foreign plant genetic resources. Flows of such materials within and across borders have been tremendous, particularly since the establishment of modern genebanks housing collections of PGRFA typically in the form of seeds and other planting materials. More than 60,000 samples are distributed annually (a 5-year moving average) just by institutes associated with the CGIAR (S. Gaiji, IPGRI, unpublished information). In a given year, samples distributed by CGIAR Centers will come from 170 or more countries, according to S. Gaiji of the CGIAR's System-wide Information Network for Genetic Resources (S. Gaiji, IPGRI, unpublished information). Virtually every country is a net recipient of such transfers (39). Interestingly, however, average distributions from CGIAR genebanks have been declining somewhat, as has the number of institutions requesting such materials (S. Gaiji, IPGRI, unpublished information).

International distributions from government genebanks vary widely. During the 1990s, the United States distributed approximately 16,300 samples of 10 crops annually, an amount estimated to be approximately half of total distributions for all crops. The Netherlands distributed 2500, and the Nordic Gene Bank provided 1550 (76). According to the FAO (8), during a five-year period in the 1990s, Brazil distributed approximately 2200 samples per annum and Canada 1500 samples.

During the period from 1990 to 1999, the United States also distributed more than 45,000 samples per annum within its own borders (76). Some countries, however, serve a domestic clientele almost exclusively. Ethiopia in recent years has provided virtually no samples to foreign researchers or institutes but distributes about 2000 a year internally (A. Demissie, Biodiversity Institute, Ethiopia. personal communication). Japan provides, on average, about 6000 samples per year, 96% to domestic users, and Germany provides 10,000 samples a year, 56% to domestic users, whereas India provides approximately 46,000 samples per year, 65% to domestic users (17). A study of utilization of germplasm of 10 crops conserved in China found that 185,000 samples were provided to more than 8600 institutes in China during the period from 1984 to 1998 (77). And CGIAR Centers provide a great deal to their own breeders, several times that sent to others in some cases (39, 58).

The U.S. and Chinese genebanks are the two largest genebanks in the world in terms of number of accessions, and both serve active plant breeding communities. Many national genebanks—particularly those in Africa, the Near East, Asia, and the Pacific—report little if any distribution of their accessions (8). In other cases, such as Thailand, materials are distributed for those crops for which there are active breeding programs, but germplasm associated with 20–30 conserved crops is not distributed or used internally (78). In fact, many national agricultural research programs employ relatively few breeders or researchers, and the demand per annum is likely to be low (79, 80). This raises an important point: Many national genebanks are apparently functioning more as closed-door conservation facilities than as sources of breeding materials. Given the information reported to the FAO and described by independent researchers (47) about the poor quality of conservation services offered by many genebanks, one is left to conclude that many facilities have difficulties both in conserving and providing genetic resources.

Smale & Day-Rubenstein's study (76) of demand for genetic resources from the U.S. germplasm system revealed interesting differences between users in developed and developing countries, differences that might help explain the lack of use of some developing country collections. They found that developing country requestors asked for landraces less frequently than developed country requestors. Instead, they sought cultivars, advanced materials, and genetic stocks that could be incorporated more readily and quickly into breeding programs. Developed country requestors, reflecting different priorities and, more importantly, different levels of research capacity, were apt to seek rarer traits or materials more suited for basic research, such as landraces and wild relatives. Consistent with this, Smale & Day-Rubenstein (76) found that private companies asked for the fewest accessions per request. On average, the requests from genebanks and public institutions were for far more samples, which may reflect that fact that both of these are likely to be involved in investigations that involve surveying numbers of accessions (76).

Smale & Day-Rubenstein's (76) data also indicate that PGRFA distributions from the United States to foreign countries "favor developing countries over developed countries in several ways, including the numbers of samples shipped, utilization rates in crop breeding programs, and the secondary benefits brought about through sharing this germplasm with other scientists." Furthermore, they found that survey respondents intended to increase their requests for germplasm from the United States in the future.

Flows of "improved" germplasm in the form of breeding lines, genetic stocks, and cultivars from public programs numerically dwarf transfers of landraces from genebanks, although comprehensive global data are not available (39). In addition to the products of public sector research, finished cultivars are also available from the private sector. In most cases, these commercial cultivars may be used as a genetic resource in breeding programs through no more complicated a procedure than purchasing seed in the manner a farmer or gardener might to use it as breeding material. In 2002, more than 8500 new cultivars were released under International Union for the Protection of New Varieties of Plants' style protection systems, legal regimes that provide for protection of plant varieties that, unlike patents, allow such use for breeding and research. That year, more than 59,000 cultivars worldwide were protected and available. It might be added that titles that cease to be in force (those cultivars that come to the end of the legal protection period) continue to remain available. During the period from 1998 to 2002, more than 22,500 cultivars fell into this category (81). The major exception to the availability of commercial protected cultivars for use in plant breeding is cultivars covered by utility patents, as in the United States.

Transfers of germplasm from genebanks are a conservative indication of need or demand, as well as an indirect measure of use of PGRFA. Because pests and diseases evolve and because commercial needs change, plant breeders routinely need new genetic resources (82). One must proceed with caution, however, in drawing conclusions about the extent to which materials are available or whether genebanks are well used from PGRFA transfer data. Despite the relatively high numbers of transfers, governments during the preparatory process for the FAO Fourth International Conference on Plant Genetic Resources reported that the potential for utilization was not being fully realized (8). Some researchers have argued that genebanks distributing a high percentage of their collection annually demonstrate a high standard of use (61). High rates might be indicative of an inefficient system and of lack of precision when making requests. And, as FAO observed, low rates of utilization do not imply poor utilization (8). They may indicate more informed, targeted requests. However, it is clear that some genebanks focus much more on their role as conservers of PGRFA and do not adequately cater to the needs of users. Virchow (61) cites the example of Russia, which distributes only about 1% of its collection annually, as compared with China, which distributed about 7% of its collections of 10 major crops per annum over a 15-year period (77).

Globally, over 400 collections—accounting for 60% of all conserved accessions—are maintained under medium- or long-term conditions (8). Such collections play an important role in conserving PGRFA and in supplying working or active collections with materials. A one-time transfer to an active collection might generate substantial use. The use of these active collections is assumed to be substantial, although the degree of use and the extent of subsequent transfers from and between active collections are not well documented.

PGRFA are obtained from genebanks by different groups of users for a variety of reasons. These include use for analysis of the extent and distribution of diversity, the study of inheritance and control of expression of specific traits in order to identify ways of improving performance, searches for resistance to biotic and abiotic stresses, evaluation as parents in crossing programs for characteristics such as combining ability, and, of course, plant breeding and direct introduction into cropping systems. Hodgkin et al. (83) explored the different ways in which genetic resources were used and noted that they were often linked. Problems in use by one group of research workers, prebreeders, or plant breeders could negatively affect use by other groups.

The conservation function of genebanks provides an insurance value (20, 75, 84). As future needs, both for basic research and for breeding, cannot be precisely predicted (82), large germplasm collections offer security. Several studies have concluded that this service is a bargain, offering benefits far in excess of costs (84, 85).

Obstacles to Availability from Genebanks Users' Perceptions

Genebanks have undoubtedly served in a very important way to conserve PGRFA and make them available to plant breeders and researchers (8, 86–89). Yet, these users have routinely criticized genebanks for deficiencies that impede access to and availability of PGRFA. They cite a number of problems—Weidong et al. (77) list 24 limiting factors—including lack of availability of seed (77), quarantine, policy, and legal obstacles (58, 90, 91).

Common to many of the surveys and commentaries and the main deficiency underlying most of the factors cited by Weidong et al. (77), for instance, is dissatisfaction with the quantity and quality of information (2, 58, 76, 77, 92–94). A survey undertaken by ten Kate & Laird found that breeders look for information that will help them pinpoint potentially useful accessions before they make a request for access (17). Presumably, lack of information would decrease requests for access and eventual use. In 1998, on the basis of reports from 154 countries, the FAO cited 10 main obstacles to the greater use of PGRFA (8). Countries identified the lack of information as the major obstacle most frequently. Not surprisingly, the FAO "Global Plan of Action for Conservation and Sustainable Utilization of Plant Genetic Resources for Food and Agriculture" (95) called for the strengthening of linkages between conservation and the user community, the implications of which were addressed in operational terms by IPGRI among others (96).

As recently as 1988, two scientists asserted that the information most needed by breeders was simply the names and addresses of germplasm collections (97). Those days have passed. Today the concern centers on characterization and, especially, evaluation data at the accession level.

Problems of Supply

From the users' point of view, genebanks need to provide the right material of the required quality at the right time, in the right quantity, and with sufficient information about it to meet user needs (98). This is a fairly substantial demand that can almost certainly never be fully met because user needs in areas such as information continuously increase and change. The genebank managers' first problem is that they have no way of determining (except possibly in rather general terms) what is likely to be the right material for different users or user groups. Indeed, different groups of users often need quite different types of material and quite different information about it. To satisfy users' needs, managers try to ensure that their collection adequately represents known diversity of the crop genepools with which they are concerned and that all the accessions in their collection are available. After that come the difficulties of ensuring that the quantity and quality of each accession is sufficient and that what is known about accessions is available to potential users.

As noted above, for many of the more important crops, substantial genetic diversity exists within collections, and for a few crops, such as wheat and rice, most of the genetic diversity may well already be conserved ex situ (8, 53, 68). For many crops that are clonally propagated or have recalcitrant seed (99), and for most minor crops and crop wild relatives, this is unlikely to be the case (65, 100). Adequate representation of genetic diversity in ex situ collections is especially difficult to achieve for crops that have to be maintained in field genebanks or in vitro, as is the case with clonally propagated species or those possessing recalcitrant seed (101). These collections suffer much greater maintenance problems and are usually much smaller than seed collections (102, 103). For these species, availability to users of the full range of their genetic diversity is likely to depend in large part on in situ conservation.

Frankel (104) argued that the large size of many collections acted as a barrier to their utilization and limited availability of their genetic resources. There were too many accessions for users to be able to identify what they wanted. This has led to the development of core collections that seek to optimally represent with minimum repetitiveness the genetic diversity of a crop species and its wild relatives within a collection (105, 106). Core collections should increase availability by providing users with a small number of accessions (often only a few hundred) in which to look for useful traits. Because they are organized to represent the whole collection, they can act as effective entry points for users, allowing them to focus on specific groups of accessions likely to possess desired traits. A survey in 1998 showed that there were over 60 established core collections involving 51 different crops in different genebanks and that the numbers were continuing to increase (105).

A more practical problem facing suppliers is often that of providing users with the required quantity of seeds of any one of several thousand or tens of thousands of accessions. This depends on building sufficient stocks of each accession and on timely regeneration or multiplication of material that is likely to be requested by users. Often the amounts of seed that can be supplied are low, especially of crop wild relatives where, for example, IRRI is reported to supply only 10–20 seeds per accession (107). This can mean that users have to multiply the accession for a generation or two to obtain sufficient material for their work. There is no obvious resolution to this problem. Core collections can help in allowing genebank managers to develop stocks of a limited set of accessions, which they can supply more frequently and in larger quantities (106), a procedure which has proved economic as a way of searching for new traits (108).

User surveys have noted problems with respect to the quality of material provided by genebanks as well as the quantity. McFerson et al. (63) reported that 27% of respondents to their survey reported frequent problems with quality and/or quantity of crucifer seed received from genebanks and that 80% reported that such problems hindered their work. Similar findings were reported by ten Kate & Laird (17). The two most important aspects seem to be identity and viability. Getting the accession that was requested is clearly important to the user. The error may be very obvious when it is large, as for example in the provision of the wrong species, but if the user is not entirely familiar with the material, errors may go undetected when related lines of similar traditional cultivars are supplied or when the wrong accession of a wild relative is sent. This is perhaps less a problem with availability per se than with the future use of a collection that becomes associated with frequent distribution errors.

More significant perhaps is low viability of a distributed accession. Loss of viability of accessions in genebanks is a widely recognized problem (8), and a number of surveys have also recorded poor viability as a problem with genebank materials (63, 77). These problems seem to result from poor storage conditions in many genebanks and from regeneration backlogs. Some genebanks face very substantial backlogs in regeneration, and it has been reported that for 44 countries an average of 48% of the accessions needed regeneration (8). Of course, individual collections vary greatly in the amount of material needing regeneration and the degree to which this affects availability, but it seems likely that even relatively well-funded collections, such as those at the CIMMYT or at the International Center for Tropical Agriculture, lack resources to carry out the required amount of regeneration and to ensure accessions have adequate seed numbers for sustained distribution over a period of years (8).

The importance of providing satisfactory information on accessions in an easily accessible form has been highlighted by nearly all surveys (76, 77, 109) and is emphasized in most discussions of plant genetic resources' conservation and use needs (8, 57, 95). Genebank managers place considerable emphasis on ensuring that adequate passport data are maintained and that accessions are fully characterized for traits that are highly heritable, expressed in all environments and can be recorded by eye (110). It has often been argued that genebanks should not become involved in evaluation of performance-related traits that may be useful in crop improvement. The levels of many of these traits depend substantially on growing conditions, and accessions are often subject to genotype-by-environment interaction so that even the order of performance may vary between environments. However, surveys suggest that users would like more information on these traits, particularly biotic and abiotic stress resistance (76, 77).

More and more information is being collected on genebank accessions, although many genebanks will admit that they still have substantial gaps in passport data and in characterization and evaluation data. Many older accessions in particular lack adequate passport data, and only the country region or local town of origin is known. Often the situation is better. Hodgkin et al. (74) found that 85% of wild *Triticum* and *Aegilops* germplasm held in the world's major collections (about 20,000 accessions) had good locality data, adequate for geo-referencing, although less than 20% possessed information on factors such as the aspect, soil, or ecology of the site where the accessions were collected. The extent to which characterization and evaluation have been carried out is also extremely variable, depending on crop and genebank. Some countries, such as China and Japan, have reported that they have characterized all of their accessions, whereas others, such as Kenya and the Czech Republic, indicated that only 50% to 60% of accessions had been characterized (8). Some genebanks have also made substantial efforts to collect evaluation data on their accessions, and many catalogues have been prepared providing performance-related data on genebank holdings (111, 112).

Making available the information that has been collected is as important to availability as collecting the information. The major advances in use of the Internet over the past decade have led to very substantial amounts of accession-level information becoming available from a number of genebanks. The CGIAR System-wide Information Network for Genetic Resources is the genetic resources information exchange network of the CGIAR Centers. It provides online access to information about the collections of genetic resources held by the CGIAR Centers (113). Online information about the U.S. Department of Agriculture germplasm collections provides accession-level information on the publicly funded collections held in the United States. In Europe, information is becoming available through the EURISCO Web catalogue (http://eurisco.ecpgr.org/_1About/index.php) that automatically receives data from the national inventories of European countries (114).

We are not aware of any investigation as to whether the availability of accession-level information online increases the use of genebanks, but it certainly has the potential to improve availability. It would be useful to monitor the way in which online access to information has altered use patterns if only to help genebanks identify the most important types of information for different user groups (83).

Availability of Germplasm Maintained In Situ

Most genetic diversity of plant genetic resources for food and agriculture continues to remain in situ, i.e., as traditional or modern cultivars or as natural populations in locations where they have been developed or evolved. Only in the case of the most important crops is the diversity of the primary genepool likely to be substantially represented in ex situ collection. In the case of the genetic diversity present in secondary or tertiary genepools, this is unlikely to be the case for any crop. There are a few cases where substantial collections of wild relatives belonging to the secondary and tertiary genepools have been developed. These include wild *Triticum* and *Aegilops* species (74), the wild *Solanum* collection in the United States, and wild *Lycopersicon* collections, which have been extensively used for tomato crop improvement (115). Availability of useful genetic diversity to plant breeders, research workers, and other institutional users therefore often depends on the availability of plant genetic resources found in situ.

The earlier emphasis on ex situ conservation of crop plant genetic resources (45) has been steadily replaced by a growing interest in in situ conservation (116–118). In situ conserved material remains a part of the production system or, in the case of many crop wild relatives, a part of the natural ecosystem. It has been argued that well-planned in situ conservation could limit the losses of diversity resulting from genetic erosion and secure genetic diversity, particularly of materials difficult to conserve ex situ, such as minor crops and crop wild relatives (119).

Genetic erosion may well be a primary cause for reductions in the amount of genetic diversity maintained in situ. The loss of local populations as a result of habitat change and the loss of traditional cultivars as new higher-yielding cultivars become available have been cited as major causes of genetic erosion (8, 47, 120) and, clearly, can act to completely prevent future availability of material. In practice, information on the extent and significance of erosion remains very limited. Very large losses in numbers of traditional cultivars have been reported (8, 14), but accompanying data are often not available on the effect this has had on loss of genetic diversity (i.e., in terms of loss of unique alleles). However, in one study of eight crops in Korea, a 75% loss of traditional cultivars over 8 years was accompanied by a progressive reduction in allelic diversity as measured by isoelectric focusing (121). Conversely, cultivar replacement may not always be accompanied by a loss of diversity, as in the case of U.K. wheat and barley between 1930 and 1990 (122).

The longer-term availability of much of the genetic diversity of plant genetic resources found in situ depends on whether it is conserved or not, whereas in the short term, availability depends much more on who the users are (whether a local farmer or some other institutional user, such as a plant breeder or researcher), what the sociopolitical framework is, and on the ability to locate the desired diversity.

Locating diversity in situ was (and remains) a central objective of most collecting missions (123). Over the past 50 years, collecting procedures have become increasingly organized and developed so as to increase the likelihood that new populations or cultivars are obtained in any one collecting expedition. Early guidelines on how to conduct collecting missions to obtain the most useful results were provided by Bennett (124), and more recently Guarino et al. (125) provided a substantial overview of the procedures to be adopted and the ways that could be used to achieve specific collecting objectives.

Ecogeographic surveys provide an important way of obtaining the knowledge required to understand the distribution of genetic diversity of a taxa or group of taxa (126). With the advent of geographic information analysis procedures, these have become increasingly sophisticated (127). Analysis procedures are now available that link geographic information to distribution of species or intraspecific genetic diversity (128, 129). Focusing on a particular crop or taxa, it is now possible to develop increasingly complete overviews of patterns of distribution of species and their genetic diversity (130) and to determine possible future patterns (42, 129, 131).

Most of these procedures have been concerned more with ensuring effective conservation of genetic diversity than with availability per se. Earlier approaches, associated with improving collecting work, were concerned with strengthening ex situ conservation, whereas more recently the procedures have been aimed at supporting both in situ and ex situ conservation activities. However, in practice, information from collecting and location work has often been used as the first step in identifying material with traits desired by users, both because diversity does not occur at random and because many useful traits are associated with specific environments or locations (132). The precise degree to which ecogeographic information can be used to locate useful traits or to determine diversity patterns in plant genetic resources has been the subject of substantial discussion, and space does not permit us to consider it here.

Most of the literature on location of diversity or specific traits in situ has been concerned with conservation. However, a survey concerned with use of plant genetic resources by plant breeding companies suggested that these have collected at least a small proportion of the material they wanted directly from the field (94). Apart from this example, there is little information on the use and effectiveness of targeted collecting either by those involved in conservation or by users.

There is a general perception that, with the entry into force of the Convention on Biological Diversity, international availability of genetic diversity from in situ sources has become increasingly limited. Anecdotal accounts are common, but data are scarce. An exception is Correa (133), who provides quantitative evidence of restrictions to access in the Andean countries. Availability to users within a country might increase as conservation efforts and knowledge of material and locations improve. However, increasing recognition of, and respect for, the interests or desires of local communities in areas where useful diversity is located might tend to limit uncontrolled access and reduce availability.

In most developing countries, farmers depend very largely on their own seed and planting material as part of informal seed systems. In Morocco, for example, 90% of wheat and *Vicia* bean seed is distributed through informal channels (134), and this is typical of many developing countries. The material includes both traditional cultivars and those originating from national or private sector breeding programs. Most of the time, farmers try to maintain their own seed, but where this is not possible, seed will be obtained from neighboring farmers or local markets. Although self-saved seed is nearly always preferred, some degree of exchange between farmers or communities is characteristic of most traditional seed systems (135, 136). This has led to the perception that traditional farmer seed supply systems are open systems with ready availability of locally adapted cultivars (137, 138), but Cleveland & Murray (139) have suggested that this is not always the case.

Available seed of locally adapted cultivars or landraces is extremely important to local communities and farmers faced with war, drought, floods, or other disasters (140). Three elements appear to be important to determining the resilience of local seed systems in disaster situations that disrupt the normal seed supply process. These are availability of seeds, whether sufficient seed can still be found for sowing and production; accessibility, whether farmers have resources to obtain seed through purchase or exchange; and utilizability, whether the seed that is available is appropriate to the production needs of the farmer (141). It can often be this last aspect—the availability of suitable and different types of materials that can be utilized by local farmers and communities—that is particularly vulnerable to war and other disasters.

Over the past few years, a number of projects have been undertaken concerned with on-farm conservation of crop plant genetic resources (43). On-farm conservation provides a way of conserving traditional crop cultivars in situ and is regarded as having a number of advantages over ex situ conservation (142). It is dynamic, maintaining the adaptive capacity of the material and allowing it to evolve and change to meet users' needs or changing environmental conditions. It ensures that users are directly involved in conservation and continue to have access to material. It is generally thought that maintaining a range of traditional cultivars provides resources for poor farmers with a risk-avoidance strategy, optimizes the use of different types of land and labor, and provides materials with a range of different uses for varied situations (143).

Most of the on-farm conservation projects that have been undertaken have been small-scale experimental actions, involving a few communities or villages in only a few locations in different countries. The effects of these actions on availability of diversity at multiple levels are difficult to determine. However, the projects seem to increase local knowledge and awareness of the diversity available within an area, and they provide a good framework for increasing the likelihood that such materials will be maintained. Information on specific useful traits possessed by individual cultivars is made available, and samples are placed in ex situ collections (D. Jarvis, IPGRI, personal communication). In Burkina Faso, the quantity of seed of traditional varieties maintained by farmers increased over the lifetime of the projects, and there was increased interest in ensuring the quality of seed maintained (144).

Although it is likely that on-farm conservation projects have a positive impact on local availability of traditional cultivars, there is no evidence that they affect availability to a wider range of users (e.g., plant breeders or research institutions) except in so far as they provide fresh materials for ex situ collections. The lack of a developed and accessible information framework for on-farm conservation activities probably limits the likelihood that in situ conservation can enhance the availability of in situ-maintained diversity (143).

In situ conservation of crop wild relatives has received much less attention that on-farm conservation in the past few years despite the value of the traits that have been obtained from such materials, as in the cases of wheat (145) and tomatoes (145), and despite the threats to these species (41). Nonetheless, there are some notable exceptions. The Sierra de Manantlan Man and Biosphere Reserve in Mexico has, inter alia, the objective of conserving teosinte, a close relative of maize. Other reserves include that established at Ammiad to conserve wild wheats and one established in Nagaland, India, to conserve wild citrus (41). These seem often to have been established almost in an ad hoc way, in contrast to the major Global Environment Facility–supported program in Turkey that led to the establishment of over 20 gene management zones for conservation of various wild crop relatives and useful wild tree species.

Generally, however, there seems to have been only limited collaboration between those interested in conserving plant genetic resources and those involved with conserving wild species or establishing and managing protected areas. This may, in large part, reflect the very different backgrounds of those involved in these different areas. Conservers and users of PGRFA almost always come from an agricultural background, whereas those involved in conservation of wild species are from environmental backgrounds.

Specific in situ conservation actions should improve the availability of the diversity in these materials. Identified populations in selected habitats will provide sources that can be more completely studied with respect to the likely possession of useful traits and can be more easily sampled. However, it will be important to ensure that an adequate range of populations is conserved so as to ensure full coverage of a taxa's ecogeographic variation (41) and to ensure that information on the conserved materials is made widely available.

POLICY, LAW, AND ACCESS

This review concentrates primarily on international aspects of PGRFA and their availability and use, yet we recognize that access can be impeded, denied, or facilitated by policy and law. Generosity has usually prevailed. The large ex situ collections are a testament to this. Disputes over genetic resources, however, date back hundreds if not thousands of years. In modern times, there have been denials of access to genetic resources for specific crops, including coffee, allspice, black pepper, turmeric, cacao, sugar cane, date palm, rubber, oil palm, and pistachio (10), and there have been blanket embargoes (76), both formal and informal (47). Today's debates are confounded by complex claims of rights (139, 146, 147) and the seemingly irresistible lure of thinking of these resources as having great economic value when determining what that value could be is impossibly complicated in the absence of a functioning market. Brush (148) has reviewed various methods of assessing the value of PGFRA. The value of PGRFA has been modeled (149), but estimating the actual value of materials conserved ex situ remains a guessing game (150).

Sovereignty and ownership issues are exceedingly complex (151), and access issues arise in different ways with different kinds of germplasm. Genetic resources may be regulated by various laws on intellectual property rights (inter alia patents, plant breeders' rights, trademarks, copyrights, and trade secrets), by two international laws (the Convention on Biological Diversity, and the International Treaty on Plant Genetic Resources for Food and Agriculture), and by health and phytosanitary laws and regulations. In both its drafting and its interpretation, one legal regime (a treaty, for instance) can be affected by another (152). Rather than generating cooperation, such processes often become politicized and contentious (14, 153).

The International Treaty (7) establishes a multilateral system for access and benefit sharing for PGRFA of most major food crops with the exception of some crops, such as soybean, groundnut, tomato, tropical forage grasses, and industrial crops. Although the Treaty will only have the force of law for those countries that are party to it, it will likely serve to set standards and regularize transfers of PGRFA for parties and nonparties alike. Access to PGRFA of crops not covered by the Treaty's multilateral system will fall, in the future, under the legal framework of the Convention on Biological Diversity. The Convention mandates that access is to be on the basis of "prior informed consent" and "mutually agreed terms" with the country of origin. This approach is legally and scientifically problematic (154–156), and there is evidence that some countries have implemented the Convention in ways that make access difficult if not impossible (133). Restrictions may have been particularly severe because of the uncertainty caused by the long and difficult process of negotiating the International Treaty.

Assembling from scratch a working genetic resource collection for a crop governed not by the Treaty but by the Convention would probably be very difficult today even if the materials were physically available in genebanks. As a generalization, and with the exception of the commercially important crops cited above, the Convention will apply to crops of lesser importance, crops that are more poorly collected and conserved. For such crops, restrictions both of access and availability will be obstacles in the future. This, unfortunately, is also likely to have a negative impact on conservation efforts.

Many countries allow for the legal protection of biological materials. The most common form of protection is plant breeders' rights, although utility patents are increasing in use in the United States, for instance (157). Plant breeders' rights and patents have very different provisions and effects on access and availability, as we use these terms in this review. Under the plant breeders' rights system, anyone can use a protected variety as breeding material to produce a new and distinct variety. With patents, protected material cannot be used for research or further breeding by anyone other than the patent holder unless permission is granted. Patent protection is available not only for cultivars in some countries but also for genes, traits, molecular constructs, and transformation procedures or enabling technologies. Use of genetic resources typically found in a farmer's field or genebank is not prevented by patents, at least if the product is made without using the isolated and purified form of DNA (157). Nevertheless, because the law and its application are evolving quickly, the situation bears monitoring in regard to the actual and cumulative effects patents may have on the availability and use of germplasm.

DISCUSSION

Aided by agriculture, world population has grown tremendously from the beginning of the Neolithic Era, when it stood at 5 million or perhaps somewhat more (158), to 2004 when it exceeds 6.3 billion (159). Obviously, global food production has increased considerably along the way. With growth in population from current levels likely, indeed already in the pipelines, further increases in production will be needed (32). Evans (158) argues that there are six main components of increased global food supply from crops. Prior to the three billion mark in world population, the most important component was the increase in the amount of land in cultivation. Since then, the most important has been increases in yield (158). Given the alternatives listed by Evans (such as clearing more land or reducing the use of feed for animals), it seems likely that increases in yield will increase in importance in the future as world population grows. It has been shown in a number of cases that much of the improvement in yields of a crop—50% or more in many cases—has been the result of plant breeding and the production of improved cultivars (160). Genetic resources are central to this process, and their continued use by breeders to obtain new variation is essential.

Use of plant genetic resources can in some ways be thought of as occurring as a process, a more or less linked chain of operations, in which the location and maintenance of diversity are the first steps and characterization, evaluation, and the provision of information the next ones. Research using available variability provides the required information on trait expression control and inheritance, and the introduction of new variability into a plant breeder's crossing program initiates the process of introducing novel diversity and results in new cultivars. Often these different stages appear more or less unlinked or occur in parallel, but effective use of plant genetic resources involves all of them (83), and limitations in one area can negatively affect the others (161).

Users of plant genetic resources may be involved in evaluation, research, and prebreeding or directly engaged in breeding programs. They have different needs and approach availability from slightly different perspectives. Plant breeders may have much higher requirements for information and want to know about general performance characteristics of different accessions. They may wish to identify accessions with optimum expression of a specific desired trait, such as pest or drought resistance. Researchers may be much more concerned with obtaining the full range of expression of particular characteristics whose control and range of expression they wish to understand. They may want to know much more about the origins of different accessions to ensure they are sampling the whole of a target genepool.

There has been criticism that genebank material is not generally available to farmers for direct use in production. Certainly utilization data suggest that the standard pattern of distribution is to formal sector research institutes and to publicly funded plant breeders. The limited use of genebank accessions made by private sector plant breeders and direct users such as farmers may reflect the fact that little attempt has been made to make material available to them in ways that are most relevant to their needs.

Availability involves more than ensuring that sufficient viable planting material is maintained of a sufficiently wide range of variation to meet passing user needs. A more active approach is required that involves genebanks understanding the difficulties faced by potential users in obtaining their material. It would seem self-evident that genebanks should seek to help potential users overcome such constraints. Genebank managers have to explore potential demand and carry out activities designed to meet and enhance it. Thus, it will often be necessary for genebanks to evaluate material for production-related traits, although many conservation workers have argued against this (162). Some genebank managers may want to go further and carry out research on topics, such as the genetic control of trait expression, for which their knowledge of the material is important to their work.

The importance of developing close links between genebanks and different user communities has been stressed by a number of authors and organizations, as well as by governments in political forums (8, 95). In practice, unless the groups are physically close together (e.g., working at the same site), it seems difficult to sustain linkages. Few crop networks have become established independent entities for any period of time.

A number of obstacles can conspire to prevent a plant breeder from obtaining and using PGRFA; among them are political and legal constraints. With the anticipated coming into force of the International Treaty on Plant Genetic Resources for Food and Agriculture, it is possible that such formal constraints may fade away for those crops covered by the Treaty's multilateral system, i.e., many of the world's most important food crops. The Treaty's guarantee of facilitated access to PGRFA could prompt us to take a fresh look at existing capacity for conserving these resources and making them available to users, as well as a fresh look at the resources themselves.

Today, the scientific community of plant breeders and researchers obtains PGRFA primarily from genebanks. One could argue that this community's basic needs could be met by a much slimmer and less costly global system than currently exists. As we have shown, an analysis of historical data indicates the presence of many duplicate samples floating about genebanks. A more rational system might be more effective at both conserving diversity and meeting user needs. But one person's original accession is another person's duplicate, and genebanks have been established with different goals and mandates, including, it would appear, conservation for its own sake, national security, and the desire not to be dependent on anyone for so vital a resource. In addition, some countries may wish to have the kind of access guaranteed by the International Treaty on Plant Genetic Resources for Food and Agriculture and also the more convenient, on-the-spot availability. These may be good and rational reasons for maintaining a number of collections (and many duplicates when viewed from a global perspective). Nevertheless, we reason that there is now an opportunity as well as a need for reevaluating the goals and practices of existing systems and institutions.

Uncoordinated or unintended duplication of accessions may be perceived as over duplication at the global level. The question is whether it causes a problem or constitutes a constraint to availability or use. It may not. Viewed globally, however, it may appear as unnecessary and as a drain on resources, particularly international funds, even though eliminating excess duplication would also have its costs.

As evidenced by the new Treaty and the recently established Global Crop Diversity Trust, there is a desire to secure the conservation, access, and availability of PGRFA. Such a goal would not, presumably, extend to excess duplicates; otherwise there would be no limit to the quantity of conserved samples or the funds needed to conserve them. Whether individual institutions choose to rationalize collections will have a lot to do with their specific mandates. But, at the international level, priorities may be viewed differently and may not extend far beyond conserving the diversity and ensuring reasonable availability for users.

If a user-oriented PGRFA conservation system is constructed, its architecture would necessarily look different crop by crop. Our own informal survey reveals that there are likely fewer than a half-dozen full-time yam breeders in the world. The number of breeders understates the crop's importance. FAO reports that more than 39 million metric tons of yams were produced in 2002, much of it in Africa (163). But the structure and arrangements best suited for yam breeders will be different from those for maize and wheat breeders.

If flows of germplasm and measures of use and incorporation are valid indicators, both access to and availability of PGRFA appear relatively good, at least for seed crops conserved in developed countries, international agricultural research centers, and a limited number of developing countries. We say this mindful of several additional caveats. Access and availability is good in regard to the primary genepools of the most globally important crops. Availability of the secondary and tertiary genepools of these crops, and of all genepools associated with most other crops, is limited by the paucity of the collections as well as lack of information about what is held. In addition, legal or policy constraints to access may exist especially for crops that are not part of the Treaty's multilateral system.

Each step in the plant breeding process—collection, selection, characterization and evaluation, exchange, enhancement, prebreeding, improvement, commercialization, and marketing—depends and builds on information and adds value (17).

To what extent is that process, specifically access to and availability of PGRFA, being constrained by lack of information, particularly accession-level data? User surveys indicate that information is their greatest concern; having more of it is their greatest desire. Certainly, in the absence of centralized databases, collection catalogs, institutional presence on the internet, and a reasonable amount of information concerning accessions (including characterization and evaluation data), many potential users will never become actual users. In fact, practical availability and use may be limited to those with personal knowledge of and even close physical proximity to the collection.

In situ conservation currently provides an unsatisfactory framework for supporting germplasm availability. This may largely reflect the limited extent of in situ conservation work and the even more limited attention given to the way in which in situ conserved resources might be made available to different user communities. However, it is likely that in situ conservation will become more important in the future for both crops and useful wild species. The conservation of additional diversity of species, such as crop wild relatives, will probably be achieved primarily through in situ conservation, and ways in which these conservation actions can be linked to user availability need to be developed.

Improvement of information about collections and accessions—ex situ and in situ—will not only stimulate demand and improve the efficiency with which researchers locate the desired materials. It will also make possible a new set of institutional arrangements that could support better and more effective use of collections. The conservation-oriented strategies implemented in the 1970s and 1980s resulted in the rescue of much diversity that otherwise would not exist or be available for use today. It was a remarkable achievement for which we have much to be grateful. If those collections can now be secured and if they can be organized, developed, and managed in ways that promote effective use of the genetic resources, future generations will have even more cause to be grateful.

ACKNOWLEDGMENT

Research for this article was funded, in part, by a grant from the Syngenta Foundation.

The *Annual Review of Environment and Resources* is online at
http://environ.annualreviews.org

LITERATURE CITED

1. Zeven AC, de Wet JMJ. 1982. *Dictionary of Cultivated Plants and their Regions of Diversity Excluding Most Ornamentals, Forest Trees and Lower Plants.* Wageningen, Neth.: Pudoc. 264 pp.
2. Natl. Research Counc. 1991. *Managing Global Genetic Resources: The U.S. National Plant Germplasm System.* Washington, DC: Natl. Acad. 171 pp.
3. Ayad WG. 1980. *A Glossary of Plant Genetic Resources Terms (English/Arabic).* Rome, Italy: Int. Board for Plant

Genet. Resour./UN Food Agric. Organ. 148 pp.
4. Glowka L, Burhenne-Guilmin F, Synge H, McNeely J, Gündling L. 1994. *A guide to the convention on biological diversity. Rep. 30*, Int. Union Conserv. Nat. Nat. Resour., Gland, Switz.
5. Callicott JB, Crowder LB, Mumford K. 1999. Current normative concepts in conservation. *Conserv. Biol.* 13:22–35
6. RAFI. 1993. *Bio-Piracy: The Story of Natural Coloured Cottons in the Americas.* Winnipeg, Can.: Rural Adv. Found. Int.
7. UN FAO. 2001. *International Treaty on Plant Genetic Resources for Food and Agriculture.* Rome, Italy: UN Food Agric. Organ.
8. UN FAO. 1998. *The State of the World's Plant Genetic Resources for Food and Agriculture.* Rome, Italy: UN Food Agric. Organ. 510 pp.
9. Harlan JR. 1975. *Crops and Man.* Madison: Am. Soc. Agron./Crop Sci. Soc. Am. 295 pp.
10. Plucknett DL, Smith NJH, Williams JT, Anishetty NM. 1987. *Genebanks and the World's Food.* Princeton: Princeton Univ. Press. 247 pp.
11. Watson AM. 1983. *Agricultural Innovation in the Early Islamic World: The Diffusion of Crops and Farming Techniques, 700–1100.* Cambridge, UK: Cambridge Univ. Press. 260 pp.
12. Brockway L. 1979. *Science and Colonial Expansion: The Role of the British Royal Botanic Gardens.* New York: Academic. 215 pp.
13. Cipolla C. 1965. *Guns, Sails and Empire: Technological Innovation and the Early Phases of European Expansion, 1400–1700.* New York: Pantheon. 192 pp.
14. Fowler C. 1994. *Unnatural Selection: Technology, Politics and Plant Evolution.* Yverdon: Gordon & Breach Sci. 317 pp.
15. Crosby A. 1972. *The Columbian Exchange: Biological and Cultural Consequences of 1492.* Westport, CT: Greenwood. 368 pp.
16. Klose N. 1950. *America's Crop Heritage: The History of Foreign Plant Introduction by the Federal Government.* Ames, IA: Iowa State Coll. Press. 156 pp.
17. ten Kate K, Laird S. 1999. *The Commercial Use of Biodiversity: Access to Genetic Resources and Benefit-sharing.* London, UK: Earthscan. 398 pp.
18. Zeven AC. 1966. Results of activities to maintain landraces and other material in some European countries in situ before 1945 and what we may learn from them. *Genet. Resour. Crop Evol.* 43:337–41
19. Harlan HV. 1936. Problems and results in barley breeding. In *Yearbook of Agriculture, 1936*, pp. 303–46. Washington, DC: US Gov. Print. Off.
20. Frankel OH, Bennett E. 1970. *Genetic Resources in Plants—Their Exploration and Conservation.* London, UK: Int. Biol. Program./Blackwell. 553 pp.
21. Vavilov NI. 1949. *The Origin, Variation, Immunity and Breeding of Cultivated Plants.* Waltham, MA: Chron. Bot. 364 pp.
22. Vavilov NI. 1926. Studies on the origin of cultivated plants. *Bull. Appl. Bot. Genet. Plant Breed.* 16:1–248
23. Simmonds NW, ed. 1976. *Evolution of Crop Plants.* London, UK: Longman. 339 pp.
24. Harlan JR. 1971. Agricultural origins: centers and noncenters. *Science* 174:468–74
25. Plucknett DL, Smith NJH, Williams JT, Anishetty NM. 1983. Crop germplasm conservation and developing countries. *Science* 220:163–69
26. Harlan JR. 1970. Evolution of cultivated plants. In *Genetic Resources in Plants—Their Exploration and Conservation*, ed. OH Frankel, E Bennett, pp. 19–32. London, UK: Int. Biol. Program./Blackwell
27. Kloppenburg J, Kleinman DL. 1988. Seeds of controversy: national property versus common heritage. In *Seeds and*

Sovereignty: The Use and Control of Plant Genetic Resources, ed. JR Kloppenburg, pp. 173–203. Durham, NC: Duke Univ. Press
28. Cooper D, Engels J, Frison E. 1994. A multilateral system for plant genetic resources: imperatives, achievements, and challenges. *Rep. 2*, Int. Plant Genet. Resour. Inst., Rome, Italy
29. Palacios XF. 1998. Contribution to the Estimation of Countries' Interdependence in the Area of Plant Genetic Resources. *Rep. 7, Rev. 1*, UN Food. Agric. Org. Comm. Genet. Resour. Food Agric., Rome, Italy
30. FAO Nutrition Division. 2001. *Nutritional Value of Some of the Crops Under Discussion in the Development of a Multilateral System. Rep. 11*, UN Food. Agric. Org. Comm. Genet. Resour. Food Agric., Rome, Italy
31. Prescott-Allen R, Prescott-Allen C. 1990. How many plants feed the world? *Conserv. Biol.* 4:365–74
32. Conway G. 1998. *The Doubly Green Revolution: Food for All in the 21st Century*. Ithaca, NY: Cornell Univ. Press. 335 pp.
33. Almekinders C, Louwaars N. 1999. *Farmers' Seed Production: New Approaches and Practices*. London, UK: ITDG Publ. 291 pp.
34. Evans LT. 1993. *Crop Evolution, Adaptation and Yield*. Cambridge, UK: Cambridge Univ. Press. 500 pp.
35. Gollin D. 1998. Valuing farmers rights. In *Agricultural Values of Plant Genetic Resources*, ed. RE Evenson, D Gollin, V Santaniello, pp. 233–45. Wallingford, UK: CABI Publ.
36. Frankel OH. 1970. Genetic conservation in perspective. In *Genetic Resources in Plants—Their Exploration and Conservation*, ed. OH Frankel, E Bennett, pp. 469–89. London, UK: Int. Biol. Program./Blackwell
37. Ford-Lloyd B, Jackson M. 1986. *Plant Genetic Resources: An Introduction to Their Conservation and Use*. London, UK: Arnold. 146 pp.
38. Maggioni L. 2002. Achievements and perspectives of the ECP/GR networking activity for the conservation and use of crop genetic resources. In *Broad Variation and Precise Characterization—Limitation for the Future*, ed. W Swiecicki, B Naganowska, B Wolko, pp. 133–42. Poznan, Pol.: Eucarpia
39. Fowler C, Smale M, Gaiji S. 2001. Unequal exchange? Recent transfers of agricultural resources and their implications for developing countries. *Dev. Policy Rev.* 19:181–204
40. Guarino L. 1995. Assessing the threat of genetic erosion. See Ref. 125, pp. 67–74
41. Meilleur B, Hodgkin T. 2004. In situ conservation of crop wild relatives: status and trends. *Biodivers. Conserv.* 13:663–84
42. Jarvis A, Ferguson ME, Williams DE, Guarino L, Jones PG, et al. 2003. Biogeography of wild arachis: assessing conservation status and setting future priorities. *Crop Sci.* 43:1100–8
43. Jarvis D, Zoes V, Nares D, Hodgkin T. 2004. On-farm management of crop genetic diversity and the convention on biological diversity's programme of work on agricultural biodiversity. *Plant Genet. Resour. Newsl.* In press
44. Palmberg C, Esquinas-Alcazar JT. 1990. The role of the United Nations agencies and other international organizations in the conservation of plant genetic resources. *For. Ecol. Manag.* 35:171–97
45. Frankel OH, Soule M. 1981. *Conservation and Evolution*. Cambridge, UK: Cambridge Univ. Press. 327 pp.
46. Harlan JR. 1975. Our vanishing genetic resources. *Science* 188:618–21
47. Fowler C, Mooney P. 1990. *Shattering: Food, Politics, and the Loss of Genetic Diversity*. Tucson: Univ. Arizona Press. 278 pp.
48. Bennett E. 1978. Threats to crop plant genetic resources. In *Conservation and Agriculture*, ed. JG Hawkes, pp. 113–22. Montclair, NJ: Allanheld, Osmun
49. Kuckuck H. 1970. Primitive wheats.

In *Genetic Resources in Plants—Their Exploration and Conservation*, ed. OH Frankel, E Bennett, pp. 249–66. London, UK: Int. Biol. Program./Blackwell
50. Bennett E. 1965. Plant introduction and genetic conservation: genecological aspects of an urgent world problem. *Scott. Plant Breed. Stn. Record*, pp. 27–113
51. Harlan JR. 1972. Genetics of disaster. *J. Environ. Q.* 1:212–15
52. Simmonds NW. 1979. *Principles of Crop Improvement*. London, UK: Longman. 334 pp.
53. Tech. Advis. Comm./UN FAO. 1986. Report of the second external program and management review of the international board for plant genetic resources. UN Food Agric. Organ., Rome, Italy
54. Williams JT. 1984. A decade of crop genetic resources research. See Ref. 164, pp. 1–17
55. Hanson J, Williams JT, Freund R. 1984. *Institutes Conserving Crop Germplasm: The IBPGR Global Network of Genebanks*. Int. Board Plant Genet. Resour./UN Food Agric. Organ., Rome, Italy
56. Tao K-L, van Sloten DH. 1989. Basecollections of crop genetic resources: their future importance in a man-dominated world. *Environ. Conserv.* 16:311–16
57. Holden JHW. 1984. The second ten years. See Ref. 164, pp. 277–85
58. Iwanaga M. 1993. *Enhancing links between germplasm conservation and use in a changing world*. Presented at Int. Crop Sci. Congr. I, Ames, IA
59. Ng NQ, Williams JT. 1979. *Seed Stores for Crop Genetic Conservation*. Rome, Italy:UN Food Agric. Organ.
60. UN FAO/ Int. Plant Genet. Resour. Inst. 1994. *Genebank Standards*. Rome, Italy: UN Food Agric. Organ./Int. Plant Genet. Resour. Inst.
61. Virchow D. 1999. Spending on conservation of plant genetic resources for food and agriculture: How much and how efficient? *Rep. 16*, Cent. Dev. Research, Bonn, Ger.
62. Comm. Germplasm Resour. Natl. Research Council. 1978. *Conservation of Germplasm Resources: An Imperative*. Washington, DC: Natl. Acad. Sci. 117 pp.
63. McFerson JR, Lamboy WF, Kresovich S. 1996. Assessing user perceptions of genetic resource collections in crucifer crops. *Crop Sci.* 36:831–38
64. Robinson J, Anishetty M. 2004. Germplasm: international and national centers. In *Encyclopedia of Plant and Crop Science*, ed. RM Goodman, pp. 531–36. New York: Dekker
65. Padulosi S, Hodgkin T, Williams JT, Haq N. 2002. Underutilized crops: trends, challenges and opportunities in the 21st century. See Ref. 165, pp. 323–38
66. Harlan JR, de Wet JHJ. 1971. Towards a rational classification of cultivated plants. *Taxonomy* 20:509–17
67. Deleted in proof
68. Lyman J. 1984. Progress and planning for germplasm conservation of major food crops. *Plant Genet. Resour. Newsl.* 60:3–21
69. Natl. Research Counc. 1993. *Managing Global Genetic Resources: Agricultural Crop Issues and Policies*. Washington, DC: Natl. Acad. 449 pp.
70. Valkoun J, Ceccarelli S, Konopka J. 1997. Barley. See Ref. 166, pp. 191–212
71. Lund B, Ortiz R, Skovgaard IM, Waugh R, Anderson SB. 2003. Analysis of potential duplicates in barley genebank collections using re-sampling of microsatellite data. *Theor. Appl. Genet.* 106:1129–38
72. van Hintum TJL, Visser DL. 1995. Duplication within and between germplasm collections II. Duplication in four European barley collections. *Genet. Resour. Crop Evol.* 42:135–45
73. van Soest L. 2001. *Verslag van een enquete onder de Nederlandse gebruikers van het CGN*, Plant Research Int., Wageningen, Neth.
74. Hodgkin T, Adham YJ, Powell KS. 1991. A preliminary survey of wild *Triticum*

and *Aegilops* species in the world's genebanks. *Hereditas* 116:155–62
75. Pardey PG, Skovmand B, Taba S, Van Dusen ME, Wright BD. 1998. The cost of conserving maize and wheat genetic resources ex situ. In *Farmers, Gene Banks and Crop Breeding: Economic Analyses of Diversity in Wheat, Maize and Rice*, ed. M Smale, pp. 35–55. Norwell, MA: Kluwer
76. Smale M, Day-Rubenstein K. 2002. The demand for crop genetic resources: international use of the US national plant germplasm system. *World Dev.* 30:1639–55
77. Weidong G, Fang J, Zheng D, Li Y, Lu X, et al. 2000. Utilization of germplasm conserved in Chinese national genebanks—a survey. *Plant Genet. Resour. Newsl.* 123:1–8
78. Sadakorn J. 1995. *Thailand: country report*. Submitted to FAO Int. Tech. Conf. Plant Genet. Resour. Food Agric. Leipzig, 1996, UN Food Agric. Organ., Rome, Italy
79. Anderson JR, Pardey PG, Roseboom J. 1993. Sustaining growth in agriculture: a quantitative review of agricultural research investments. *Agric. Econ.* 10:107–23
80. Pardey P, Beintema N. 2001. *Slow Magic: Agricultural R & D a Century after Mendel*. Washington, DC: Int. Food Policy Research Inst.
81. Off. Union. 2003. *Plant Variety Protection Statistics for the Period 1998–2002*. Geneva, Switz.: Int. Union Prot. New Var. Plants
82. Duvick D. 1986. Plant breeding: past achievements and expectations for the future. *Econ. Bot.* 40:289–97
83. Hodgkin T, Rao VR, Cibrian-Jaramillo A, Gaiji S. 2003. The use of ex situ conserved plant genetic resources. *Plant Genet. Resour.* 1:19–29
84. Pardey PG, Koo B, Wright BD, Van Dusen ME, Skovmand B, Taba S. 2001. Costing the ex situ conservation of genetic resources: maize and wheat at CIMMYT. *Crop Sci.* 41:1286–99
85. Dep. Agric. Sci. 2002. *Crop Diversity at Risk: The Case for Sustaining Crop Collections*. Wye, UK: Imperial Coll.
86. Chang TT. 1989. The case for large collections. See Ref. 167, pp. 123–35
87. Shands H. 1990. Plant genetic resources conservation: the role of the gene bank in delivering useful genetic materials to the research scientist. *J. Hered.* 81:7–10
88. Duvick D. 1984. Genetic diversity in major farm crops on the farm and in reserve. *Econ. Bot.* 38:161–67
89. Comm. Genet. Vulnerability Major Crops Natl. Research Council. 1972. *Genetic Vulnerability of Major Crops*. Washington, DC: Natl. Acad. Sci. 307 pp.
90. Marshall DR. 1989. Limitations to the use of germplasm collections. See Ref. 167, pp. 105–20
91. Peeters JP, Williams JT. 1984. Towards better use of genebanks with special reference to information. *Plant Genet. Resour. Newsl.* 6:22–32
92. Frankel OH, Brown AHD. 1984. Plant genetic resources today: a critical appraisal. See Ref. 164, pp. 249–57
93. Erskine W, Williams JT. 1980. The principles, problems, and responsibilities of the preliminary evaluation of genetic resources samples of seed-propagated crops. *Plant Genet. Resour. Newsl.* 41:19–33
94. Olsen N, Swanson T, Gillett H. 1996. The use of plant genetic resources in agriculture. In *Industrial Reliance Upon Biodiversity*, pp. 99–121. London, UK: UK Dep. Environ. Darwin Initiat.
95. UN FAO. 1996. *Global plan of action for the conservation and sustainable utilization of plant genetic resources for food and agriculture*. Presented at UN Food Agric. Organ. 4th Int. Tech. Conf. Plant Genet. Resour. Food Agric., Leipzig, Ger.
96. Engels JMM, Visser L, eds. 2003. *A Guide to Effective Management of Germplasm Collections. IPGRI Handbooks*

for Genebanks No. 6. Rome, Italy: Int. Plant Genet. Resour. Inst.
97. Peeters JP, Galway NW. 1988. Germplasm collections and breeding needs in Europe. *Econ. Bot.* 42:503–21
98. Weltzien E, vom Brocke K. 2001. Seed systems and their potential for innovation: conceptual framework for analysis. In *Targeted Seed Aid and Seed-System Interventions: Strengthening Small-Farmer Seed Systems in East and Central Africa*, ed. L. Sperling, pp. 9–14. Cali, Columbia: Int. Cent. Trop. Agric. (CIAT)
99. Chin HF. 1988. Recalcitrant seeds: a status report. *Rep.* Int. Board Plant Genet. Resour., Rome, Italy
100. Miller JC, Tanksley SD. 1990. RFLP analysis of phylogenetic relationships and genetic variation in the genus *Lycopersicon*. *Theor. Appl. Genet.* 80:437–48
101. Engelmann F, Engels JMM. 2002. Technologies and strategies for ex situ conservation. See Ref. 165, pp. 89–104
102. Engelmann F. 1996. *Management of field and in vitro collections*. Presented at Consultation Meet., Int. Cent. Trop. Agric. (CIAT), Cali, Colombia
103. Dulloo ME, Charrier A, Dussert S, Anthony F, Tesfaye S, et al. 2001. *Conservation of coffee genetic resources—constraints and opportunities*. Presented at 19th World Colloq. Coffee Sci., Trieste, Italy
104. Frankel OH. 1984. Genetic perspectives of germplasm conservation. In *Genetic Manipulation: Impact on Man and Society*, ed. WW Arber, K Llimensee, WJ Peacock, P Starlinger, pp. 161–70. Cambridge, UK: Cambridge Univ. Press
105. Brown AHD. 1995. The core collection at the crossroads. In *Core Collections of Plant Genetic Resources*, ed. T Hodgkin, AHD Brown, TJL van Hintum, EAV Morales, pp. 3–20. Chichester, UK: Wiley
106. van Hintum TJL, Brown AHD, Spillane C, Hodgkin T. 2000. Core collections of plant genetic resources. *Rep. 3*, Int. Plant Genet. Resour. Inst., Rome, Italy
107. Jackson MT, Loresto GC, Rao SA, Jones M, Guimaraes EP, Ng NQ. 1997. Rice. See Ref. 166, pp. 273–91
108. Holbrooke CC. 1999. Testing and utilization of a core collection for the US germplasm collection of peanut. In *Core Collections for Today and Tomorrow*, ed. RC Johnson, T Hodgkin, pp. 68–73. Rome, Italy: Int. Plant Genet. Resour. Inst.
109. Widrlechner MP, Burke LA. 2003. Analysis of germplasm distribution patterns for collections held at the North Central Regional Plant Introduction Station, Ames, Iowa, USA. *Genet. Resour. Crop Evol.* 50:329–37
110. IBPGR./Int. Cent. Research Semi-Arid Trop. 1992. *Descriptors for Groundnut*. Rome, Italy: Int. Board for Plant Genet. Resour. 125 pp.
111. Erskine W, Witcombe JR. 1984. *Lentil Germplasm Catalog*. Aleppo: ICARDA. 363 pp.
112. Dajue L, Mingde Z, Rao VR. 1993. *Characterization and Evaluation of Safflower Germplasm*. Beijing: Geological. 260 pp.
113. System-wide Inf. Netw. Genet. Resour. (SINGER). 2004. *System-wide genetic resources programme*. Consult. Group. Int. Agric. Research. Rome, Italy. http://www.sgrp.cgiar.org.
114. 2004. European Cooperative Programme for Plant Genetic Resources. Rome, Italy: Int. Plant Genet. Resour. Inst.
115. Rick CM. 1987. Genetic resources in *Lycopersicon*. In *Tomato Biotechnology*, ed. D Nivens, R Jones, pp. 17–26. New York: Liss
116. Altieri MA, C. ML. 1987. In situ conservation of crop genetic resources through maintenance of traditional farming systems. *Econ. Bot.* 41:86–96
117. Brush S, ed. 2000. *Genes in the Field: On-farm Conservation of Crop Diversity*. Boca Raton, FL: Int. Plant Genet. Resour. Inst./Int. Dev. Resour. Cent./Lewis. 288 pp.

118. Berg T, Bjørnstad Å, Fowler C, Skrøppa T. 1991. Technology options and the gene struggle. *Rep. 8*, Nor. Cent. Int. Agric. Dev., Ås, Nor.
119. Brush S. 2000. The issues of in situ conservation of crop genetic resources. See Ref. 117, pp. 3–28
120. Heywood VH. 1997. Conservation of the wild relatives of cultivated plants native to Europe: introduction. *Bocconea* 7:15–18
121. Ahn WS, Kang JH, Yoon MS. 1996. Genetic erosion of crop plants in Korea. In *Biodiversity and Conservation of Plant Genetic Resources in Asia*, pp. 41–55. Tokyo: Jpn. Sci. Soc.
122. Donini P, Law JR, Koebner RMD, Reeves JC, Cooke RJ. Temporal trends in the diversity of UK wheat. *Theor. Appl. Genet.* 100:912–17
123. Brown AHD, Marshall DR. 1995. A basic sampling strategy: theory and practice. See Ref. 125, pp. 75–92
124. Bennett E. 1970. Tactics of plant exploration. In *Genetic Resources in Plants–Their Exploration and Conservation*, ed. OH Frankel, E Bennett, pp. 157–79. London, UK: Int. Biol. Program./Blackwells
125. Guarino L, Ramanatha Rao V, Reid R. 1995. *Collecting Plant Genetic Diversity: Technical Guidelines*. Wallingford, UK: Int. Plant Genet. Resour. Inst./CABI Publ. 748 pp.
126. Maxted N, van Slageren MW, Rihan JR. 1995. Ecogeographic surveys. See Ref. 125, pp. 255–86
127. Guarino L, Jarvis A, Hijmans RJ, Maxted N. 2002. Geographic information systems (GIS) and the conservation and use of plant genetic resources. See Ref. 165, pp. 387–404
128. Jones PG, Guarino L, Jarvis A. 2002. Computer tools for spatial analysis of plant genetic resources data: 2. FloraMap. *Plant Genet. Resour. Newsl.* 130:1–6
129. Hijmans RJ, Guarino L, Cruz M, Rojas E. 2002. Computer tools for spatial analysis of plant genetic resources data: 1. DIVA-GIS. *Plant Genet. Resour. Newsl.* 127:15–19
130. Greene SL, Gritsenko M, Vandermark G, Johnson RC. 2002. Predicting germplasm differentiation using GIS-derived information. See Ref. 165, pp. 405–12
131. Jarvis A, Guarino L, Williams DE, Williams K, Vargas I, Hyman G. 2002. Spatial analysis of wild peanut distributions and the implications for plant genetic resources conservation. *Plant Genet. Resour. Newsl.* 131:29–35
132. Bradshaw AD. 1984. Ecological significance of genetic variation between populations. In *Perspectives on Plant Population Ecology*, ed. R Dirzo, D Sarukhan, pp. 213–28. Sunderland, MA: Sinauer
133. Correa C. 2003. The access regime and the implementation of the FAO International Treaty on Plant Genetic Resources in the Andean group countries. *J. World Intellect. Prop. Rights* 6:795–806
134. Tahiri A. 2004. Seed systems in Morocco. See Ref. 168. In press
135. McGuire SJ. 2002. Farmers' views on management of sorghum diversity in Western Hararghe, Ethiopia: implications for collaboration with formal breeding. In *Farmers, Scientists and Plant Breeding: Integrating Knowledge and Practice*, ed. DA Cleveland, D Solieri, pp. 107–36. Wallingford, UK: CABI Publ.
136. Louette D, Charrier A, Berthaud J. 1997. In situ conservation of maize in Mexico: genetic diversity and maize seed management in a traditional community. *Econ. Bot.* 51:20–38
137. Richards P. 1986. *Coping with Hunger: Hazard and Experiment in an African Rice-Farming System*. London, UK: Allen & Unwin. 176 pp.
138. Richards P. 1995. Farmer knowledge and plant genetic resource management. In *In Situ Conservation and Sustainable Use of Plant Genetic Resources for Food and Agriculture in Developing Countries*, ed. JMM Engels, pp. 52–93. Rome, Italy: Int. Plant Genet. Resour. Inst.

139. Cleveland DA, Murray SC. 1997. The world's crop genetic resources and the rights of indigenous farmers. *Curr. Anthropol.* 38:477–516
140. Sperling L. 1997. *War and crop diversity. Rep. 75*, Overseas Dev. Inst., London, UK
141. Remington T, Maroko J, Walsh S, Omanga P, Charles E. 2002. Getting off the seed and tools treadmill with CRS seed vouchers and fairs. *Disasters* 26:302–15
142. Brush SB. 1995. In situ conservation of landraces in centers of crop diversity. *Crop Sci.* 35:346–54
143. Jarvis DI, Myer L, Klemick H, Guarino L, Smale M, et al. 2000. *A Training Guide for In Situ Conservation On-farm. Version 1*. Rome, Italy: Int. Plant Genet. Resour. Inst. 161 pp.
144. Balma D, Ouedraogo JT, Sawadogo M. 2004. Seed systems and crop genetic diversity on-farm. See Ref. 168. In press
145. Appels R, Lagudah ES. 1990. ES manipulation of chromosomal segments from wild wheat for the improvement of bread wheat. *Aust. J. Plant Physiol.* 17:253–66
146. Genet. Resour. Action Int. 1995. *Towards a Biodiversity Community Rights Regime*. Barcelona, Spain: Genet. Resour. Action Int.
147. Fowler C, Lower R. 2004. The politics of plant breeding. *Plant Breeding Reviews* 25:In Press
148. Brush SB. 1996. Valuing genetic resources. *J. Environ. Dev.* 5:416–33
149. Zohrabian A, Traxler G, Caudill S, Smale M. 2003. Valuing pre-commercial genetic resources: a maximum entropy approach. *Am. J. Agric. Econ.* 85:429–36
150. Smale M, Bellon MR, Pengali PL. 1998. Farmers, gene banks, and crop breeding: introduction and overview. In *Farmers, Gene Banks, and Crop Breeding: Economic Analyses of Diversity in Wheat, Maize and Rice*, ed. M Smale, pp. 3–18. Boston, MA: Kluwer
151. Correa C. 1994. Sovereign and property rights over plant genetic resources. *Rep. 2*, UN Food Agric. Organ. Comm. Plant Genet. Resour.
152. Andersen R. 2002. The time dimension in international regime interplay. *Glob. Environ. Polit.* 2:98–117
153. Görg C, Brand U. 2000. Global environmental politics and competition between nation-states: on the regulation of biological diversity. *Rev. Int. Polit. Econ.* 7:371–98
154. Fowler C. 2001. Protecting farmer innovation: the convention on biological diversity and the question of origin. *Jurimetrics* 41(4):478–88
155. Hardon JJ, Vosman B, van Hintum TJL. 1994. Identifying genetic resources and their origin: the capabilities and limitations of modern biochemical and legal systems. *Rep. 4*, UN Food Agric. Organ. Comm. Genet. Res. Food Agric., Rome, Italy
156. Menon U. 1995. Access to and transfer of genetic resources. *Int. J. Technol. Manag.* 10:311–24
157. Falcon W, Fowler C. 2002. Carving up the commons—emergence of a new international regime for germplasm development and transfer. *Food Policy* 27:197–222
158. Evans LT. 1998. *Feeding the Ten Billion*. Cambridge, UK: Cambridge Univ. Press. 247 pp.
159. Popul. Ref. Bur. 2004. *Population reference bureau*. http://www.prb.org/
160. Fehr WR, ed. 1984. *Genetic Contributions to Yield Gains of Five Major Crop Plants*. Madison, WI: Crop Sci. Soc. Am./Am. Soc. Agron. 101 pp.
161. Knight J. 2003. Crop improvement: A dying breed. *Nature*, vol. 421:568–70
162. Frankel OH. 1989. Principles and strategies of evaluation. See Ref. 167, pp. 245–62
163. UN Food Agric. Organ. 2004. http://apps.fao.org/page/collections?subset=agricultur
164. Holden JHW, Williams JT. 1984. *Crop*

Genetic Resources: Conservation and Evaluation. London, UK: Allen & Unwin. 296 pp.
165. Engels J, Rao VR, Brown AHD, Jackson MT, eds. 2002. *Managing Plant Genetic Diversity*. Wallingford, UK: CABI Publ. 487 pp.
166. Fucillo D, Sears L, Stapleton P. 1997. *Biodiversity in Trust*. Cambridge, UK: Cambridge Univ. Press. 371 pp.
167. Brown AHD, Frankel OH, Marshall DR, Williams JT, eds. 1989. *The Use of Plant Genetic Resources*. Cambridge, UK: Cambridge Univ. Press. 382 pp.
168. Jarvis D, Smale M, eds. 2004. *Seed Systems and Crop Genetic Diversity On-Farm*. Proc. Workshop, Sept. 16–20, 2003, Pucallpa, Peru, ed. D Jarvis, R Sevilla, T Hodgkin. Rome, Italy: Int. Plant Genet. Resour. Inst. In press

# Construction Materials and the Environment

Arpad Horvath

Department of Civil and Environmental Engineering, University of California, Berkeley, California 94720; email: horvath@ce.berkeley.edu

Key Words concrete, cement, aggregates, recycling, life cycle

■ **Abstract** No other industry in the United States uses more materials by weight than the construction industry. Because of its economic strength and societal importance, it is also a significant polluter and a target of growing stakeholder scrutiny. This review offers an extended, supply chain inclusive framework for the study of the construction industry that serves all the life-cycle stages of society's infrastructure systems, and it summarizes selected literature on the life-cycle environmental assessment of construction materials, designs, and processes. On the basis of identified knowledge gaps, a research agenda is discussed for lesser-studied questions in order to first understand and then eventually reduce the environmental impacts of construction materials, processes, and activities.

CONTENTS

INTRODUCTION 181
THE IMPORTANCE OF THE CONSTRUCTION INDUSTRY IN THE
  U.S. ECONOMY 183
MATERIALS USE IN CONSTRUCTION 185
ENVIRONMENTAL EFFECTS OF CONSTRUCTION MATERIALS
  AND DESIGNS 187
  Life-Cycle Assessment of Construction Materials 188
  Comparison of Construction Materials and Designs 190
ARE SHORTAGES OF CONSTRUCTION MATERIALS EXPECTED? 192
END-OF-LIFE OPTIONS FOR CONSTRUCTION MATERIALS 194
CONCLUSIONS AND FUTURE RESEARCH 196

INTRODUCTION

The construction industry has to support a world of continuing population growth and social and economic development. The twentieth century witnessed an unparalleled increase in infrastructural investments, especially in the industrialized countries (e.g., highways, dams, power plants, pipelines, and railways). The public has tightened its scrutiny of construction activities' environmental impacts. In fact, the notion of NIMBY (not in my backyard) has been turning into BANANA (build absolutely nothing anywhere near anything). Opposition to large-scale construction projects (e.g., dams, pipelines, and power plants) is growing worldwide. Although heavy civil construction is increasingly faced with considerable public opposition, residential construction has enjoyed strong growth in the industrialized countries primarily owing to renovations and retrofits (a result of increased disposable income), urban sprawl (a desire to own a residential home in the suburbs), and automobility.

Increased public examination has caught up with the U.S. construction industry that is already a tough business: Contractors routinely see meager profit rates of a few percentages, and a significant number of the construction businesses go bankrupt each year. In addition to cutthroat competition fueled by a sea of contractors and tight economics, environmental challenges have been adding to this business' problems. Other large sectors of the economy, e.g., automobile manufacturing, chemicals, petrochemicals, paper, and electronics, have been striving for green design, engineering and management investments for more than a decade now, affording in-house or outsourced environmental management and stewardship services. However, most of the construction companies (except for the larger, more integrated firms) are routinely ill-prepared to face environmental problems. Dealing with environmental problems and liabilities may further eat into their profits, completing a vicious circle.

By virtue of its size, construction is one of the largest users of energy, material resources, and water, and it is a formidable polluter. Just how large is still being debated because information and data about the environmental impacts of the built environment are still not being collected and analyzed systematically. The assessment is complicated by the fact that it should be extended to a myriad of components and facilities of societal infrastructure (for example, residences, commercial buildings, transportation, government and military installations, roads, bridges, utilities, ports, and railways), including private and public construction, and every input and output of the life-cycle stages of the built environment: raw materials acquisition and processing, manufacturing, construction, operation, maintenance, and end-of-life option.

However, the construction industry must not only comply with the ever-growing number of environmental rules and regulations but go beyond compliance, proactively internalizing environmental performance in a way similar to that of other industries. The other large sectors of the economy, notably vehicle, electronics, and chemical manufacturing have already made significant progress in reducing their environmental footprint, and industrial ecology studies have documented these efforts (1).

This review focuses on the environmental performance of the construction industry and its materials by providing a study framework that accounts for supply chain effects, synthesizing the major research thrusts, and outlining an agenda for future research directions.

THE IMPORTANCE OF THE CONSTRUCTION INDUSTRY IN THE U.S. ECONOMY

Construction involves numerous manufacturing sectors [e.g., building materials (such as cement concrete) and building systems (such as heating, ventilation, and air conditioning)] and service sectors (e.g., engineering, project management). It is also one of the largest industries in any country of the world with a vast number of participants.

One typically thinks of construction [sector 23 in the North American Industry Classification System (NAICS)] (2) as a sector that

> comprises establishments primarily engaged in the construction of buildings and other structures, heavy construction (except buildings), additions, alterations, reconstruction, installation, and maintenance and repairs. Establishments engaged in demolition or wrecking of buildings and other structures, clearing of building sites, and sale of materials from demolished structures are also included. This sector also includes those establishments engaged in blasting, test drilling, landfill, leveling, earthmoving, excavating, land drainage, and other land preparation.

In the United States, by this definition alone, there were 709,590 establishments with 6.57 million paid employees in 2000 (3). Typical construction employers include contractors (general and specialty), construction management firms, and maintenance companies. The value of new construction put in place was $842.5 billion in 2001 in current dollars, or 8.4% of the U.S. gross domestic product (GDP) that year. Construction services contributed 4.7% to the GDP, i.e., over three times more than agriculture, forestry, and fishing, and almost four times more than motor vehicles and equipment manufacturing. The U.S. construction industry's contribution to the GDP in 2000 was larger than the GDP of 212 countries of the world (out of 231 total) (4). California alone generated more value added in construction than the GDP of 150 world economies.

However, construction has a much broader definition when complete project delivery and servicing the built environment are included. Architectural and engineering design firms, mines, material processors and manufacturers (e.g., rock, gravel, sand, cement, concrete, glass, steel, asphalt concrete, aluminum, plastics, chemical additives), construction equipment manufacturers (e.g., dump truck, backhoe, concrete mixer), building system manufacturers (e.g., electrical, heating, ventilation and air conditioning, elevators), electrical, electronics and software companies (e.g., computer systems for traffic control, software for design and project management), facilities management firms, and others should be counted as well. In fact, through its extensive supply chain, the entire national economy is involved in supplying to the construction industry. For example, a $1000 demand of ready-mixed cement concrete, a basic construction material, generates another $1166 of demand in the various other sectors of the economy (Table 1), some of which are direct inputs into concrete production and delivery of materials (cement, sand,

TABLE 1 Economy-wide demand as a result of $1000 in ready-mixed concrete purchases; total for all U.S. economic sectors and for the top 25 sectors in 1992 dollars (5)

	Economic sector	Dollars
	Total for all U.S. economic sectors	2186
1	Ready-mixed concrete	1020
2	Cement, hydraulic	166
3	Trucking and courier services, except air	117
4	Sand and gravel	99
5	Wholesale trade	77
6	Crude petroleum and natural gas	43
7	Electric services (utilities)	41
8	Industrial inorganic and organic chemicals	40
9	Dimension, crushed, and broken stone	35
10	Petroleum refining	33
11	Natural gas distribution	30
12	Real estate agents, managers, operators, and lessors	25
13	Railroads and related services	24
14	Water transportation	22
15	Other repair and maintenance construction	21
16	Banking	17
17	Advertising	14
18	Automotive repair shops and services	12
19	Coal	12
20	Computer and data processing services	12
21	Royalties	11
22	Telephone, telegraph communications, and communications services, not classified elsewhere	11
23	Miscellaneous repair shops	10
24	Legal services	9
25	Eating and drinking places	8

gravel, stone, chemicals, energy, trucking, railroads, water transportation), but also others which are closer or further "upstream" in the supply chain (wholesale trade, real estate services, repair and maintenance construction, banking, advertising, automotive and other repair, computer services, royalties, legal services, eating and drinking places) (5). (Note the circularity effect that a $1000 ready-mixed concrete demand generates an additional $20 worth of concrete demand throughout the supply chain, i.e., concrete is needed to manufacture concrete.) In total, 127 economic sectors (25 of which are shown in Table 1) contribute at least $1 to $1000 of cement concrete demand. An economy-wide, supply chain inclusive approach is also necessary for a comprehensive environmental assessment of construction materials, services, processes, and activities.

MATERIALS USE IN CONSTRUCTION

By volume used, the major construction materials in the United States are crushed rock, gravel, sand, cement, cement concrete, asphalt concrete, timber products, clay brick, concrete block, drywall, roofing materials, steel, aluminum, copper and other metals, plastics, paper, paints, glues, and numerous chemical products. Construction in other parts of the world uses locally available materials as well (e.g., bamboo in Southeast Asia). Natural aggregates (crushed rock, gravel, sand) that make up the bulk of portland cement concrete and asphalt concrete are used in the largest volume. In recent years, coal combustion products (fly ash, bottom ash, boiler slag), blast furnace slag, and foundry sand have become viable replacements for natural aggregates. Coal fly ash has become a common substitute for up to 50% of portland cement in concrete in the United States.

Construction has been the largest documented consumer of materials in the United States by weight for almost a century. Crushed stone, sand, and gravel use (primarily in road base, cement concrete, and asphalt concrete) have grown significantly from ∼33% in 1900 to 70% to 73% of all materials used in 1998 (6). Natural aggregate use has reached 2.78 gigatons (Gt) (Figure 1), or one half of all

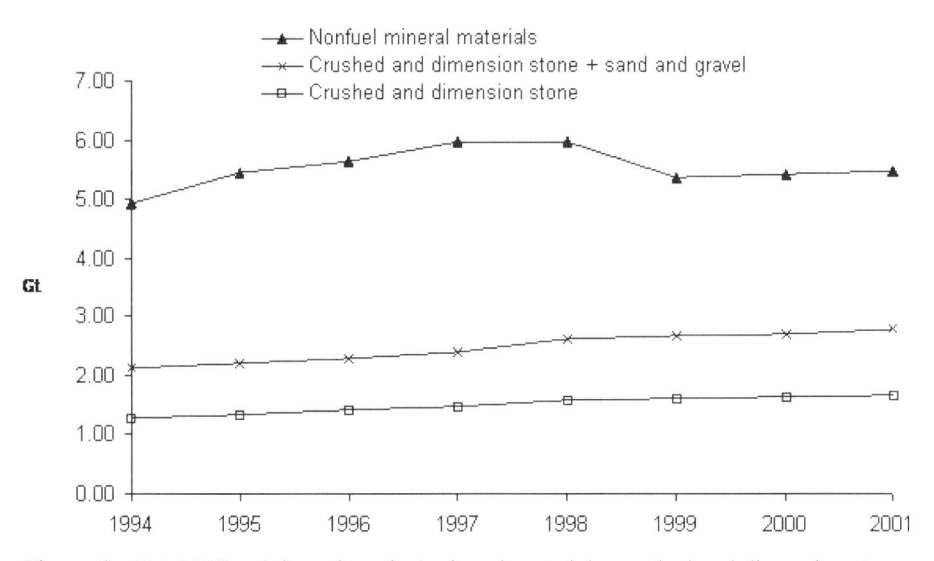

Figure 1 Total U.S. mining of nonfuel mineral materials, crushed and dimension stone, and construction sand and gravel, measured by gigaton (Gt) (7).

TABLE 2 Use of construction mineral and material commodities in the United States in tons (1950–2000) (8)

	Cement	Crushed stone	Dimension stone	Coal combustion products	Iron and steel slag	Construction sand and gravel
1950	40,891,000	228,000,000	1,890,000		22,600,000	321,000,000
1960	55,526,000	557,000,000	2,250,000		26,100,000	628,000,000
1970	67,476,000	788,000,000	1,830,000	4,630,000	30,600,000	830,000,000
1980	70,173,000	893,000,000	1,830,000	11,300,000	22,900,000	692,000,000
1990	80,964,000	1,110,000,000	3,680,000	19,300,000	22,100,000	831,000,000
2000	110,470,000	1,569,000,000	5,850,000	28,600,000	17,500,000	1,120,000,000

nonfuel minerals mined in the United States in 2001 (7). Table 2 shows that apparent consumption (domestic production + imports − exports − stocks) of construction mineral and material commodities has increased steadily and significantly between 1950 and 2000 by a factor of nearly three (for cement) to seven (for crushed stone), with stagnating iron and steel slag use (8).

Construction material production is significant in economic terms as well. Of the major materials, $7.2 billion worth of cement, $20.2 billion worth of ready-mixed concrete, and $6.1 billion worth of asphalt paving mixtures and blocks were shipped from U.S. plants in 2001 (9); these shipments accounted for 0.3% of the GDP.

Enormous amounts of materials and energy are embedded in the built environment, but data are still scarce and come largely from overseas. For example, a study of a typical office building in Finland (10) estimates building material consumption at 1.307 Mg/m^2 of floor space and an additional 0.133 Mg/m^2 in the operation and maintenance phase over a 50-year lifetime. The energy demand (electricity use and heating) over 50 years is 8.53 MWh/m^2. New house construction in Japan is estimated to require 0.45 Mg of material or 5.8 GJ of energy per m^2 of floor area on average (11). In Shanghai, the construction of high-rise hotels and commercial structures has increased from 2–8 per year between 1980 and 1986 to 14–45 per year between 1987 and 1990, with a consistent growth in the number of floors (12). From 1990 to 1993, 20 million m^2 of floor space were constructed (13), adding up to 9.27 million tons of material or 119.5 PJ of up-front energy investment (14). Billions of Mg of material and energy are embedded in the 121.5 million U.S. housing units with more than 18.7 billion m^2 of floor area and the 4.7 million commercial buildings with 6.3 billion m^2 of floor space (3).

Overall, buildings are estimated to be responsible for two fifths of the world's material and energy flows, one sixth of its freshwater withdrawals, and one quarter of its wood harvest (15). In the United States, 54% of energy consumption is directly or indirectly related to building construction and operations. The use of other materials (e.g., plastics, chemicals) in construction is not well documented.

ENVIRONMENTAL EFFECTS OF CONSTRUCTION MATERIALS AND DESIGNS

Although building energy use has been studied quite extensively and research efforts have been implemented in practice [e.g., (16, 17)], the environmental impacts of other parts of the infrastructure (for example, roads and bridges), especially construction materials and processes, and nonuse phase impacts (e.g., construction, maintenance, demolition) have thus far garnered unjustifiably limited research attention. A first comprehensive roadmap for built environment sustainability (18) and construction ecology publications (19, 20), analogous to industrial ecology studies for other sectors, have appeared recently, but a critical mass of literature, including detailed analyses and practical recommendations, is still missing. For example, the emergence of the Leadership in Energy and Environmental Design (LEED) green building certification system (21) and a recent green checklist for rebuilding the World Trade Center (22) are commendable, but their success will depend on the availability of comprehensive data and willingness of the stakeholders to adopt environmentally better performing construction materials, processes, activities, and designs.

In addition to the huge amounts of materials and energy used to construct, operate, and maintain it, the built environment is responsible for formidable amounts of pollution and waste generation (23) at millions of locations worldwide. In contrast to some other large economic sectors that have fewer plants and locations (e.g., there are about 180 petroleum refineries in the United States), construction materials processing and manufacturing are distributed. For example, the 1.35 billion Mg of crushed stone were produced in 3400 U.S. quarries, and the 1 billion Mg of sand and gravel came from 5300 operations in 1998 (6). There are some 210 cement plants in the United States (24), but as many as 7500 across China (in 1994) (25). Cement concrete is produced in 4000 to 5000 ready-mix plants in the United States (24). In 2001, 1.6 million privately-owned housing units started construction in the United States, at nearly as many distinct locations (3).

The use of common building materials has associated health hazards, although the bulk of the literature is on indoor air issues. For example, better indoor environments may bring substantial annual health cost savings, estimated at $6–$14 billion from reduced respiratory disease, $1–$4 billion from reduced allergies and asthma, $10–$30 billion from reduced sick building syndrome symptoms, as well as $20–$160 billion from worker productivity gains unrelated to health (26).

Materials flows signify the magnitude of renewable and nonrenewable materials production and consumption, the energy needed to extract, transport, and prepare them for further use, the corresponding emissions and wastes, and the potential for depletion of viable stocks. However, materials flows only tell a limited environmental story. Assessment of environmental performance and attainment of environmentally sustainable solutions require the adoption of holistic approaches.

Life-Cycle Assessment of Construction Materials

For the total environmental balance of a product, process, or service, an established analytical method is life-cycle assessment (LCA). LCA is needed for systematic analysis of not just the direct but also the indirect environmental effects of construction materials. Direct effects relate to the energy and material use in the materials production stage, whereas indirect effects reveal the contributions of the supply chains. For example, asphalt concrete production in a mixing plant has lower energy demand than the mining, processing, manufacturing, and transportation of the main constituents (bitumen, crushed rock, and gravel) throughout their extensive supply chains.

There are two widely practiced approaches to LCA. Process-based LCA uses process flow analysis to model life-cycle activities and stages (27, 28). The major material and energy inputs and outputs are identified and quantified, and the impacts from the resulting environmental emissions are estimated. The International Organization for Standardization created ISO 14040, a voluntary international standard that provides guidance in developing LCAs (27). Because of time, cost, and data restrictions, process-based LCA typically requires that an analysis boundary be set. Often this means that many of the supply chain environmental effects, especially the further upstream ones, have to be left out of the analysis (29). The other LCA approach, EIO-LCA, solves this problem by using the economic input-output data (for the United States, from the Department of Commerce) and resource input and environmental output data from various publicly available sources to quantify both direct and supply chain effects (30). Both approaches have advantages and limitations. The strengths of the two models include the ability of process-based LCA to provide analysis of direct and indirect environmental effects (within a set boundary), using product-specific data, whereas EIO-LCA provides an estimate of both direct and supply chain effects for commodities using average U.S. national data. The two approaches have thus far been used largely independently, but applied together in a hybrid approach (29), they could assess the total life-cycle environmental effects of construction materials or other products, processes, or services comprehensively.

The literature on the LCA of construction materials and designs is limited. Of all the facilities of the built environment, commercial, industrial, and residential buildings have been studied the most intensively, in particular, design for energy efficiency. Tools to aid in green building material selection have appeared [e.g., (31)]. LCAs of full buildings are still rare, and it is difficult to derive general principles from them, especially between regions or countries [for residential buildings, see (32, 33), and for commercial buildings, see (10)].

The most significant problems with LCA studies have been the issues with boundary definition, data acquisition, data quality, uncertainty, and interpretation of results. Various assessments of the same material may yield radically different results because of varied assumptions about scope and data sources. The next section illustrates this as well as the state of current research on one of the major construction materials, cement concrete.

CEMENT CONCRETE The components of cement concrete are aggregates (crushed stone, gravel, sand), cement, water, coloring, and chemical additives (to control setting time and workability). Concrete is used in the construction of every part of the built environment, including buildings, roads, bridges, dams, ports, and storage tanks. For example, approximately 260 million Mg of concrete are used annually in U.S. highway and road construction (34), even though only a small fraction of the overall more than 6 million km of paved roads in the United Statesis are made of cement concrete. Similarly, of the 1,471,000 km of roads under the oversight of the Federal Highway Administration (35), only 95,000 km are concrete pavements, and another 166,000 km are concrete pavements that have been overlaid with asphalt. The rest is asphalt concrete.

On a per unit basis, cement is the most energy- and pollution-intensive component of concrete. The 1.45 billion Mg of global cement production are accountable for about 2% of the global primary energy or close to 5% of the total global industrial energy consumption, about 5% of the global anthropogenic CO_2 emissions (25), and significant emissions of SO_2, NO_x, particulate matter, and other pollutants (36, 37). Average primary energy intensity globally is around 4.8 GJ/Mg of cement, and 5.4 GJ/Mg in North America. On average, 0.222 Mg of C is released from producing 1 Mg of cement worldwide (25), and 0.242 Mg C in North America. One Mg of cement requires 1.45 to 1.6 Mg of various raw material inputs (24). The United States is the third largest cement manufacturer in the world with about 110 million Mg, and this activity demands about 0.6% of the U.S. total energy use annually, even though cement manufacturing is only about 0.06% of the GNP (24).

In the last several decades, one of the indicators of development of a country was thought to be the rate of cement use. Although infrastructure investments are still high in the industrializing world [e.g., China has become the largest manufacturer of cement (25)], this indicator is now disappearing because of the realization that with the slowing rate of public works projects, construction activities in the industrialized economies are shifting toward maintenance and renovation, and cement use may not be the most accurate measure of the intensity of such construction investments. Global usage of other construction materials, such as asphalt concrete, steel, aluminum, and plastics, is also very large.

Despite the global annual production of over 12 billion Mg of concrete (38), the environmental assessment literature on cement concrete is limited and inconclusive, focusing largely on energy input and associated CO_2 emissions. For example, the embodied energy of concrete varies significantly from one source to another, depending on assumptions about analysis boundary, fuel mixes, concrete mixes, and technological differences. Four studies (39), two from Europe and two from the United States, estimated it between 70 and 6000 MJ/Mg, another (40) reported 700–1600 MJ/Mg, whereas Wilson (24) listed it at 950 MJ/Mg (Table 3). CO_2 emissions were estimated at 0.375 Mg and total particulate (dust) emissions at 0.180 Mg per Mg of concrete (24).

As shown in Table 1, economic effects of the purchase of concrete, supply chain impacts are also crucial in estimating the total environmental effects of cement concrete. Table 4 lists the top 25 energy contributors to producing $1000

TABLE 3 Embodied energy for cement and concrete production (24)

	% by weight	Btu per ton Materials	Hauling	Btu/yd³ concrete	% energy
Cement	12	5,792,000	504,000	1,574,000	94[a]
Sand	34	5,000[b]	37,000[b]	29,000	1.7
Crushed stone	48	46,670	53,000	100,000	5.9
Water	6	0	0	0	0
Concrete	100	817,600		1,700,000	100

[a]Energy requirements for cement production are provided using 1990 numbers from the Portland Cement Association (24).
[b]Energy requirements for aggregate (sand and stone) and hauling are computed using data from the Portland Cement Association and assuming (a) the cement is hauled 50 miles to ready-mix plant; (b) the aggregate is hauled 10 miles to plant; (c) the concrete mix is hauled 5 miles to building site; and (d) the concrete mix is 500 lbs. cement, 1400 lbs. sand, 2000 lbs. crushed stone, and 260 lbs. water per yd³ (24).

worth of concrete. The two largest contributors, as expected, are cement production and the final mixing of concrete (at the ready-mix plant), with 27% and 25% of the total, respectively. The supply chain (everything but the ready-mix plant) contributes 75% of the energy to the production of concrete. Although the first 12 on the list plus number 16 (crude petroleum and natural gas extraction) appear in Table 1 as well (although in different order), the bottom 12 of this list are sectors that were not part of the top 25 economic contributors to concrete production. Similarly to Table 1, which lists surprise sectors, such as banking and advertising among the top 25, Table 4 shows that there are major energy consumers in the supply chain, such as air transportation and fertilizer and paper manufacturing, that one would not intuitively associate with concrete production. However, they appear in the supply chain because of the induced economic effects of concrete manufacturing. Supply chain inclusive analysis is, therefore, critical in comprehensive environmental assessment.

A perennial question inquires about the contribution of transportation to the total environmental effect of construction materials. Ready-mix cement concrete transport from the plant to the construction site is limited by technological reasons (without special chemical admixtures, typically up to about 20 miles). Thus for a typical concrete mix (500 lbs cement, 1400 lbs sand, 2000 lbs crushed stone, 260 lbs water per yd³), transportation was found to contribute only on the order of 12% to the embodied energy, assuming 50 miles of cement and 10 miles of aggregate trucking to the ready-mix plant and 5 miles of concrete hauling to the construction site (24).

Comparison of Construction Materials and Designs

Rather than focusing on one material's environmental effects, which may not provide much of an explanation out of context, it is often more valuable to perform a comparative assessment of construction materials and designs.

TABLE 4 Energy use of the supply chain of $1000 worth of ready-mixed concrete purchases; total for all U.S. economic sectors and for the top 25 sectors (1992 data) (5)

Economic sector	Total GJ
Total for all U.S. economic sectors	28.33
1 Cement, hydraulic	7.59
2 Ready-mixed concrete	6.99
3 Electric services (utilities)	5.13
4 Trucking and courier services, except air	2.58
5 Sand and gravel	0.89
6 Industrial inorganic and organic chemicals	0.75
7 Water transportation	0.72
8 Petroleum refining	0.51
9 Railroads and related services	0.32
10 Natural gas distribution	0.28
11 Dimension, crushed, and broken stone	0.24
12 Wholesale trade	0.22
13 Blast furnaces and steel mills	0.20
14 Air transportation	0.18
15 Minerals, ground or treated	0.16
16 Crude petroleum and natural gas	0.14
17 Nitrogenous and phosphatic fertilizers	0.12
18 Automotive rental and leasing, without drivers	0.10
19 Sanitary services, steam supply, and irrigation systems	0.08
20 Paper and paperboard mills	0.07
21 Chemicals and chemical preparations, not classified elsewhere	0.06
22 Surface active agents	0.06
23 Clay, ceramic, and refractory minerals	0.05
24 Other state and local government enterprises	0.04
25 Coal	0.04

Although attempts have been made to evaluate the life-cycle effects of complete buildings [e.g., (10, 32, 33, 48)], most studies thus far have analyzed only specific construction materials and life-cycle phases. For example, a comparison of wood, steel, and concrete structural frames for commercial buildings has been performed (41), but only for energy use and greenhouse gas emissions, excluding the end-of-life stage. A study of concrete and steel building frames (42) found little environmental difference between the two structures, but most construction and demolition activities had been excluded. A recent study of concrete and steel structural frames for a typical U.S. office building (43) accounted for the construction effects, the material supply chains, and transportation, and the study still found the two structural systems to be environmentally comparable in terms of energy use and several types of emissions.

Comprehensive environmental assessments of other parts of the infrastructure are rare [for example, the water treatment and distribution infrastructure has only been a subject of a few papers, e.g., (44, 45)], and existing studies are still mostly incomplete from an LCA perspective. For example, a comparison of asphalt concrete and portland cement concrete surface courses for pavements (39) found that steel-reinforced concrete pavements have higher energy use and environmental emissions, but the report did not conclusively quantify the effects of maintenance and recycling. A study of steel and steel-reinforced concrete bridges (46) estimated that the concrete design has lower environmental burdens, but the recycling of steel bridges needed to be studied further. The service life of the two bridge designs had been assumed similar, which in reality may not be the case.

In some studies, environmental assessment of the materials manufacturing, construction, and maintenance phases is simply approximated or skipped. Although the longest life-cycle phase, use/operation, is thought to be often the most energy- and emission-intensive, more research is needed to assess the environmental impacts of the materials manufacturing, construction, and maintenance stages. For example, materials manufacturing, construction, and maintenance phases may be relatively insignificant in the overall service life of coal and natural gas power plants because of their gargantuan fossil fuel use (47), but they can be relatively and absolutely significant for other power plants. For example, materials manufacturing, construction, and maintenance were estimated to contribute 8% to 17% to the total global warming effect (GWE) of the Glen Canyon hydroelectric plant (3 to 6 Tg of CO_2 equivalent, measured 20 years after construction) (47). The GWE of materials manufacturing, construction, and maintenance was also estimated for a solar photovoltaic plant and a wind farm with comparable annual energy production to Glen Canyon. Measured 20 years after construction, the GWE was found to be 10 Tg of CO_2 equivalent for the solar plant and 0.8 Tg of CO_2 equivalent for the wind farm.

Further, for some buildings and particular emissions, the construction phase alone is not to be ignored. For example, for a typical U.S. office building, construction of the structural frame is found to contribute to 10% to 15% of its lifetime (50 years) energy use, 10% of NO_2, and 5% of PM emissions (43). Similar numbers have been reported for Finland (10, 48).

ARE SHORTAGES OF CONSTRUCTION MATERIALS EXPECTED?

One of the uses of materials flow and balance studies is to help determine the short- and long-term stocks and flows, and another is the geographic distribution of construction materials used. Are we—globally—in danger of running out of them? A method proposed by Graedel & Klee (49) helps estimate the ratio of the current consumption rate to a "sustainable rate" of current and anticipated consumption over an assumed planning period. For the United States, the steps are (49, 50)

1. Establish the available supply of the resource. Allocate the reserve base (presently economically extractable plus known but currently not economically viable resources) for each year over a 50-year time horizon.
2. Allocate the resource supply by dividing it equally among 7.5 billion people, the anticipated average world population over the next 50 years.
3. Determine the sustainable use rate including reuse and recycling. Factor into the resource base reused and recycled materials.
4. Compare the current U.S. consumption rate to the global sustainable use rate. Divide the current U.S. demand by the U.S. population to find the U.S. consumption rate, and contrast it to the global sustainable use rate.

For materials used in construction, the U.S. consumption rate is estimated to be less than the world sustainable use rate for sand and gravel (50), iron ore, and soda ash (used in glass manufacturing), but the United States exceeds the world sustainable use rate of petroleum and zinc (used in steel galvanizing, brass, and bronze) (49). Similar estimates have not yet been calculated for other common construction materials, such as cement, steel, aluminum, bitumen, plastics, and glass. Of course, many construction materials share a resource depletion concern with many other industries that also use large amounts of them (e.g., aluminum and plastics).

Globally, major construction material resources may be plentiful, but energy is being used at an unsustainable rate. If it saves energy and other resources and prevents pollution and waste generation, reuse and recycling of materials may become increasingly important because of limited economically feasible energy supplies or local material shortages. At the regional level, construction material shortages are already a concern, and transporting these materials to construction sites from large distances will not only make them more expensive but will increase their environmental burden as well. For example, shortages of crushed rock, sand, and gravel are increasing in urban and industrialized areas as a result of local zoning regulations that restrict mining. The sand and gravel consumption rate is several times higher for some states than the national average consumption (Table 5). There is anecdotal evidence that the San Francisco Bay Area and some cities in Texas are already experiencing local shortages of aggregates and are forced to import aggregates from large distances (e.g., from British Columbia in the case of the Bay Area), and/or use recycled aggregates for cement and asphalt concrete.

Increased need for conservation of natural resources and reuse and recycling of construction materials could be one reason for establishing extended producer responsibility programs for built facilities (50), which are already gaining ground

TABLE 5 Annual use rate of construction sand and gravel for several U.S. states and the national average (50)

Location	Use rate [tons/person/year]
United States	4.0
Texas	3.9
California	4.4
Oregon	4.8
Michigan	7.6
Arizona	11.5
Nevada	18.2

in similar forms for other industries, notably take-back policies for automobiles, electrical and electronic goods, and household appliances in the European Union.

END-OF-LIFE OPTIONS FOR CONSTRUCTION MATERIALS

Construction and demolition (C&D) waste is 13% to 29% of solid waste entering landfills in Australia, Finland, Germany, The Netherlands, and the United States (51). Detailed statistics are appearing regionally and locally. In California, construction waste is 0% to 55% of municipal solid waste, depending on the municipality (52). Building-related demolition debris is estimated at around 65 million tons annually in the United States (53). Two thirds of it by weight and about one half by volume is cement concrete (24). To help future estimates, demolition waste intensity units for different building types have been published for Seoul, Korea (54), a useful endeavor.

There are significant opportunities and challenges for reuse and recycling of construction materials. Opportunities arise from potential environmental and economic savings realizable through reuse (such as old steel bridge girders or timber beams) and recycling (e.g., asphalt and steel) (55). Although there are many technically feasible ways to recycle construction materials (Table 6), in practice, only asphalt concrete, steel, aluminum, and wood have been recycled in significant volumes in the United States owing to their positive secondary market value after deconstruction and demolition. Cement concrete recycling also holds potential. In general, the secondary material with the most profitable reuse or recycling will determine the choice of demolition method for a facility.

Challenges exist largely because of economic and market issues, lack of information, and a tendency of recycled material users to continue with the old

CONSTRUCTION MATERIALS C-1

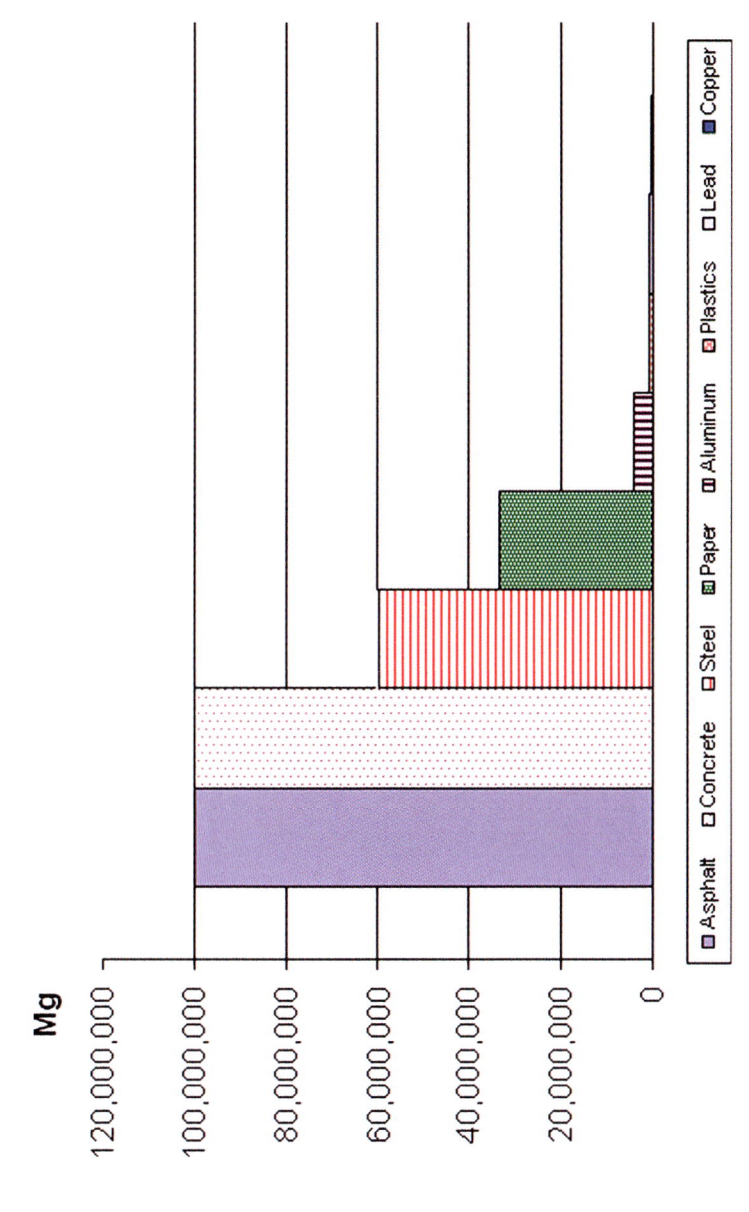

Figure 2 Current quantities of various recycled materials in the United States. Sources are asphalt (65), portland cement concrete (65), steel (66), paper (67), aluminum (68), plastics (69), lead (70), and scrap consumption of total copper consumed (71).

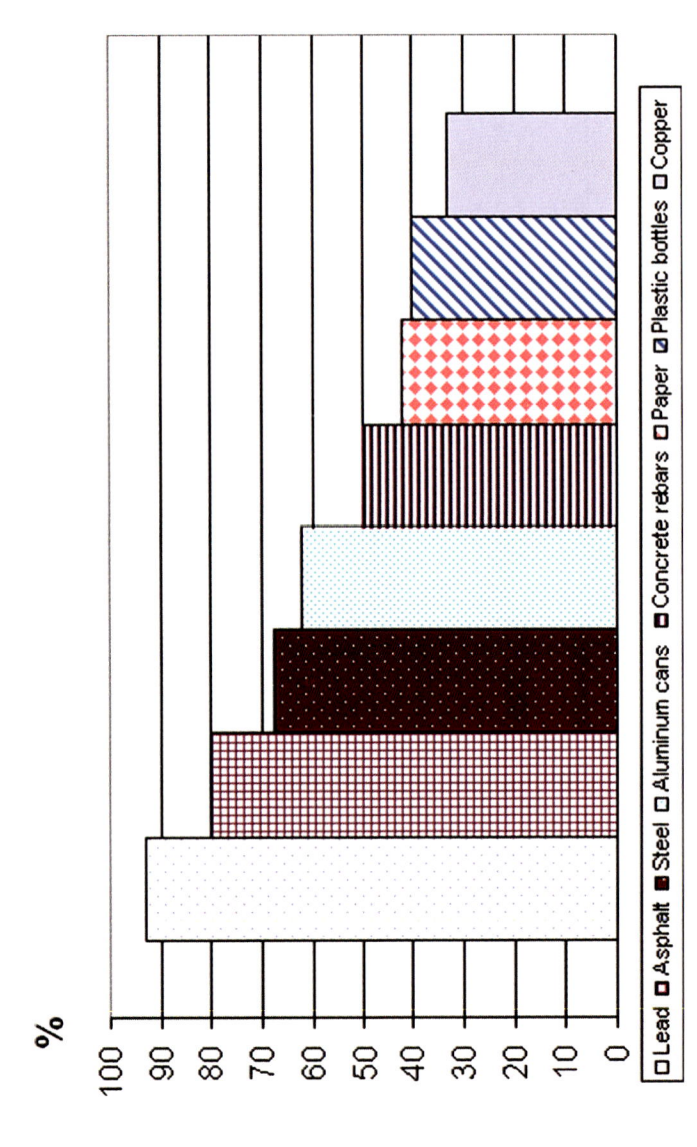

Figure 3 Current U.S. recycling rates of various materials. Sources are lead (70), asphalt (65), steel (66), aluminum cans (72), steel reinforcing bars in concrete (66), paper (67), plastic bottles (69), and scrap consumption of total copper consumed (71).

TABLE 6 Potential uses for recycled construction materials (50)

Material	Potential uses
Wood	Reuse or shred for fuel, animal bedding, mulch, manufactured building products, compost
Bricks	Reuse or crush to make aggregate
Asphalt	New asphalt paving, or roadbed
Concrete	Crush to make base material for roads, foundations, fill; aggregate for asphalt or concrete
Drywall	Gypsum for soil amendment, drywall
Roofing	Asphalt shingles for asphalt paving, reuse clay tiles
Metal	Scrap metal feedstock
Plastic	Plastic lumber, highway barriers, traffic cones

practices (e.g., virgin materials use) without embracing change and new technologies. Secondary construction material markets are mainly internal to a company (waste material from one construction site can be reused or recycled at another) or local (e.g., intercompany trades of asphalt concrete for pavements) (55). Regional markets are few, and the viability of a national secondary construction materials market is very limited owing to high transportation and storage costs despite the appearance of some waste construction materials at the Chicago Board of Trade in the late 1990s (56).

The majority of C&D waste is landfilled, although reuse and recycling have been gaining ground. In 1996, 20% to 30% of building-related C&D waste was estimated to have been recycled in the United States (53). Nonbuilding-related recycling could be higher. In fact, secondary asphalt and concrete amounts, each with about 100 million Mg annually, outweigh all other materials in recycling, even steel (Figure 2, see color insert). As much as 80% of waste asphalt is recycled (Figure 3, see color insert), two thirds into road base, one third into new hot-mix asphalt (6). Construction steel has high recycling rates; approximately 95% of structural beams and plates and 47.5% of reinforcing bars and miscellaneous steel were recycled in 2000 (57), but steel recycling is only about 67% throughout the economy. The 100 million Mg of waste concrete is still a small fraction ($<5\%$) of the total annual demand for more than 2 billion Mg of aggregates in the United States (Table 2). About 66% of secondary concrete is used in road base, 3% in high-value riprap, 7% in low-value products such as general fill, and 7% in other applications (6). Only one seventh is recycled into high-value applications, such as new concrete mixes (6%) and hot-mix asphalt (9%).

Old-growth wood structural members are typically removed by hand and reused. For example, salvaged redwood timber from demolished buildings has a high resale value not the least because long timber beams are very rare nowadays and, if available, very expensive.

Rather than being simply stockpiled or landfilled, the use of industrial by-products in construction has been increasing. Coal combustion products (fly ash, bottom ash, boiler slag, flue gas desulfurization material), blast furnace slag, foundry sand, glass cullet, and crumb rubber have become viable substitutes for natural aggregates. Coal fly ash can currently replace up to 50% of the cement in cement concrete and asphalt concrete. In fact, in a not unusual case, all cement concrete purchased from the largest concrete plant in San Francisco contains at least some coal fly ash.

As with other materials in the economy, reuse and recycling of construction materials have been driven by economic benefits. An articulated obstacle to more recycling has been industry-wide reluctance to accept the uneven quality of recycled aggregates (6), and rather than in high-value products, such as road wearing course and structural concrete, recycled aggregates mostly end up as road base material, replacing natural aggregates. However, as recycling becomes more ubiquitous, the use of recycled materials is expected to increase.

Infrastructure materials also hold the potential for reduced energy and other inputs and lower environmental emission and waste rates relative to the extraction, processing, manufacturing, and transportation of virgin resources. However, despite its importance, the literature on such quantitative assessments is limited.

CONCLUSIONS AND FUTURE RESEARCH

Because of their size, economic strength, and profound societal importance, construction activities and processes are among the largest consumers of materials and energy and significant polluters on the global scale. For these reasons, more attention should be devoted to understanding, researching, and ultimately reducing their environmental impacts.

It is important to observe that the construction industry has a broader definition and encompasses more than just the contractors and employees that build facilities. The industry is organized as a large tree of suppliers with many branches of builders, materials and equipment companies, and other professionals that contribute to every life-cycle stage of the infrastructure. Therefore, a comprehensive assessment should encompass the entire supply chain. For example, creating environmentally less damaging asphalt concrete for pavements may not start at the asphalt plant, but at the aggregate mines, mine equipment manufacturers, petroleum refineries, and asphalt paver manufacturers.

The literature on environmental impacts of infrastructure is still limited. Most attention has been devoted to the use-phase energy consumption of residential, commercial, and industrial buildings, especially in heating, ventilation, air conditioning, and lighting. Although future research should continue with the study of the use phase and energy issues, it should also focus more on the other life-cycle stages of the infrastructure that have received limited attention but are just as important. A larger number of quantitative studies are needed on the materials and processes related to roads, railroads, airports, bridges, dams, ports, off-shore platforms, telecommunications facilities and lines (e.g., fiber-optic cables), and utilities (water, sewer, natural gas, and oil pipelines; water and wastewater treatment plants; power plants; and power lines). In order to fully assess the impacts of the built environment, environmental analysis must extend to the other lifecycle stages: raw materials extraction and processing, materials manufacturing, maintenance, and end-of-life options (reuse, recycling, landfilling). Material and energy inputs are important in all of these stages, but so are less-studied processes, such as the equipment and labor demand for construction activities. In particular, processes related to construction and life-long maintenance need to be assessed. For buildings, this includes excavation/earthwork; cast-in-place concrete; steel and concrete structural work; fire protection; wood and steel framing; roofing; installation and maintenance of mechanical, electrical, and plumbing systems and of heating-ventilation-air conditioning systems; interior finishes; flooring; roofing; exterior walls; and landscaping. Many other processes are needed to start and operate other parts of the infrastructure, for example, road and bridge construction and maintenance. Too little has been published on end-of-life treatment of infrastructure, such as deconstruction and demolition, and the options related to the outputs of this phase, as well as the economical, environmentally preferable, and technically feasible reuse and recycling of infrastructure materials.

A number of other important questions worthy of further study emerge.

- What are the materials flows and uses of all construction materials in the United States and worldwide? Research on material cycles is appearing in print [e.g., (58)]. Although there are data (at least in the United States) on crushed rock, gravel, sand, cement, cement concrete, asphalt concrete, timber products, clay brick, drywall, roofing materials, and steel, the construction uses of aluminum, other metals, plastics, paper, paints, glues, numerous chemical products, and additional items need to be mapped, especially on a regional level. The list is much longer if regionally or locally used materials are also included (e.g., bamboo). It is impossible to measure and characterize the environmental burdens of construction materials when data about the volumes are nonexistent. What are the magnitudes of uses and cycles of renewable and nonrenewable construction materials around the world?

- How much resource consumption is associated with construction when the supply chains are analyzed? What is the demand for nonconstruction materials and services when construction materials and services are purchased? Through its extensive supply chains, the construction industry induces the consumption of numerous other major commodities and hundreds of other materials. What does the supply chain of each construction material contain? How stable are these supply chains over time, and how do they change with varying economic and technological conditions? How much water does construction use? What is the water demand of the built environment in the United States, in the industrialized countries, and the world?

- How much emissions and wastes are associated with construction materials and processes in all life-cycle phases? Research has traditionally focused on materials and energy use (in weight and energy units), and emissions inventories have typically reported greenhouse gases, particulate matter, and a few criteria pollutants and toxic chemicals. More comprehensive emission inventories are needed that include all criteria pollutants and toxic substances from the entire supply chain. Waste generation rates in materials manufacturing, on-site construction, transportation, maintenance, and end-of-life treatment need to be calculated in order to devise effective reduction programs. There is a need to quantify the environmental, economic, and engineering effects of reuse and recycling of construction materials. Is it environmentally beneficial to recycle old concrete into new applications? Is it feasible to reuse "post first-use" steel bridge girders in another building project locally and regionally? Is it environmentally and economically beneficial to ship them overseas if there is demand for them? Can construction (and other industrial) wastes be recycled economically and beneficially for the environment?

- What are the environmental impacts of construction materials? All too often studies report emissions of a few pollutants and look for "vector dominance." If one material has uniformly higher emissions than its alternative, it is labeled environmentally unfriendly. Just as in environmental analysis in general, inventory analysis of construction materials and processes has to be followed by impact analysis that accounts for the fate and transport of pollutants in the environment. Barring eliminating all emissions and wastes, what are the sustainable emission and waste rates and levels in a particular geographical region in the short, medium, and long-term period? As is likely for many construction materials, supply chains extend through the entire national economy (e.g., natural aggregates for concrete might come from local quarries, but coal combustion products might be shipped from afar) or even to foreign industries (e.g., steel bridge components needed in the United States may be manufactured in Japan). How can the environmental impacts of entire supply chains be reduced?

- How do the environmental effects of construction products vary from one geographic region to another? For example, the energy efficiency of basic construction materials production varies worldwide, e.g., by 50% for cement and 30% for iron and steel (59). Emissions may vary regionally and locally as well because of different input energy mixes and technologies, stricter environmental regulations, and other reasons. Therefore, it is important that the environmental impacts of construction materials production be analyzed using data on appropriate geographical levels in order to avoid incorrect generalizations.

- What are the environmental impacts of the construction materials under development? Amid a clear deficit in knowledge about the environmental implications of currently used construction materials, new materials, in particular composites, are emerging. For example, the engineering, the economic, as well as the environmental burdens of fiber-reinforced polymer (60) and engineered cementitious composites (61) ought to be studied, and the findings relayed to the public and private stakeholders. Can these new materials be recycled environmentally, economically, and technologically feasibly?

- How long does infrastructure last? The answer to this question is crucial in designing and planning for a service life that may be different from the design life (intended at the time of planning) (62, 63) and in normalizing environmental emissions by the planning horizon of a facility. Functional obsolescence of facilities (when they no longer serve their users satisfactorily) dictates that they should be either designed for shorter life spans or for continuous maintenance and periodic, complete renovations that extend their useful life. Some facilities may be overdesigned given their actual service life. It is commonly assumed that parts of the built environment last for a long time. This is true for much of the infrastructure that is perpetually maintained and periodically renovated or reconstructed (e.g., roads, railways), but it is not necessarily true for all facilities. For example, bridges are often demolished and replaced because traffic volumes outgrow them and thus render them functionally obsolete (e.g., the Clark Bridge at Alton, Illinois, on the Mississippi River and the Woodrow Wilson Bridge on the Capital Beltway around Washington, D.C.). Seismically unsafe buildings have been replaced after just a few decades of service life, much sooner than planners intended. There are examples of office buildings (from the 1950s through the 1970s) that are completely stripped down to the bare structure to be rebuilt to today's functional expectations and safety, seismic, or technological standards. Airport passenger terminals are demolished to give space to larger buildings. Statistics on the expected service life of buildings, bridges, dams, and other parts of infrastructure are needed for better engineering, economic, and environmental planning. The availability of such fundamental data is currently limited.

- How will shorter service life spans and increased need for reconstruction and renovation affect the environmental performance of the construction industry? Already there is anecdotal evidence that parts of the infrastructure live a shorter service life than intended, and this trend is expected to continue. How will this affect the supply of construction materials and energy? Will reuse and recycling become more economically and environmentally feasible or even necessary because of local shortages of materials and energy? Will prohibitively expensive landfill tipping fees force construction to divert materials into recycling and reuse? Can this be done such that it is environmentally and technologically beneficial? But even if recycling rates increase, how will it be possible to keep recycling the same materials repeatedly when the need for traditional materials may diminish in order to give space to new, composite materials? Can materials be recycled in perpetuity (i.e., how many cycles will they last before they cannot be used any more)?

- What are societal trends of importance to the built environment, and what challenges do they pose for environmental performance? As societal trends change, they affect the infrastructure. Automobility created sprawling cities and suburban shopping malls. Increased globalization and mobility is steadily leading to more international travel and tourism. The construction industry has served these changing trends faithfully. It will be valuable to understand what the predictable trends hold for this industry, which is already a large strain on natural resources. For example, in the industrialized world, a shift in share of construction activities from new construction to maintenance and renovation (e.g., for roads and power plants) is emerging. What are the corresponding environmental effects?

- How can reuse and recycling of construction materials be assured feasible when it will become actual 30, 50, or 100 years from now? The generally long, but varying lifetimes of facilities pose a challenge for reuse and recycling of construction materials. What will be the engineering requirements and the economics of recycling then?

- What are the societal costs of construction materials? In addition to comprehensive and supply chain–oriented life-cycle assessment of all construction materials and corresponding processes, valuation of environmental emissions and impacts (e.g., on human health and the built environment) (64) and other externalities (e.g., private costs of road closures and congestion due to construction) is important. Construction needs to be compared with the rest of societal activities through an assessment of full social costs.

- How to communicate results about the environmental impacts of construction materials to stakeholders? The construction industry, through its supply chains and customers, has a myriad stakeholders scattered around the nation and the world. They do not necessarily communicate with each other regularly or at all, and they demand various ways of communication. How can these stakeholders be educated about the environmental impacts of materials, equipment, and processes, and how can they be convinced to start implementing changes identified through life-cycle assessments that would result in decreased environmental loadings? What methods, tools, and practices will facility owners, architects, engineers, construction contractors, customers, and other stakeholders need to start demanding the use of environmentally less damaging construction materials, processes and activities?

With growing population, especially in urban areas worldwide, ever-increasing and changing societal requirements, and continuously growing and shifting demand for infrastructural services, there is a definite need for better environmental quality through a more sustainable development of infrastructure systems.

ACKNOWLEDGMENT

The author wishes to acknowledge the financial support of the Faculty Early Career Development (CAREER) Program from the National Science Foundation's Division of Civil and Mechanical Systems.

The *Annual Review of Environment and Resources* is online at
http://environ.annualreviews.org

LITERATURE CITED

1. Graedel TE, Allenby BR. 2003. *Industrial Ecology*. Upper Saddle River, NJ: Prentice Hall. 2nd ed.
2. US Census Bur. 1997. *1997 economic census, construction*. http://www.census.gov/epcd/www/97EC23.HTM
3. US Census Bur. 2002. *Statistical abstract of the United States 2002*. Washington, DC. http://www.census.gov/prod/2004pubs/03statab/roster.pdf
4. US Central Intell. Agency. 2003. *The World Factbook 2003*. Washington, DC: CIA
5. Carnegie Mellon Univ. Green Design Initiat. 2004. *Economic input-output life cycle assessment*. http://www.eiolca.net
6. US Dep. Inter. US Geol. Surv. 2000. Recycled aggregates–profitable resource conservation. *Fact Sheet FS-181-99*, Feb., Reston, VA
7. Ewell ME. 2001. Mining and quarrying trends. In *Minerals Yearbook*, Vol. I. *Metals and Minerals*. Reston, VA: US Geol. Surv. http://minerals.usgs.gov/minerals/pubs/myb.html
8. Kelly T, Buckingham D, DiFrancesco C, Porter K, Goonan T, et al. 2003. Historical statistics for mineral and material commodities in the United States. *Open-File Rep. 01-006*, US Geol. Surv. Reston, VA
9. US Dep. Commer. 2003. Value of product shipments: 2001. *Annual Survey of Manufactures, Rep. M01(AS)-2*, US Dep. Commer, Washington, DC
10. Junnila S, Horvath A. 2003. Life-cycle environmental effects of an office building. *J. Infrastruct. Sys.* 9(4):157–66
11. Suzuki M, Oka T, Okada K. 1995. The estimation of energy consumption and CO_2 emission due to housing construction in Japan. *Energy Build.* 22:165–69
12. Gaubatz P. 1999. China's urban transformation: patterns and processes of morphological change in Beijing, Shanghai and Guangzhou. *Urban Stud.* 36:1495–521
13. Yuemin N. 1998. City planning and urban construction in the Shanghai metropolitan area. In *The Dragon's Head: Shanghai, China's Emerging Megacity*, ed. HD Foster, DC Lai, N Zhou, pp. 229–45. Victoria, BC: West. Geogr.
14. Decker EH, Elliott S, Smith FA, Blake DR, Rowland FS. 2000. Energy and material flow through the urban ecosystem. *Annu. Rev. Energy Environ.* 25:685–740
15. Augenbroe G, Pearce AR, Kibert CJ. 1998. Sustainable construction in the United States of America, a perspective to the year 2010. *CIB-W82 Rep.*, Georgia Inst. Technol., Atlanta, GA
16. Bevington R, Rosenfeld, AH. 1990. Energy for buildings and homes. *Sci. Am.* Sept., pp. 77–86
17. US EPA. 1994. Green Lights: Third Annual Report. *(6202J), EPA 430-R-94-005*, Off. Air Radiat.,Washington, DC
18. Vanegas JA. 2003. Road map and principles for built environment sustainability. *Environ. Sci. Technol.* 37(23):5363–72
19. Kibert CJ, Sendzimir J, Guy GB. 2002. *Construction Ecology: Nature as the Basis for Green Buildings*. London, UK: Spon
20. Forman RTT, Sperling D, Bissonette JA,

Clevenger AP, Cutshall CD, et al. eds. 2003. *Road Ecology*. Washington, DC: Island
21. US Green Build. Counc. 2003. *LEED—Leadership in energy & environmental design*. http://www.usgbc.org/LEED/LEED_main.asp
22. Borg RF, Gambatese J, Haines K Jr, Hendrickson CT, Hinze J, et al. 2003. Rebuilding the World Trade Center. *Pract. Period. Struct. Design Constr.* 8(3):137–45
23. Hendrickson CT, Horvath A. 2000. Resource use and environmental emissions of U.S. construction sectors. *J. Constr. Eng. Manag.* 126(1):38–44
24. Wilson A. 1993. Cement and concrete: environmental considerations. *Environ. Build. News* 2(2):7–12
25. Worrell E, Price L, Martin N, Hendriks C, Ozawa Meida L. 2001. Carbon dioxide emissions from the global cement industry. *Annu. Rev. Energy Environ.* 26:303–29
26. Fisk WJ. 2000. Health and productivity gains from better indoor environments and their relationship with building energy efficiency. *Annu. Rev. Energy Environ.* 25:537–66
27. Int. Organ. Stand. 1997. Environmental Management—Life Cycle Assessment—Principles and Framework. *Rep. ISO 14040*, Geneva, Switz.
28. Curran MA, ed. 1996. *Environmental Life-Cycle Assessment*. New York: McGraw-Hill
29. Suh S, Lenzen M, Treloar GJ, Hondo H, Horvath A, et al. 2004. System boundary selection in life-cycle inventories. *Environ. Sci. Technol.* 38(3):657–64
30. Hendrickson CT, Horvath A, Joshi S, Lave LB. 1998. Economic input-output models for environmental life-cycle assessment. *Environ. Sci. Technol.* 32(4):A184–91
31. Build. Environ. Econ. Sustain. (BEES). 2000. *Technical Manual and User's Guide*. Gaithersburg, MD: Natl. Inst. Stand. Technol.
32. Keoleian GA, Blanchard S, Reppe P. 2000. Life-cycle energy, costs, and strategies for improving a single-family house. *J. Ind. Ecol.* 4(2):135–56
33. Ochoa L, Hendrickson C, Matthews HS. 2002. Economic input-output life-cycle assessment of U.S. residential buildings. *J. Infrastruct. Sys.* 8(4):132–38
34. Kelly T. 1998. Crushed cement concrete substitution for construction aggregates—a materials flow analysis. *Circ. 1177*, US Geol. Surv., Reston, VA
35. US Dep. Transp. 2000. Highway Statistics. *Rep. 1980–2000*, FHWA, Off. Highw. Inf. Manag., Washington, DC
36. US EPA. 1999. *National Emission Standards for Hazardous Air Pollutants for Source Categories; Portland Cement Manufacturing Industry; Final Rule*, 40 CFR Part 63 (June 14)
37. van Oss HG, Padovani AC. 2003. Cement manufacture and the environment. Part II: Environmental challenges and opportunities. *J. Ind. Ecol.* 7(1):93–126
38. van Oss HG, Padovani AC. 2002. Cement manufacture and the environment. Part I: Chemistry and technology. *J. Ind. Ecol.* 6(1):89–105
39. Horvath A, Hendrickson CT. 1998. A comparison of the environmental implications of asphalt and steel-reinforced concrete pavements. *Transp. Research Record* 1626:105–13
40. Demkin JA, ed. 1998. *Environmental Resource Guide: Concrete—Material Report*, New York, NY: Wiley
41. Cole RJ. 1999. Energy and greenhouse gas emissions associated with the construction of alternative structural systems. *Build. Environ.* 34:335–48
42. Jönsson A, Bjorklund T, Tillman A-M. 1998. LCA of concrete and steel building frames. *Int. J. Life-Cycle Assess.* 3(4):216–24
43. Guggemos A, Horvath A. 2004. Comparison of environmental effects of steel and concrete framed buildings. *J. Infrastruct. Syst.* In press
44. Herz R, Lipkow A. 2002. Life cycle

assessment of water mains and sewers. *Water Sci. Technol.: Water Supply.* 2(4):51–58
45. Friedrich E. 2002. Life-cycle assessment as an environmental management tool in the production of potable water. *Water Sci. Technol.* 46(Part 9):29–36
46. Horvath A, Hendrickson CT. 1998. Steel vs. steel-reinforced concrete bridges: environmental assessment. *J. Infrastruct. Syst.* 4(3):111–117
47. Pacca S, Horvath A. 2002. Greenhouse gas emissions from building and operating electric power plants. *Environ. Sci. Technol.* 36:3194–200
48. Junnila S, Horvath A, Guggemos A. 2004. Life-cycle assessment of office buildings in Europe and the U.S. *J. Infrastruct. Syst.* In press
49. Graedel TE, Klee RJ. 2002. Getting serious about sustainability. *Environ. Sci. Technol.* 36(4):523–29
50. Guggemos A, Horvath A. 2003. Strategies of extended producer responsibility for buildings. *J. Infrastruct. Syst.* 9(2):65–74
51. Bossink BAG, Brouwers HJH. 1996. Construction waste: quantification and source evaluation. *J. Constr. Eng. Manag.* 122(1):55–60
52. Calif. Integr. Waste Manag. Board (CIWMB). 2002. *Construction and demolition debris recycling.* http://www.ciwmb.ca.gov/condemo/default.htm
53. Franklin Assoc. 1998. Characterization of building-related construction and demolition debris in the United States. *Rep. EPA530-R-98-010*, US EPA, Washington, DC
54. Seo S, Hwang, Y. 1999. An estimation of construction and demolition debris in Seoul, Korea: waste amount, type and estimating model. *J. Air Waste Manag. Assoc.* 49(8):980–85
55. Hendrickson CT, Horvath A, Lave LB, McMichael FC. 1996. New markets for old materials. *TR News* 184:32–35
56. Lave LB, Horvath A. 1997. The market for recyclables: prospects and problems. *Proc. Market Tools Green Goals Conf.*, ed. P Alonzi P, RF Kosobud, DS Atallah, pp. 75–93. Chicago, IL: Board Trade City Chic.
57. Steel Recycl. Inst. 2002. *Fact sheet.* http://www.recycle-steel.org/index2.html
58. Graedel TE, Bertram M, Kapur A, Reck B, Spatari S. 2004. Exploratory data analysis of the multilevel anthropogenic copper cycle. *Environ. Sci. Technol.* 38(4):1253–61
59. Metz B, Ogunlade D, Swart R, Pan J. 2001. *Climate Change 2001: Mitigation,* ed. Intergov. Panel Clim. Change Work. Group III. Cambridge, UK: Cambridge Univ. Press
60. Ehlen MA. 1997. Life-cycle costs of fiber-reinforced-polymer bridge decks. *J. Mater. Civil Eng.* 11(3):224–30
61. Li VC. 1998. Engineered cementitious composites—tailored composites through micromechanical modeling. In *Fiber Reinforced Concrete: Present and the Future,* ed. N Banthia, A Bentur, A Mufti, pp. 64–97. Montreal, Can.: Can. Soc. Civil Eng.
62. Marland G, Weinberg AM. 1988. Longevity of infrastructure. In *Cities and Their Vital Systems,* ed. JH Ausubel, R Herman. Washington, DC: Natl. Acad.
63. Lemer AC. 1996. Infrastructure obsolescence and design service life. *J. Infrastruct. Syst.* 2(4):153–61
64. Matthews HS, Lave LB. 2000. Applications of environmental valuation for determining externality costs. *Environ. Sci. Technol.* 34(8):1390–95
65. Wilburn DR, Goonan TG. 1998. Aggregates from natural and recycled sources—economic assessment for construction applications—a material flow analysis. *US Geol. Surv. Circ. 1176,* US Dep. Inter. US Geol. Surv., Reston, VA
66. Anonymous. 2002. Steel recycling rate remains high. *Recycl. Today,* Apr. 12. Accessed Jan. 12, 2004. http://www.recyclingtoday.com/news/news.asp?ID=2163
67. US EPA, Off. Solid Waste. 2002. *Recycling.* http://www.epa.gov/epaoswer/nonhw/muncpl/recycle.htm
68. Alum. Assoc. 2002. *Recycling.* http://www.

aluminum.org/Content/NavigationMenu/The_Industry/Recycling/Recycling.htm
69. Am. Plastics Council. 2002. *Plastics resource.com*. http://www.plasticsresource.com/recycling/recycling_rate_study/index.html
70. *E-Wire*. 2002. *Lead-acid batteries top list of recycled products*. Accessed Jan. 12, 2004. http://www.ewire-news.com/wires/3AF08D65-49A2-48B5-A61D930D0D456C01.htm
71. Copper Dev. Assoc. 2002. Copper at a crossroads. *Recycl. Today*, Apr. 16
72. Anonymous. 2002. UBC recycling rate hits 55.4 percent. *Recycl. Today*, Apr. 27

CONTESTED TERRAIN: Mining and the Environment

Gavin Bridge

*Department of Geography, Syracuse University, Syracuse,
New York 13214; email: gbridge@maxwell.syr.edu*

Key Words mining, natural resources, environment, development, sustainability

■ **Abstract** This review critically surveys an extensive literature on mining, development, and environment. It identifies a significant broadening over time in the scope of the environment question as it relates to mining, from concerns about landscape aesthetics and pollution to ecosystem health, sustainable development, and indigenous rights. A typology compares and contrasts four distinctive approaches to this question: (*a*) technology and management-centered accounts, defining the issue in terms of environmental performance; (*b*) public policy studies on the design of effective institutions for capturing benefits and allocating costs of resource development; (*c*) structural political economy, highlighting themes of external control, resource rights, and environmental justice; and (*d*) cultural studies, which illustrate how mining exemplifies many of society's anxieties about the social and environmental effects of industrialization and globalization. Each approach is examined in detail.

CONTENTS

CONTESTED TERRAIN: THE NEW REALITY OF MINERAL DEVELOPMENT	206
ENVIRONMENT: AN INCREASINGLY INCLUSIVE FIELD	208
Earth Moving: Mining as Physical Landscape Modification	209
The Big Sink: Mining Wastes as Pollution	210
Ecosystems: Mining as a Driver of Regional and Global Environmental Change	214
Community: Mining and the Social Environment	216
CLEANER PRODUCTION: ENGINEERING AND MANAGEMENT APPROACHES TO MINING AND ENVIRONMENT	217
Eco-Efficiency and Environmental Performance	218
Innovation for Pollution Prevention	221
New Drivers of Environmental Performance	222
SUSTAINABLE DEVELOPMENT: PUBLIC POLICIES FOR HARNESSING MINERAL WEALTH AND PREVENTING POLLUTION	225
Development: Minerals and the Resource Curse	225

1543-5938/04/1121-0205$14.00

Environment: Internalizing Externalities 230
Sustainable Development 233
DEPENDENCY, RIGHTS, AND JUSTICE: POLITICAL ECOLOGIES
OF EXTRACTION 234
Extraction, Governance, and the State 236
Land Rights, Resistance, and Environmental Justice 238
THE MINING IMAGINARY: THE CULTURAL POLITICS OF
EXTRACTION 240
The Underground 242
Modern Alchemy: Mining as Transformation 243
SUMMARY 245

CONTESTED TERRAIN: THE NEW REALITY OF MINERAL DEVELOPMENT

From diamonds to phosphates and alabaster to zinc, a stunning array of commodities is wrested from the earth. By convention these materials are divided into *metals* (e.g., copper, gold, bauxite, iron, nickel), *fuel minerals* (e.g., oil shale, coal, uranium), *industrial minerals* (e.g., phosphates, salt, gypsum), and *construction materials* (e.g., stone, sand, gravel). Exploration, mining, and mineral processing describe the steps by which these materials are located, extracted, and refined. Stretching from mine to market, this production chain binds mineral-rich regions into a network of market exchange that can drive changes in local land values and transform existing land uses. As a consequence of its transformative capacities, mining raises questions about where and how resources will be accessed, mineral revenues distributed, and processing wastes disposed.

Environmental effects from mining and mineral processing "have been experienced, complained about and—at least temporally—solved for at least seven centuries" (1). It was not until the mid-1980s, however, that the environment emerged as a core strategic issue for the mining industry. Over the past two decades, the mining industry "has come under tremendous pressure to improve its social, developmental and environmental performance" (2). It is now widely held that the industry is at an historic juncture and faces a "new reality of mineral development," the contours of which are becoming increasingly clear (3). The three most prominent indicators of this new reality are (*a*) that full legal compliance with state environmental regulations is a necessary but increasingly insufficient means of satisfying society's expectations on environmental issues. This erosion of legal compliance as a guarantor of a mining firm's ability (if not its right) to access resources, or deposit wastes in the environment, is frequently described in terms of the need for a social license to operate. Thus, (*b*) a range of nontraditional, nonstate institutions—from financial institutions to environmental organizations and human-rights groups—increasingly intrude on areas of decision making that were once considered the preserve of mine management. As a result, (*c*) the canvas of environmental issues is now very broad, and it extends significantly beyond conventional questions of technology choice or management practice to include the preservation of cultural integrity and the development of sustainable, postmining land uses.[1]

This review sorts through the complex relationships surrounding resource development and the environment by distinguishing between four different analytical approaches used to explain the links between mining and environmental change. It identifies critical differences in the way mining's environmental problem is defined, the causal mechanisms invoked to explain the environmental impacts of mining, and the different solutions that follow from these analyses. Following this introduction, the second section discusses the meaning of environment in the context of mineral extraction. It argues that environment has become a progressively more inclusive term over the past 20 years and distinguishes four successive waves of environmental concern related to mining. The third section discusses a literature on the environmental performance of mining firms and the opportunities for adopting cleaner production techniques. This body of work explains differences in environmental performance among large mining firms by reference to a firm's capacity for technological innovation and improved environmental management. The fourth section addresses a large policy-oriented literature on the opportunities and challenges of mineral-based economic development, and it discusses major shifts in environmental policies toward mining. It highlights specific issues associated with the informal mining sector and with operationalizing the concept of sustainable development for nonrenewable resources.

The fifth section addresses research that explores the relationships between mining, development, and the environment using the theories and methods of structural political economy. This literature on the political ecologies of extraction emphasizes the institutional obstacles to achieving environmental protection in an industry characterized by frontier-type environments and high degrees of external control, and much of this literature adopts indigenous rights and social and environmental justice as a framework to explain contemporary political struggles over natural resource development. The sixth section examines a literature that occupies the borders between cultural studies, anthropology, and the history of science. Focusing on the popular imaginaries of mining, the principal insight of this work is its indication of how debates over mining and the environment can be understood as a displacement onto mineral extraction of a much broader set of anxieties about the scale of human intervention in the environment, the social and ecological costs of globalization, and the capacity of communities for self-determination. The final section presents a summary of the four perspectives and discusses their implications for understanding current conflicts over mineral development.

---

[1] A number of recent institutional initiatives are indicative of this juncture, including the Global Mining Initiative (GMI), the Mining, Minerals and Sustainable Development Project (MMSD) to which the GMI gave rise, the Extractive Industries Transparency Initiative of the U.K. government, and the World Bank's Extractive Industries Review (EIR).

ENVIRONMENT: AN INCREASINGLY INCLUSIVE FIELD

Societies have wrestled with the issue of whether—and if so, how—rights should be granted to miners for access to land or for the release of wastes to air and water for hundreds of years (4). The venerable tradition of contesting the environmental impacts of mining is illustrated in Agricola's oft-cited claim—based on his meticulous observations of mining in sixteenth century Saxony—that the primary argument against mining was its effects on forests, rivers, and wildlife:

> ...the strongest argument of the detractors is that the fields are devastated by mining operations.... Also they argue that the woods and the groves are cut down, for there is need of an endless amount of wood for timbers, machines and smelting of metals. And when the woods and groves are felled, then are exterminated the beasts and birds.... Further when the ores are worked, the water which has been used poisons the brooks and streams, and either destroys the fish or drives them away.... Thus, it is said, it is clear to all that there is greater detriment from mining than the value of the metals which mining produces (5).

For much of the nineteenth and twentieth centuries, the environmental depredations identified (and subsequently dismissed) by Agricola have been little more than marginalia in the scholarly literature. Mining's ability to secure sufficient availability of nonrenewable resources, however, has been a central problematic in classical political economy from Ricardo to Malthus, Smith, and Marx. For much of the past 200 years, the critical environmental question concerning mining has not been the effect of mineral production on the environment but the ability of the environment (defined as a storehouse of resources) to provision the economy. Publication of the Club of Rome Report on *The Limits to Growth* (6, 7) pushed this long-standing intellectual joust into popular consciousness, fueling a public debate during the 1970s that pitted physical, thermodynamic definitions of resource scarcity (as measured, for example by the crustal abundance of various elements) against economic, price-based definitions of scarcity in which the market—rather than nature—was the arbiter of whether a mineral was scarce or abundant. The falling price of many basic commodities on world markets during the 1980s and 1990s significantly dampened this debate, although questions of resource supply have resurfaced in the last few years in the context of work on the availability of global oil supplies (8). Thus, it is only in the past two decades or so that mining's environmental problem has come to be understood chiefly in terms of its effects on the receiving environment. There is now widespread recognition of how mining and mineral processing have historically relied upon the capacity of the environment for dispersing and assimilating wastes and the extent to which these capacities have become overwhelmed by the massive expansion of mineral production during the twentieth century.

Earth Moving: Mining as Physical Landscape Modification

Common to all extractive activities is the need to move earth. A frequent entry point for considering the environmental impacts of mining, therefore, is to consider the physical landscape modifications that occur in the process of extracting and refining valued materials from the earth. Research on mining as a form of landscape modification is characterized by two contrasting approaches. On the one hand are quantitative, material-flow studies that calculate the volume, weight, and rate of earth movements associated with mineral extraction and urbanization at local, regional, and global scales (9). These seek to account for the hidden flows associated with mining by including both the mass (or volume) attributable to the target mineral and that associated with the overburden and waste that must be moved in the course of mining (10). Douglas & Lawson (10) estimate that mining and quarrying worldwide move over 57 billion tons per year, a figure that rivals natural, geomorphological processes of earthmoving: Material moved by water erosion each year is estimated at 53 billion tons (11). Industrial countries dominate material flows on a per capita basis (for example, per capita production of sand and gravel in the United States is 7.8 tons; in China 4.2 tons; and in India 0.39 tons), although developing economies (and China in particular) have seen rapid and substantial growth in their material use (10).

On the other hand are qualitative, site-specific histories of former mining districts (12, 13). Undertaken by historians, industrial archaeologists, or cultural geographers, these studies typically address the ways in which mining, milling, and smelting rework local topography; alter drainage systems, land use, and vegetation patterns; and introduce both new structures and new meanings to the landscape. Much of this literature follows the standard format of local history—it is organized chronologically and is resolutely parochial in its focus. Yet a few accounts explicitly address the connection between local landscape change and broader-scale economic processes (14, 15). Schwantes (16), for example, adopts the concept of landscape as an organizing principle in a history of the Phelps Dodge Corporation. He shows how the physical and working environment was transformed at the company's mines in Arizona over a 150-year period through the application of scale economies and the introduction of new concentrating and smelting techniques. Morse (17) makes explicit the links between local landscape change and economic and political processes operating over broader spatial scales in her environmental history of the Yukon gold rush. She locates the placer miners of the Klondike and Yukon Valleys at the center of a network of trade, supply, and financial relations that radiated out to San Francisco, the agricultural heartlands of the Great Plains, and Washington, D.C., at the end of the nineteenth century.

The range of landscape modifications introduced by mining includes pits, waste piles, built structures (headframes, stacks, aqueducts, tramways) and secondary (i.e., downstream) geomorphological features, such as debris fans, sand bars, and turbid rivers. Frequently described as "visual intrusions," the interpretation of these landscape features as "unsightly or even repellent" (18) is far from universal.

Robertson (19) documents how residents of mining communities in Oklahoma, Illinois, and Colorado have invested waste piles from lead, zinc, and coal mining with meaning as enduring markers of personal and community identity. Ethnographic research reveals both the symbolic attachments that residents of mining communities often form with the mined landscape, and the tensions that can arise between historic preservationists seeking to maintain evidence of earlier mining and those concerned with the protection of public safety or exposure to legal liability.

The Big Sink: Mining Wastes as Pollution

The landscape perspective treats the environment as an integrated, physical unit but is unspecific about the range of geophysical and geochemical processes by which mining and minerals processing introduce wastes into the environment. An approach focused on pollution places the mineral processing flow sheet at the center of the analysis and seeks to quantify releases to the environment from each of the controlled chemical interactions that occur during mineral processing and to identify the extent to which mining accelerates naturally occurring geochemical and hydrological processes. Although stone, sand, and gravel top the list of earthmoving endeavors, the complex geochemistry of metal ores and the use of reagents for mineral processing mean that the pollution effects of metal mining can be much more severe than those associated with the extraction of construction materials.

Analyses of metal-mining wastes typically distinguish between physical pollution and chemical pollution (20). Physical pollution results from the ingress of particulates into the atmosphere (as dust and aerosols), into water, or onto land. Although lacking the aura of toxicity that accompanies chemical pollutants (such as mercury, arsenic, or cyanide), suspended solids, dusts, and solid wastes have historically been the primary focus of objections to mining and continue to be a significant form of pollution (20). Figure 1 schematically reviews the range of wastes from metal mining. It disaggregates the mine-to-metal process into exploration, extraction, and beneficiation stages; identifies emissions from each stage; and indicates how these releases to the environment can become hazardous to health.[2]

Waste outputs vary from mine to mine as a function of the range of mineral substances extracted from the earth and the diversity of environments in which extraction takes place. The salient characteristic of metal mining, however, is that mineral processing is a *segregative process* by which a relatively small amount of a valued substance is isolated from a much larger mass of less valuable material. Segregating the valued component occurs through a series of steps, each producing a separate waste stream. Figure 2 illustrates the mineral-to-waste ratios for 12 commodities that account for the largest total material flows worldwide: Over 99.5% of the material mined to produce copper, for example, is rejected as

---

[2]Figure 1 suggests that there are no impacts from exploration. This is not the case: A major point of contention over the last few years has been the effects of oil, gas, and metal mine exploration activity on relatively undisturbed lands.

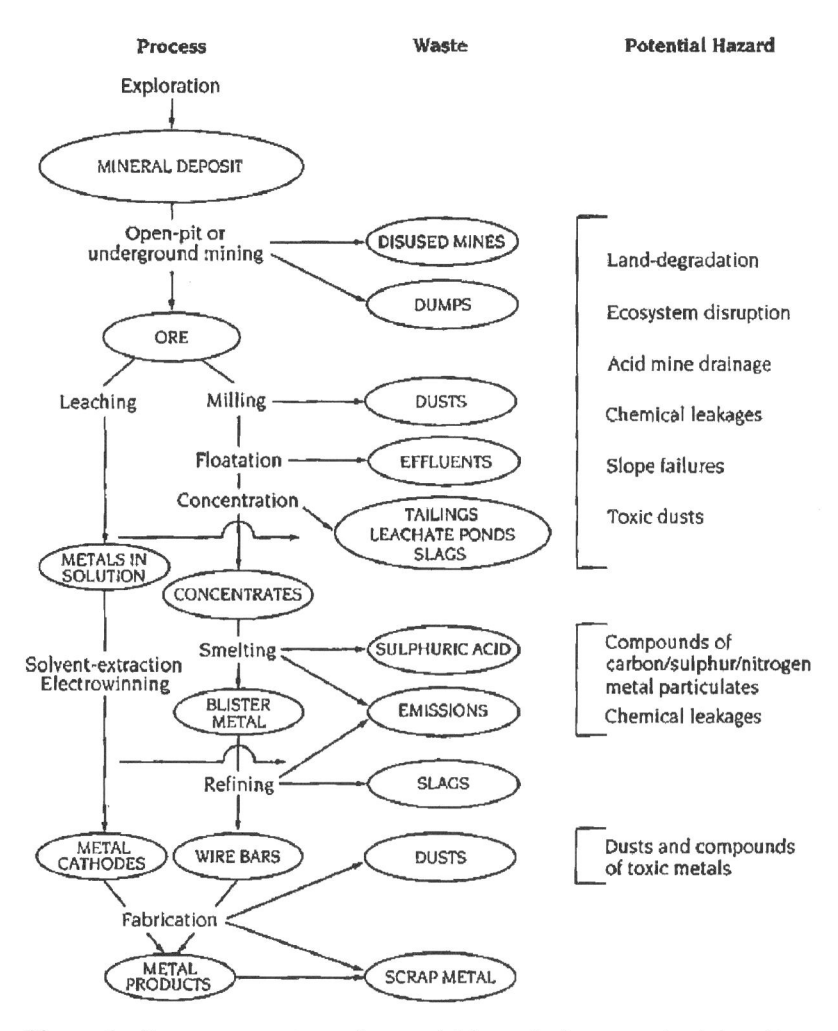

Figure 1 Processes, wastes and potential hazards from metal mining. From Reference 21.

waste during processing. The average Canadian metal mine rejects 42% of the mined material immediately as waste rock, a further 52% from the mill as tailings, and an additional 4% from the smelter as slag: The remaining 2% comprises the values for which ore is mined (22). The challenge of waste disposal is not restricted to metal mines. The extraction and processing of phosphates, for example, requires separating phosphate from a matrix of sand and clay: Clay wastes (known as slimes) constitute over half the total plant waste and require large settling ponds for disposal (18). In many cases there are no markets for mineral wastes (or the low value/high weight ratio of many waste by-products imposes restrictive transportation costs) and so low-cost disposal options have to be found. Waste disposal

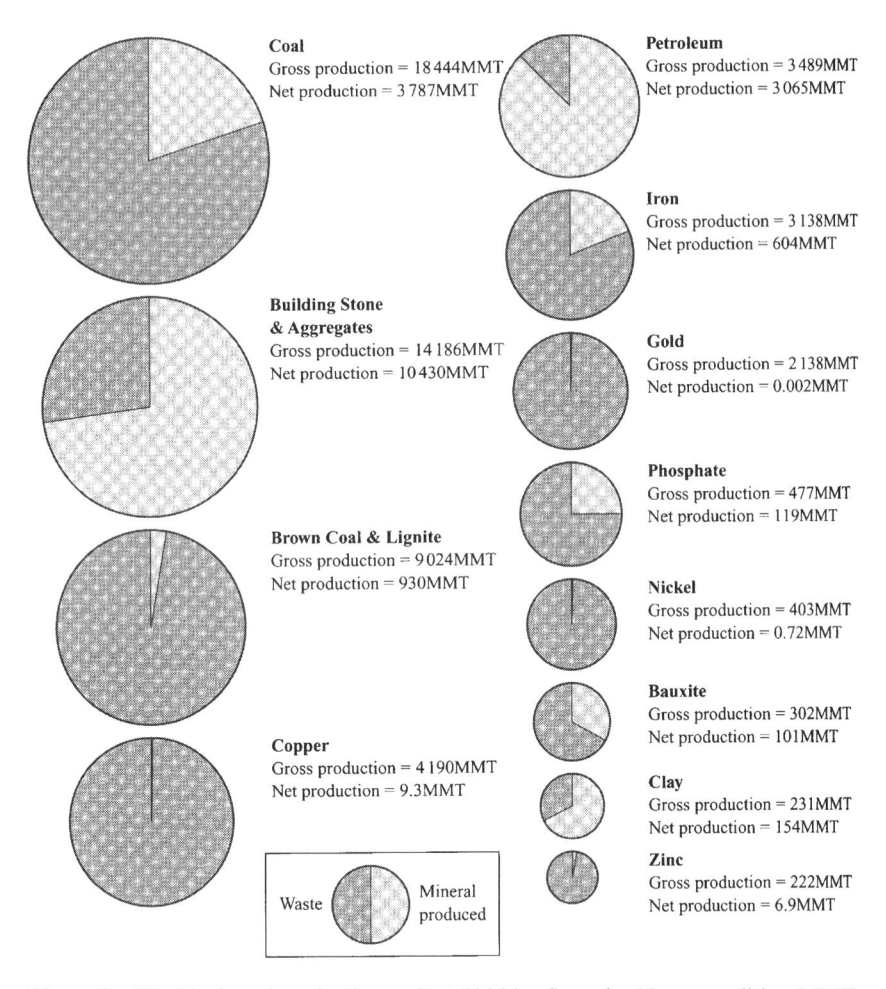

Figure 2 World mineral production and total hidden flows for 12 commodities. MMT, million metric tonnes. From Reference 10.

is now a defining problem for the mining industry. In some jurisdictions, large-scale mineral producers are chafing against regulatory limits on waste disposal established decades ago.[3] In addition, the industry meets increasingly stiff public opposition around the world to standard waste disposal practices (such as tailings

---

[3]For example, a 1997 ruling by the solicitor of the Department of the Interior on the mill-site claim provision of the U.S. General Mining Law (which determines the amount of land that can be claimed for mineral processing, including waste storage, versus the amount of land that can be claimed for mining) effectively blocked development of the Crown Jewel Mine in Washington state (23). The ruling was subsequently overturned by the U.S. Congress.

ponds or submarine tailings disposal) and faces so-called legacy-effects, i.e., the current costs of managing historic waste disposal practices.

Waste volume is frequently only part of the problem as waste streams are often chemically reactive. Overburden and waste rock may be the most significant waste streams by weight, but they are not necessarily the most contaminating because the concentration of contaminants in waste typically increases with the degree of processing. Studies of waste streams from copper processing in the Clark Fork River basin of Montana, for example, demonstrate how arsenic concentrations increase from 1070 ppm for heap-roasting slags to 2960 ppm in mill tailings and 10,400 ppm in smelter residues (for comparison, background arsenic concentrations are 10 ppm) (24). These studies (24) point to tailings ponds as one of the primary contamination sources associated with metal extraction because the concentration of potential pollutants, such as arsenic, cadmium, copper, lead, and zinc, is significantly higher in tailings than in waste rock. The failure of over 30 tailings dams in the last 12 years—including failure at mines operated by firms acknowledged as leaders in best-practice environmental management—has "created a serious image problem for the global mining industry, particularly for international mining companies operating in developing countries" (25). Among the most significant failures were (*a*) the Omai Mine in Guyana (1995) in which 4.2 million cubic meters of cyanide slurry were released into the Essequibo River; (*b*) El Porco in Bolivia (1996) where 400,000 tons of tailings were deposited up to 300 km downstream in the Pilocomayo River; and (*c*) the failure at the Los Frailes mine in Spain (1998) where 6.8 cubic meters were released, covering thousands of hectares of farmland and part of the internationally protected Doñana wetlands (26, 27). Incidents like these have generated technical assessments and policy discussions regarding the specific challenges of tailings dams (28).

Chemical pollution can occur via two basic routes: (*a*) release to the environment of reagents added during mineral processing and (*b*) oxidation of naturally occurring minerals in the ore as a result of exposure to air. In the former category are chemicals used in mineral processing (e.g., sulfuric acid for the leaching of copper oxides and mercury or cyanide for the extraction of gold) that may be added to ores under controlled conditions but which can escape into the environment if not adequately managed. In the latter category, the primary challenge arises from sulfide deposits. Many metal ores (nickel, copper, and lead, for example) occur as sulfides, and in the presence of oxygen and water, these oxidize to form sulfuric acid. The oxidation of sulfide ores can generate acid rock drainage (ARD) if it is not effectively managed. ARD is "arguably the most serious environmental problem facing the mining industry" (23) and the industry's "largest environmental liability" (29). The pollutant effects of ARD have been recognized for a long time: Studies of fish populations in former mining regions in England and Wales during the 1930s demonstrated the negative impacts of acid drainage on aquatic life (30). It was not until the 1980s, however, that the chemical and biological processes of sulfide oxidation that generate ARD were really understood. It is now recognized, for example, that ARD formation is autocatalytic because the ferrous iron produced via sulfide oxidation is itself then oxidized to ferric iron and becomes the dominant oxidizing agent for exposed sulfides. The generation of ARD is very hard to stop once started (31). Research has also delineated how the oxidation of sulfides is catalyzed by the presence of bacteria (notably *Thiobacillus ferrooxidans*), which obtain their energy by oxidizing ferrous iron, thiosulfate, sulfur, and metallic sulfides and which can increase the rate of oxidation by as much as a factor of one million (32, 33). Because ARD takes other metals into solution if it is not neutralized, mine drainage is frequently accompanied by high metal loadings [typical contaminants include aluminum, arsenic, cadmium, copper, mercury, lead, and zinc]. The U.S. Forest Service estimates that between 5000 and 10,000 miles of streams in the United States are subject to ARD, and the U.S. Environmental Protection Agency states that mining has contaminated headwater reaches of more than 40% of the watersheds in the western states (34).

Pollution, then, provides the primary lens through which mining's environmental impacts have been viewed in the recent past (35–41). In the early 1990s, however, the debate over mining's environmental consequences began to shift. As Ripley et al. (22) note, an approach to pollution that focused on "counting fish kills and examining the composition of grasses" was increasingly recognized as insufficient. Researchers began to focus on the transport, behavior, and fate of pollutants in the environment and to identify nonlinearities and irreversibilities in environmental responses to mining pollution. Increasingly, then, the analytical framework of the production flow sheet has been supplemented by the ecosystem, a significantly broader unit of analysis.

Ecosystems: Mining as a Driver of Regional and Global Environmental Change

A central tenet of research on the environmental impacts of mining until recently has been that because mines occupy a relatively small land area (when compared, for example, to other land uses like forestry or agriculture), the effects of mining on the environment will be localized. Mining occupies considerably less than 1% of the world's terrestrial land surface. Estimates for the United States—a country with an extensive mining history—indicate that mineral extraction occupies only 0.25% of the land area (and only 0.025% for metal mining) in comparison with 3% for urban areas and 70% for agriculture (42). The influential progenitor of American environmentalism, George Perkins Marsh (43), largely dismissed the impacts of mining because they "must always be too inconsiderable in extent to deserve notice in a geographical point of view." A growing body of research in environmental science has challenged this view of discrete, localized impacts (22, 44). Adopting an ecosystem perspective, this work addresses the ways in which wastes interact with ecological processes in the receiving environment and the implications of these interactions for ecosystem function and ecosystem health. In contrast to studies of mining pollution emerging from engineering, the ecosystem perspective broadens the definition of impact beyond the boundaries of the industrial process or the mine itself to consider the way mining modifies ecological processes operating over broad geographical scales. This perspective informs work in three areas: (*a*) the effects of air and water emissions and solid wastes on the biological productivity of receiving ecosystems [e.g., the effect of mine tailings on rates of primary productivity or the availability of spawning sites in aquatic ecosystems (22)]; (*b*) the contribution of mining to biogeochemical processes that are regional or global in scope (e.g., the effects of coal combustion or energy use in mining on the global carbon cycle, the contribution of smelting to the sulfur cycle, or the impact of mining and smelting on the global flux of trace metals, such as copper, arsenic, and mercury); and (*c*) the role of mining in driving regional land-cover conversion, habitat fragmentation, and associated effects on biodiversity.

The ecological approach is exemplified in Moore & Luoma's (24) study of the transport and redistribution of copper mining wastes in Montana by fluvial processes. They identify a complex catena of chemical, biological, and hydrological interactions as wastes become part of the ecosystem into which they are deposited, producing different contamination effects along a river's profile. Wastes initially deposited close to the mine are subsequently transported away from the site via hydrologic and atmospheric processes, generating secondary and tertiary contamination in rivers, groundwater, soils, and air. This can occur across large areas: Moore & Luoma identify contamination at 10 times the background levels nearly 400 km downstream from the primary site of waste disposal. Other studies highlight how ecosystem processes can alter the chemical composition of potential contaminants. Work on the speciation of mercury, for example, demonstrates how water temperature and turbidity play a critical role in determining the chemical form that mercury takes in the environment and, therefore, its bioavailability (45).

Since the 1980s, research has explored the extent to which emissions from mining and smelting modify global biogeochemical cycles, the natural and anthropogenically driven flows of minerals between mineral stocks stored in the lithosphere, atmosphere, hydrosphere, and biosphere. Mining and smelting modify the global biogeochemical cycle of minerals, such as sulfur, copper, and mercury, by mobilizing materials locked up in the lithosphere so that "sooner or later, traces of all the 'new' metals that are mined will be dissipated to the biosphere" (46). A series of papers by Nriagu (47, 48) shows that anthropogenic fluxes of lead, cadmium, vanadium, and zinc exceed natural fluxes 28-, 6-, 3-, and 3-fold, respectively, whereas anthropogenic fluxes of arsenic, copper, mercury, nickel and antimony are between 100% and 200% of natural fluxes. Thus, "cumulative industrial releases of heavy metals into our environment are...massive and pervasive and have overwhelmed the natural biogeochemical cycles of metals in many ecosystems" (48). Mining and smelting are the primary contributors to the anthropogenic releases for most metals, accounting for 67%, 65%, and 55% of the anthropogenic emissions of copper, arsenic, and zinc, respectively.

Geographical shifts in the location of mining investment (see Dependency, Rights, and Justice section, below) have intensified long-standing concerns about the impact of mining on global biodiversity and critical ecosystems. An increasing proportion of mineral exploration and investment expenditures during the 1990s targeted the tropical Andes, the Guiana Shield, Indonesia, Papua New Guinea, the Philippines and, to a lesser extent, tropical west Africa (49–51).[4] Because tropical regions have significantly higher measures of biological diversity than temperate latitudes, much current investment is taking place in areas that are ecologically sensitive and/or have high conservation values. The World Resources Institute finds, for example, that at the global scale 75% of active mines and exploration areas overlap with areas of high conservation value and areas of watershed stress, that over 25% of active mines and exploration sites overlap with or are within a 10-km radius of a strictly protected area, and that nearly one third of all active mines and exploration sites are located within intact ecosystems of high conservation value (26).

Community: Mining and the Social Environment

The conditions of the mine working environment have long been a source of socio-political struggle. In 1842, the Royal Commission Report into coal mining practices in England, for example, provided a harrowing account of the physical effects of underground mine work on women, men, and children, leading to the passage of laws banning women and boys under the age of 10 from employment in mines. Over time, however, the definition of social impact has broadened from issues of worker safety (a dominant theme in Europe and the United States in both the nineteenth and twentieth centuries) and occupational health (which emerged to prominence in the period following the Second World War) to questions of community stability, cultural integrity, and indigenous rights. Occupational health and safety issues—such as the risk of coal mine explosions or premature death from respirable dusts in underground mines—remain a core concern, however, particularly in developing and transition economies. A boom in small-scale gold mining operations that began in the 1980s in South America (53, 54), Africa (55), and Asia (56)—operations that use mercury for recovering gold—has drawn attention to the way mining can expose small-scale miners, mining communities, and communities downstream to heavy metals. Ogola et al. (57), for example, found that concentrations of mercury, lead, and arsenic in river sediments exceeded acceptable levels at gold mining operations in Kenya. Their study demonstrates, however, how mercury is seldom the only occupational hazard: In addition to careless handling of mercury during panning and amalgamation, primary health hazards for gold miners in Kenya include inhaling large amounts of siliceous dust, the malarial risks of waterlogged pits and trenches, and limited ventilation in underground mines. Recent studies point to HIV/AIDS as a leading mining hazard, particularly in South Africa where the combination of widespread poverty and the system of migrant mine labor that developed under apartheid established social

---

[4]Warhurst & Franklin (52) note that of 17 megadiversity countries identified by Conservation International, 8 appear on a list of emerging markets compiled by the Mining Journal.

conditions conducive to the rapid transmission of sexually-transmitted diseases (58). The World Bank (59) estimates 20% of coal miners and 30% of gold miners in South Africa are HIV positive (prevalency rates 17% higher than in the base population), and productivity losses from the disease are estimated around 20%.

The predominant approach to understanding the social issues surrounding mining, then, has been to focus on how the physical processes of mining effect human bodies and collectivities, whether it be the physical hazards of explosions and rockfalls, the risk of contracting black lung disease,[5] or exposure to mercury poisoning. Over the past decade, however, communities affected by mining (and some mine-worker organizations) have increasingly expressed their concerns as issues of social and environmental justice, the preservation of cultural integrity and/or indigenous rights, and the ability to participate in decisions about mineral development from a position of prior informed consent. A core component of the new reality of mineral development is that many communities now reject technical and managerial definitions of mineral extraction as a politically neutral process of economic development, producing social and environmental side effects that can be mitigated. Mining communities and influential nongovernmental organizations are instead choosing to frame the debate over mining and the environment as a fundamentally political process of negotiation (and contestation), involving decision making about the ownership and exercise of rights (to land and water), the criteria and processes for valuing land, and the legal rights of the state vis-à-vis the moral rights of local peoples.

CLEANER PRODUCTION: ENGINEERING AND MANAGEMENT APPROACHES TO MINING AND ENVIRONMENT

A distinctive approach to understanding the relationship between mining and the environment emerged during the 1990s. It diagnosed emissions and wastes from mining as symptoms of production inefficiency and traced this inefficiency to underinvestment in technology, lack of capital, or insufficient acquisition of technical and/or managerial skills. The implications of differential production efficiency—between state and private firms, for example—are a long-standing concern of development economics. Its application to understanding the environmental impacts of mining during the 1990s, however, reflected a growing enthusiasm for the ideas of Porter (61) as a means of framing the challenge of environmental

---

[5]Belated recognition of the extent of so-called black lung disease among U.S. coal miners—a general category that includes coal workers' pneumoconiosis and silicosis caused by prolonged inhalation of dusts—played a role in passage of the 1969 Federal Coal Mine Health and Safety Act (60).

management.[6] Porter argues against the prevailing wisdom that economic and environmental objectives constitute an intractable trade-off. Rather than a zero-sum game in which economic growth (jobs) is only possible at the expense of the environment, Porter proposed a win-win hypothesis in which firms could be both clean and competitive by improving resource productivity (64). These ideas gained analytical weight from a growing body of research on the manufacturing sector that indicated how reengineering production processes to prevent pollution could be more cost-effective than adopting "end-of-pipe" technologies that control potential emissions (65, 66). Application of concepts of eco-efficiency and pollution prevention to mining was first systematically developed by Warhurst (67) [with the Mining and Environment Research Network (63)], who undertook a series of comparative studies of the environmental performance of mining firms in a range of economic and political contexts [see also (68)]. The objective of these studies was to understand why some firms adopted technologies and/or management practices that reduced emissions (or set new standards for environmental performance at greenfield operations), and to explain differences between good and bad performers on the basis of differential access to (and ability to mobilize) capital, technology, and skills. Firms demonstrating environmental best practices were then contextualized as vanguards of a new environmental paradigm.

Eco-Efficiency and Environmental Performance

A simple observation marks the point of departure for much of the research on cleaner mineral production: Standards of environmental performance vary widely among mining firms, even among firms within the same regulatory jurisdiction. This is a provocative observation because it suggests that factors internal to the firm may be more significant than government regulation in determining the effect of mineral extraction on the environment. Warhurst and colleagues (63), for example, found that "environmental degradation tends to be greatest in low-productivity operations with obsolete technology, limited capital, inefficient energy use and poor human resource management" and that "the environmental performance of a mining enterprise is more closely related to its innovative capacity than to the regulatory regime under which it operates." Because the factors influencing environmental performance vary from firm to firm, different firms can be expected to illustrate varied capacities for responding to regulatory and market pressures.

---

[6]This approach to the relationship between mining and environment rearticulates conventional modernization theories of development, which explain underdevelopment (in this case poor environmental performance) as a result of capital scarcity, insufficient investment, and lack of technology. Compare, for example, Bauer & Yamey (62) who argue that foreign investment introduces new technology to the periphery, supplements, or substitutes for local capital, driving growth, which then diffuses throughout the economy, with Warhurst (63) who argues that, under certain conditions, foreign mining investment in the developing world can upgrade obsolete mineral processing technology, introduce capacities for innovation, and, in the process, become a means to more sustainable forms of development.

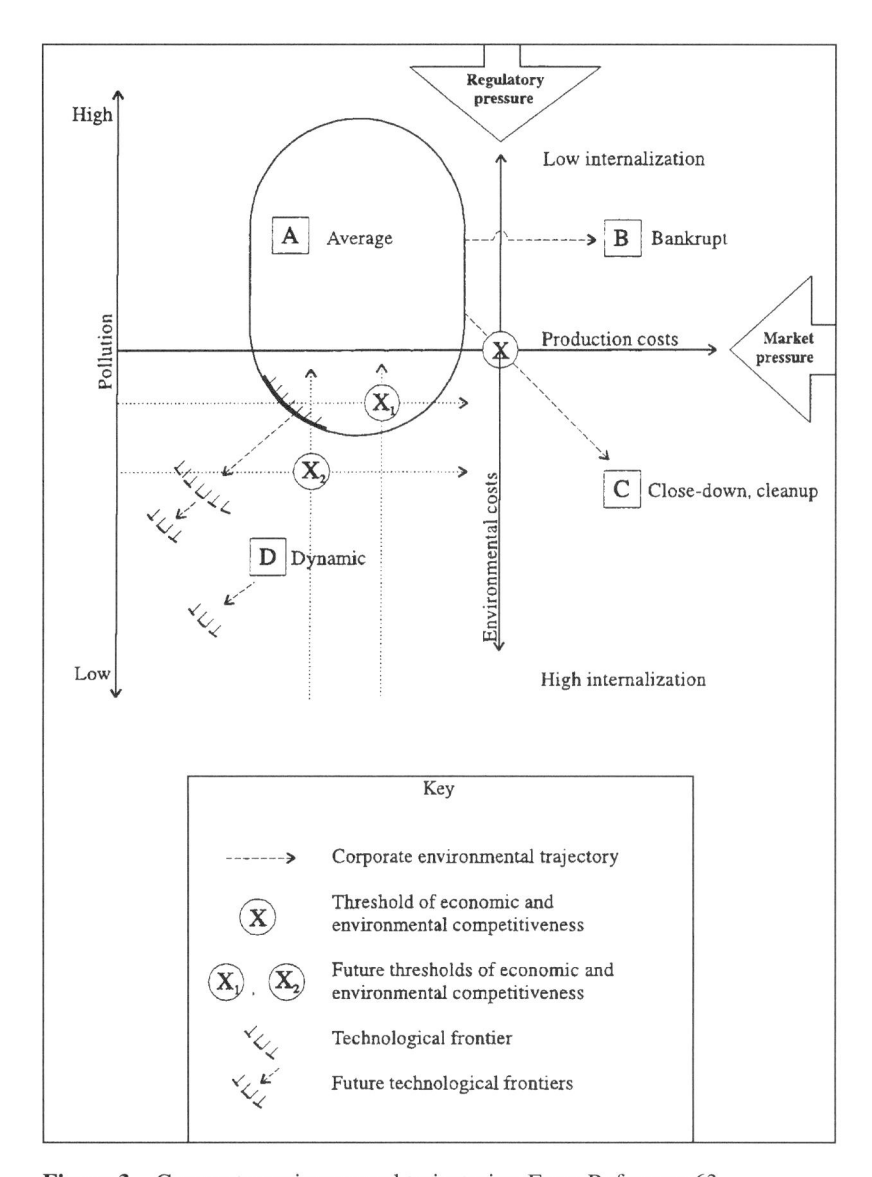

Figure 3 Corporate environmental trajectories. From Reference 63.

Warhurst outlines three environmental trajectories that schematically describe the range of possible responses to external pressures (Figure 3). Trajectories A → B and A → C increase the costs of production beyond a competitive threshold and lead to closure. Trajectory A → D indicates a response that reduces both production costs for the firm and the impact of the firm's operations on the environment. Innovation is central to this trajectory because, unlike Trajectory A → C, pollution is reduced without using add-on, end-of-pipe controls that increase costs to the firm. Warhurst characterizes firms moving toward D as dynamic because of their ability to respond in ways that deliver benefits to both the firm and to society at large. Although Figure 3 is a useful schematic, it provides an incomplete picture of the full range of strategic responses available to the firm. Regulatory pressures, for example, are seldom exogenous forces beyond the reach of corporate strategy and are often a target of corporate efforts to improve or preserve operational flexibility.

The argument that a firm's environmental performance is positively related to its competitive position is intriguing because it suggests that the globalization of mineral investment—and in particular, investment by multinational mining firms in the developing world—may be able to deliver environmental and developmental benefits to society. Privatization and the adoption of policies to attract foreign mining investment, for example, provide a vehicle for improving the competitive and environmental performance of former state-run mines, with track records of poor production efficiency and obsolete technology. Investments by acknowledged best-practice firms at greenfield sites in the developing world are also a potential mechanism for transferring critical capacities for technological innovation and environmental management (69). Although broadly sympathetic to these arguments, several studies describe the obstacles to diffusion and adoption of cleaner process techniques and propose policy mechanisms by which they may be overcome. Hilson (70), for example, considers the legislative, technological, and economic barriers that prevent implementation of cleaner technologies and practices. Questionnaire data from North America indicate a substantial difference in the application of these techniques between large mining houses and the smaller, junior mining firms: Whereas most gold mines operated by the large mining companies have implemented state-of-the-art measures, operations owned by the juniors lag far behind (71). Recommendations range from legislative reform to remove disincentives for investment, adjusting fiscal policy to provide credits for environmental innovation, development of closer partnerships with government and academia, and an intensification of research on specific technologies, such as biological oxidation, that hold the greatest promise for cleaner mineral production (71). Collectively, these studies provide conditional support for the main argument in this literature: The industry is evolving, albeit often slowly and unevenly, toward cleaner production techniques.

More recent contributions question the extent to which concepts (eco-efficiency and pollution prevention) developed in the manufacturing and service sectors are applicable to mining. This discussion revolves around two issues. First, the environmental impacts of mineral extraction can be reduced but not eliminated: Process inputs (water, energy, and reagents) can be reduced; waste management improved; and mining sites rehabilitated—yet the extraction of minerals necessarily modifies the environment to some degree (72). Pollution prevention—understood as the elimination of pollution at the source by not producing pollution in the first place—does not take account of this essentially extractive component. Second, operationalizing eco-efficiency in the mining sector is complicated by the fact that mining (unlike manufacturing) is a segregative process that necessarily produces large volumes of waste (see above). The decline in average metal ore grades over time means that the volume of wastes produced in relation to metal product is increasing rather than decreasing, i.e., it is moving in the opposite direction from that advocated by proponents of eco-efficiency. These differences between mining and manufacturing mean that "complications can arise if industrial environmental management terminology is interpreted (for the mining sector) in an excessively cavalier manner" (72).

Innovation for Pollution Prevention

Technological innovation is central to the eco-efficiency argument because it provides the means by which firms can combine savings in production costs with environmental improvements. Accordingly, there is now a substantial literature on environmentally significant innovation in the mining and mineral-processing industry (73, 74). The range of technological approaches include more efficient production techniques, redesigning process flow sheets to produce waste streams that are easier to manage (by, for example, reducing the dispersion of toxins or producing wastes in forms that are more chemically and physically stable), state-of-the-art management systems, new approaches to metals recovery from wastes (such as smelter slags and tailings), and evolving techniques for environmental remediation and rehabilitation (71).

The most storied successes of environmental innovation concern the redesign of metal smelting techniques (74). Smelter emissions were the first environmental issue to affect the mining industry in a systematic and sustained way. During the 1970s, SO_2 emissions from metal smelters were identified as a principal contributor to acid rain in Europe and North America. Increased regulation of atmospheric emissions, together with rising energy prices, spurred research interest in smelting technologies for sulfidic ores that could reduce energy consumption and that would enable the cost-effective capture of sulfur dioxide. Flash smelting technologies—which reduce fuel demand by utilizing the exothermic properties of sulfide ores and which produce a concentrated off-gas stream facilitating sulfur dioxide capture and its fixation as commercially marketable sulfuric acid—are frequently discussed as paradigmatic examples of innovation for pollution prevention. Warhurst & Bridge (69) and Hilson (72), for example, describe the development and commercialization of flash smelting technology by the Canadian company INCO and by Outokumpu from Finland. Until the mid-1990s, INCO's operation of an aged and obsolete reverberatory smelter at Sudbury, Ontario, made it the greatest single source of SO_2 emissions in North America with a peak output in 1965 of 2,500,000 tons of SO_2. Having reached the limits of efficiency improvement with this smelter design and unable to meet increasingly stringent air quality regulations, INCO invested in research and development that produced an oxygen flash smelter. This not only reduced smelter emissions by over 100,000 tons per year but also helped transform INCO into one of the world's lowest-cost nickel producers. Similarly, the technology collaboration between Outokumpu and Kennecott in the development of flash smelting and flash converting technology at Garfield, Utah, is often regarded as a best-practice case: Improving sulfur capture from 93% to 99.9%, the project set a new benchmark for smelter performance worldwide and was expected to reduce operating costs for the company by over 50%.

In addition to driving smelter innovation, the ratcheting of air quality regulations has also spurred a search for alternatives to pyrometallurgical techniques of metal recovery over the past two decades. The technical literature on extractive metallurgy attests to an evolving interest in the development of hydrometallurgy—the use of leaching processes to recover metals—for the treatment of sulfidic ores and concentrates. Unlike smelting, hydrometallurgical processing produces no gaseous emissions, and sulfur is either oxidized to water-soluble sulfate or to the inert, readily storable form of elemental sulfur (75). Hydrometallurgical techniques, therefore, have been proposed as a cleaner processing route for some metals, principally because they avoid the traditionally dirty smelting phase. A major area of innovation within the past two decades has been bacterially assisted mineral leaching. Known collectively as biohydrometallurgy, these processes harness the ability of a group of bacteria (the obligate chemolithoautotrophs) to oxidize insoluble inorganic sulfides of ferric iron (the same process that produces ARD). Several new bioleaching techniques were developed to the commercial scale during the 1990s for extracting gold, copper, and nickel from sulfide ores and concentrates, and biohydrometallurgy is often identified as a leading-edge approach for cleaner metal production (69, 76). Significant challenges remain, however, in managing and monitoring the impacts of hydrometallurgical processes on surface- and groundwater.

Most studies of cleaner mineral production focus on the downstream phases of mineral processing (an implicit acknowledgment of the challenge the upstream, extractive phase poses for pollution prevention). A few studies, however, take the road less traveled and track the possibilities for cleaner production back up the production chain to the mine itself. These address the opportunities for preventing pollution by changing mine design to reduce the formation of acid mine drainage, improve the economics of backfilling, or reduce the mine's overall ecological footprint. Krauss (77), for example, reports the experience of Homestake's McLaughlin mine in northern California, which, by many measures, provides a showcase of best-practice environmental management. Central to the environmental success of McLaughlin was a mine plan that included detailed assessments of the acid-generating potential of the ore body; a selective mining method to divide wastes into those that were acid generating and those that were not, facilitating waste handling and storage; and the siting and design of waste impoundments, improving the effectiveness of storm water management.

New Drivers of Environmental Performance

If the opportunities for process innovation are the primary evidence used to substantiate the win-win claims of cleaner production, then an important secondary argument is the emergence of new driving forces, which reward firms that achieve higher standards of environmental performance. The discussion of new drivers typically focuses on either nongovernmental organizations (NGOs), whose grassroots activity is often conceptualized as exerting an influence from below, or on providers of credit and insurance who, by virtue of the fact that they hold the purse strings of project financing, are considered to exert their influence from above. NGOs have not only proliferated in number and turned their attention to issues of resource extraction, but NGOs also are increasingly adept at accessing media outlets and organizing campaigns that influence the perception of mining among metropolitan audiences far removed from sites of extraction. *Cultural Survival Quarterly* (78) recently reviewed this rapid globalization of mining activism and concluded that "for better or worse anti-mining activism is a global social movement." NGOs are significant beyond metrics of their increase in number or geographical scope: They constitute a diversity of new actors that supplement—and sometimes supplant—the state's formal role in setting standards for environmental performance.

The emergence of a complex web of national and international environmental agreements has raised the stakes for banks and other institutions providing credit and insurance coverage to mining projects. These agreements provide important leverage for NGOs in their relations with mining companies and can change the perceived risk-reward ratio for investors. Thus the risk of expropriation by national governments may have declined, but the financial risk associated with land-use conflict and the social and environmental performance of mining projects has increased. Notable examples of institutional initiatives harnessed by NGOs in recent years include: international environmental designations, e.g., those of the UN Educational, Scientific, and Cultural Organization or the World Conservation Union; declarations concerning indigenous peoples, such as Convention 169 of the International Labor Organization; constitutional reforms that redefine the state as multiethnic and pluricultural and codify indigenous rights, such as those in Bolivia, Colombia, Ecuador, and Venezuela (79); and high-profile popular campaigns, such as the U.K.'s Extractive Industries Transparency Initiative. As a consequence, financial institutions began attaching new environmental conditions to their lending and insurance agreements with mining firms during the 1990s. The withdrawal of political risk insurance by the U.S. Overseas Private Investment Corporation from the Grasberg Mine in Irian Jaya at the end of 1995—citing tailings disposal plans that would negatively affect river and forest environments—provided an early indication of how insurers could reappraise their exposure to risks in the light of a company's environmental performance (80).

This process has intensified. In 2003, a group of major commercial banks established the Equator Principles, which describe a set of commitments and procedures for assessing the social and environmental risks of project financing. Pratt (81) illustrates how the increased sensitivity of financial institutions to environmental risk is, in part, a function of the ability of NGOs to leverage the relationship between a mining firm and its major creditors. The author describes how a small

U.S.-based NGO was able to change proposals for a mine haulage road through a national park (and international biosphere reserve) in the Peruvian Andes by engaging the creditors of the international consortium that was developing one of the world's largest copper mines. A recent survey of biodiversity reporting by oil, gas, and mining firms conducted by a U.K. asset management company (82) is indicative of the scrutiny now paid by investors to the environmental record of mining firms on account of the risk such records pose "for restricted access to land, biodiversity-related liabilities and reputational damage." The survey found a wide gap between best and worst performers and noted that some of the most economically significant companies ranked at the bottom of the list (82).

The principal contribution of the cleaner production literature is to illustrate how a firm's access to technology and capacity for environmental management determine the impact of mineral extraction on the environment. Acknowledgment of this internal differentiation and recognition of the technologically dynamic nature of what is often considered a mature industrial sector are something that other approaches to mining and the environment tend to overlook (discussed below). The cleaner production approach, however, is limited in its ability to explain the way mining affects the environment in at least three respects. First, the focus on reductions in environmental burden per unit of output via process reengineering illuminates only one of several possible mechanisms by which mining can drive environmental change. It illustrates very clearly what Frederickson (83) terms the technique effect, yet largely ignores environmental impacts due to expansion in the number and size of mining investments (the scale effect) and the concentration of environmental impacts that occurs when a national or regional economy specializes in extraction (the composition effect). Second, the argument for improving environmental performance via increased process efficiencies is, at base, an argument for better housekeeping. Although studies confirm the considerable scope for efficiency improvements (and their potential to deliver cost savings to firms and benefits to society), opportunities for good housekeeping are likely to face diminishing returns. There is no guarantee that the economic threshold that limits further investments in efficiency improvements—the point at which the marginal costs of investment are equal to the marginal benefits in terms of efficiency gains—equates to an adequate level of environmental protection. Third, and most significant, relatively few of the major challenges facing mining companies today are narrowly environmental in nature. Although environmental issues are frequently raised in opposition to mining projects, many contemporary conflicts over mineral development are not about environmental performance per se. There is an increasing divergence between a firm's ability to deliver high standards of environmental performance and its ability to overcome resistance and bring a project into production. The environment may still be "the single most important issue facing executives in every sector of the extractive industry," but today the environmental issue for mining is defined in significantly broader terms than those of environmental performance or cleaner production (84).

SUSTAINABLE DEVELOPMENT: PUBLIC POLICIES FOR HARNESSING MINERAL WEALTH AND PREVENTING POLLUTION

Resource extraction is a double-edged sword. It holds the promise of wealth sufficient to sever a society from the constraints of nature, but such liberation is only won through environmental and social change. Whether interpreted positively or negatively, the social, economic, and ecological effects of mining are nearly always described as a transformative process. These transformations are the target of public policies for allocating the costs of mineral extraction, capturing and distributing its potential gains, and determining the conditions under which extraction will take place. Public policy approaches to mining are traditionally framed by two concerns: (*a*) economic development and (*b*) environmental protection. Since the Earth Summit in 1992, a number of countries have adopted sustainable development as a framework for resource and environmental decision making, and as a result, these two areas of policy have increasingly fused into a third debate (*c*) over the policy mechanisms needed to make nonrenewable resource extraction more compatible with sustainability.

Development: Minerals and the Resource Curse

Mining has long been regarded as the starting point for a series of economic and social changes that constitute development. Proponents of mining as an agent of development point to the historical experience of countries, such as Australia, Canada, Sweden, and the United States, where mineral extraction and processing preceded industrialization. Policy makers in developing countries with significant resource endowments often describe foreign direct investment in the mineral sector as a key that will unlock the country's buried treasure (85) and set in motion a virtuous cycle of socioeconomic change. This treasure chest theory of resource-based economic development is widespread and gains its justification from a remarkably diverse array of intellectual traditions. These include (*a*) the theory of comparative advantage [countries with large natural resource endowments should specialize in extracting and exporting minerals and use the wealth generated to import other goods and services (86)]; (*b*) theories of resource-based industrialization via autarkic policies of import substitution [which seek to develop indigenous natural resources and downstream processing capacity as a way to reduce dependency on imports and provide the basis for domestic industrialization (87)]; (*c*) geopolitical theories about national security and state-led strategies of resource acquisition in order to stave off resource famines and ensure the availability of strategically significant minerals (88); and (*d*) growth pole theories that view mining investment as a form of pump priming to address uneven patterns of economic development.

The mobilization of mineral wealth may be a constant theme of development policy, yet the past 50 years have seen significant shifts in the policies promoted to achieve this objective. These shifts can be seen with particular clarity in the debate within development economics over whether large capital projects, such as mines, dams, and railroads, should be financed through foreign direct investment or by the domestic state (89). Classical modernization theory stresses foreign direct investment in the mineral sector as a means of generating foreign exchange earnings, enhancing state revenues, and upgrading professional and technical skills. The historical experience of colonial and neocolonial resource development, however, gave rise to a trenchant critique of this approach and led many countries during the 1960s to adopt policies of import substitution and state-led development as alternatives. The policy tools of import substitution include nationalization of mines and smelters, restrictions on equity participation by foreign corporations, incentives to undertake the value-added stages of refining and fabrication domestically in order to capture a greater share of mineral product value, and the formalization of small- and medium-scale mining as part of land-reform initiatives. As the development policy literature began to shift in the 1960s and 1970s from economic growth concerns to the fulfillment of basic needs, so the debate over the design of policy frameworks for mineral-based development also changed. Policies increasingly targeted technology transfer, capacity building, and the opportunities for mining to contribute to poverty reduction (90). The attention given to bottom-up initiatives of community-based development stemmed in part from recognition of how the socioeconomic benefits of mineral-based development (taxes, royalties, export earnings) typically accrue at one spatial scale (the national government), whereas many of the costs (social disruption, environmental impacts) fall locally. It also acknowledged that redistributive policy mechanisms within many mineral economies have been ineffective in addressing this scalar mismatch in the geographies of mining's costs and benefits.

Since the mid-1980s, the development policy pendulum has swung away from state-led approaches back toward the market. Over 90 countries have reformed their mining investment laws and mining codes in the past two decades and these policies are credited with attracting significant inflows of mining investment (69). A sizeable literature has developed around these mineral reforms and includes guides for mining code reform, assessments of international best practices, and critical accounts of the impact of mineral law reform on the social and geographical distribution of mining rights (91). Figure 4 illustrates the geographical distribution of capital expenditures in the nonferrous mining sector during the 1990s and demonstrates the significant gains experienced by South America (chiefly Chile and Peru) and by Southeast Asia (principally Indonesia and Papua New Guinea).

The standard measures used to evaluate the effectiveness of neoliberal economic development policy are its effect on macroeconomic indicators like gross domestic product, the value of foreign direct investment, or the trade balance. At the same time, however, a parallel literature looks beyond these macroeconomic indicators to examine how mining contributes to goals of poverty reduction, job creation, the empowerment of women, and community development. It is in this context that increased attention has been paid to the informal mining sector, which is estimated to provide employment for approximately 13 million people worldwide

MINING AND THE ENVIRONMENT   227

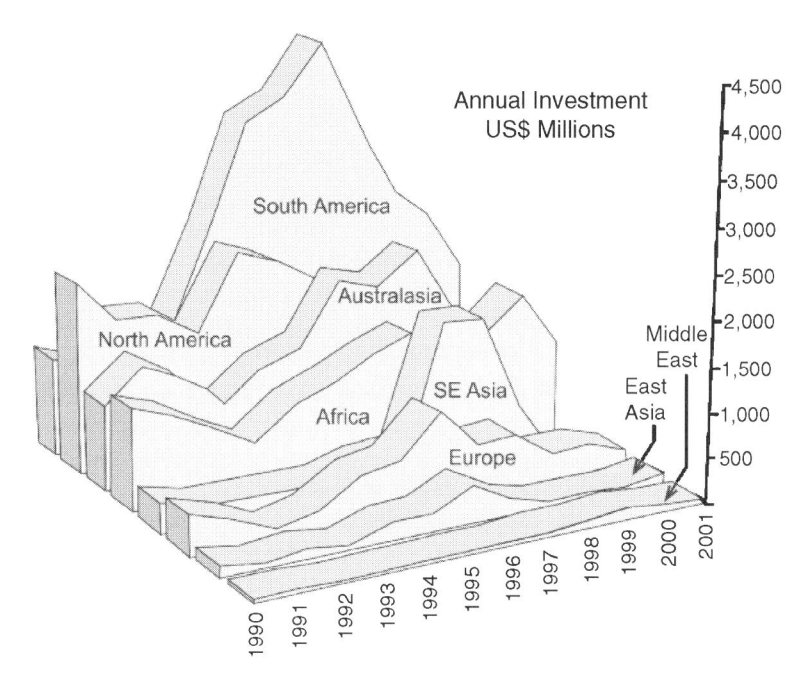

Figure 4 Capital expenditures on mine development excluding iron ore, bauxite, and fuel minerals, by geographical region from 1990 through 2001. From Reference 51.

and which affects the livelihood of an estimated 80 to 100 million. The informal mining sector is characterized by low capital intensity, relatively small volumes of output per operation, and insecurity of land tenure. The sector presents a number of policy challenges (92–95), including (*a*) tensions between informal and formal (and frequently large-scale) mining sectors over access to mineral deposits; (*b*) conflict between informal sector miners and other land users over the expansion of mining; (*c*) lack of title in the informal mining sector; and (*d*) a series of direct and indirect environmental and health impacts associated with the expansion of informal mining (see above).

These challenges notwithstanding, research on the informal sector indicates that it has considerable potential for poverty alleviation: A comparative study of small-scale mining in Niger, Peru, and the Philippines (96) found that small-scale mining can help stem rural-urban migration and make a major contribution to foreign exchange earnings. The liberalization of mining in Tanzania during the 1990s is considered by some to have reduced poverty in rural areas "on a scale far surpassing the impact of donor-funded job-creation efforts." The study's authors, however, are careful to point out that maintaining these benefits requires policies for growth management if they are not to be transitory (97). Research has also focused on the opportunities of the small-scale mining sector for reducing gender inequities in economic development (98). Female employment in Suriname's informal mining sector raised household income and decreased women's dependency during the country's gold mining boom, but it also introduced new axes of conflict to households, a finding consistent with other studies of the impact on gender equity of women's employment in the informal sector (99).

A strong counter-refrain permeates discussions of mining and development policy. It questions the received wisdom that "the extraction and processing of natural resources are at the heart of economic development" and suggests that this may be more "folk economics" than sound policy advice (100). Observing that the record of mining as an agent of long-term, broad-based development is remarkably weak under both laissez-faire and autarkic development regimes, this perspective makes the argument that mineral extraction is a uniquely difficult form of economic development that has "long been the pariah of development economics" (101). Auty (102–105), for example, draws on the historical experience of mineral economies in Zambia, Bolivia, Saudi Arabia, Kazakhstan, Peru, Chile, Botswana, and Papua New Guinea to argue that mineral-rich countries perform less well (by both simple growth measures and by more sophisticated measures of wealth distribution) than economies that are resource poor. Accordingly, several authors have claimed that large resource endowments may prove to be a curse rather than a blessing (106).

The paradox of mineral wealth impeding economic performance hinges on the relationship between the extractive and nonextractive sectors of the economy, and the political structures that often develop around resource windfalls (102): (*a*) Mineral booms tend to concentrate revenues on the government, which uses them to mask or postpone the need for economic reform; (*b*) as a result, resource-rich countries develop states that are factional or predatory rather than those that have sufficient autonomy to pursue economic policies that are coherent and that seek to raise social welfare; (*c*) mineral development siphons financial and human resources away from other sectors, leaving them underdeveloped and noncompetitive when a mineral boom ends; and (*d*) mineral windfalls are often absorbed too quickly, leading to inflation and appreciation of the exchange rate, which slows the diversification into nonmineral tradeables, i.e., those sectors of the economy that produce for export but which are not mineral based. This last argument—that mineral booms negatively affect the performance of other export sectors via a form of "medium term deindustrialization" (101)—is also known as the Dutch Disease after the shrinkage of the Dutch tradables sector, following the production of natural gas in the Groningen field from the late 1960s (107). Working at the rather different spatial scale of "extractive-dependent communities" in the western United States, Power (100) finds similarly weak multiplier effects between extractive industries and economic development: Research on Idaho's Silver Valley, for example, found that expansion in the nonmining economy was most rapid during periods when mining declined. As a result, Power argues that mineral-centric development policies are a "dangerous distortion" because they mistake real development, which he defines as a shift to nonextractive uses, for economic decline. Policies that encourage communities to specialize in mining, Power (100) argues, express the "economics of the rear view mirror." A summary assessment by Freudenburg & Wilson (108) also finds that "extractive activity is not only not the source of economic vitality, it is often a source of economic instability and depression."

Debate over the resource curse is far from settled. Central questions are whether the association between mineral extraction and limited growth reflects causation, or whether it is better understood as a correlation that masks the operation of other factors (such as weak government and/or degree of ethnic diversity). Davis (101), for example, argues that pessimism over mineral economies is misplaced and that, if taken to its logical conclusion, policies to combat the Dutch Disease lead to perverse policy recommendations, such as making mineral exploration illegal, counting mineral discoveries as debits in national accounts, and leaving minerals in the ground. Elsewhere Davis (109) rebuts arguments in political science that claim a connection between mineral rents and an inflexible state government, which, in turn, retards economic growth (110). He finds no evidence that minerals affect the state's capacity to govern as a general rule but finds a strong association between ethnic fractionalization and the capacity to govern, leading him to argue that "the necessary ingredient for economic failure remains ethnic diversity, rather than mineral resources."

The appropriateness of the extractive paradigm for alleviating poverty in the developing world has moved from being a largely technical, policy discussion to a public debate in the past few years (111, 112). In a widely publicized report released in 2001 (113), Oxfam America highlighted the negative effects of mineral dependence on income inequality, child welfare, and vulnerability to external shocks. It asked international financial institutions to adopt a much more cautious approach to the extractive sector, restricting lending to those states that are democratic and that have a demonstrated commitment to fighting poverty. Davis & Tilton (114) offer a robust rebuttal of the Oxfam report on the grounds that it mistakes correlation for causation and makes sweeping claims on the basis of very limited evidence. They also argue that the Oxfam report (and other statements like it) center on the wrong question: Rather than asking whether developing countries should pursue mineral development, they argue instead that the "appropriate policy question is...where should we encourage (mining) and how can we ensure that it contributes as much as possible to economic development." Although such thoughtful rebuttals highlight an emerging consensus that some ecologically and culturally protected areas should be off-limits to mining and that mineral development is not an unalloyed benefit in all circumstances, they largely sidestep the questions of how and by whom no-go areas will be determined. The leading edge of mineral development policy today, therefore, is not the fine-tuning of tax or investment policy, but the design of participatory decision-making processes and metrics of development with which to evaluate the social and spatial distribution of both mining's benefits and its socioeconomic and environmental costs.

Environment: Internalizing Externalities

For much of the nineteenth and twentieth centuries, the environmental costs of rapidly expanding mineral production were allocated through the courts via reference to the laws of property. Issues such as fugitive dusts or lost agricultural productivity, resulting from unrestrained smelter emissions, were handled either by nuisance law or via market compensation. The death of 1000 cattle, 800 sheep, and 20 horses during the first year of operation of the Anaconda smelter in 1902, for example, was managed via compensation payments, a financial arrangement between smelters and downwind farmers that became common throughout the American West (4, 24). Environmental regulation, primarily a product of the second half of the twentieth century, is a state-based administrative framework, organized around the three environmental media of air, water, and land, which sets science-based standards for the type and quantities of materials that may be emitted into the environment. It reflects the progressive expansion of the state's authority to protect the public interest and to offset some of the political and economic tensions arising from the externalization onto society of the environmental costs of postwar economic expansion. In the developing world, this expansion of state-based regulatory frameworks has occurred rather later and often in conjunction with conditions attached to multilateral loans or, as in the case of Chile, with the adoption of democratic reforms.

As state-based environmental regulations developed in industrial economies during the 1960s and 1970s, legislation followed a pattern in which local and regional air pollution was typically the first issue to be addressed. The political action to introduce such legislation, however, often occurred only after scientific and anecdotal evidence had accumulated for decades and, in many cases, was precipitated by an extreme event. Passage of the Clean Air Act (1955) in the United States, for example, was spurred in part by the Donora disaster of 1948. Twenty people died and about 7000 became ill during a 5-day period when a thermal inversion trapped atmospheric emissions from a zinc smelter located in the town of Donora, in the Monongahela River Valley near Pittsburg, Pennsylvania (115). Over time, the focus of concern has broadened from local air pollution (e.g., particulates) to address pollutants of regional and global concern. The U.S. Clean Air Act Amendments of 1977, for example, greatly restricted the amount of sulfur dioxide that smelters (located predominantly in the western states) and coal-burning power plants could emit in order to address acid rain, the effects of which were experienced predominantly in eastern states and in Canada.

As the substantive focus of environmental regulation has expanded to embrace water pollution, solid wastes, and toxics, the debate over the regulation of mining has shifted in significant ways. Most discussion of environmental policy and mining during the 1960s and 1970s focused on the costs of compliance and the relative environmental benefits to be gained from placing these costs on industrial producers. As national governments increasingly have sought to place restrictions on the production and management of solid wastes, the argument has turned to whether mining is fundamentally different from manufacturing in ways that should exempt it from solid waste regulations designed primarily for industries that assemble products, rather than for an industry that segregates metals from ore. In the United States, for example, the mining industry used this argument to obtain an exemption—the Bevill Amendment—to the Resource Conservation and Recovery Act. Efforts to regulate toxic materials have renewed the debate over mining's exceptionalism. Many of the toxic releases attributed to mining include naturally occurring materials that are mined, transported, and dumped on-site, and some of the listed metal toxics, copper and nickel, are the very products that mining firms produce. In the United States, environmental organizations have seized on the fact that mining, which was first included in the U.S. Toxics Release Inventory (TRI) in 1997, now heads the national list of toxic releases. Data for 2001 indicate that the U.S. metals mining industry accounted for 45% of releases of copper, silver, and gold, releasing about 1.35 million tons of listed materials out of a national total of 3.05 million tons (for comparison, the electric utility and chemical industries accounted for 17% and 9.5%, respectively) (116). Caution is warranted in interpreting these data. Of all the industries covered by TRI, mining had the lowest ratio of "off-site" release to "total releases," underscoring how the bulk (99%) of mining's releases by weight are on-site solid waste (compared to 57% as an average for all industrial classes covered by the TRI). More generally, the weight of releases is a poor proxy for the environmental and health effects of toxic materials. Risks associated with toxic releases depend on a range of factors, including the toxicity of the chemical, its fate in the receiving environment, and the amount and duration of exposure to the chemical after its release (117).

A secondary axis of contention concerns the effectiveness of policy design in achieving policy objectives. There is a long tradition of opposing environmental legislation on the grounds that it imposes excessive costs, but a distinctive argument emerged in the 1990s claiming that environmental policy was ineffective in its own terms and that the goals of environmental policy could be better served by rethinking the form of environmental regulation. The debate revolved around the relative effectiveness of policy approaches that specified technology standards [so-called best available technology standards (BAT)] and those that focused on performance standards (such as the concentration of pollutants per unit volume or mass emitted per time period). The significant difference is that performance standards do not identify the technologies or methods by which emission targets should be met and, therefore, provide companies with a degree of flexibility in how to meet them. This debate was supported by microeconomic studies of firm behavior, which indicated how BAT approaches could create perverse incentives by requiring firms to adopt a particular technology when other methods might offer greater environmental gains at lower cost. The 1990s, therefore, saw a critique of command-and-control regulations mandating specific pollution controls and promotion of performance-based standards as a means to encourage firms to develop innovative approaches that would not simply control pollution but would actually prevent it (see above).

Policies to prevent pollution, however, do not address mining's legacy effects, the contemporary pollution effects caused by historic releases to the environment. Commenting on the impacts of several hundred years of lead mining in the north of England, Kelly (118) notes that "the miners' memorial may be thousands of church roofs, miles of lead pipes and the ammunition which defended an empire but their bitter legacy remains just where they left it. Heavy metals are not a problem that will just go away." Recognition of the large environmental costs (and lack of revenue to pay for its cleanup) that can be left once a mine closes has underpinned recent efforts to develop mine closure policies, identify techniques for separating (historic) pollution stocks from (contemporary) pollution flows, and specify a range of best-practice techniques that can reduce the costs of closure (119, 120). The unplanned closure of the Summitville gold mine in the Rocky Mountains of Colorado in 1992 became an object lesson in how the environmental costs of mining can be passed onto society in the absence of adequate reclamation bonding (121). In the wake of Summitville, both developing and developed economies have introduced closure planning regulations. Pasquale & Maxwell (122) discuss this process in the context of mine closure legislation in Indonesia. Others have advocated that the most successful way to limit long-term liabilities associated with mining is to move beyond thinking of closure as clean up and walk away to embrace a "custodial transfer process" based on a "postmining sustainable use plan" (123). The point is to obviate Lovins' aphorism that "mines grow no second crop" by encouraging mining firms to regard land use as a temporary custodial duty and to identify postmining land uses and future custodians as early as possible (124, 125).

The most striking feature of work on environmental policy and mining is its almost exclusive focus on the fairly narrow question of how to do mining better. Most studies proceed from the assumption that the flow of minerals into the economy will increase as economies develop and that ways need to be found to reduce the impact each mine has on the environment. Starting from this position leaves unquestioned the more substantial issues of how resources are used in the economy, what functions they perform, whether such functions are socially necessary (as opposed to profitable), and other means of providing those functions. In comparison to a plethora of studies on policies and technologies to improve practices of mineral supply, there has been very little research into more comprehensive approaches that would address mineral demand, such as taxing resource use, creating incentives for recovery and recycling, or phasing out subsidies for extraction (126, 127). Thus Young (128) observes that the "de facto materials policies of industrial nations have always been to champion the production of virgin minerals" rather than "maximiz(ing) conservation of mineral stocks already circulating in the global economy." This bias toward extraction, he argues, leads to a rhetorical trap in which development and prosperity are directly linked to the quantity of materials drawn from the earth. The way out of this trap is to separate mineral use from mineral extraction by making greater use of those materials that have already been extracted. Because it is the extraction and processing of minerals, not their use, that poses the greatest threat to the environment[7] policies that encourage recycling and decrease the incentive to use virgin materials will serve to decouple the wealth-creating potential of material use from the environmental effects of extraction.

Sustainable Development

Many commentators have noted that there is something incongruous about nonrenewable resource extraction making claims to sustainability. As noted by Joyce & Thomson (129), the Earth Summit in Rio de Janeiro in 1992 launched sustainable development as a guiding framework but said very little about how mining would fit within these goals. What policy approaches might enable an industry invested in a linear economy (so decried by advocates of closing the loop via materials recovery and recycling) to further the goal of "meeting the needs of present without compromising the ability of future generations to meet their own needs" (130)? Standard formulations developed for renewable resources—such as sustainable harvesting of fish stocks or sustainable yield forestry—are irrelevant for mineral resources because of their inability to regenerate over timescales that are meaningful to humans. The argument that mining is compatible with sustainable development rests on a couple of theoretical propositions: First, mineral extraction and processing are processes of capital conversion, through which stocks of irreplaceable natural capital are converted into replaceable human capital; and second, wealth creation is central to the antipoverty agenda of sustainable development (131, 132). The second of these propositions repackages the standard argument that mineral development generates wealth and, therefore, is not especially distinctive. The first proposition, however, illustrates how at the heart of sustainable development is a debate over what is being conserved over the long run (133). To Solow (134), the key measure of conservation is *productive capacity*, which he defines as "a generalized capacity to produce economic well-being." In the context of exhaustible resources, the conservation of productive capacity can only be achieved if society replaces the resources used up with something else. Economists, like Solow, view mining as a process of wealth creation and capital conversion through which natural capital is converted into human capital (expressed variously as wealth, skills, or infrastructure). The policy objective is to ensure that the human capital created by mining at least compensates for the depletion of the mineral asset, so that the present generation passes to the next a stock of capital equivalent or greater than that which it inherited. Mikesell (135) outlines a practical proposal for meeting this objective, arguing that sustainability can be achieved by saving and reinvesting each year an amount equal to the present value of the annual net revenue from the sale of mineral products. These analyses assume a high degree of substitutability between human capital and natural capital, but as Tilton (136) points out, the extent

---

[7]This is true for most metals but not for fuels or metals with dissipative uses, such as the use of lead as a gasoline additive.

to which it is feasible to make investments compensate for losses in natural capital depends on the elasticity of substitution. There are some forms of natural capital, biodiversity for example, that cannot be substituted.

Much of the literature on mining and sustainable development implicitly accepts—rather than critically tests—these assumptions of substitutability and moves directly to the task of operationalizing macroeconomic abstractions of sustainability (ecology, equity, futurity) into tools for environmental management (triple bottom-line reporting, stakeholder mapping techniques, indicators of sustainability). Considerable energy has been invested over the past decade in refining a suite of management tools for mining and sustainable development and in designing metrics for evaluating and reporting a firm's environmental performance and contribution toward sustainability. This work, however, is often constrained by the way it reduces sustainability to a series of technical, managerial, and economic questions, excluding social questions such as the ownership of land and water rights, local control of resource decisions, or the right of host communities to consent to mining. The contemporary language of sustainable development is the language of partnership and shared goals, not the language of rights. As Cooney (137) points out in a refreshingly candid discussion of the challenges facing negotiations between mining firms and local communities, "One needs to consider whether the right of the community to maintain its integrity…may be superior to the rights of an investing corporation. Understandably, corporations will seek to shift the conversation away from rights towards sustainable development, where the objective is to engage stakeholders in shared decisions and possibly joint action…." The reduction of sustainability to a set of management tools that obscure underlying resource and environmental politics has led some observers to argue that sustainable development—initially a call for a new set of development goals—has become the means du jour to the conventional ends of resource access and extraction.

DEPENDENCY, RIGHTS, AND JUSTICE: POLITICAL ECOLOGIES OF EXTRACTION

Critiques of mining as an agent of sustainable development emerge most forcefully in a body of work on the political economy of mineral development. The hallmarks of this approach are its focus on questions of resource ownership, access, and control and the way it brings asymmetries of economic and political power (between firms and states, between states and communities) to the center of analysis. Advocates of this perspective argue that to assess the capacity of mining to contribute to sustainable development, one has to look beyond the choice of technology and management of the flow sheet and understand how mineral extraction is situated at the end of a chain of relationships that stretch from the mine to corporate headquarters, to the state, to international capital and commodity markets, and to the actions of multilateral lending agencies. A central argument is that these relationships structure the timing and extent of mineral investment and condition the practices adopted by investing firms.

Structural political economy evinces a long-standing concern with resource exploitation (and mining in particular), whether in debates over European imperialism in the early twentieth century, in the extensive literature on Latin American and African underdevelopment that formed around the dependency school of development theory in the 1970s, or in contemporary studies in political ecology, anthropology, and environmental justice of the political alliances and struggles that form around mining projects. Core issues include (*a*) the social and geographical distribution of the costs and benefits of mining; (*b*) the relationship between the domestic state, national elites, and transnational capital; (*c*) the ways in which accounting techniques, e.g., transfer pricing, minimize the revenues received by host countries and block opportunities for domestic accumulation; and (*d*) the existence of dual economies (or enclave economies) in which there are few productive linkages between an export-oriented modern mining sector and a stagnant, domestic agricultural sector.

Much of the work on mining and development from the 1970s, for example, opens with the "baffling paradox" (138) that, after centuries of colonial mineral extraction in Latin America (and decades in Africa), these regions were still beset with grinding poverty. As Lanning & Mueller (138) observed in the early 1970s, Africa produced 80% and 75% of the world's gold and diamond production as well as 30% of the output of chrome, vanadium, manganese, and antimony yet continued to slip further and further behind in development. Similarly, Frank (139), in one of the classic statements of structural political economy, uses Chilean nitrates as an example of how mineral extraction is structured in ways that systematically benefit the core rather than the periphery: The extraction and shipping of Chilean nitrates netted British capital £16 million between 1880 and 1913 while Chile retained only £2 million, leading the author to conclude that Chilean nitrates developed European agriculture at the expense of Chilean agricultural development. The analysis of underdevelopment in the peripheries of the Third World has been applied to other extractive regions. Examples of internal peripheries include the coal mining regions of the Appalachian Mountains in the eastern United States (140); uranium and coal mining on Native American reservations in the western United States (141); bauxite, uranium, and diamond mining on aboriginal lands in Australia (142; although for a dissenting view, see Reference 143); nickel development in maritime provinces of Canada (144); and lead and zinc mines in Ireland (145).

Integrating the environment with work on the political economies of mining has produced several innovative approaches that move beyond the primary concern of dependency theory with the appropriation and accumulation of economic surplus in the economic core of the global economy. These studies can be grouped into two categories: (*a*) efforts to understand the historical association of mineral extraction with both political-economic marginalization and environmental degradation, including the role of the state in both mediating these tensions and facilitating resource access; and (*b*) an interest in the resistance struggles of indigenous peoples to mining operations and the way ostensibly environmental issues (such as tailings disposal, water pollution, or expressions of concern over cyanide management) articulate broader concerns about social justice.

Extraction, Governance, and the State

The dual meaning of extraction—as a physical concept describing the separation and removal of one component of a larger ecosystem and as an economic concept denoting the accumulation and transfer of economic surplus—has led some researchers to consider whether the association of mineral development with environmental degradation and persistent poverty may be more than an historical contingency. Research on the underdevelopment of the Amazon by Bunker (146), for example, considers how the extraction and export of mineral commodities is structured by the laws of thermodynamics in ways that produce uneven forms of development. Resource extraction, he argues, produces both useful forms of energy (those temporarily preserved in mineral products) and useless forms of energy (in the form of disruption to ecological systems). While the former are traded out of the region and incorporated into industrial economies (enabling these economies to develop more complex forms of social organization), the extractive economy loses useful energy, becoming more simplified and impoverished in both economic and environmental terms (146). Barham et al. (147) argue that environmental degradation in the extractive periphery can be particularly acute because property rights are often poorly defined, the market valuation of land for nonmining purposes is low, and monitoring and enforcement costs in the periphery are high. A similar argument is made by other studies that examine how industrial countries increasingly import sustainability by sourcing resource-intensive products from overseas. Muradian & Martinez-Alier (148), for example, argue that geographical shifts in resource extraction (following the adoption of neoliberal economic reforms in many developing countries during the 1990s) have led resource-rich developing countries to specialize in the environmentally intensive production of natural resources, a process they term primarization. The authors argue, therefore, that the specific way in which developing countries are integrated into the world economy as resource producers peripheralizes the environmental effects of international consumption, exacerbating existing inequalities between North and South.

Because the liberalization of investment regimes requires specific action by national governments, and because expanding mineral production can exacerbate political tensions over the allocation of the costs and benefits of extraction, political-economic approaches to mining and environment pay particular attention to the role of the state. The treatment of the state in political economy, however, is quite different from that in public policy literature. Although studies of public policy are necessarily about the state, the primary concerns of that literature are to sketch out the normative goals of public policy and identify the technical design of policies to achieve those goals. Political-economic approaches to the state are primarily interested in questions of governance, i.e., the ways in which political and economic relations between states and other actors in society (firms, foreign states, NGOs) structure the actions (and inactions) of the state on issues of resource development and environmental protection. Because taxes and royalty payments on mineral extraction generate revenue for national governments, the state frequently shares the economic interests of mining firms who want access to national mineral resources. These interests can be sufficiently powerful to resist other pressures on the state (resource conservation, nonmining land uses, or environmental protection, for example), particularly in economies that have limited diversification and that rely heavily on mining for export earnings and tax revenues. A central theme in this literature, therefore, is the effect that capture of the state by transnational mining interests can have on the environment. Leith (149), for example, outlines the relationships between the Suharto regime in Indonesia and the Louisiana-based company Freeport McMoran, which operates one of the world's largest and lowest-cost copper and gold mines on Irian Jaya. The author concludes that the mining firm's economic and political significance "encouraged the development of mutually beneficial and supportive relationships between the company, the Indonesian president, his military, and the nation's political elite" and that, in return, Freeport was politically and physically protected by the regime.

Secondary themes are the specific practices taken by the state to promote mining and the ways in which multinational mining firms are dependent on the authority and legitimacy of state power to realize mineral development. These actions include infrastructure development, the allocation of title to land and resources, and the establishment (and enforcement) of the procedures by which other parties can participate in decisions over land use. At one end of the spectrum, this involves the state's ability to condemn land for resource development, remove existing users (by force if necessary), and establish the terms of compensation. There is a long history of states overriding or ignoring existing land uses and appropriating land for mining. Much has been written, for example, on the forcible subjugation and removal of Native Americans in the United States during the nineteenth century to facilitate a series of gold, silver, and copper rushes (150). Other authors have documented how Australia's mining boom of the 1960s and 1970s resulted in the loss of aboriginal lands and that there were close links between emerging states in Melanesia and Australian mining firms during the same period (142, 151). Denoon (152), for example, reports how the incipient state of Papua New Guinea (which in the late 1960s was still an Administrative Trust Territory of Australia) was initially "crushed between mining logistics and village politics" but that, in the face of community resistance on the island of Bougainville, it ultimately used force to carry out land surveys, remove existing land users, and appropriate 57,000 acres of land for the Panguna copper and gold mine.

More recent research indicates how the capture of the state by mining interests is historically contingent. Economic diversification in economies once dominated by extractive uses, for example, can drive the state to support increasingly strict environmental requirements, remove lands from mineral development, and act to ensure the protection of customary title to land. Among the more striking examples of a divergence in the interests of mining firms and the actions of the state is Australia's Mabo decision. In 1992, the Australian High Court rejected the long-standing doctrine of *terra nullius*, which held that Australia was a land without owners prior to colonization. The Mabo decision not only recognized native title prior to colonization but also said native title survived historical annexation by the British Crown and was not dependent on a grant of rights from the state (153). From the perspective of mineral developers, the initial effect of the Mabo decision was to increase uncertainty surrounding land access and security of tenure. With the actions of the state no longer so closely aligned with those of mining firms, mineral producers have had to work more directly with aboriginal groups and embrace a wider range of stakeholders in order to develop mineral prospects (154).[8]

If conventional political economies of mining are characterized by an interest in the active role of the state in resource decisions, a significant new focus has been on cases of weak governance or state failure in which the administrative state is conspicuously absent. This work is spurred by a proliferation of resource-based conflicts in which revenues from resources (most notably oil and diamonds) fuel violence between armed belligerents (155, 156). Natural resource extraction gained popular notoriety during the 1990s through its association with civil wars in Sierra Leone, Angola, and the Democratic Republic of Congo. The Conflict Diamonds and Fatal Transactions campaigns led by Global Witness, a London-based NGO, highlighted the role of the international diamond trade in funding regional wars in Africa and culminated in the Kimberley Process of diamond tracking and certification. In these conflicts, the state conspicuously fails to govern, as competing factions wage war for control of mining areas and the trading networks that produce the revenue to sustain conflict. The demonstrable weakness of the state in these cases—together with the apparent influence of nonstate actors, such as Global Witness, and international institutions, like the UN's Fowler Commission and the World Diamond Council—provokes an analytical challenge for conventional state-centric approaches to political economy. Work on resource violence, therefore, exemplifies how political-economic approaches to mining and environment are increasingly recognizing that governance is the product of a diverse range of actors operating at multiple spatial scales (157).

Land Rights, Resistance, and Environmental Justice

In the past 10 years, a substantial body of literature has emerged that focuses on the effects of multinational mining operations on indigenous peoples (141, 142, 151, 158–160). Much of this literature comes from, or is written in partnership with,

---

[8]Canada's Whitehorse Mining Initiative (1992–1994) expresses a similar process: The Initiative sought to build alliances and partnerships between mining firms; environmental groups; indigenous people's organizations; labor organizations; and federal, state, and provincial ministries in the context of a series of legal decisions on environment and land-use questions in the late 1980s and early 1990s that were unfavorable to the industry.

NGOs and self-consciously oppositional movements. Common features of this work are that it (*a*) stresses the asymmetries of power between mining firms and indigenous peoples; (*b*) focuses on the political struggles that take place between firms, indigenous peoples, and the state over resource access, land rights, revenue distribution, and environmental impacts; and (*c*) in most cases describes these struggles in explicitly moral terms, using the language of justice, human rights, and indigenous rights. Specific examples include a study of the impacts on social groups and the environment following the adoption of a new mining code in the Philippines in 1995 (161); descriptions of the effects on rivers, forests, and indigenous people following a surge in gold mining exploration on the Guianan Shield during the 1990s (162); and a discussion of how the environmental and social impacts of mining at Ok Tedi in Papua New Guinea require transnational forms of justice that go beyond "those conceptions of justice functional for commodity exchange" (163). These and other examples suggest that contemporary struggles over mining are not adequately captured as environmental disputes. Banks (164), for example, argues that controversies over large-scale mining operations in Melanesia (Ok Tedi and Porgera in Papua New Guinea, Grasberg in Irian Jaya, and the Gold Ridge mine in the Solomon Islands) are better understood as disputes over community control of resources and the right of community members to control the direction of their lives.

Most studies adopting the political-economic approach eschew the language of stakeholders in describing the relationships between multilateral lending institutions (like the World Bank), mining firms, government agencies, and activist groups. If stakeholder approaches understand society as a set of actors existing on a level playing field, each with an equal opportunity to influence the terms of the debate, then political-economic approaches to mining and environment view society as composed of interest groups with differential levels of access to power. An historical literature, for example, explores class formation and racial division in mining communities (165), and some of the most insightful studies of social differentiation originate in anthropology (166): Taussig (167), Godoy (168) and DeWind (169), for example, document how material and symbolic relationships between mining and agriculture are transformed as mining becomes increasingly capitalized in predominantly peasant societies in Bolivia and Peru.

Researchers have expanded from the traditional foci of class and race as axes of differentiation to include gender. Scheyvens & Lagisa (170), for example, discuss the gendered impacts of mining in Papua New Guinea, observing how many of the impacts from mining fall initially and most acutely on women. They argue that "women also bear a disproportionate share of the responsibility for dealing with the social and environmental mess which accumulates" following mining and logging activities in the Pacific and that these inequalities are the cause of politicization and social unrest at a range of scales from domestic strife in the household to protests and roadblocks around the mine. The questions asked by researchers about gender and mining are increasingly diverse and include studies of the role played by gender in antimining activism (171); the sexualization of work relations around mining that lead to sex-segregation and gender-typing of mine jobs (172); and the historical role of women as prospectors and developers in frontier mining activities (173).

For all its attention to differentiations in society, however, political-economic approaches have paid insufficient attention to the way mining capital itself is highly differentiated. For example, junior exploration companies are structured by quite different objectives and constraints than those for large, integrated mining firms, and they have different degrees of motivation for adopting environmental management plans, embracing public participation, or subscribing to principles of sustainable development (71). Similarly, the markets for capital, ownership structure, and final demand vary considerably across the range of mined commodities (consider, for example, gold, coal, and iron). These differences are not trivial because they affect the way the industry works, the relationships between producers and end users, and the industry's responsiveness to social pressure.

The political-economic approach is generally skeptical of the extent to which mining is able to transcend its historical practices, a function of its analytical claim that the effects of mining flow from the social relations surrounding capitalist production. This perspective is often poorly understood by industry practitioners who make the argument that the mining industry is in fact nothing more than a collection of individuals, many of whom believe in environmental goals, care deeply about their actions, and who recognize that expectations of environmental performance have changed dramatically. This voluntarist perspective is largely rejected by political economy, which understands the behavior of transnational mining firms as being structured primarily by the dynamics of capitalism (competition, profitability, demands of the capital markets, corporate concentration). As Frank (139) puts it, foreign investment is an object "not of voluntary decisions...but of the needs and contradictions of capitalism and their historical resolution." More pointed still is Girvan's (174) assessment of the conflicts between multinational mining firms and state governments during the 1960s and 1970s in Chile (copper) and Guyana and Jamaica (bauxite): "rather than constituting unfortunate episodes that can be handled by adroit management and 'rational' behavior, such conflict should be seen as the manifestation of profound antagonisms among groups within the international capitalist order." Contemporary political economy approaches to mining, environment, and development have evolved beyond simplistic assessments of a struggle between states and corporations and vague invocations of a capitalist order, yet they retain a profound skepticism of mining's ability to reduce—rather than reproduce—inequalities in wealth and livelihood opportunities.

THE MINING IMAGINARY: THE CULTURAL POLITICS OF EXTRACTION

The preceding sections have addressed mining as a set of technological, economic, and political relationships. Discussions of mining and environment conventionally stop at this point and do not consider the way that mining also has significant cultural power. With its capacity for generating both tremendous wealth and intense environmental transformation, mining is a potent metaphor for the energies and contradictions of development (175).[9] The argument in this section is that much of the contemporary debate over mining and environment reflects society's displacement onto mining of more general anxieties about the scale of human intervention in the environment, the globalization of business, a perceived loss of local control, and rapid social and ecological change. A significant component of the new reality of mining, in other words, is the cultural and environmental politics surrounding extraction that intrudes directly (and with concrete consequences) into the practical debates over proposals to open new mines or expand the scale of existing operations. The most technically competent, meticulously caveated, and robustly financed proposal to open a mine, therefore, encounters a rich cultural ferment of contentions and disagreements about the practices, meaning, and significance of mining. To understand contemporary debates over mining and environment, therefore, it is necessary to recognize how mineral development is unavoidably situated within a moral landscape: as Williams (176) argues, the mining environment "is a technological one—but it is also a mental landscape, a social terrain, and an ideological map."

The historical juxtaposition of mining with the processes of industrialization, militarism, imperialism, and dispossession constitutes a collective cultural memory that fuels contemporary opposition to mineral development. For example, the harsh social and ecological realities of mining during the period of coal-fired industrialization [cf. the exploitation of women and children in English coal mines, as expressed in the Royal Commission Report (1842)] provide a cultural reference point that informs contemporary interpretations of the way large-scale, industrial mining in the developing world can radically transform established social conventions. Thus, mineral extraction has become a lightning rod for concerns about environment, human rights, and the discontents of development. There is now a substantial literature that addresses the meaning and cultural power of both the mine and mining within western society. Schematically, this literature can be considered as addressing two distinctive areas: (*a*) the moral geographies of the underground and the ways in which the physical working environment of the mine has historically subverted or suspended the social conventions prevailing above ground; and (*b*) the spatial and temporal imaginaries that surround mining, particularly the construction of mining as the alchemic transition of mere dirt into wealth beyond the dreams of avarice, a transformation that propels social, political,

---

[9]As Mumford brilliantly observed seventy years ago, "on the one hand, mining stands as a triumph of human ingenuity and fortitude over the fickle reluctance of nature....Minerals are liberated from the earth, turning hostile and unproductive terrain into a fount of civilized wealth, freeing society from the drudgery of nature. On the other hand, the act of wresting minerals from the earth has historically required the subjugation and demeaning of both nature and humankind, as faceless pairs of hands and unseen laboring backs descend into the dark, inhuman hell of tunnels to strip away the organs of nature" (175, 176).

economic, and environmental changes, the nature and significance of which are highly contested. Each of these perspectives is discussed below.

The Underground

As a cultural landscape, the mine sits at the nexus of history, politics, and culture, the focal point of a contested moral landscape. In debates over mining and the environment, the concepts of the mine and mining are a cultural currency traded and exchanged among individuals and groups as a way of articulating meanings about development, environment, democracy, and even life itself. A significant part of the contention over the meaning of mining concerns the physical, topographical space of the mine itself and, in particular, that of the underground. A radically unfamiliar space in an experiential sense, this space is nonetheless culturally familiar because the mine (and, in particular, the coal mine) is extensively storied in both art and literature. In a wide-ranging collection of papers, Thesing (177) explores coal mining as "a metaphor for the times" and analyzes the different ways in which gender, race, ethnicity, and class have been portrayed in art, film, and literature on coal mining during the nineteenth and twentieth centuries. Studies like these demonstrate how artists have sought to represent the relationship between the physical mining environment and the formation of individual and collective identity, and the studies point to the ways in which the unfamiliarity of the mining landscape can provoke alienation and distrust. Mines are places in which "day has been abolished and the rhythm of nature broken;" artificial lighting, artificial ventilation, and the absence of anything organic render the mine a place apart from the rest of the world (175, 176). The underground is also a space without a horizon, "an inner outdoors where night and day coexist and boundaries disappear" (178). The landscapes of mining, then, challenge conventional coordinates of space and time. Whether through the absence of the horizon, the lack of light in the underground, or the vertiginous sense of scale and the lack of familiar organic landmarks (such as vegetation) that make it difficult to comprehend the size of some open pits, the physical geography of mining landscapes can create a profound sense of dislocation.

The insight from these cultural studies is that the fundamental unfamiliarity of these environments makes them morally uncertain spaces, places in which codes of conduct are not yet settled and over which different groups make competing claims. From this perspective, disputes between mining companies, the state, and a range of NGOs over whether mines will be opened and/or how they will be operated can be understood as struggles to define the social contract. The place-specific agreements through which these disputes are mediated are, therefore, more than simply local solutions because they define incipient modes of social order. Whether in the context of a gold mine in the proximity of Yellowstone National Park (e.g., Crown Butte Resources) or in the agricultural lowlands of Peru (e.g., Manhattan Minerals' Tambogrande project), the hard political work of defining the social, economic and environmental terms for mining and winning a social license to operate is also a struggle to shape the nature of globalization. Similar to the sweatshop and the *maquiladora*, mines have become defining spaces through which to understand contemporary problematics, such as development, globalization, or imperialism (179).

Modern Alchemy: Mining as Transformation

It is a rare account of mining that does not refer to its capacity for transformation. Whether interpreted as a supreme emblem of a heroic Age of Progress or as a culture of massive disturbance that is cruelly disruptive (13, 176), mining is frequently held to represent an historic disjuncture, a hinge point in the history of social and ecological relations, a means by which to "locate a place in time" (180). Portrayed as an irreverent intrusion or a jarring juxtaposition symbolic of modernization, mines are frequently described (in art, literature, and travelers accounts) as either disrupting the natural sublime or terminating a pastoral idyll by wrenching peasants from their time-honored ways. These two different strands have deep historical roots but are remarkably persistent: They can be found, for instance, in many contemporary struggles over proposed mines in the vicinity of wilderness areas or hot spots of global biodiversity (the twenty-first century equivalent of the natural sublime) or in the context of proposals to open mines in areas with a long history of agricultural production. In both cases, the moral landscape of mining is contrasted to that of an imagined space of preindustrial integrity and harmony. In many accounts, the technologies and rationalities of mining intrude to produce a "dis-spirit of place," a set of physical and mental changes that are interpreted as a fall from grace.

This sense of mining as an epochal shift is most clear in work that contrasts mineral extraction with agriculture. Hyndman (181), for example, describes how the arrival of large-scale mining in the western province of Papua New Guinea during the 1970s represents an historical hinge point between subsistence and capitalist relations, fundamentally changing the way traditional land users in Melanesia related with the wider economy. Although both mining and agriculture are primary sector activities predicated on the extraction of value from nature, the two sectors are rhetorically counterposed—structured by very different logics. Whereas agriculture is organic and structured by the rhythms and cycles of nature, mining is inorganic, a "leaden landscape of perpetual winter" structured entirely by human logics; agriculture is renewable and productive of sustenance, and mining is nonrenewable, "evacuative" (182), and produces nothing that can be ingested to support life. Lewis Mumford, the first to seriously consider the links between mining and modernity, for example, was particularly exercised by the fact that the mining environment was "completely inedible;" agriculture supports life, yet extraction is lifeless, "not a living world, but a dead mine" (175).

Williams (176) takes this sense of transition further to argue that the logic of mining is one of urbanization. Technologies of surveying, lifting, and construction pioneered in mining are imported into the city; the rationalities of ecological simplification and radical abstraction that underpin geological science become the hallmark of urban design; and the dominance of "artificial means" epitomized by the mine come to characterize the experience of urban life. Brechin (183) develops a similar argument in a compelling account of the environmental history of San Francisco, which grew to prominence in the California Gold Rush and subsequently financed the silver mines of the Comstock Lode, the gold mines of South Dakota, and the copper mines of Montana. The cycling of mineral wealth through the city, and its fixation in urban space, leads Brechin to argue that the skyscrapers of San Francisco are technologically, economically, and philosophically the inverted mines of the city's massive hinterland. Thus, many of the objections to mining mirror long-standing and conflicted attitudes within western societies to the intrusion or encroachment of urban and industrial activities into rural spaces (184).

Authors from a wide range of traditions—economics, public policy, political economy—all concur that the transition to mining is difficult (although they disagree on whether such difficulties need to be managed and if so, on the mechanisms by which to do it). The individual and collective trauma of the changes ushered in by mining is central to many contemporary discourses about the impacts of mining on environments and communities. Mumford's (175) comment on the "devilishly sinister" nature of mining is indicative of the way monster imagery is often used to capture this sense of an intimate encounter with an omnipotent, transformational force beyond individual control. Devilish or monstrous figures appear in a number of writings as a figurative device for expressing the individual and collective bargains through which miners and mining communities submit to the risks and privations of mining in order to earn a living. In a classic account, Taussig (167) discusses the extensive use of devil imagery by miners in Columbia and identifies it as a creative response under conditions of proletarianization: Peasants drafted into the mines use the devil as a way of negotiating one of the central contradictions of capitalism (that between use value and exchange value). The sense of the monstrous, something that contravenes all natural laws, continues to inform much of the rhetoric surrounding mining and the environment. The scale of mining, for example, is often represented by its detractors as something inhuman because of the way it rivals nature in geomorphological efficacy and sheer, awesome power.

Nature, however, holds no monopoly on the sublime. Nye (185) convincingly argues that the location of the sublime in American thought underwent a noticeable shift early in the twentieth century as attributes of grandeur and unfathomable power that had formerly been associated with nature were increasingly applied to industrial technologies. Mining exemplifies this technological sublime with its celebration of size, ambition, and skillful control of nature. This heroic tale of mining fills most mining histories and is presented at mining museums and pit overlooks. The Kennecott copper pit in Utah (now 2.5 miles wide and 0.75 miles deep) is a classic example and is frequently described as one of the few human constructions that can be seen from space. For much of the twentieth century, such "brute force technologies" have been celebrated precisely for their ability to transform landscapes and sever humankind from the drudgery of nature (186). Thus for many, mining constitutes the "fine flower of industrial achievement" (187) because "without mining, man would still be just another animal, seeking nothing more than a full belly and a refuge against other animals more savage than himself" (188).

Such muscular development narratives have largely given way to a proliferation of discourses about mining and sustainability, following the environment's rise to prominence as a strategic issue for mining companies since the 1980s. It is tempting to see this "ecological phase" (189) of mining capital as a definitively new metaphor of resource husbandry and planetary stewardship that draws a distinction between the dirty past and a cleaner, greener future. It is better understood, however, as a variant of two long-standing, mutually reinforcing narratives about mining and development: the idea of mining as a moral enterprise ensuring social and natural order (or, more generally, civilization); and the construction of mining as a skilled, professional endeavor conducted by "masters of technical excellence" whose technological prowess and personal integrity enable the production of value from nature (180, 190). Current discourses of sustainable mining, for example, rearticulate these long-standing themes. The language of reclamation, for example, is a moral discourse through which lost landscapes are redeemed, set aright, and made productive. Engineering activities, such as burying waste rock, grading waste piles, covering them with topsoil, and seeding, are celebrated for the way they physically restore an aesthetic and ecological order. Extraction—the business of getting the minerals out of the ground—is reframed in the metaphors of agricultural science: Resources are stewarded or harvested, land use is temporary, and, in the discussions of closure planning, merely borrowed in readiness for the next user. Thus, the core of contemporary debates over mining and the environment include defining the role of mining in the context of sustainable development and increasing claims for local resource control. It is widely accepted that cleaner process technology and environmental management practices geared toward pollution prevention will be important, even essential, components going forward as the mining industry seeks a social license to operate. Yet the most contentious issues—those which frustrate resource development even where firms are in full legal compliance and adopt best-practice technologies—are far less susceptible to technological solutions and involve issues of land rights, resource control, and cultural perceptions of the value, meaning, and significance of mining relative to other land uses.

SUMMARY

This review surveyed a broad body of literature on mining, development, and environment and identified four distinctive approaches: (*a*) technology- and management-centered accounts, which define the issue of mining and environment in terms of environmental performance; (*b*) public policy studies on the design of effective institutions for capturing benefits and allocating costs of resource development; (*c*) structural political economy, highlighting themes of external control, resource rights, and environmental justice; and (*d*) cultural studies, examining mining as a metaphor for expressing anxieties about the social and environmental effects of industrialization and globalization. Table 1 presents a summary of these perspectives in the form of a typology. It identifies the guiding paradigms that inform each approach and the different definitions of the mining and environment problem to which these paradigms give rise. Table 1 also contrasts the objectives of research undertaken within each perspective and highlights significant differences in how the relationship between scientific research and social change is understood. For studies of cleaner production, for example, the primary objective is to assist mining firms in efforts to improve environmental performance; for sustainable development, the objective is to improve public policies for capturing the benefits of mineral development and minimizing its environmental costs, whereas work informed by political economy documents inequalities in the social and geographical distribution of mining's costs and benefits in order to shift the balance of power in negotiations between mining firms and communities. Table 1 illustrates, therefore, how each approach leads to a distinct political stance regarding the possibilities for improving the relationship between mining and the environment, and that this arises out of the approach's core claims and whether they conceptualize mining as a predominantly technological, socioeconomic, political, or cultural endeavor.

The most contested environmental issues raised by mining have evolved over time. Aesthetic and physical safety concerns have been progressively supplemented by struggles over the impacts of mining on human health, agricultural productivity, and ecosystem function. The range of environmental media has also broadened—often in response to national environmental regulations—from an initial focus on air quality, to surface- and groundwater, solid wastes, toxics, and, more recently, biodiversity. Today the most pressing environmental issues associated with mining concern access to land and the challenge of waste disposal. This evolution in the focus of concern is, in part, a function of the fact that many of the emissions from mining and mineral processing to air and water have proven responsive to technological change and better environmental management. Atmospheric emissions from smelters demonstrate the greatest improvement not only in postindustrial societies but increasingly in developing and transition economies too. The management of surface-water quality at mine sites has also improved significantly (through, for example, advances in prevention and treatment technologies for acid mine drainage), although impacts to surface- and groundwater remain a problem at long-established mining operations. The extent and significance of environmental modernization in the mineral sector, therefore, should not be underestimated. Although continuing incidents, such as tailings dam failures (Baie Mare in Romania, Los Frailes in Spain) and cyanide spills (Tarkwa, Ghana), indicate pollution from mining has not been solved in any permanent sense, there is evidence to support the optimistic claim that, on matters of environmental performance and environmental management, leading mining firms today operate quite differently than those of a number of years ago.

Yet the key environmental issues facing the mining industry today (land access and options for waste disposal) are not primarily technological or even managerial. Resource access and the increasing ratio of wastes to metal are intractable problems at the corporate level. It is not possible for an individual firm, given the constraints of competition, to reduce its need for land or absorb the costs of backfilling the increasing volume of waste from processing low-grade ores (national or international policies to promote secondary recovery and decouple mineral use from mineral extraction would, however, make this far less intractable). Geographical shifts in the focus of mineral investment have exacerbated the structural constraints of the need for land and for low-cost waste disposal options. From the Canadian Arctic to the Great Basin of Nevada, and from eastern Siberia to Papua New Guinea, mining investment increasingly coincides with hot spots of ecological and cultural diversity. In many cases, the mining investment boom of the 1990s propelled mineral exploration and development into areas remote from centers of urbanization, where formal state control is relatively weak; in regions which have not experienced intensive colonization; and where significant indigenous or tribal populations remain.[10] The emergence of an international socio-political environment in which indigenous rights are increasingly recognized by law (and in which state governments face internal demands for devolution of authority and increased political autonomy) has rendered ineffective those time-honored practices for negotiating land access that rely on the state's authority for mineral negotiations, its powers for zoning land and allocating land title, and its police powers for enforcing land claims.

There is an irony here. Frequently derided as a mature, even anachronistic industry, mining now finds itself in the vanguard of a halting, yet ineluctable, move toward increased corporate social responsibility. As a lightning rod for broad demands for a change in the social contract between corporate activity and society, the mining sector is at the sharp end of the adaptive process of ecological modernization (190a). Its development of environmental management capacity, investments in cleaner production techniques, embrace of corporate environmental reporting, and even, on occasion, its forswearing of rights of access for mineral development are part of a strategic process of experimentation to internalize (and reduce) some of the costs mining once externalized onto society, in order to remain competitive and preserve social legitimacy in a climate of changed social expectations. How one interprets these changes—as historic transition, cosmetic modification ("greenwash"), or something in between—depends largely on the way one

---

[10]This generalization holds for many cases, but there are exceptions. The contentious Tambogrande mining project in Peru's San Lorenzo Valley is one such exception. It is located in a region with a long history of high-value export-oriented agriculture and with relatively strong economic and political connections to Lima when compared with other mining regions in the Andean Highlands or the Amazon Basin.

TABLE 1 Summary of approaches to mining, development, and environment

	Cleaner production	Sustainable development	Dependency, rights and justice	The mining imaginary
Problem definition	Process inefficiencies; lack of capital and/or skill; changing strategic environment	Social inefficiencies (and inequities) in how resources are priced and in the allocation of mining's costs/benefits over time and space	Asymmetries in economic and policial power between mining firms and communities (plus high degree of external control) make mining a poor engine of meaningful economic development	Political opposition to resource development reflects a displacement onto mining of a much broader set of anxieties about the form and scale of human intervention in the environment. Mining is a moral landscape as well as a technical and economic process
Guiding paradigm	Industrial ecology	Welfare economics	Political economy and ecological economics	Poststructuralism and cultural politics
Objective	To improve processes of engineering and management to better deliver environmental performance	To create institutional structures that better connect mining activities with socioeconomic development goals	To map the social and geographical distribution of mining's costs and benefits; to expose inequities in their distribution; and to achieve more effective community participation in decisions over mining development	To deconstruct popular discourses about mining and show how these cultural forms do political work in the contemporary period
Core claims	Improving environmental performance is good business (win-win or lean and clean)	The boom-bust cycle of mining and the exhaustible nature of non-renewable resources create serious	Mining reproduces inequalities in the distribution of wealth and power and creates	Mining is a powerful metaphor for expressing aspects of the relationship between society and environment

MINING AND THE ENVIRONMENT 249

Conceptual approach to mining	Mining as a technological process that transforms matter through the application of energy and/or as a value chain delivering returns to shareholders	Mining as a socioeconomic activity capable of delivering a stream of benefits and costs to society; social expectations about the balance of these costs/benefits vary over time and space and are judged in relation to other activities	Innovation and new investment are key to improving environmental performance (via transfer of skills, technologies and practices) challenges for extractive communities Institutional innovation is necessary to safeguard against socioeconomic dislocation (both during mining and post-closure) and to help nonrenewable resource extraction approach the goals of sustainable development long-term ecological damage Mining is incompatible with all but the narrowest definitions of development and, historically, has proven to be a poor engine for improving livelihoods and social welfare	Mining as a set of political relationships that are in tension (sometimes in overt struggle, sometimes in uneasy collaboration) that, if unchallenged, 'work' to siphon wealth out of mineral-rich regions while also creating cultural and environmental degradation Because the cultural significance of these metaphors was forged in distinctive historical and geographical contexts (imperialism, industrialization, racism, gender and class oppression), contemporary discussions about mining disclose anxieties about much broader relations between rich and poor nations and between industries, people and environment Mining as a cultural metaphor for thinking about social and ecological relations
Academic disciplines	Management, business, engineering	Public policy, public administration Welfare economics and sociology	Political economy, anthropology, geography, environmental history	Cultural studies, anthropology, geography

understands the structure of the modern capitalist economy. If the economy is regarded as a set of relationships between individual actors who represent the basic factors of production (land, labor, and capital) along with a range of other stakeholders (governments, civil society), then the environmental imperative poses a fundamental challenge to business as usual. The changes one observes constitute an historic, epochal shift because they broaden and deepen the networks of relationships between these actors and, at a minimum, require firms to consult with a much broader range of stakeholders than before. If, however, capitalism is a set of relationships between those with property and those without—a structural inequality in economic and political power that is maintained by, among other things, the role of the state in determining who has rights of access to property (i.e., land and resources), how those rights are obtained, and which among an array of competing rights and potential uses have priority, then the relationship between mining and the environment today looks little different (in fact, the privatization of many state-owned mining firms during the 1990s has, by this measure, increased inequality).

From this latter perspective, the true test of an historic shift in the relationship between mineral extraction and the environment does not hinge on whether a firm adopts cleaner production techniques or is certified to meet international environmental management standards. Rather it lies in the extent to which processes of stakeholder dialogue and public participation enable communities to reject mining as a land use or to impose significant conditions on its form, rate, and extent. Many contemporary public policy discussions around mining and environment are animated by this critical tension between stakeholder consultation and the right of a community to give its informed consent prior to mining (191). This tension emerges in the debate over the Extractive Industries Review (EIR) commissioned by the World Bank in 2000 to provide it with guidance on future involvement in oil, gas, and mining projects. The EIR initially made a number of recommendations that alarmed the international mining industry, including that the World Bank cease to support coal mining, phase out financing for oil projects by 2008, and "require companies to engage in consent processes with communities and groups directly affected by projects in order to obtain their free prior and informed consent" (192). Although its affirmation of informed consent has earned endorsements from a wide range of environmental and human rights groups, the EIR Report has been extensively critiqued by mining firms and by some developing country governments who fear it will lead to a reduction in foreign mining investment, and it has created an internal dispute within the Bank about whether to accept its specific recommendations. Senior representatives of the mining industry have recently indicated that, in specific cases related to biodiversity, the industry may be prepared to cede rights of access and yield them to other land uses, even when a mining firm is in possession of full, state-sanctioned rights of access and extraction (193). Whether this constitutes an historic shift in the political economy of mineral development is, as yet, unclear. It does suggest, however, that this may be a particularly propitious moment in the debate over mining and environment.

ACKNOWLEDGMENTS

I thank Gerardo Castillo for his work on the initial literature search that informed this review. I wish to acknowledge support from an NSF CAREER grant SBR 9874837 for research on mining investment as a driver of land-use change. I would also like to recognize the support of a Ciriacy-Wantrup Fellowship in Natural Resource Studies at the University of California, Berkeley, where this article was completed.

The *Annual Review of Environment and Resources* is online at
http://environ.annualreviews.org

LITERATURE CITED

1. Down CG, Stocks J. 1977. *Environmental Impact of Mining*, p. 7. New York/Toronto: Wiley
2. Min. Miner. Sustain. Dev. 2003. *Breaking New Ground: The Report of the MMSD Project*. London/Sterling, VA: Earthscan
3. Clark AL, Clark JC. 1999. The new reality of mineral development: social and cultural issues in Asia and Pacific nations. *Resour. Policy* 25(3):189–96
4. Smith D. 1987. *Mining America*. Lawrence: Univ. Kans. Press
5. Agricola G. 1556 (1950). *De Re Metallica*, p. 8. New York: Dover
6. Meadows DH. 1972. *The Limits to Growth: A Report for the Club of Rome's Project on the Predicament of Mankind*. New York: Universe Books
7. Simon JL. 1981. *The Ultimate Resource*. Princeton, NJ: Princeton Univ. Press
8. Campbell CJ, Laherrere JH. 1998. The end of cheap oil. *Sci. Am.* 278(3):60–65
9. World Resour. Inst. 1997. *Resource Flows: The Material Basis of Industrial Economies*. Washington, DC: World Resour. Inst.
10. Douglas I, Lawson N. 2000. Material flows due to mining and urbanization. In *A Handbook of Industrial Ecology*, ed. U Ayers, LW Ayers, pp. 351–64. Cheltenham, UK/Northampton, MA: Elgar
11. McNeill JR. 2000. *Something New Under the Sun: An Environmental History of the Twentieth-Century World*. New York: Norton
12. Quivik FL. 1997. The historic industrial landscape of Butte and Anaconda, Montana. In *Images of An American Land: Vernacular Landscapes in the Western United States*, ed. T Carter, pp. 267–90. Albuquerque: Univ. N. Mex. Press
13. Black B. 2000. *Petrolia: The Landscape of America's First Oil Boom*. Baltimore: Johns Hopkins Univ. Press
14. Francaviglia R. 1982. Copper mining and landscape evolution: a century of change in the Warren Mining District, Arizona. *J. Ariz. Hist.* 23(3):267–98
15. Buckley GL. 1988. The environmental transformation of an Appalachian valley, 1850–1906. *Geogr. Rev.* 88(2):175–98
16. Schwantes C. 2000. *Vision and Enterprise: Exploring the History of Phelps Dodge Corporation*. Tucson: Univ. Ariz. Press
17. Morse K. 2003. *The Nature of Gold: An Environmental History of the Klondike Gold Rush*. Washington/London: Univ. Wash. Press
18. Weisz J. 1970. The environmental effects of surface mining and mineral waste generation. In *Environmental Side Effects of Rising Industrial Output*, ed. A van Tassel, pp. 291–312. Lexington, MA: Heath Lexington Books

19. Robertson D. 2000. Heaps of history: Toluca and the historic Longwall mining district. *J. Ill. Hist.* 3(3):162–84
20. UNESCAP. 1992. *Environmental Impact Assessment, Guidelines for Mining Development*, p. 6. New York/Bangkok: UN Econ. Soc. Comm. Asia Pacific
21. Warhurst A. 1994. The limitations of environmental regulation in mining. In *Mining and the Environment. International Perspectives on Public Policy*, ed. RG Eggert, pp. 133–72. Washington, DC: Resour. Future
22. Ripley EA, Redman RE, Crowder AA. 1996. *Environmental Effects of Mining*, p. 9. Delray Beach, FL: St Lucie Press
23. Humphries M. 2003. *Mining on Federal Land*. Congr. Res. Serv. Issue Brief Congr. Washington, DC: Congr. Res. Serv.
24. Moore J, Luoma S. 1990. Hazardous wastes from large scale metals extraction: a case study. *Environ. Sci. Technol.* 24:1278–85
25. Ramos HC, Cabalda MV, Banaag MA. 2000. *Tailings dam accidents and the use of chemicals in mining: issues, policy response and lessons learned from the Philippines.* http://www.mineralresourcesforum.org/workshops/regulators/2000/docs/Ramos.pdf
26. World Resour. Inst. 2004. *Mining and Critical Ecosystems: Mapping the Risks.* Washington, DC: World Resour. Inst.
27. TailingsInfo. 2004. *Tailings accidents.* http://www.tailings.info/accidents.htm
28. UN Environ. Program. 2001. *Tailings Dams: Risk of Dangerous Occurrences, Lessons Learnt from Practical Experiences, Bull. 121.* Paris: UN Environ. Program., Div. Technol., Industry Econ. Int. Comm. Large Dams
29. Nat. Resour. Can. 2004. *Mining environment neutral dainage (MEND).* http://www.nrcan.gc.ca/mms/canmet-mtb/mmsl-lmsm/mend/default_e.htm
30. Jones J. 1940. The fauna of the river Meliddwr, a lead polluted tributary of the river Rheidol in north Cardiganshire, Wales. *J. Anim. Ecol.* 9:188–201
31. Allan R. 1995. Impact of mining activities on the terrestial and aquatic envirnoment with emphasis on mitigation and remedial measures. In *Heavy Metals: Problems and Solutions*, ed. W Salomons, U Forstner, P Mader, pp. 119–40. Berlin: Springer-Verlag
32. Singer PC, Stumm W. 1970. Acidic mine drainage: the rate determining step. *Science* 167:1121–23
33. Mitchell PB. 2000. Prediction, prevention, control and treatment of acid rock drainage. In *Environmental Policy in Mining: Corporate Strategy and Planning for Closure*, ed. A Warhurst, L Noronha, pp. 117–43. London/New York: Lewis
34. EPA. 2004. *Liquid assets 2000: Americans pay for dirty water.* http://www.epa.gov/water/liquidassets/dirtywater.html
35. Sengupta M. 1993. *Environmental Impacts of Mining Monitoring, Restoration, and Control.* Boca Raton, FL: Lewis
36. UN Environ. Program. 1991. Environmental aspects of selected non-ferrous metals ore mining: a technical guide. *UN Environ. Program, Tech. Rep. Ser. 5*, New York
37. Azcue J, ed. 1999. *Environmental Impacts of Mining Activities: Emphasis on Mitigation and Remedial Measures.* Berlin/New York: Springer-Verlag
38. Dhar B. 2000. *Mining and Environment.* New Delhi: APH
39. Hester RE, Harrison RM, eds. 1994. *Mining and Its Environmental Impact.* Cambridge: R. Soc. Chem.
40. Mudder T, Botz M, Smith A. 2004. *The Cyanide Compendium.* London: Mining J. Books
41. Lacerda LD, Salomons W. 1998. *Mercury from Gold and Silver Mining: A Chemical Time Bomb?* Berlin: Springer-Verlag
42. Hodges CA. 1995. Mineral resources,

environmental issues and land use. *Science* 268(5215):1305–12
43. Marsh GP. 1864 (1965). *Man and Land: or Physical Geography as Modified by Human Action*, p. 462. Cambridge: Harvard Univ. Press
44. Furness RW, Rainbow PS. 1990. *Heavy Metals in the Marine Environment*. Boca Raton, FL: CRC
45. Kim C, Bloom N, Rytuba J, Brown G. 2003. Mercury speciation by x-ray absorption fine structure spectroscopy and sequential chemical extractions: a comparison of speciation methods. *Environ. Sci. Technol.* 37:5102–8
46. Nriagu JO. 1990. Global metal pollution. *Environment* 32(7):7–11, 28–33
47. Nriagu JO. 1994. Mercury pollution from the past mining of gold and silver in the Americas. *Sci. Total Environ.* 149(3):167
48. Nriagu JO. 1996. History of global metal pollution. *Science* 272(5259):223–24
49. Bowles IA, Prickett GT. 2001. The growing footprint: resource investments expand further into the humid tropics. In *Footprints in the Jungle: Natural Resource Industries, Infrastructure, and Biodiversity Conservation*, ed. IA Bowles, GT Prickett, pp. 3–6. New York: Oxford Univ. Press
50. Conserv. Int. 2000. *Lightening the Lode: A Guide to Responsible Large Scale Mining*, p. 1. Washington, DC: Conserv. Int. Policy
51. Bridge G. 2004. Mapping the bonanza: geographies of mining investment in an era of neo-liberal reform. *Prof. Geogr.* 56(3):406–21
52. Warhurst A, Franklin K. 2001. Biodiversity conservation, minerals extraction and development: towards a realistic partnership. See Ref. 49, pp. 183–203
53. Cleary D. 1990. *Anatomy of the Amazon Gold Rush*. Iowa City: Univ. Iowa Press
54. Peterson G, Heemskerk M. 2001. Deforestation and forest regeneration following small-scale gold mining in the Amazon: the case of Suriname. *Environ. Conserv.* 28(2):117–26
55. Hilson G. 2002. Small-scale mining in Africa: tackling pressing environmental problems with improved strategy. *J. Environ. Dev.* 11(2):149–74
56. Howard M. 1993. Small-scale mining and the environment in SE Asia. In *Asia's Environmental Crisis*, ed. M Howard, pp. 73–110. Boulder, CO: Westview
57. Ogola J, Mitullah W, Omulo M. 2002. Impact of gold mining on the environment and human health: a case study in the Migori gold belt, Kenya. *Environ. Geochem. Health* 24(2):141–58
58. *Eng. Min. J.* 1995. AIDS now number one South African mining hazard. *Eng. Min. J.* 196(11):14
59. The World Bank. 2004. *HIV/AIDS and mining*. http://www.worldbank.org/ogmc/wbminingaids.htm
60. United Mine Work. Am. 2004. *Black Lung*. http://www.umwa.org/blacklung/blacklung.shtml
61. Porter ME. 1990. *The Competitive Advantage of Nations*. New York: Free Press
62. Bauer PT, Yamey BS. 1957. *The Economics of Under-Developed Countries*. Chicago: Univ. Chicago Press
63. Warhurst A, ed. 2001. *Mining and the Environment: Case Studies from the Americas*. Ottawa: Int. Dev. Res. Cent.
64. Porter ME, van der Linde C. 1995. Green and competitive: ending the stalemate. *Harv. Bus. Rev.* 73(5):120–37
65. Schmidheiny S, Zorraquin F. 1996. *Financing Change: The Financial Community, Eco-Efficiency and Sustainable Development*. London: MIT Press
66. Hilson G. 2003. Eco-efficiency: improving environmental management strategy in the primary extraction industry. *J. Environ. Syst.* 29(1):1–11
67. Warhurst A. 1991. *Environmental degradation from mining and mineral processing: corporate policies and national responses*. Discuss. Doc. Phase 1 Min.

Environ. Res. Network. Sci. Policy Res. Unit, Univ. Sussex
68. Purcell S, Anderson K. 1993. Pollution prevention in mining and mineral processing. *Proc. Int. Conf. Pollut. Prev. Min. Miner. Process., Snowmass Village, Colo.*, Aug. 24–27. Golden: Colo. Sch. Mines
69. Warhurst A, Bridge G. 1997 Economic liberalization, innovation and technology transfer: opportunities for cleaner production in the minerals industry. *Nat. Resour. Forum* 21(1):1–12
70. Hilson G. 2000. Barriers to implementing cleaner technologies and cleaner production practices in the mining industry: a case study of the Americas. *Miner. Eng.* 13(7): 699–717
71. Hilson G, Murck B. 2001. Progress toward pollution prevention and waste minimization in the North American gold mining industry. *J. Clean. Prod.* 9:405–15
72. Hilson G. 2002/2003. Eco-efficiency: Improving environmental management strategy in the primary extraction industry. *J. Environ. Syst.* 29(1):1–14
73. Sanchez M, Vergara F, Castro H, eds. 1996. *Clean Technology for the Mining Industry.* Concepción, Chile: Univ. Concepción
74. Brundenius C, ed. 2003. *Technological Change and the Environmental Imperative: Challenges to the Copper Industry.* Cheltenham, Engl./Northampton MA: Elgar
75. Monhemius A. 1996. Hydrometallurgy—the clean solution for metal production? See Ref. 73, pp. 13–23
76. Brewis T. 1995. Metal extraction by bacterial oxidation. *Min. Mag.*, Oct., pp. 197–207
77. Krauss R. 1994. Homestake's McLauglin Mine. In *Proc. Int. Conf. Pollut. Prev. Min. Miner. Process.*, *Snowmass Village, Colo.*, Aug. 24–27, 1993, pp. 108–16. Golden: Colo. Sch. Mines
78. Ali S, Behrendt L. 2001. Mining and indigenous rights. *Cult. Surviv. Q.* 25(1):6–8
79. Offen K. 2003. The territorial turn: making black territories in Pacific Colombia. *J. Lat. Am. Geogr.* 2(1):43–73
80. Warhurst A, Bridge G. 1997. Financing environmental performance strategies. *Min. Finance* April:54–56
81. Pratt DJ. 2001. Corporations, communities, and conservation: the Mountain Institute and Antamina Mining Company. *Calif. Manag. Rev.* 43(3):38–43
82. ISIS Asset Manag. 2004. *Are extractive companies compatible with biodiversity? Extractive industries and biodiversity: a survey.* Available from ISIS Asset Manag., London. http://www.isisam.com
83. Frederickson P. 1999. Trade, global policy, and the environment: new evidence and issues. In *Trade, Global Policy and the Environment*, ed. P Frederickson, pp. 1–11. Washington, DC: World Bank
84. 1990. *Environment: the bottom line. Mining J.* 23 (Suppl.):1
85. Bomsel O. 1990. *Mining and Metallurgy Investment: The End of Large Projects?* Paris: OECD
86. Pearson LB. 1969. *Partners in Development: Report of the Commission on International Development.* New York: Praeger
87. Braz. Secr. Plann. 1984. *The Greater Carajás Program: Legislation and Norms.* Brasília: Pres. Repub. Braz.
88. Freyman A. 1974. Mineral resources and economic growth. *Finance Dev.* 11(1):20–23, 34
89. Banks G. 1993. Mining multinationals and developing countries: theory and practice in Papua New Guinea. *Appl. Geogr.* 13(4):313–27
90. Bosson R, Varon B. 1977. *The Mining Industry and the Developing Countries.* New York: World Bank/Oxford Univ. Press
91. Naito K, Remy F, Williams JP. 2001. *World Bank Review of Legal and Fiscal*

Frameworks for Exploration and Mining. London: Min. J. Books
92. Bugnosen E, Twigg J, Andrew S. 2000. Economic issues: small-scale mining legislation and regulatory frameworks. *Ind. Environ.* 23:50–54
93. Quiroga E. 2002. The case of artisanal mining in Bolivia: local participatory development and mining investment opportunities. *Nat. Resour. Forum* 26(2):127–39
94. Hollaway J. 1997. Mining and sustainable development. Small-scale mining: how to combine development with low environmental impact. *Ind. Environ.* 20(4):44–49
95. Barry M. 1996. Regularizing informal mining. *Summary Proc. Int. Roundtable Artisanal Min.* Washington, DC: World Bank/Ind. Energy Dep.
96. Jennings NS, Soumaïla A, Martínez-Castilla Z, Estrella-Gust D. 1999. *Child labour in small-scale mining: examples from Niger, Peru and Philippines.* Sect. Act. Program. Geneva: Int. Labor Organ.
97. Phillips LC, Semboja H, Shukla GP, Sezinga R, Mutagwaba W, et al. 2001. *Tanzania's Precious Minerals Boom: Issues in Mining and Marketing.* Equity Growth Econ. Res. (EAGER). Arlington, VA: US Agency Int. Dev.
98. Labonne B. 1996. Artisanal mining: an economic stepping stone for women. *Nat. Resour. Forum* 20(2):117–22
99. Heemskerk M. 2003. Self employment and poverty alleviation: women's work in artisanal gold mines. *Hum. Organ.* 62(1):62–73
100. Power TM. 1996. *Lost Landscapes and Failed Economies: The Search for a Value of Place*, p. 238. Washington, DC: Island Press
101. Davis GA. 1998 Learning to love the Dutch disease: evidence from mineral economies. *World Dev.* 23:1766–79
102. Auty RL. 1993. *Sustaining Development in Mineral Economies: The Resource Curse Thesis*, p. 1. New York: Routledge
103. Auty RM. 1991. Mismanaged mineral dependence—Zambia 1970–90. *Resour. Policy* 17(3):170–83
104. Auty RM. 1994. The resource curse thesis: minerals in Bolivian development, 1970–90. *Singapore J. Trop. Geogr.* 15(2):95–111
105. Auty RM. 1998. Mineral wealth and the economic transition: Kazakstan. *Resour. Policy* 24(4):241–49
106. Gelb B. 1988. *Oil Windfalls: Blessing or Curse?* World Bank: Oxford Univ. Press
107. Kremers J. 1986. The Dutch disease in the Netherlands. In *Natural Resources and the Macroeconomy*, ed. JP Neary, S van Wijnbergen, pp. 96–136. Cambridge, MA: MIT Press
108. Freudenburg WR, Wilson LJ. 2002. Mining the data: analyzing the economic implications of mining for nonmetropolitan regions. *Sociol. Inq.* 72:549–78
109. Davis GA. 1998. The minerals sector, sectoral analysis, and economic development. *Resour. Policy* 24(4):217–28
110. Shafer DM. 1986. Undermined: the implications of mineral export dependent for state formation in Africa. *Third World Q.* 8:916–52
111. McPhail K. 2000. How oil, gas, and mining projects can contribute to development. *Finance Dev.* 37(4):46–49
112. Friends Earth. 2002. *Phasing out international financing institutions financing for fossil fuel and mining project: demanding local community self-determination.* http://www.foe.org/res/pubs/pdf/FFMeng
113. Ross M. 2001. *Extractive sectors and the poor.* Boston/Washington: Oxfam Am. http://www.oxfamamerica.org/pdfs/eireport.pdf
114. Davis GA, Tilton JE. 2002. *Should developing countries renounce mining? A perspective on the debate.* Int. Counc. Miner. Met.. http://www.icmm.com/uploads/62TiltonDavisfinalversion.pdf
115. Penn. Dep. Environ. Prot. Donora smog kills 20, Oct., 1948. http://www.dep.

state.pa.us/dep/Rachel_Carson/donora.htm
116. US EPA. 2004. Toxic release inventory (TRI) explorer online. *Chem. Rep.*, *(Met. Min. Ind. SIC Code 10) for all chemicals, U.S., 2001 data*. http://www.epa.gov/triexplorer/
117. US EPA. 2001. *Toxic release inventory (TRI) explorer online. Chem. Rep. Note Ind. (Met. Min. SIC Code 10) Chem. Releases Rep*. www.epa.gov/triexplorer/industry.htm. TRI Progr. Div., Office Info. Anal. Access, Environ. Prot. Agency, Wash., D.C.
118. Kelly M. 1988. *Mining and the Freshwater Environment*, p. ix. London/New York: Elsevier Appl. Sci.
119. Warhurst A, Noronha L. 2000. *Environmental Policy in Mining: Corporate Strategy and Planning for Closure*. Boca Raton, FL: Lewis
120. World Bank. 2002. *It's Not Over When It's Over: Mine Closure Around the World*. Washington, DC: World Bank
121. Warhurst A, Mitchell P. 2000. Corporate social responsibility and the case of Summitville mine. *Resour. Policy* 26(2):91–102
122. Pasquale C, Maxwell P. 2003. Mine closure legislation in Indonesia: the role of mineral industry involvement. *Nat. Resour. Forum* 27(1):42–52
123. Robertson AM, Shaw SC. 1999. The concept of custodial transfer of mined land. *Mine Water Environ., Int. Mine Water Assoc. Congr., Sevilla, Spain, 13–17 Sept.*
124. Lovins A. 1973. *Red Alert: Open Pit Mining*. London: Earth Island
125. Wellmer FW, Becker-Platten JD. 2002. Sustainable development and the exploitation of mineral and energy resources: a review. *Int. J. Earth Sci.* 91:723–45
126. Natl. Res. Counc. 2004. *Materials Count: The Case for Material Flows Analysis*. Washington, DC: Natl. Acad. Sci.
127. Geiser K. 2001. *Materials Matter: Towards a Sustainable Materials Policy*. Cambridge, MA: MIT Press
128. Young J. 1992. *Mining the Earth*. Washington, DC: WorldWatch Inst.
129. Joyce S, Thomson I. 2002. Two cultures of sustainable development. *PDAC Commun*. Toronto, Can: PDAC
130. World Comm. Environ. Dev. 1987. *Our Common Future*. Oxford/New York: Oxford Univ. Press
131. Sterna DI. 1995. The contribution of the mining sector to sustainability in developing countries. *Ecol. Econ.* 13(1):53–63
132. Eggert R. 1995. Editorial: Sustainability and resources policy. *Resour. Policy* 21(1):34–35
133. Blignaut JN, Hassan RM. 2002. Assessment of the performance and sustainability of mining sub-soil assets for economic development in South Africa. *Ecol. Econ.* 40(1):89–101
134. Solow R. 1993. An almost practical step toward sustainability. *Resour. Policy* 19(3):162–72
135. Mikesell R. 1994. Sustainable development and mineral resources. *Resour. Policy* 20(2):83–86
136. Tilton JE. 1996. Exhaustible resources and sustainable development: two different paradigms. *Resour. Policy* 22(1/2):91–97
137. Cooney J. 2001. Nongovernmental organizations: friend or foe? In *Politics of Mining: What They Don't Teach You in School*, ed. D Malhotra, pp. 87–96. Littleton, CO: Soc. Min. Metall. Explor.
138. Lanning G, Mueller M. 1973. *Africa Undermined: Mining Companies and the Underdevelopment of Africa*. Harmondsworth, Engl.: Penguin Books
139. Frank AG. 1967. *Capitalism and Underdevelopment in Latin America: Historical Studies of Chile and Brazil*. New York: Monthly Rev. Press
140. Gaventa J. 1980. *Power and Powerlessness: Quiescence and Rebellion in an*

Appalachian Valley. Urbana: Univ. Ill. Press
141. Gedicks A. 1993. *The New Resource Wars: Native and Environmental Struggles Against Multinational Corporations.* Boston: South End Press
142. Cousins D, Nieuwenhuysen J. 1984. *Aboriginals and the Mining Industry: Case Studies of the Australian Experience.* Sydney/London: Allen & Unwin
143. Tsokhas K. 1986. *Beyond Dependence: Companies, Labour Processes and Australian Mining.* Melbourne: Oxford Univ. Press
144. Lowe M. 1998. *Premature Bonanza: Stand-off at Voisey's Bay.* Toronto: Transcontinental
145. Regan C, Walsh F. 1976. Dependence and underdevelopment: the case of mineral resources and the Irish Republic. *Antipode* 8(3):46–59
146. Bunker S. 1985 *Underdeveloping the Amazon: Extraction, Unequal Exchange, and the Failure of the Modern State.* Urbana: Univ. Ill. Press
147. Barham B, Bunker S, O'Hearn D. 1994. *States, Firms, and Raw Materials: The World Economy and Ecology of Aluminum.* Madison: Univ. Wis. Press
148. Muradian R, Martinez-Alier J. 2001. *Globalization and Poverty: An Ecological Perspective.* Berlin: Heinrich Boll Found. http://www.boell.de/en/04_thema/1190.html
149. Leith D. 2002. Freeport and the Suharto regime, 1965–1998. *Contemp. Pac.* 14(1):69–100
150. Spude R. 1989. Native Americans and Gold Rushes: two views, 1860s Arizona and the Apaches, 1900s Alaska and the Eskimo. In *Towards a Social History of Mining in the 19th and 20th Centuries,* ed. K Tenfelde, pp. 213–22. Munich: Verlag CH Beck
151. Howitt R, Connell J, Hirsch P, eds. 1996. *Resources, Nations and Indigenous Peoples: Case Studies from Australasia, Melanesia and Southeast Asia.* Melbourne/New York: Oxford Univ. Press
152. Denoon D. 2000. *Getting Under the Skin: the Bougainville Copper Agreement and the Creation of the Panguna Mine.* Victoria: Melbourne Univ. Press
153. Strelein L, Behrendt L. 2001. Old habits die hard: indigenous land rights and mining in Australia. *Cult. Surviv. Q.* 25(1):51–53
154. Shanahan T. (n.d.) *CEO Chamber of Minerals and Energy, Western Australia.* Cited in *National Native Title Tribunal, 10 Years of Native Title Information Kit.* http://www.nntt.gov.au
155. Le Billon P. 2001. The political ecology of war: natural resources and armed conflicts. *Polit. Geogr.* 20(5):561–84
156. Watts M. 2001. Petro-violence: community, extraction, and political ecology of a mythic commodity. In *Violent Environments,* ed. N Peluso, M Watts, pp. 189–212. Ithaca/London: Cornell Univ. Press
157. Sadler D. 2004. Trade unions, coalitions and communities: Australia's construction, forestry, mining and energy union and the international stakeholder campaign against Rio Tinto. *Geoforum* 35:35–46
158. Howitt R. 2001. *Rethinking Resource Management: Justice, Sustainability and Indigenous Peoples.* London/New York: Routledge
159. Evans G, Goodman J, Lansbury N, eds. 2002. *Moving Mountains: Communities Confront Mining and Globalization.* London/New York: Zed Books
160. O'Faircheallaigh C. 2001. Resource development and inequality in indigenous societies. *World Dev.* 26:381–95
161. Tujan A, Bella Guzman R. 2002. *Globalizing Philippine Mining.* Manila: IBON Found.
162. Forest Peoples Programme. 2000. *Undermining the Forests: The Need to Control Transnational Mining Companies.*

Moreton-in-Marsh, UK: Forest Peoples Programme

163. Low N, Gleeson B. 1998. Situating justice in the environment: the case of BHP at the Ok Tedi Copper Mine. *Antipode* 30:201–26

164. Banks G. 2002. Mining and the environment in Melanesia: contemporary debates reviewed. *Contemp. Pac.* 14(1):39–67

165. Klubock T. 1998. *Contested Communities: Class, Gender, and Politics in Chile's El Teniente Copper Mine, 1904–1951*. Durham, NC: Duke Univ. Press

166. Ballard C, Banks G. 2003. Resource wars: the anthropology of mining. *Annu. Rev. Anthropol.* 32:287–313

167. Taussig MT. 1980. *The Devil and Commodity Fetishism in South America*. Chapel Hill: Univ. N.C.

168. Godoy R. 1990. *Mining and Agriculture in Highland Bolivia: Ecology, History, and Commerce Among the Jukumanis*. Tucson: Univ. Ariz. Press

169. DeWind J. 1987. *Peasants Become Miners: The Evolution of Industrial Mining Systems in Peru, 1902–1974*. New York: Garland

170. Scheyvens R, Lagisa L. 1998. Women, disempowerment and resistance: an analysis of logging and mining activities in the Pacific. *Singap. J. Trop. Geogr.* 19(1):51–70

171. Bantjes R, Trussler R. 1999. Feminism and the grass roots: women and environmentalism in Nova Scotia, 1980–1983. *Can. Rev. Sociol. Anthropol.* 36(2):179–97

172. Tallichet SE. 2000. Barriers to women's advancement in underground coal mining. *Rural Sociol.* 65(2):234–52

173. Zanjani S. 1997. *A Mine of Her Own: Women Prospectors in the American West 1850–1950*. Lincoln/London: Univ. Neb. Press

174. Girvan N. 1976. *Corporate Imperialism: Conflict and Expropriation, Transnational Corporations and Economic Nationalism in the Third World*, p. 3. White Plains, NY: Sharpe

175. Mumford L. 1934. *Technics and Civilization*, p. 70. New York: Harcourt Brace

176. Williams R. 1990. *Notes on the Underground*. Cambridge, MA: MIT Press

176a. Lord Ashley. 1842. *Rep. Comm. Labour Women Child. Mines. Parliam. Pap. XV-XVII*. London: Br. Parliam.

177. Thesing WB, ed. 2000. *Caverns of Night: Coal Mines in Art, Literature and Film*, p. xii. Columbia: Univ. S. C. Press

178. Gall S. 2003. *Subterranea*. New York/London: Umbrage/Turnaround

179. Bridge G. 2001. Resource triumphalism: postindustrial narratives of primary commodity production. *Environ. Plann. A* 33:2149–73

180. Trigger D. 1997. Mining, landscape and the culture of development ideology in Australia. *Ecumene* 4(2):161–80

181. Hyndman D. 2001. Academic responsibilities and representation of the Ok Tedi crisis in postcolonial Papua New Guinea. *Contemp. Pac.* 13(1):33–54

182. Watts M. 1999. *Petro-Violence: some thoughts on community, extraction and political ecology*. Berkeley Workshop Environ. Polit., Work. Pap. 99–1

183. Brechin G. 2002. *Imperial San Francisco: Urban Power, Earthly Ruin*. Berkeley/Los Angeles: Univ. Calif. Press

184. Marx L. 1964. *The Machine in the Garden: Technology and the Pastoral Ideal in America*. Oxford/New York: Oxford Univ. Press

185. Nye DE. 1994. *American Technological Sublime*. Cambridge, MA: MIT Press

186. Josephson P. 2002. *Industrialized Nature: Brute Force Technology and the Transformation of the Natural World*. Washington, DC: Island Press

187. Rickard TA. 1932. *A History of American Mining*. New York/London: McGraw-Hill

188. Heath KC. 1975. Foreword. In *Minerals*

and the Environment: Proceedings of an International Symposium, London, 4–7 June 1974, pp. x–xi, ed. M Jones, Inst. Min. Metall., Inst. Quarr. Inst. Min. Eng.
189. O'Connor M. 1992. The system of capitalized nature. *Capital. Nat. Social.* 3(3):86–89
190. Quam-Wickham N. 1999. Rereading man's conquest of nature: skill, myth and the historical construction of masculinity in western extractive industries. *Men Masc.* 2(2):135–51
190a. Mol A. 2001. *Globalization and Environmental Reform: The Ecological Modernization of the Global Economy*. Cambridge/London: MIT Press
191. Environ. Law Inst. 2004 *Prior Informed Consent and Mining: Promoting the Sustainable Development of Local Communities*. Washington, DC: ELI
192. Extr. Ind. Rev. 2003. Striking a better balance. *Final Rep. Extr. Ind. Rev.* http://www.eireview.org
193. Wilson R. 2003. *The Extractive Industries and Protected Areas.* Chairman's Speech, World Parks Congr., Durban, South Afr., 16 Sept. http://www.icmm.com/news/161WPC-RPWpresentation160903.pdf

GRAZING SYSTEMS, ECOSYSTEM RESPONSES, AND GLOBAL CHANGE

Gregory P. Asner,[1,2] Andrew J. Elmore,[1] Lydia P. Olander,[1] Roberta E. Martin,[1] and A. Thomas Harris[1]

[1]*Department of Global Ecology, Carnegie Institution of Washington, Stanford, California 94305; email: aelmore@globalecology.stanford.edu, lolander@globalecology.stanford.edu, robin@globalecology.stanford.edu, thomas@globalecology.stanford.edu*

[2]*Department of Geological and Environmental Sciences, Stanford University, Stanford, California 94305; email: gasner@globalecology.stanford.edu*

Key Words agriculture, deforestation, desertification, land-use change, woody encroachment

■ **Abstract** Managed grazing covers more than 25% of the global land surface and has a larger geographic extent than any other form of land use. Grazing systems persist under marginal bioclimatic and edaphic conditions of different biomes, leading to the emergence of three regional syndromes inherent to global grazing: desertification, woody encroachment, and deforestation. These syndromes have widespread but differential effects on the structure, biogeochemistry, hydrology, and biosphere-atmosphere exchange of grazed ecosystems. In combination, these three syndromes represent a major component of global environmental change.

CONTENTS

INTRODUCTION	262
THE GLOBAL FOOTPRINT OF GRAZING SYSTEMS	263
Basic Demographic Patterns	263
GIS Analysis of Bioclimatic and Edaphic Conditions	263
Regional Syndromes in the Global Grazing Footprint	269
DESERTIFICATION	271
Ecosystem Structure	271
Biogeochemistry	273
Trace-Gas Emissions	275
Hydrology	276
Climate Interactions	277
WOODY ENCROACHMENT	278
Ecosystem Structure	278
Biogeochemistry	280
Trace-Gas Emissions	281

1543-5938/04/1121-0261$14.00

Hydrology	281
Climate Interactions	282
DEFORESTATION	282
Ecosystem Structure	282
Biogeochemistry	283
Trace-Gas and Aerosol Emissions	284
Hydrology	285
Climate Interactions	286
ECOSYSTEM RESPONSES TO MANAGED GRAZING	286
Response Typologies	286
Knowledge Gaps and Research Needs	289

INTRODUCTION

Managed grazing occupies more than 33 million square kilometers or 25% of the global land surface, making it the single most extensive form of land use on the planet. Managed grazing systems are defined here as any geographically extensive operation designed for the production of animals for consumption, including for meat, milk, and any major animal products. Recent work indicates that managed grazing systems have increased more than 600% in geographic extent (from about 5.3 M km^2) during the past three centuries (1). More than 1.5 billion "animal units" (AU)[1] were present in managed grazing systems on Earth in 1990 (2).

Despite these impressive statistics, there are surprisingly few synthetic reports on how managed grazing systems affect global ecological, atmospheric, or hydrological processes. The predominance of site-specific perspectives on ecosystem responses to managed grazing has led to a fragmented understanding of this important land use as a contributor to global environmental change. Given the importance of managed grazing systems to the subsistence of the human population, and given the increasing role that land degradation plays in determining the long-term sustainability of pastoral practices throughout the world (3), a global-scale overview based on available scientific data is overdue.

In this review, we develop a perspective on ecosystem responses to managed grazing. We employ a basic geographic information system (GIS) analysis and a literature review to determine the environmental "footprint" of grazing systems throughout the world. In this case, the footprint represents responses of ecosystems to managed grazing relative to global bioclimatic and edaphic variability. We find that managed grazing occupies bioclimatically and edaphically marginal lands throughout much of the world and that these conditions predispose current rangelands to three regional syndromes—desertification, woody encroachment, and deforestation. We use these syndromes as an organizing framework to synthesize

---

[1]An animal unit (AU) is defined as the number of cattle, buffalo, sheep, goats, horses, and camels weighted by their relative size and growth rates [AU = n (cows + buffalo) + 0.2 n (sheep + goats) + 1.2 n (horses + camels)] (2).

GRAZING SYSTEMS AND GLOBAL CHANGE   C-1

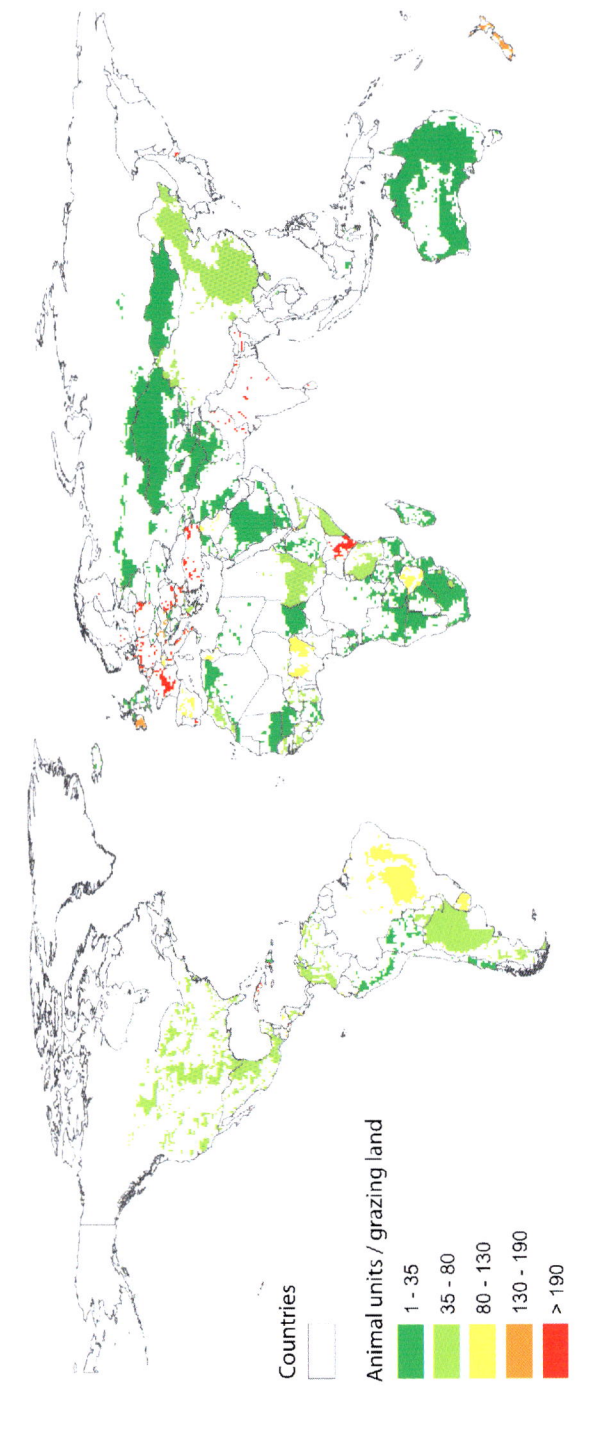

Figure 1 The present global distribution of grazing extent and intensity (stocking rates), derived by combining References 1 and 2.

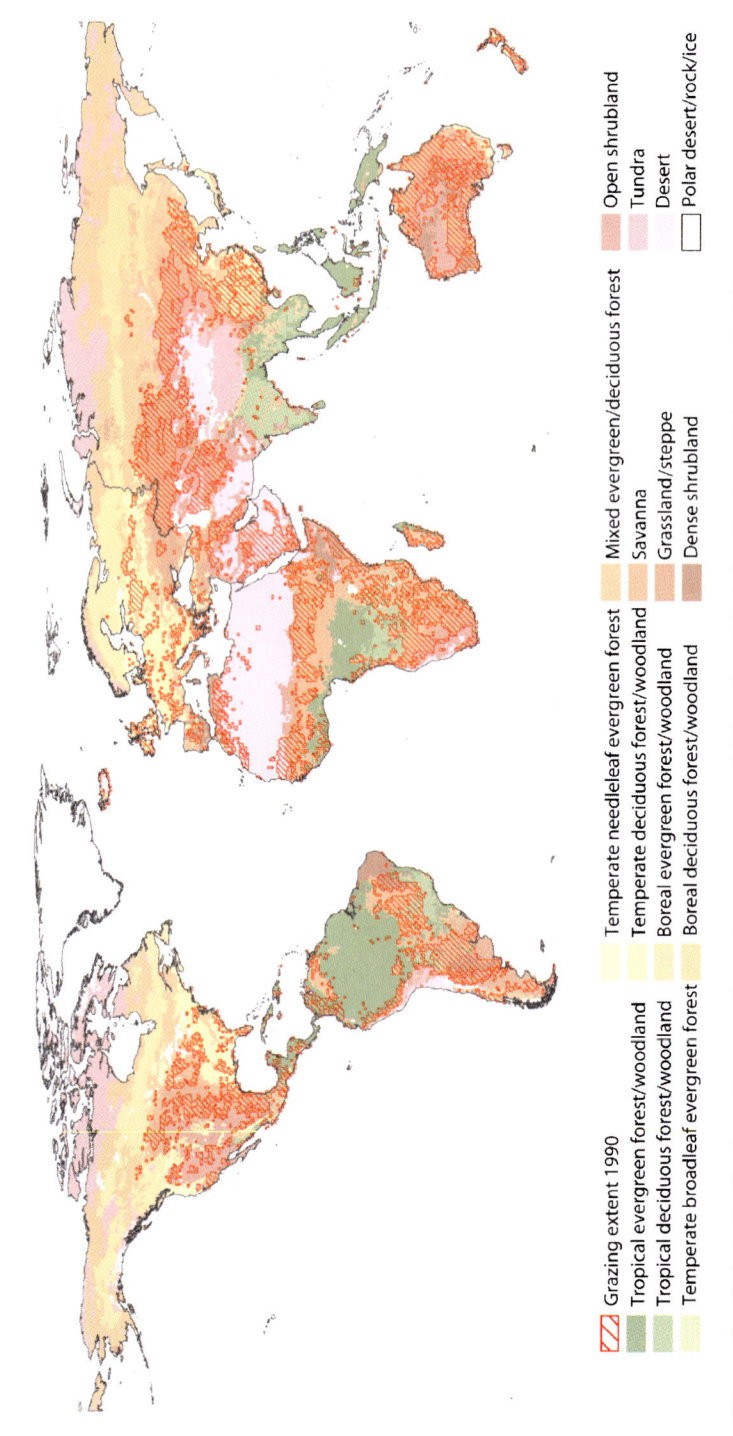

Figure 3 Global distribution of managed grazing systems overlaid on the global distribution of biomes (1, 160).

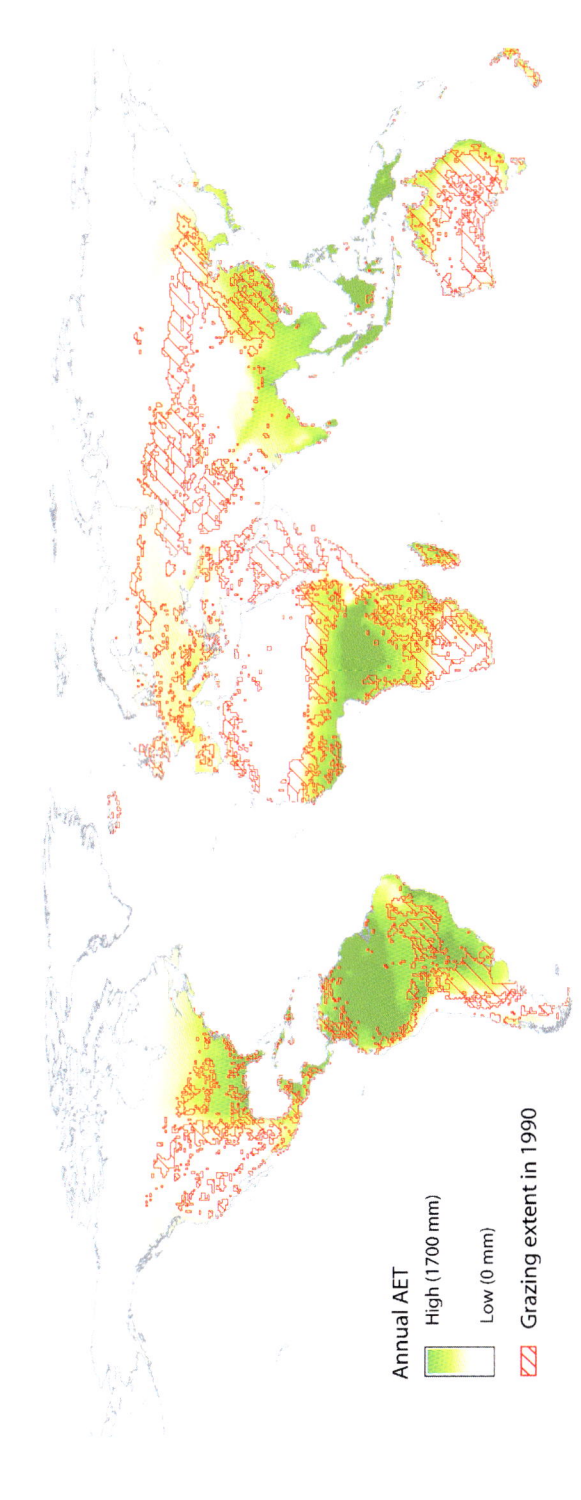

Figure 4a Global distribution of managed grazing systems and actual evapotranspiration (AET), a metric of bioclimatic stress. Derived by combining References 1 and 8.

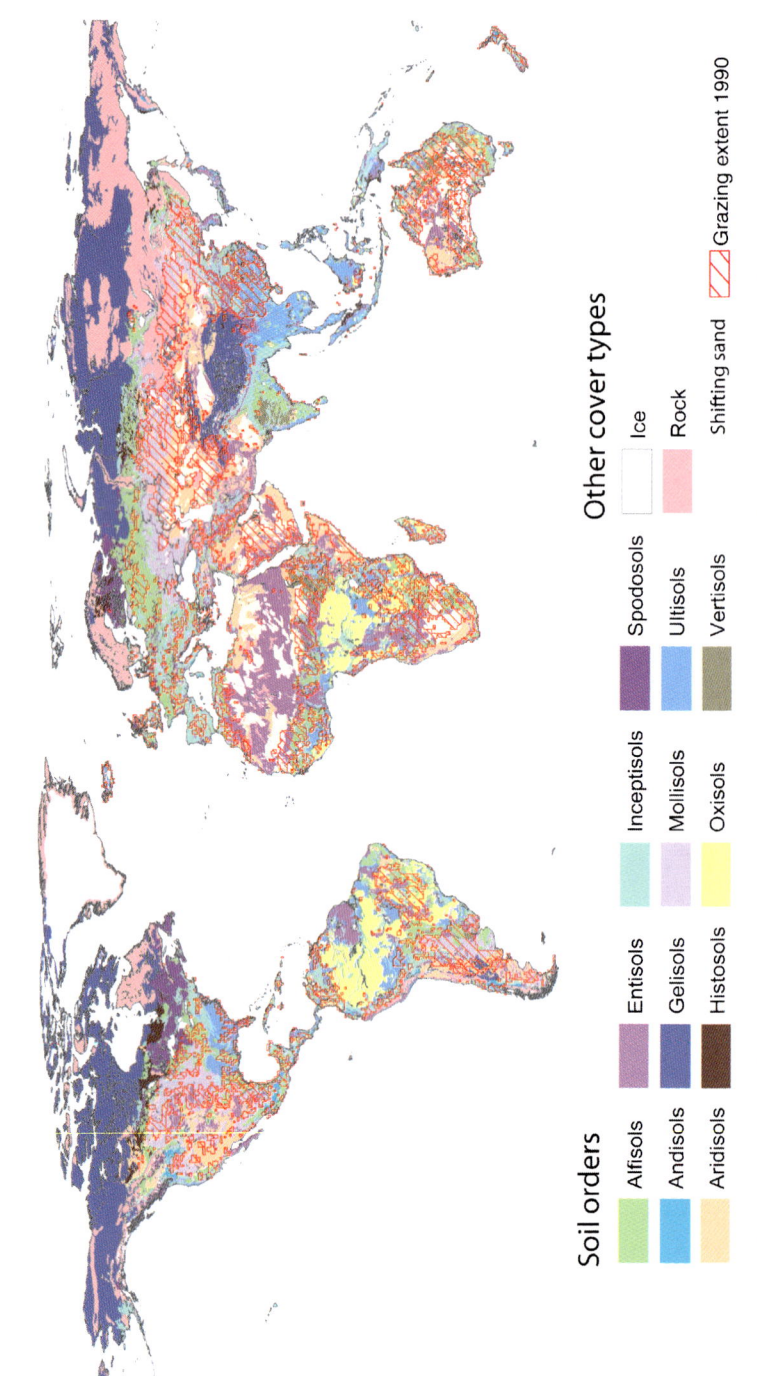

Figure 4c Global distribution of managed grazing systems and soil taxonomic order. Derived by combining References 1 and 10.

the impacts of managed grazing on ecosystem structure, biogeochemistry, hydrology, and biosphere-atmosphere interactions. We contend that these syndromes, when taken in combination, represent a major component of global environmental change.

THE GLOBAL FOOTPRINT OF GRAZING SYSTEMS

Basic Demographic Patterns

Combining global grazing area in 1990 (1) with country-level stocking rates [AU per grazed area; (2)], we estimated the geographic extent and intensity of managed grazing systems worldwide (Figure 1, see color insert). The five countries with most land area in grazing systems are Australia, 4.4 M km^2; China, 4.0 M km^2; United States, 2.4 M km^2; Brazil, 1.7 M km^2; and Argentina, 1.4 M km^2. However, based on the fraction of total land area each nation uses for grazing, Mongolia, Botswana, and Uruguay lead with 80%, 76%, and 76%, respectively. Countries with the highest stocking rates are Malaysia, 320 AU km^{-2}; India, 272 AU km^{-2}; N. Korea, 213 AU km^{-2}; and Vietnam, 184; others are found in central Europe and the Middle East. Countries containing large tracts of dryland grazing systems, such as in Australia, Argentina, and the United States, have low stocking rates.

Our GIS analyses of grazing extent, grazing intensity, and human demographic statistics reveal very few correlates (Figure 2). Grazing land area is well correlated with total land area of each country (r = 0.79, $p < 0.05$). However, the total number of animal units per country is weakly correlated with both grazing area (r = 0.50, $p < 0.05$) and total land area (r = 0.60, $p < 0.05$). Grazing intensity—stocking rates at the country level—is not correlated with grazing area or total land area (Figure 2). By far the strongest relationship is found between human population and the number of grazing animals per country (r = 0.91, $p < 0.01$). Human population growth is likely to increase demand for meat and dairy products, which will have to be met by a combination of increasing intensification and continued extensification, as has been observed over the past 300 or more years. Evidence reported in the following sections suggests that grazing extensification cannot occur without continued major changes in global land cover, and that intensification will also have significant environmental impacts.

GIS Analysis of Bioclimatic and Edaphic Conditions

The global footprint of managed grazing, which implicitly represents human decisions on where to develop grazing systems, spans a gradient of identifiable environmental conditions presented in this section. We show that managed grazing dominates in the marginal bioclimatic and edaphic regions of drylands. Grazing occurs in the best bioclimatic areas of temperate forests and woodlands but is employed on marginal soils found throughout much of the humid tropics.

Country-level correlates

Grazing land area (km²) → Number of animals   0.50
Number of animals
Animal units / area grazing land
Mean annual PPT
Mean annual T
Topography
Land area (km²) → Grazing land area (km²)   0.79
Population 2000 → Number of animals   0.60
Population growth rate 2000
Percentage urban in 2000 ┐
Population density 2000 │
Fertility rate 1999   │
Birth rate 2000   └→ Number of animals   0.91
Net migration 2000
Death rate 2000
Life expectancy 2000
Infant mortality 2000
Literacy rate 2000
Gross domestic product 1999

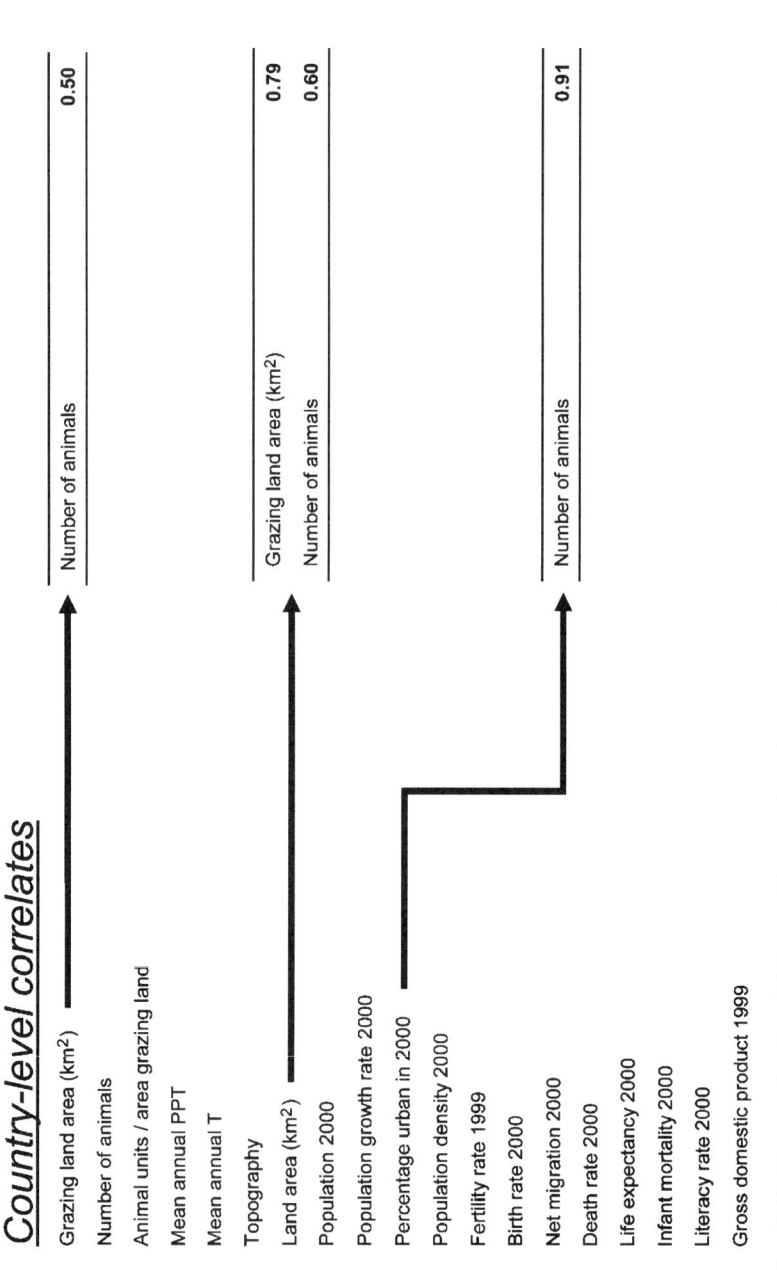

Figure 2 (*left*) Country-level variables used in a series of Pearson product-moment correlation analyses. (*right*) Correlations (r-values) of particular importance to determining linkages between land area, stocking rate, and human population size (all p-values < 0.05). All unreported correlations were weak and statistically insignificant. Derived by combining References 1, 2, and 8.

GIS analyses of global grazing by biome reveal that savannas, grasslands, shrublands, and deserts support the largest extent of managed pastoral systems (Figure 3, see color insert). In combination, these dryland biomes cover more than 67 M km^2 of the ~132 M km^2 total global biome area (Table 1). Although these biomes contribute about 51% of the total land area on the planet, they support a disproportionately high 78% of the global grazing area.

Outside of these dryland systems, other biomes support substantial levels of managed grazing. Roughly 30% and 56%, respectively, of temperate deciduous and temperate evergreen broadleaf forests and woodlands are now supporting grazing systems (Table 1); however, some studies indicate that the extent of grazing systems is decreasing in temperate forests following historically higher levels (4). About 1.7 M km^2 (or 10%) of tropical evergreen broadleaf forests have been cleared for managed grazing, and this area is growing annually in regions such as the Amazon basin, Congo, and Southeast Asia (5). Many believe that humid tropical ecosystems represent the only viable way to expand global grazing systems beyond its current geographic extent (6).

We sought to uncover the environmental conditions under which managed grazing occurs globally. Actual evapotranspiration (AET) was selected as an integrating metric of bioclimatic stress for vegetation growth, because AET is low in cold and/or dry regions and high in warm and/or wet areas. We analyzed the spatial extent of managed grazing relative to the AET for each biome (Figure 4a, see color insert). There is a clear bioclimatic footprint throughout global pastoral systems, evident even in using the coarse analyses afforded by available global GIS data (Table 1). In savannas, grasslands, and deserts, grazing systems persist in areas where AET is 20% to 25% lower than the average AET of each biome. Managed grazing is preferentially employed in areas that are much drier than the biome mean, as shown in Table 1, with the ratios of grazed biome:total biome annual precipitation ranging from 0.69 to 0.82 for savannas, grasslands, and deserts. These results suggest that the bioclimatically marginal portions of drylands service the global grazing enterprise and that other forms of land use (e.g., agriculture and urbanization) occupy the fraction of dryland biomes with less bioclimatic stress. Indeed, by overlaying the global extent of croplands (7) on the AET map (8) shown in Figure 4a, we found that agriculture persists on the fraction of dryland biomes with 47% to 203% higher AET than the biome average (map not shown).

In contrast to drylands, AET rates of grazing systems in temperate deciduous, evergreen, and mixed forests are 30% to 75% higher than their biome mean AET (Table 1). This trend persists in the extreme cold boreal and tundra regions. The managed grazing footprint is evident as grazing AET:mean biome AET ratios are from 1.20 to 1.75, most of which is explained by the preferential use of warmer regions for grazing practices in these cold ecoregions. Temperature conditions in the portion of boreal evergreen forests used for managed grazing are more than 300% warmer than the biome mean annual temperature. However, these are the extreme cases; boreal and tundra biomes support less than 1% of the global grazing enterprise (Table 1).

TABLE 1 Biome statistics of land area, managed grazing, and climatology

Biome[a]	Total area (M km²)	Percent of global land area	Area grazed (M km²)	Percent biome grazed	Mean grazing area AET	Mean biome AET	Grazing: biome AET	Grazing: biome MAP[b]	Grazing: biome MAT
Savanna	19.31	15	9.48	49.1	595	781	0.76	0.69	0.90
Grassland/steppe	14.22	11	7.68	54.0	321	401	0.80	0.75	0.59
Desert	15.45	12	1.97	12.8	71	88	0.81	0.82	0.95
Dense shrubland	6.01	5	2.73	45.4	314	339	0.93	0.90	0.96
Tropical evergreen forest/woodland	17.43	13	1.72	9.9	1114	1141	0.98	0.97	0.87
Temperate broadleaf evergreen forest/woodlands	1.26	1	0.71	56.0	821	818	1.00	1.00	1.00
Tropical deciduous forest/woodland	5.96	5	1.20	20.2	935	859	1.09	1.04	1.04
Boreal evergreen forest/woodland	6.36	5	0.08	1.2	424	354	1.20	0.78	3.03
Open shrubland	12.09	9	3.98	32.9	297	243	1.22	1.22	1.26
Boreal deciduous forest/woodland	2.18	2	0.02	1.1	435	352	1.24	1.45	0.45
Temperate deciduous forest/woodland	5.10	4	1.49	29.1	793	611	1.30	1.62	1.32
Temperate needleleaf evergreen forest/woodland	3.62	3	0.76	20.9	689	463	1.49	1.59	2.23
Evergreen/deciduous forest/woodland	15.68	12	1.26	8.0	642	369	1.74	1.50	1.67
Tundra	7.32	6	0.17	2.3	431	247	1.75	1.74	0.01

[a]Biomes are ordered by the ratio of actual evapotranspiration (AET) in grazed portions of each biome compared to the biome mean AET. Source data: Ramankutty & Foley (160), Hearn et al. (8), and Goldewijk et al. (1).
[b]Other abbreviations are MAP, mean annual precipitation, and MAT, mean annual temperature.

Mean annual AET is a metric of the average bioclimatic conditions of an ecosystem, but the manageability of grazing systems (and other forms of land use) is also largely determined by climate variability, which is not captured in a mean AET estimate. Regions with large interannual precipitation and temperature variation undergo climatic boom-bust cycles that strongly affect vegetation production, grazing capacity, and human living conditions. It is extremely difficult to assess the global footprint of grazing systems with respect to climate variability because long-term, spatially explicit climate records are not readily available. We used a 17-year satellite record of the normalized difference vegetation index (NDVI) (monthly temporal resolution; $1° \times 1°$ spatial resolution) to map the global interannual variability of vegetation greenness, which is highly correlated with primary production (9). We calculated absolute NDVI anomalies from the average annual climatic cycle, 1982–1999. We then compared this measure of vegetation variability to the global distribution of managed grazing (Figure 4b). This analysis shows that global grazing systems persist in nearly all regions with high NDVI variation (darker gray). Biomes with the highest NDVI variation are, in descending order of variance: savannas, temperate deciduous forest, shrublands, grasslands, and boreal systems. Within these biomes, grazing systems occur in zones that are 5% to 63% more variable in terms of vegetation cover and condition than the mean biome variability. Managed grazing is thus practiced in the biomes and within the regions of these biomes that experience substantial climatological and ecological variation.

Managed grazing systems also have a distinguishable global edaphic footprint. Soil types are shown by taxonomic order (10) along with global grazing extent in Figure 4c (see color insert). We calculated the statistical mode of soil type presence by taxonomic order for grazed areas of each biome and compared it to the mode of soil presence for the entire biome (Table 2). In savanna, shrubland, and desert biomes, grazing systems are predominantly found on marginal soils, such as aridisols and entisols, relative to the most common soils, alfisols, found globally in these biomes. In the colder boreal biomes, grazing takes place preferentially on alfisols and spodosols but not on frozen gelisols, which are the most common soil order found in these regions.

There also exists a clear edaphic footprint of grazing in humid tropical regions. Ultisols dominate grazing systems found in the Amazon basin, Congo, and Southeast Asia (Figure 4c), yet the most common soils found in these regions are oxisols (Table 2). Oxisols are widely recognized as nutrient poor and thus marginal for managed grazing systems (11). Ultisols, are more manageable in terms of fertility but are also often considered biogeochemically marginal. This global footprint of grazing systems is probably not a coincidence because ranch managers often select the best available soils (ultisols) (6). It is nevertheless surprising to observe a global footprint of managed grazing on soils in the humid tropics, as this area represents the summed effect of millions of ranch managers operating at small geographic scales throughout the world. Tropical deforestation is largely driven by an increasing need for grazing land, with grazing systems expanding in the humid tropics at a rate of $>15,000$ km^2 year^{-1} (12). The need for additional

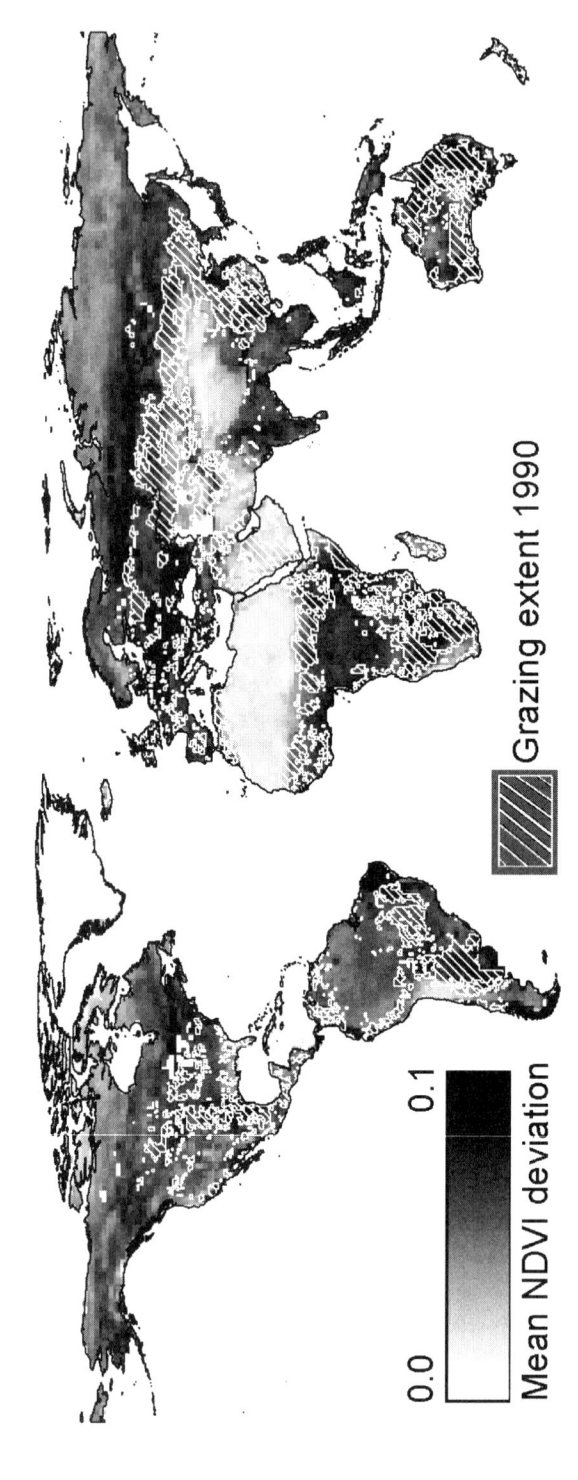

Figure 4b The global distribution of managed grazing systems and the interannual variability of vegetation production, as indicated by the satellite metric normalized difference vegetation index (NDVI). Mean NDVI deviation is the interannual variability of vegetation greenness, after accounting for mean monthly greenness. This record represents the period from 1982 to 1999. Derived from combined References 1 and 161.

TABLE 2 Global distribution of managed grazing systems by biome and taxonomic soil order

Biome[a]	Mode of soil order of grazing areas	Mode of soil order	
Tropical evergreen forest/woodland	Ultisols	Oxisols	⎫ Grazing on the more fertile soil
Tropical deciduous forest/woodland	Ultisols	Oxisols	⎭
Temperate broadleaf evergreen forest/woodlands	Ultisols	Histosols	
Temperate needleleaf evergreen forest/woodland	Alfisols	Alfisols	
Temperate deciduous forest/woodland	Inceptisols	Inceptisols	
Boreal evergreen forest/woodland	Alfisols	Gelisols	⎫
Boreal deciduous forest/woodland	Spodosols	Gelisols	⎬ Grazing on the unfrozen soils
Evergreen/deciduous mixed forest/woodland	Inceptisols	Gelisols	⎭
Grassland/steppe	Mollisols	Mollisols	
Savanna	Entisols	Alfisols	⎫
Dense shrubland	Aridisols	Alfisols	⎬ Grazing on the less fertile soils
Open shrubland	Aridisols	Alfisols	
Desert	Aridisols	Entisols	⎭

[a]Source data: Klein Goldewijk et al. (1), Ramankutty & Foley (160), USDA (10).

grazing land results in part from human population growth but also from pasture degradation caused by the dominance of low fertility soils (see the deforestation section).

These GIS analyses illuminate the climatic and edaphic factors limiting the expansion of grazing systems. Considering the current extent of grazing and a growing population, expansion of grazing systems in arid and semiarid regions will require the conversion of cropland systems, a land-use change that is unlikely to occur given the pressure for grain production worldwide (13). Intensification of animal production and grazing systems is likely to continue, requiring expensive management or causing greater degradation of already marginal lands. Any further extensification of global grazing systems will likely occur through the conversion of forests to pastures, as is well under way in the humid tropics.

Regional Syndromes in the Global Grazing Footprint

At the global scale, endogenous environmental conditions set the stage for determining both the ecosystem responses to grazing and the limitations imposed by climate and soils on the expansion and intensification of grazing practices worldwide. The bioclimatically marginal nature of grazing lands in arid and semiarid

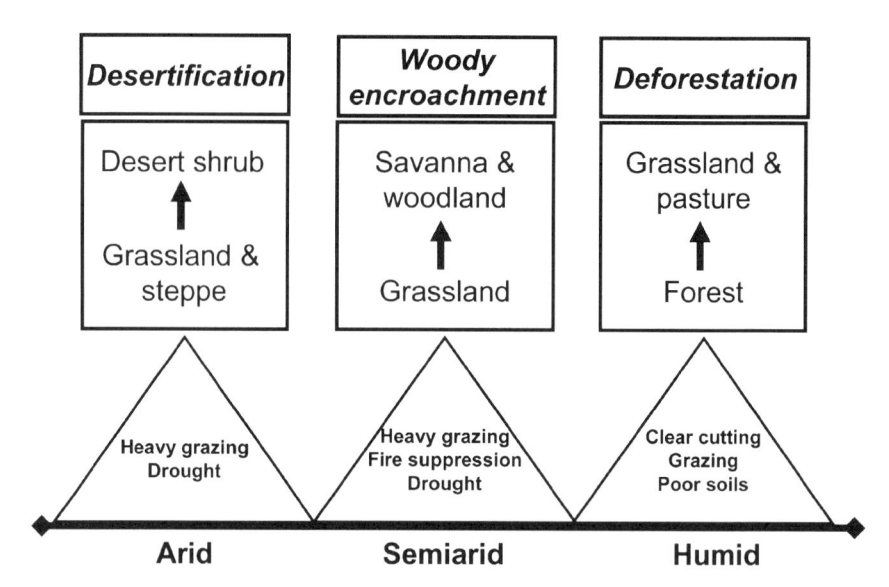

Figure 5 Three regional syndromes resulting from managed grazing practices across global-scale gradients of bioclimatic and edaphic conditions.

regions plays a key role in two regional syndromes widely reported throughout the literature—desertification and woody encroachment. The marginal biogeochemical nature of humid tropical soils accelerates the process of deforestation, a third regional syndrome (Figure 5).

One problem in describing these syndromes lies in the definitions of desertification, woody encroachment, and deforestation. The most difficult to define is desertification. In the past, a reduction in net primary productivity (NPP; vegetation growth) has been used as an indicator of desertification (14). Others have focused more on the composition and structural configuration of vegetation types (15), whereas the common observation of increased bare soil (exposed and eroded surfaces) has been the most definitive trait in yet other studies (16). Ash et al. (17) argue that desertification can best be analyzed in terms of secondary production losses (e.g., cattle, sheep, and human). In contrast, woody encroachment has been defined as the increased geographic extent of woody vegetation in ecosystems. Expansion of woody vegetation may or may not be a component of desertification; and when it is, the structural features of the woody cover changes are different from that of woody encroachment. Most notably, in woody encroachment, herbaceous cover in the intercanopy zones is typically left intact, whereas in desertification, these zones become bare soil surfaces with decreased soil resources (e.g., organic matter). Deforestation has been described as the conversion of forest landscapes to grazing systems (pastures), but this use is complicated by variation in the definition of forest. Some focus on primary or mature forest; others include areas of secondary or regrowing forest.

To present our synthetic perspective on the common syndromes inherent to grazing systems worldwide, we simply define all three processes, desertification, woody encroachment, and deforestation, in terms of changing ecosystem structure (Figure 5). *Desertification* is the replacement of herbaceous cover by shrub cover and bare soil. *Woody encroachment* is the addition of woody canopies without major losses of herbaceous cover, although herbaceous production may decrease. *Deforestation* is operationally defined as the replacement of forest cover with herbaceous pasture systems.

Independent of the precise definition of each regional syndrome, the bioclimatic and edaphic conditions under which managed grazing occurs have, to some degree, contributed to the development of these three syndromes. It is widely understood that desertification has occurred in arid regions of the world (e.g., southwest United States, Australia, South Africa, and Argentina) as a result of large-scale grazing and pronounced climatic variability (Figure 5) (3). Woody encroachment, as defined above, has occurred in semiarid to mesic environments as a result of large-scale grazing, fire suppression, and climatic variability (18). Deforestation continues to expand in the humid tropics (and elsewhere) in part because of grazing development on infertile soils that often cannot sustain large-scale managed pastoral operations (6). These three syndromes are regional in nature, but they are present throughout grazing systems on a global scale.

The remainder of this review provides a synthetic perspective on the ways that managed grazing has altered ecosystems across a bioclimatic gradient from arid to mesic to humid conditions. Synthesis of vegetation structural and the biogeochemical, hydrological, and atmospheric effects of grazing systems are presented using the syndromes as the organizing framework. In doing so, we demonstrate how managed grazing systems contribute significantly to global environmental change.

DESERTIFICATION

Ecosystem Structure

The myriad perspectives and intended audiences of studies on grazing systems lead to variation in vegetation classifications and, thus, in the observations, analyses, and conclusions in the literature. Most published studies use one or very few classifications to describe vegetation-grazing interactions. Common classifications in grazing studies are woody versus herbaceous (19) or perennial versus annual (20). Relatively few studies break the vegetation down into classes of C3 versus C4 physiology (21), evergreen versus deciduous life forms (22), or by nitrogen fixing abilities (23). Few studies have focused at the species level (24), and those that do often involve the introduction or spread of invasive plants (25, 26). Drawing from the scientific literature, managed grazing appears to play a central role in altering the biophysical structure of grazed ecosystems globally. We use *ecosystem structure* to discuss the spatial extent and configuration of major vegetation lifeforms (trees, shrubs, and herbaceous cover). This is useful because the majority of studies describe changes in ecosystem structure that appear to be caused or accelerated by grazing practices.

The literature highlights a consistent set of ecosystem structural changes involved in desertification. These changes can be described in three major features and one overarching pattern. The features include (*a*) increased bare soil surface area, (*b*) decreased herbaceous cover, and (*c*) increased cover of woody shrubs and shrub clusters. The overarching pattern is one of increased spatial heterogeneity of vegetation cover and a concomitant increase in the spatial variance of belowground resources, such as organic matter, nutrients (see the Biogeochemistry section), and soil moisture (see the Hydrology section).

Many grazing systems experiencing desertification in the southwestern United States, Australia, and Africa are now dominated by one or a few woody shrub species, with little herbaceous canopy remaining on the landscape (27–29). Okin et al. (16) suggested wind erosion removes soil nutrients and carbon from shrub interspaces. Once established, a combination of biogeochemical and hydrological feedbacks sustains these shrub systems in a new stable state, very different from the prior grassland (Figure 6) (15).

Desertification can also happen without a major increase in woody plant cover but rather as an increase in bare soil causing fragmented herbaceous cover (30). Van de Koppel et al. (31) suggested the following progression of events leading to a fragmented landscape. Herbaceous cover decreases in areas preferential to

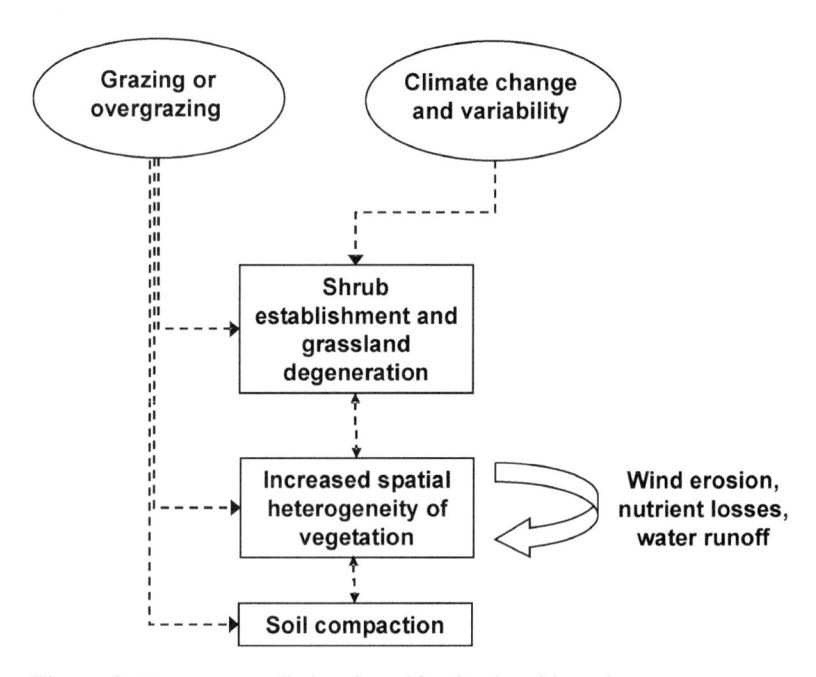

Figure 6 Processes mediating desertification in arid grazing systems.

grazers, leaving compacted bare soils that allow rainfall to run off into remaining vegetation patches. This increases the productivity of remaining patches, which stimulates increased grazing and, thus, loss of these patches, eventually leading to total ecosystem collapse. There is currently little empirical evidence to test this model, but another modeling study concurs that patch dynamics are mediated by grazing, climate variability, and surface hydrological transport (32).

A phenomenon related to managed grazing, land degradation, and desertification is the human-mediated dispersal of African grasses worldwide. Introduced African grasses have made their ecological mark in dryland (and tropical) systems in North America, Central and South America, Australia, and Oceania (33). These grasses compete effectively with native grass species and can alter nutrient cycling and other ecosystem processes (34–36). African grasses are typically fire tolerant and quite flammable, increasing fire frequency and promoting their further geographic expansion (26).

Biogeochemistry

Some changes in ecosystem structure (abundance, cover, and configuration of life-forms) described above are directly attributable to grazing. These structural alterations result in a cascade of change in other ecosystem processes, such as water drainage, wind and water erosion, species invasion, disturbance types and frequency (e.g., fire), carbon cycling, and the biophysical and biochemical characteristics of soils (21, 31).

Where desertification is occurring, degradation often results in reduced productivity or vegetative cover, which brings with it a change in the carbon (C) and nutrient stocks and cycling of the system (Figure 7) (37–43). The primary ecosystem response to desertification is an increase in the heterogeneity of vegetation cover, with concomitant increases in the spatial variability of soil C and nutrients (15, 54). Overall, reduced vegetative cover and total aboveground biomass seem to result in a small reduction in aboveground C stocks and a slight decline in C fixation, measured as NPP, but there is significant variability by vegetation type with topographic and edaphic factors (43). Because total nutrient pools are relatively small, any decline in total nutrient stocks has a significant impact on productivity.

Despite small, sometimes undetectable changes in aboveground biomass and NPP, both total soil C and nitrogen (N) usually decline (38). The reduced soil organic N may result from increased N lost in surface runoff, increased trace-gas flux, and vegetation removal by grazers. Decreased infiltration and increased runoff elevate losses of both inorganic and organic N in overland flow; however, these losses are smaller than inputs to the system from deposition in some regions (39, 55). Nitrogen trace-gas losses, particularly as nitrous oxide, are large relative to the total N pool (see the next section). Most studies on biogeochemical changes caused by desertification are from Northern Chihuahuan ecosystems in New Mexico, United States of America. A recent study by Asner et al. (37) in Argentina also found that desertification resulted in little change in woody cover, but there was

274   ASNER ET AL.

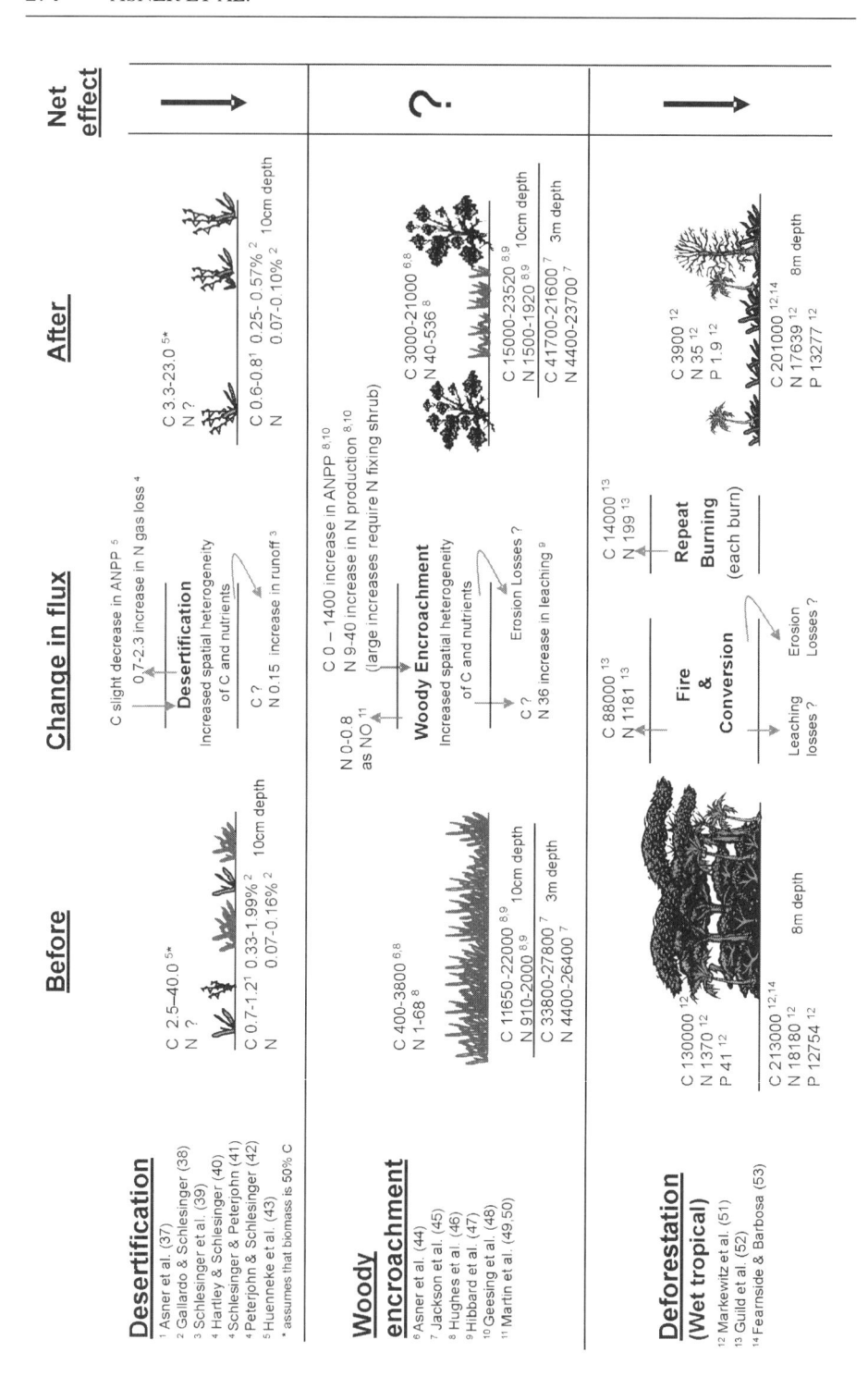

Before	Change in flux	After	Net effect
Desertification C 2.5–40.0 [5]* N ? C 0.7–1.2 [1] 0.33–1.99% [2] 10cm depth N 0.07–0.16% [2]	C slight decrease in ANPP [5] 0.7–2.3 increase in N gas loss [4] **Desertification** Increased spatial heterogeneity of C and nutrients C ? N 0.15 increase in runoff [3]	C 3.3–23.0 [5]* N ? C 0.6–0.8 [1] 0.25–0.57% [2] 10cm depth N 0.07–0.10% [2]	→
Woody encroachment C 400–3800 [6,8] N 1–68 [8] C 11650–22000 [8,9] 10cm depth N 910–2000 [8,9] C 33800–27800 [7] 3m depth N 4400–26400 [7]	N 0–0.8 as NO [11] C 0 – 1400 increase in ANPP [8,10] N 9–40 increase in N production [8,10] (large increases require N fixing shrub) **Woody Encroachment** Increased spatial heterogeneity of C and nutrients C ? → Erosion Losses ? N 36 increase in leaching [9]	C 3000–21000 [6,8] N 40–536 [8] C 15000–23520 [8,9] 10cm depth N 1500–1920 [8,9] C 41700–21600 [7] 3m depth N 4400–23700 [7]	↻
Deforestation (Wet tropical) C 130000 [12] N 1370 [12] P 41 [12] C 213000 [12,14] N 18180 [12] P 12754 [12] 8m depth	C 88000 [13] N 1181 [13] **Fire & Conversion** Leaching losses ? → Erosion Losses ? C 14000 [13] N 199 [13] **Repeat Burning** (each burn)	C 3900 [12] N 35 [12] P 1.9 [12] C 201000 [12,14] N 17639 [12] P 13277 [12] 8m depth	→

Desertification
[1] Asner et al. (37)
[2] Gallardo & Schlesinger (38)
[3] Schlesinger et al. (39)
[4] Hartley & Schlesinger (40)
[5] Schlesinger & Peterjohn (41)
[4] Peterjohn & Schlesinger (42)
[5] Huenneke et al. (43)
* assumes that biomass is 50% C

Woody encroachment
[6] Asner et al. (44)
[7] Jackson et al. (45)
[8] Hughes et al. (46)
[9] Hibbard et al. (47)
[10] Geesing et al. (48)
[11] Martin et al. (49, 50)

Deforestation (Wet tropical)
[12] Markewitz et al. (51)
[13] Guild et al. (52)
[14] Fearnside & Barbosa (53)

a 25% to 80% decline in soil organic C and N storage in areas with long-term grazing.

Soil compaction reduces infiltration and increases runoff, resulting in faster and greater flow through waterways and greater channel and gully erosion (see the Hydrology section). As a result, soil is lost, and sediment loads increase in waterways (56). In systems where soil erosion is substantial, resulting losses of soil C, N, and P may also be important but have not been well quantified. Wind erosion could also be important and enhanced by increased bare soil in the case of desertification (16). Phosphorus in arid ecosystems is often bound to calcium carbonates and retained in the mineral soils; thus, erosion tends to mobilize C and N more so than it does P (57). Grazing also breaks up and reduces coverage of cryptobiotic soil crusts found in many arid regions. Although disturbing these crusts can increase infiltration of water, it also reduces inputs of C and N fixed by biological activity of the crusts (58).

Trace-Gas Emissions

Increases in greenhouse trace gases (CO_2, CH_4, N_2O, and O_3) since preindustrial times have led to a warming of the Earth's surface and other climate changes (59). Though anthropogenic emissions of trace gases from fossil-fuel burning and fertilizers account for the majority of trace-gas emissions, soils account for more than 30% of biogenic trace-gas emissions (60). Soil trace-gas production and consumption vary spatially and temporally, and they are governed by factors such as soil nutrient stocks and cycling rates, soil temperature and moisture content, and vegetation cover (61), all of which are changed by grazing (previous sections).

Nitric and nitrous oxide gases (NO and N_2O) are produced in the soil during the processes of nitrification and denitrification, and these fluxes are mediated by vegetation litter inputs. The partitioning of NO and N_2O fluxes at the soil-air interface is dependent upon the soil water content, with a shift from NO production to N_2O production as the soil water increases (62). Nitric oxide is a key component in regional-scale ozone regulation.

Woody vegetation cover changes associated with desertification have measurable impacts on soil NO emissions. Hartley & Schlesinger (40) found higher NO emissions from soils under woody canopies than in intercanopy zones. These findings support the concept of enhanced nutrient stocks and cycling under woody vegetation canopies, thereby resulting in enhanced N gas emissions at the plot scale. Although there were little to no N_2O emissions measured in the field from

---

Figure 7 Effects of three syndromes of managed grazing on biogeochemical properties of arid/semiarid, mesic, and humid tropical ecosystems. Carbon (C), nitrogen (N), and phosphorus (P) stocks and fluxes are taken from literature sources cited to the left. All pools are in kg/hectare (ha) except those noted as a percentage, and all fluxes are in kg/ha/year except for the tropical systems where they are kg/ha/burn. Values for tropical ecosystems are averages across multiple studies.

bare soils due to the aridity, laboratory studies indicated N_2O emissions from soils collected under shrub canopies can potentially be two times greater than those collected in a nearby grassland (63).

Methane (CH_4) is generated in soils during anaerobic respiration, and it has a global warming potential 24.5 times that of CO_2. In some cases, soil compaction due to grazing limits soil aeration and stimulates CH_4 production (64). Grazing affects the atmosphere through the direct emission of CH_4 gas from ruminants and via increases in ammonia (NH_3) production from livestock excreta. Globally, approximately 54 terragrams (Tg) N-NH_3 are emitted each year, with the largest fraction (~40%) from animal waste (65). Excreta deposited on grassland by grazing animals stimulated N_2O production, contributing up to 22% of the total N_2O emission from a U.K. grassland (66). The current estimate of CH_4 from ruminant animals and animal waste is 100 Tg CH_4, nearly a fifth of the total global emissions (59). CH_4 emissions from livestock have increased about fivefold over the last century in close step with the increasing rate of cattle production (67).

Hydrology

The balance between plant-available water and evapotranspiration (ET) regulates soil moisture and ultimately determines many characteristics of ecosystem structure and functioning on grazed lands (68). In grazing systems, ET (calculated as the sum of evaporation from bare soil and plant surfaces and from transpiration through plant stomata) is often the largest loss of water from the system (Figure 8) (56, 69, 70). Controls over this flux are the relative fractions of soil and vegetation cover, leaf area index (LAI), and plant-available soil moisture. Grazing influences each of these variables.

Vegetation cover and LAI decline as grazers remove plant matter. Reduced plant surface area results in lower transpiration and retention of soil moisture throughout the root zone (Figure 8) (71). Grazing thus leads to increased soil

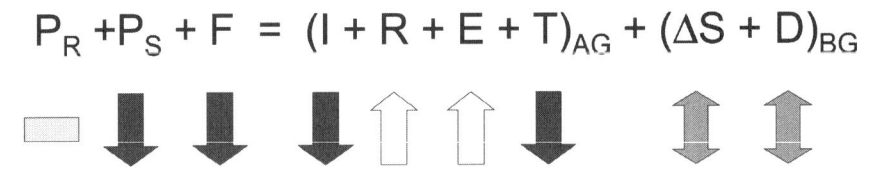

$$P_R + P_S + F = (I + R + E + T)_{AG} + (\Delta S + D)_{BG}$$

Direction of change with managed grazing

Figure 8 Components of the hydrologic cycle and reported directions of change with managed grazing. Processes are divided into aboveground$_{(AG)}$ and belowground$_{(BG)}$ components. Other abbreviations are P_R, rainfall; P_S, spring snow melt; F, fog or cloud condensation on aboveground plant matter; I, canopy interception; R, runoff; E, evaporation from soil surfaces; T, transpiration from the canopy; S, the change in soil moisture; and D, discharge through subsurface flow vertically and horizontally away from plant roots. P_S and F are not applicable in all environments.

moisture relative to nongrazed pastures (72–74). Grazing also increases bare soil surface area, resulting in greater radiative heating of soil surfaces and increased evaporation (71). Therefore, net changes in soil moisture can be assessed with regard to the balance between LAI and bare soil surface changes resulting from grazing. Reductions in LAI alone will increase soil moisture; increases in bare soil area will decrease soil moisture; and when both occur, the change in soil moisture is uncertain (75).

Grazing compacts soil and exposes soil surfaces, both of which lead to lower infiltration, increased runoff, and higher erosion rates (Figure 8) (56). Trimble & Mendel (76) found that infiltration decreased from approximately 50 mm h^{-1} on lightly grazed to 25 mm h^{-1} on heavily grazed land, but they also highlighted the large variance in field measurements. Infiltration is sensitive to many factors, including soil conditions at the time of grazing and the degree of bare soil exposed following grazing. The link between higher runoff and erosion rates follows logically because increased surface flow can carry larger sediment loads. Grazing reduces vegetation cover, leading to bare and unstable soil surfaces; therefore, the effects of grazing on erosion can be notably larger than the impact of climatic changes, such as increased precipitation (77). Conversely, the absence of grazing results in litter buildup, which has been found to reduce runoff and erosion (78). The balance between infiltration and runoff depends on the hydrologic conductivity and spatial heterogeneity of soil and vegetation surfaces (79).

Desertification involves specific hydrologic changes that include increased spatial heterogeneity of soil moisture and less effective transfer of precipitation to soil moisture (15). Net primary production per unit of precipitation may decrease (80), creating landscapes, with a low rain-use efficiency, that resemble deserts. There is evidence that grazing, combined with feedback mechanisms in the climate system, eventually makes these symptoms permanent (31). The process may begin in areas with vegetation cover removed and soils compacted, resulting in declining infiltration rates and moisture in surface soils. Deeper soil layers and soils where vegetation cover remains high may continue to receive recharge from large storm events (81). The landscape thus becomes more heterogeneous, with patches of vegetation helping to maintain higher infiltration, soil stability, and nutrient retention. Meanwhile, bare soil interspaces become increasingly depauperate in soil moisture and nutrient resources. With continued grazing and high climate variability, vegetated areas become increasingly rare, shifting systems even further toward a desert-like state.

Climate Interactions

Early studies of desertification suggested that changes in surface albedo caused by increased bare soil cover could have regional and even global climate effects. Charney et al. (82) predicted that increases in surface albedo due to Sahelian desertification would increase radiative heat losses from the Sahara, thus reducing rainfall. Additional studies incorporating albedo, transpiration, and roughness found that a positive feedback reduced rainfall in the Sahel as well as on the Indian subcontinent (83).

In Sonoran drylands, surface temperatures were generally 2°–4° higher on the brighter, more heavily grazed Mexican side of the border than on the U.S. side (84). In this case, temperature differences were shown to impact soil moisture and cloudiness, but no changes in precipitation were apparent. A more recent study, using Landsat Thematic Mapper data, found only small Arizona/Sonora trans-border differences in albedo and radiant temperature along 25 one-kilometer transects (85).

WOODY ENCROACHMENT

Ecosystem Structure

There are hundreds of documented cases of increased woody plant cover in semiarid, subtropical rangelands of the world [(86); http://cnrit.tamu.edu/]. In North and South America, Africa, Australia, and elsewhere, woody vegetation cover has increased significantly in grazing systems during the past few decades. Cited causes of woody encroachment include overgrazing of herbaceous cover that reduces competition for woody seedlings, fire suppression that enhances woody plant survival, atmospheric CO_2 enrichment that favors C3 (woody) plant growth, and nitrogen pollution that favors woody encroachment (Figure 9) (18, 87).

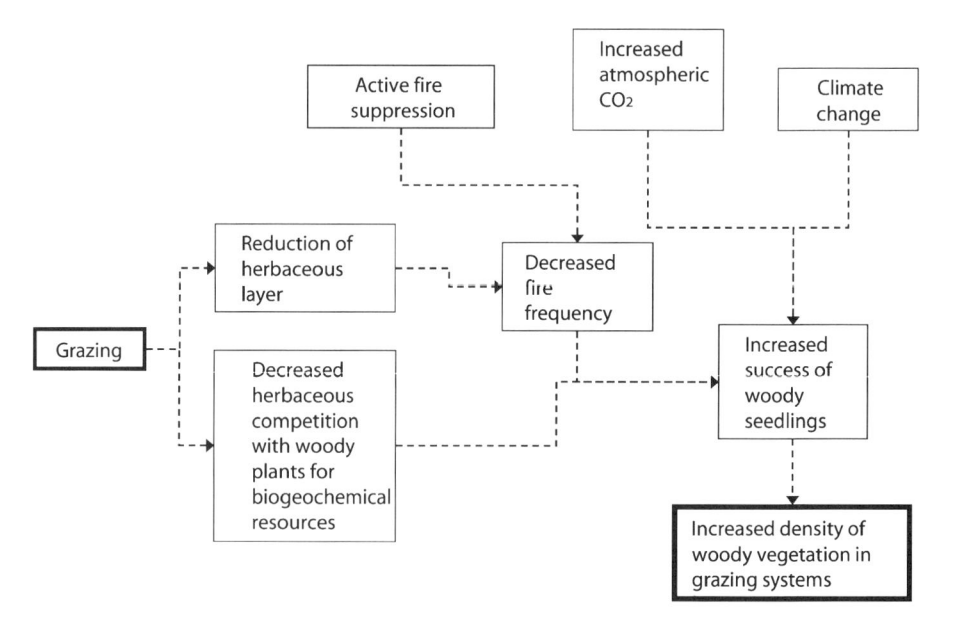

Figure 9 Processes mediating woody vegetation encroachment in semiarid and mesic grazing systems.

It is noted in most encroachment studies that the woody plants were present somewhere on the landscape prior to the installment of managed grazing. For example, in a southern Texas rangeland containing a diverse array of trees, shrubs, and subshrubs, heavy grazing caused increases in the cover of the nitrogen-fixing tree *Prosopis glandulosa* var. *glandulosa* (mesquite). Long-term records and aerial photographs indicate that mesquite encroachment then facilitated the establishment of other woody plants in its understory, which subsequently outcompeted mesquite for light and other resources (88). Mesquite remnants are commonly found among well-developed patches of woody vegetation known not to have existed a century ago (89). The same species of mesquite has increased dramatically in cover in a northern Texas rangeland during the past century (44), but there are very few other woody species established in this region. Most other species are confined to riparian zones; thus few woody plants can be found in association with the mesquite cover (90). Precipitation conditions are similar between the northern (650 mm) and southern (680 mm) Texas sites, but temperatures are substantially lower in the north, with values below freezing in many months (91). Low temperatures in the north likely preclude the presence of many warm-climate woody plants found in the south (*Acacia, Diospyros* spp.), and thus the ecological dynamics of woody encroachment are very different between sites.

There are some basic trends in vegetation-grazing interactions associated with woody encroachment in global drylands. Five vegetation properties are consistently highlighted in the literature as changing with respect to grazing and/or the release from grazing: (*a*) woody vegetation cover, (*b*) herbaceous vegetation cover, (*c*) surface litter cover, (*d*) dominance by perennial herbaceous plants, and (*e*) dominance by annual herbaceous plants (Figure 10).

At light grazing intensity, most studies indicate slight increases in woody cover if the woody plants are present in the area (Figure 10) (92). Somewhat independent of woody vegetation dynamics, most reports show a decrease in herbaceous vegetation biomass and/or cover and in surface litter cover/biomass (24, 93). In light grazing scenarios, some studies mention decreases in perennial grasses, although a clear trend among annuals is not evident (94). Changes are much more pronounced in cases of long-term, heavy grazing (Figure 10).

Many studies indicate dramatic increases in woody cover or biomass if the woody plants are already present or introduced to the region (86). Both herbaceous and surface litter (cover and biomass) are found to decrease under conditions of heavy grazing (37, 78). Shifts from perennial to annual grasses are more obvious in heavy grazing regimes (95, 96). Following heavy grazing, a release, or substantial rest period, woody cover often remains elevated (Figure 10); that is, there are few if any studies showing decreases in woody cover following release from heavy grazing, but herbaceous and surface litter cover and biomass typically do increase (97). A few studies indicate that annual grasses may initially increase following release from grazing, but often the grasses are replaced by perennials over periods of years or a few decades (98). A net outcome of heavy grazing, even following a release from such practices, can be an increase in woody cover regionally.

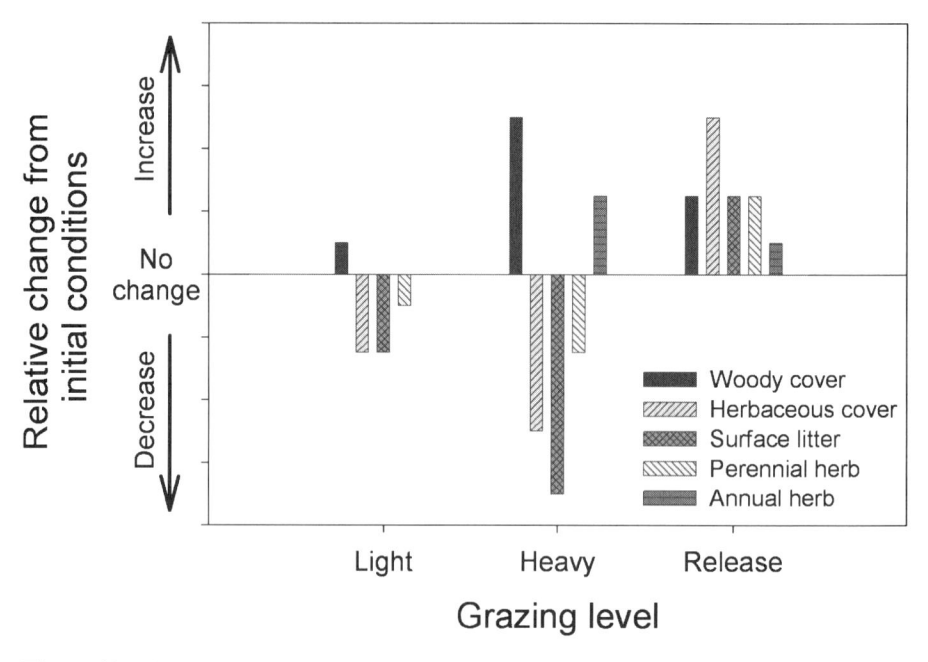

Figure 10 Commonly reported responses of five-dryland ecosystem structural properties to light and heavy grazing and to release from grazing. Bars show relative, directional responses as reported in the literature.

Biogeochemistry

Woody encroachment reduces the quality of land for animal production (39), yet in some cases, it enriches total ecosystem C and N stocks (Figure 7). As previously discussed, the shift from herbaceous to woody vegetation is different from desertification in that the woody cover increases without a major loss of herbaceous cover. With the shift to woody vegetation comes a large increase in aboveground NPP and C storage. Increases in aboveground NPP of up to 1400 kg C ha^{-1} year^{-1} have been observed when the dominant woody species is a nitrogen fixer (48, 90). Increases in the aboveground C pool can range from 300 to 44,000 kg C ha^{-1} in less than 100 years of woody encroachment (44). When the dominant woody species is a nitrogen fixer, nitrogen accumulation can be 9–40 kg N ha^{-1} year^{-1} greater in the woody areas than the grasslands (48), with aboveground nitrogen increasing 39–468 kg N ha^{-1} following encroachment (46).

Despite an increase in aboveground C and N with encroachment, the trends in soil organic C and N are highly variable. Measuring soil carbon to 3 m depth, Jackson et al. (45) found that woody encroachment increased soil C and N in drier grassland regions but reduced it in regions with mean annual precipitation greater than ~500 mm. They found the decline in soil C in wetter ecosystems was sufficient to offset aboveground gains from woody encroachment, resulting in no net ecosystem C gain. In contrast, Boutton et al. (99) studied grasslands with annual precipitation of 700 mm and found a 27% to 103% increase in soil C in the upper 10 cm. Likewise, Geesing et al. (48) measured soil organic C increases of 40% to 80% across a range of sites with mean annual precipitation of ~700 mm.

As with soil C, there is some uncertainty in how total soil N changes with woody encroachment. Jackson et al. (45) found trends similar to those observed for C, an increase in N stocks in drier regions and a decrease in wetter regions. In contrast, Hibbard et al. (47) found a clear increase in soil N in the top 10 cm of a wetter site, and Martin & Asner (49) measured an increase in soil N pools following 30–70 years of woody encroachment. Clearly, our understanding of how woody encroachment changes soil resources, and thus the long-term productivity and sustainability of semiarid regions, remains highly fragmented.

Trace-Gas Emissions

Woody encroachment has a measurable effect on soil nitrogen oxide emissions. In northern Texas rangelands, encroaching *Prosopis glandulosa*, a N-fixing species, caused C and N storage to increase in surface soils, which resulted in enhanced soil nitric oxide (NO) fluxes during nitrification (49, 50). Aboveground woody biomass was the best spatial predictor of NO emissions, with values increasing 20-fold (0.04–0.78 mg NO-N m^{-2} day^{-1}) across a 70-fold biomass gradient (5–350 g m^{-2}). Emissions also covaried with soil pH and clay content. Temporally, NO emissions and nitrification were positively correlated with temperature. Precipitation events elevated NO emissions fourfold over 24-hour periods and produced small amounts of N$_2$O. Overall, mesquite encroachment in these grasslands increased NO emissions in a spatially explicit manner determined by the woody biomass and soil type, which was then temporally mediated by temperature and secondarily by precipitation (49, 50).

At a regional scale, desertification and woody encroachment appear to have very different effects on the N status of dryland ecosystems. Desertification promotes nutrient accretion in soils under woody plant canopies, but the surrounding bare soil areas have very low-nitrogen contents. When the fractional covers of woody clusters with higher NO emissions and bare soils with low-NO emissions are taken into account, there is ~0.4 kg N ha^{-1} year^{-1} (53%) decrease in NO emissions regionally, in comparison to the preexisting grassland (40). In contrast, when woody encroachment involves an N-fixing species in a grassland, and when woody expansion does not decrease the herbaceous cover significantly, NO gas emissions increase beyond that of the original grasslands by ~1.0 kg N ha^{-1} year^{-1} or 29% (49).

Hydrology

Woody and herbaceous life-forms utilize soil moisture from different depths in the soil profile (100, 101). Woody plants take advantage of deeper soil moisture, and herbaceous plants access moisture only in the upper soil layers. It has often been theorized that variation in soil moisture, both vertically and horizontally, determines the relative fraction of woody and herbaceous cover (102). Grazing affects soil moisture through compaction and reduced infiltration and through the exposure of bare soil surfaces. Increased evaporative losses from bare soils increase the disparity between shallow and deep soil moisture, and such losses support the notion that surface soil moisture is more sensitive to grazing intensity than deep soil moisture (103). These changes in soil moisture may drive changes in the relative balance between woody and herbaceous cover, favoring the deep-rooted shrub species.

Woody encroachment may be controlled by changes in the annual timing of precipitation (32) or the relative proportion of rainfall occurring in large precipitation events (100). Particularly in the presence of grazing, high-rainfall events or several months of elevated precipitation are effective in recharging deep soil layers, thereby creating soil moisture conditions that favor woody species. Modeling studies confirm the importance of temporal precipitation patterns in determining the relative abundance of herbaceous and woody plants, but grazing activity must be included for full transitions between plant life-forms in these models (32).

Climate Interactions

At the scale of individual canopies, shading, litter accumulation, and canopy interception of precipitation causes soils beneath woody vegetation to receive less solar irradiance and to have lower temperatures and water contents compared to intercanopy areas (104, 105). However, recent work suggests that the albedo changes resulting from shrubland encroachment have been slight. For example, Grover & Musik (106) showed that mean daily albedo for a creosote bush shrubland and a grassland were not significantly different (0.2 and 0.27, respectively), and these did not differ from other creosote bush, mesquite, or grassland communities. They concluded that increasing spatial heterogeneity of woody cover does not significantly impact surface albedo and climate. In contrast, Hoffman & Jackson (107) attributed a decline in precipitation of approximately 10% to a reduction in roughness length and to an increase in albedo. They also found that deeper rooting had a small positive effect on latent heat flux, with a corresponding reduction in sensible heat.

In comparison to canopy-scale processes, the impacts of woody encroachment on regional climate variables are virtually unknown. It is thought that the effects of woody encroachment on surface energy fluxes, critical to the formation of clouds and precipitation, are small relative to evaporative fluxes from other forms of land use (e.g., irrigated croplands). However, the spacing of vegetation in semiarid regions can affect the development of local wind circulations that contribute to cumulus cloud formation and precipitation (108).

DEFORESTATION

Ecosystem Structure

At first glance, the ecosystem structural changes caused by forest-to-pasture conversion might seem obvious. Biologically diverse, large-stature forest is cut (and often burned) in geometric patterns easily discernable from satellite imagery. This is true, and in humid tropical regions, the "installed" herbaceous species are predominantly African grasses (33, 109). However, tropical pasture development is carried out across an enormous range of environmental, social, and economic conditions, leaving the installed pasture in an equally broad number of biophysical states. In the humid tropics, the biophysical structure of pastures ranges from highly managed monospecific grasslands to savanna-like systems containing varying densities of palm and secondary forest species. In a study of 145 pastures in the central Amazon, Asner et al. (110) found that shrub and secondary forest vegetation cover ranged from 0% to 45%, and palms covered 20% to 60% of pasture areas. Although variation in pasture cover causes concomitant variation in biogeochemical, atmospheric, and hydrological processes (see below), vegetation structure is rarely quantified in published studies. Therefore, our synthesis implicitly incorporates the complicating effects of structural variability in pastures, but it does not determine the effects of this variation.

Biogeochemistry

In forests and woodlands, the largest impacts of grazing result from the conversion of the system to herbaceous cover, and deforestation for cattle pasture occurs across a wide range of climatic conditions. We discuss both dry and wet tropical forest conversion, where future conversion is most likely to take place on a large scale. With tropical dry forest conversion followed by repeated burning, up to 90% of aboveground C and N stocks and nearly 50% of the aboveground phosphorus (P) can be lost (111). C, N, and P are volatilized, whereas calcium (Ca) and the remaining C, N, and P are deposited as ash, much of which is lost in wind erosion immediately after the fire. Water erosion and soil loss can be significant for a few months after fire (112), and concentrations of dissolved mobile nutrients [e.g., NO_3 and potassium (K)] can be substantially elevated in overland flow (113). For a short period after burning, large increases in available soil N and nitrification rates are observed because NH_4 is mineralized during fire (114). Fire has little direct effect on total soil nutrients (C, N, and P); losses of these nutrients are mainly from the aboveground pools, and the size of these losses is small relative to the size of total soil nutrient pools (111, 115). However, it is estimated that it would take a century or more of recovery for a dry forest ecosystem to accumulate the nutrients lost during slash and burn (111).

With the global expansion of grazing systems, further conversion is most likely in humid forests. In contrast to dry forests, humid tropical forests are often found on highly weathered soils (ultisols and oxisols) rich in available N and poor in P and base cations [e.g., Ca and magnesium (Mg)], which are weathered and leached from the original rock (116, 117). Losses of P and Ca during deforestation are thus important to future pasture productivity (Figure 7). Many studies show that the initial burning of slashed primary forest results in combustion of ~48% of biomass, or 88 Mg C, 1181 kg N, and 107 kg sulfur (S) per hectare (52). The percentage of aboveground nutrients lost through combustion and transport of particulates average roughly 90% of N, 45% of P, and over 30% of Ca, Mg, and K (118). For about a decade after conversion, pastures release significantly more N_2O (nitrous oxide) trace gas than the forest but then decline to background forest levels (see the Trace-Gas section). Following deforestation, soil pH and exchangeable cations remain elevated in pastures, but a recent synthesis showed that neither soil C nor N changed in a consistent manner (11, 119). However, a detailed reaccounting of changes in soil C that considered the effects of soil compaction and management practices suggests an average loss of 12 tons C ha^{-1} in tropical lands maintained as pasture (53).

Repeated burning is often used as a management tool to remove woody regrowth and weeds and to renew nutrient availability in pastures (120). In the Brazilian Amazon, repeated burning of cattle pasture consumes up to 46% of aboveground biomass (slash, grass, and litter), with ∼14 Mg C, 199 kg N, and 16 kg S per hectare lost to the atmosphere (52). Losses of P, Ca, and K in one experimental burn were nearly 33 kg ha^{-1} (120). With repeated fires over a six-year period, over 1900 kg N ha^{-1} is lost, which is equivalent to ∼90% of the aboveground pool in a mature tropical forest. As a result, repeated burning can lead to N limitation even in previously nitrogen-rich tropical systems (121).

Results from the literature are inconsistent in describing how P changes with deforestation and repeating burning of pastures (11, 51, 118). Available P in ash after the initial fire may remain in the system, rapidly sorbing to soil minerals or consumed by vegetation and soil microbes. In many cases, available P seems to accumulate in soil organic material, which can remain enriched in pastures for years after conversion (11, 122–124). Others do not find the missing available P in the soil (51).

With long-term grazing (e.g., decades), total soil P usually declines; Ca, K, and Mg often decline as well; and N may also decline if there is frequent burning (44, 118, 125). The mechanisms for P loss are uncertain but include combustion, erosion of ash, and leaching to deep soils. Another possibility is that P is transferred into a bound form that is not easily detected with methods currently used. In any case, available phosphorus declines and grass productivity in pastures is often P limited. Phosphorus fertilization (∼50 kg ha^{-1} every 5–10 years) is thus becoming more common in some regions, such as the eastern Brazilian Amazon (121, 126). Despite these recent and more localized trends, many studies show that tropical pastures accumulate and cycle fewer nutrients than forest, redistribute cations from trees to soils, lose most of the C and N that was stored in aboveground forest biomass, and maintain reduced soil nutrient availability (Figure 7). These reported trends are induced and mediated by poor edaphic conditions inherent to many humid tropical forest regions.

Trace-Gas and Aerosol Emissions

Tropical forest soils are the largest biogenic source of N_2O, accounting for 25% to 50% of the global source (59). NO emissions from tropical forests are also significant, accounting for up to 20% of global emissions (127). The disturbance and initial volatilization of nutrients during burning associated with forest-to-pasture conversion increases trace-gas emissions for months to years, but emissions often return to or drop below initial forest or savanna levels as pastures age. Studies in Costa Rica demonstrated that soil N_2O emissions and CH_4 production were higher for 15 years following conversion, but returned to background levels after 18 years (128). In a synthesis, Davidson et al. (129) found for a variety of tropical sites in Costa Rica, Puerto Rico, and Brazil that old tropical pastures produce consistently lower NO fluxes than old-growth tropical forests. The reasons for these differences were changes in the environmental factors that control N oxide emissions, such as soil water, temperature, nutrient status, pH, diffusion, and plant biomass.

Biomass burning is a common tool for the establishment and management of pastures for grazing, most recognized in tropical rain forests and savanna regions but also in grasslands worldwide (130, 131). Biomass burning is a significant source of globally relevant trace gases (CO_2, NO_x, CO, and CH_4) and aerosols (130, 132). Climatological effects include the formation of photochemical smog, hydrocarbons, and NO_x that rapidly produce O_3. Long-range transport of smoke plumes may be redistributed locally, transported throughout the lower troposphere, or entrained in large-scale circulation patterns in the mid and upper troposphere. The perturbation of these gases to the atmosphere is evident in satellite observations of high-O_3 and -CO levels over large areas of Africa, South America, and the tropical Atlantic and Indian Oceans (133).

Pyrogenic aerosols from pasture biomass burning dominate the atmospheric concentration of aerosols over the Amazon basin and Africa (132, 134). Concentrations of aerosol particles are highly seasonal, with a clear maximum in the dry (burning) season, contributing to cooling both through increasing atmospheric scattering of incoming light and the supply of cloud condensation nuclei (CNN). High-CCN concentrations from biomass burning stimulate rainfall production and affect large-scale climate dynamics (135). The cooling effect of smoke alone may be minimal (-0.3 watts m^{-2}) compared to the heating from anthropogenic greenhouse gases [2.45 watts m^{-2} globally (136)].

Hydrology

The conversion of forest to pasture is the primary driver of grazing-induced hydrologic change in mesic to wet climate zones (137). The majority of research conducted in tropical environments is in regions where deforestation has occurred recently and is likely to continue (5). Higher surface albedo, lower surface aerodynamic roughness, reduced LAI, and shallower rooting depths combine to reduce ET in pastures relative to forests. This model is supported by stable isotope studies, which reveal that water vapor above forest sites is derived from plant transpiration, in the eastern Amazon, whereas water vapor above pasture is derived primarily from surface evaporation (138). Lower ET and reduced infiltration rates within pastures culminate in increased average long-term discharge (139). Where changes in infiltration rates are modest, reduced ET alone can increase rainy season runoff (140). Decreases in dry-season flow are also theorized to result from deforestation, but evidence of this effect is limited (141). Initial increases in stream discharge decline over time as forests regenerate (137, 142).

Climate Interactions

Forest-to-pasture conversion causes substantial decreases in land-to-atmosphere moisture transport. Early global-scale numerical simulations, using drastic levels of deforestation, predicted a 25% decrease in precipitation associated with a 30% decrease in evapotranspiration and a 2.5°C increase in surface temperature (143). However, recent mesoscale modeling studies suggest that, in spatially complex mosaics of forest and pasture lands, moisture fluxes from the land to the atmosphere can be enhanced, as can reciprocal fluxes of precipitation (144). Recycling of water by up to 25% to 35% was attributed to interactions between increased albedo, sensible heat flux, and mixed-layer height in pastures relative to forest (144, 145). Modeling studies also suggest that changes in surface energy dynamics can affect the upper atmosphere, perturbing tropical circulation patterns, shifting the position of the Hadley circulation, and altering planetary waves that propagate moisture to upper- and midlatitudes (146). Nonetheless, the effects of managed grazing and deforestation on climate, like that of desertification and woody encroachment, are poorly understood.

ECOSYSTEM RESPONSES TO MANAGED GRAZING

Response Typologies

Managed grazing has flourished for thousands of years, but the spatial extent and intensity (e.g., stocking rates) of grazing systems have increased substantially in the past several decades to centuries. The typologies of ecosystem response to managed grazing are regional in nature because they vary with bioclimatic and edaphic conditions. Not all grazing systems or practices lead to the syndromes of desertification, woody encroachment, and deforestation highlighted in this synthesis. We have a poor understanding of how much land has been affected by these phenomena. Nonetheless, scientific reports tend to address common environmental concerns, and these are the phenomena that often emerge as identifiable syndromes of managed grazing.

In arid regions, ecosystem responses to grazing practices are mediated by extreme climatic conditions combined with nutrient-poor soils. Low and highly variable precipitation causes ecological boom-bust cycles (Figure 4b), and yet managed grazing occurs on the most variable and climatologically marginal portions of these biomes (Table 1). When grazing systems are implicated in cases of desertification, thresholds in ecosystem resistance and resilience to drought are often crossed owing to the persistence of grazing at the worst of times climatologically (27, 147). The results are long-term losses of surface herbaceous cover, increases in bare soil extent, and, at times, increases in woody shrub cover (Table 3). A cascade of biogeochemical and hydrological feedbacks then takes place, such as nutrient

TABLE 3 Relative effects of land-cover change due to grazing on land surface properties that mediate biosphere-atmosphere interactions. Larger arrows indicate the dominant change within the ecosystem syndromes listed

	Deforestation	Woody proliferation	Desertification
Albedo	↑	↓	↑
Roughness length	↓	↑	↓
Turbulence	↑	↑	—
Vegetated fraction	↓	↑	↓
Evaporation	↓	—	↑
Transpiration	↓	↑	↓

losses via runoff and wind erosion, soil compaction, reduced soil water infiltration and increased patchiness of soil moisture (Table 4). Structural, biogeochemical and hydrological processes change to the point where an alternative "stable" state ecosystem then persists (15, 148). Additional feedbacks to the atmosphere result from changing albedo, surface temperature, and trace-gas emissions (Table 3). The scientific community is only beginning to understand the potential effects of desertification at the ecosystem-atmosphere interface. Whether these changes alter regional climate in ways that may enhance or dampen the effects of desertification on the global climate system is not known.

In semiarid and mesic biomes, woody encroachment is a widely reported ecosystem response to managed grazing (Table 4); however, other critically important cofactors are climate variability, fire suppression, and the presence of woody plant seed sources (Figure 9). Fire suppression favors woody seedling recruitment and survival, especially when grazers are actively consuming the herbaceous layer. In contrast to desertification, which appears to entail a combination of extreme climate variability and heavy grazing, even light-to-moderate grazing intensities can promote woody encroachment in semiarid and mesic environments (86, 149) (Figure 10). Like that of desertification, the spatial heterogeneity of aboveground and belowground resources such as vegetation cover and soil organic matter often increases. However, woody vegetation increases tend not to be well linked to large-scale losses of herbaceous cover. Biogeochemical responses include soil compaction, increased carbon storage and nutrient stocks (especially when nitrogen fixing woody species are implicated), and increased greenhouse gas emissions. The hydrology of these systems shows a typological response as well, with increased heterogeneity of soil moisture with depth, increased runoff and erosion, and decreased soil water infiltration (Table 3). Virtually nothing is known regarding the effects of woody encroachment on the climate system.

The major effects of managed grazing in humid forest regions are determined by deforestation and pasture maintenance (Table 4). Forests are replaced by herbaceous systems, which decrease ecosystem carbon storage and nutrient stocks

TABLE 4 Summary of most commonly reported changes in ecosystem properties for desertification, woody encroachment, and deforestation

	Regional syndrome		
Ecosystem properties	**Desertification**	**Woody encroachment**	**Deforestation**
Vegetation structure	• Decreased herbaceous, increased bare soil • Increased woody cover • Increased spatial heterogeneity	• Increased woody cover • Increased spatial heterogeneity	• Increased herbaceous • Decreased forest cover
Biogeochemistry	• Increased spatial heterogeneity of nutrients and carbon • Increased nutrient loss via runoff and erosion • Decreased soil nutrient stocks • Soil compaction	• Increased carbon storage • Increased soil nutrient stocks, when N-fixing plants are present and active • Soil compaction	• Decreased carbon storage • Decreased soil nutrient stocks over time • Nutrient losses via burning and aerosol
Biosphere-atmosphere exchange	• Increased albedo • Increased surface temperature • Increased ammonia and methane production	• Increased N trace-gas production • Increased ammonia and methane production	• Changed surface energy budget • Short-lived increase in soil N trace gas emission • Increased ammonia and methane production • Aerosol production
Hydrology	• Increased spatial heterogeneity of soil moisture • Increased runoff and erosion • Reduced infiltration	• Increased vertical heterogeneity of soil moisture • Increased runoff and erosion • Reduced infiltration	• Decreased transpiration • Decreased infiltration • Increased temporal variation in streamflow

(Table 3). Nutrient losses and greenhouse gas emissions may persist in cases of repeated burning of pastures. Substantial hydrologic changes occur via decreased plant transpiration, decreased soil infiltration, and increase variability in runoff and stream flow (Table 3). In humid tropical systems, the global dominance of nutrient-poor ultisol and oxisol soils (Figure 4c, Table 2) are widely implicated in the decline of productivity in ranching systems (53, 109). Tropical deforestation has been a regional syndrome largely driven by nutrient-poor soils, underlying a social and political demand for cattle production (150). Climatological impacts of deforestation have been heavily studied, suggesting overall decreases in continental-scale precipitation but possible increases in rainfall at the landscape-to-regional levels.

As the human population grows and land scarcity increases, intensification and shifts in traditional animal production are occurring globally. Traditional extensive pastoral systems are declining in some arid regions, and integrated pastoral farm management is disappearing in tropical highlands. These are being replaced by more concentrated grazing systems that can lead to greater degradation of pasture land (151). In the northeastern United States, northwestern Europe, and densely populated areas of Asia, animal production has become mechanized and dependent on external fertilizer and feed inputs. Industrial meat production is growing rapidly. From 1991 to 1993, it provided 37% of global meat production and 43% by 1996 (152). In these systems, animal waste exceeds the absorptive capacity of the land and pollutes the surrounding environment (153). Excess nitrogen and phosphorus from livestock is a substantial source of nonpoint pollution in the United States, causing eutrophication of freshwater and marine ecosystems, toxic algal blooms, and fish kills (154). Excess nitrogen in the environment can have many negative impacts on human health (155). Other biogeochemical impacts of intensification are only starting to be studied and quantified.

Knowledge Gaps and Research Needs

We contend that a combination of three regional syndromes—desertification, woody encroachment, and deforestation—represents a major component of global environmental change promoted and mediated by managed grazing activities. There is a rich literature on the ways that cropland expansion and intensification have altered both terrestrial and aquatic ecosystems (156, 157). There are also clear effects of urban and suburban land use on regional ecological dynamics, and the role of urbanization on climate is now being recognized at the global scale (158). Managed grazing systems cover more of the Earth's surface than any other form of land use, yet pastoral operations are spatially diffuse and natural looking (except in the case of deforestation). Nonetheless, managed grazing has resulted in typological responses of ecosystems during the past few centuries if not beforehand. These responses can be organized by climate-edaphic conditions on a regional basis, and in doing so, the global footprint of grazing systems appears to be quite large. This synthesis helps stitch together this globally relevant land use into a single framework for further study and perspective.

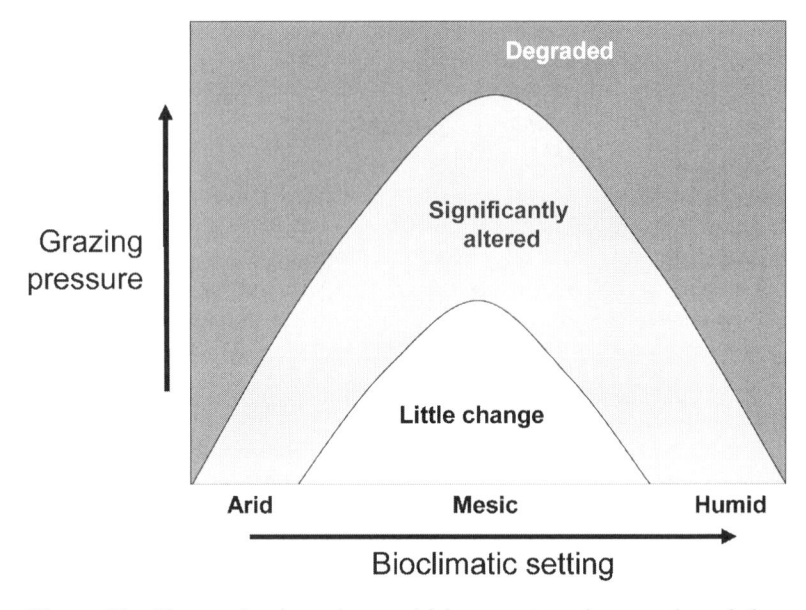

Figure 11 The grazing intensity at which ecosystems become degraded or are significantly altered changes with bioclimatic setting, with greater impacts and lower sustainability in very dry and very humid ecosystems.

As the result of the emergent themes from our synthesis, we hypothesize that ecosystem responses to grazing vary along a bioclimatic gradient from arid to mesic to humid environments (Figure 11). The literature suggests that mesic environments, such as in temperate grasslands, can endure the highest grazing intensities (19). At some point, however, changes in the structure, biogeochemistry, and hydrology of these systems occur, and the degree of such changes will be mediated by management practices. Arid environments are predisposed to changes in ecosystem structure, biogeochemistry, and hydrology in ways that truly degrade the land, even at relatively low grazing pressures. Humid forest ecosystems (especially tropical) are immediately and significantly altered by grazing systems, and degradation of pastureland often occurs under poor edaphic conditions.

These hypotheses are well supported by the scientific literature, but our overall understanding of ecosystem responses to managed grazing remains somewhat diffuse and fragmented for several reasons. The extent and intensity of managed grazing operations are very poorly known at regional, continental, or global scales. The GIS maps presented and synthesized here are state of the art, yet we recognize the generality and inaccuracy of them, especially in regions, such as the Indian subcontinent, the U.S. southwest, South America, and northern Mexico. Remote sensing technologies cannot identify grazing lands without going to very high-spatial and -biogeophysical resolution (37, 44, 80). Such approaches are impractical at the global scale, but a strategic global sampling would be tractable if we knew how to stratify such a sampling, using process-level knowledge of grazing systems and the resulting regional syndromes.

Our lack of process-based knowledge not only impedes our ability to make the appropriate observations for analysis and monitoring, but it also limits our predictive capabilities. We are currently unable to forecast the onset of desertification, woody encroachment, or even deforestation because we lack the approaches to understand the interaction between ecological, climatological, and socioeconomic factors. Recent synthetic work has made some progress in this regarding desertification (159) and deforestation (6), but the basic observations of when, where, and under what conditions these regional syndromes occur are still lacking. Even remote sensing studies of tropical deforestation produce wide-ranging estimates of the amount of pastureland emplaced annually (5, 12). In sum, the observations are limited by technological barriers, whereas the scientific understanding of grazing systems and global change are limited by insufficient observations. Research and progress are needed on both fronts to better understand the role of managed grazing in the global environment.

ACKNOWLEDGMENTS

We thank A. Cooper and A. Warner for technical assistance, and R. Naylor and P. Matson for thoughtful comments on the manuscript. This work was funded by NASA New Investigator Program grant NAG5-8709, the National Science Foundation, and the Mellon Foundation.

The *Annual Review of Environment and Resources* is online at
http://environ.annualreviews.org

LITERATURE CITED

1. Goldewijk K, Battjes CGM, Battjes JJ. 1997. A hundred year (1890–1990) database for integrated environmental assessments (HYDE, version 1.1). *Rep. 422514002*, Natl. Inst. Public Health Environ. (RIVM), Bilthoven, Neth.
2. World Resour. Inst. 1990. *World Resources 1990–1991*. New York: Oxford Univ. Press
3. UN Environ. Programme. 1994. *UN Earth summit. Convention on desertification*. Presented at UN Conf. Environ. Dev., Rio de Janeiro, Brazil
4. Caspersen JP, Pacala SW, Jenkins JC, Hurtt GC, Moorcroft PR, Birdsey RA. 2000. Contributions of land-use history to carbon accumulation in US forests. *Science* 290:1148–51
5. Achard F, Eva HD, Stibig HJ, Mayaux P, Gallego J, et al. 2002. Determination of deforestation rates of the world's humid tropical forests. *Science* 297:999–1002
6. Geist HJ, Lambin EF. 2001. What drives tropical deforestation? *LUCC Rep. Ser. 4*, Land Use Cover Change Int. Project Off., Louvain-la-Neuve, Belg.
7. Ramankutty N, Foley JA. 1998. Characterizing patterns of global land use: an

analysis of global croplands area. *Glob. Biogeochem. Cycles* 12:667–85

8. Hearn P, Hare T, Scruben P, Sherrill D, LaMar C, Tsushima P. 2001. Global GIS database: digital atlas of the world. *Rep. Digit. Data Ser. DDS-62-H*, US Geol. Surv., Reston, VA

9. Field CB, Randerson JT, Malmström CM. 1995. Global net primary production: combining ecology and remote sensing. *Remote Sens. Environ.* 51:74–88

10. US Dep. Agric. 1999. Soil taxonomy: a basic system of soil classification for making and interpreting soil surveys. *Rep. 486*, USDA, Nat. Resour. Conserv. Serv. Washington, DC

11. McGrath DA, Smith CK, Gholz HL, Oliveira F. 2001. Effects of land-use change on soil nutrient dynamics in Amazônia. *Ecosystems* 4:625–45

12. DeFries RS, Houghton RA, Hansen MC, Field CB, Skole D, Townshend J. 2002. Carbon emissions from tropical deforestation and regrowth based on satellite observations for the 1980s and 1990s. *Proc. Natl. Acad. Sci. USA* 99:14256–61

13. Rosegrant MW, Paisner MS, Meijer S, Witcover J. 2001. *Global Food Projections to 2020: Emerging Trends and Alternative Futures.* New York: Int. Food Policy Research Inst.

14. Prince SD, Colstoun EBd, Kravitz LL. 1998. Evidence from rain-use efficiencies does not indicate extensive Sahelian desertification. *Glob. Change Biol.* 4:359–74

15. Schlesinger WH, Reynolds JF, Cunningham GL, Huenneke LF, Jarrell WM, et al. 1990. Biological feedbacks in global desertification. *Science* 247:1043–48

16. Okin GS, Murray B, Schlesinger WH. 2001. Degradation of sandy arid shrubland environments: observations, process modelling, and management implications. *J. Arid Environ.* 47:123–44

17. Ash AJ, Stafford-Smith DM, Abel N. 2002. Land degradation and secondary production in semi-arid and arid grazing systems: What is the evidence? See Ref. 163, pp. 111–34

18. Archer S, Schimel DS, Holland EA. 1995. Mechanisms of shrubland expansion: land use, climate or CO_2. *Clim. Chang.* 29:91–99

19. Milchunas DG, Lauenroth WK. 1993. Quantitative effects of grazing on vegetation and soils over a global range of environments. *Ecol. Monogr.* 63:327–66

20. Valone TJ, Meyer M, Brown JH, Chew RM. 2002. Timescale of perennial grass recovery in desertified arid grasslands following livestock removal. *Conserv. Biol.* 16:995–1002

21. Hughes L. 2003. Climate change and Australia: trends, projections and impacts. *Austral Ecol.* 28:423–43

22. Kerley GIH, Knight MH, DeKock M. 1995. Desertification of subtropical thicket in the Eastern Cape, South Africa: Are there alternatives? *Environ. Monit. Assess.* 37:211–30

23. Saleem MAM. 1998. Nutrient balance patterns in African livestock systems. *Agric. Ecosyst. Environ.* 71:241–54

24. Oba G, Weladji RB, Lusigi WJ, Stenseth NC. 2003. Scale-dependent effects of grazing on rangeland degradation in northern Kenya: a test of equilibrium and non-equilibrium hypotheses. *Land Degrad. Dev.* 14:83–94

25. Oconnor TG. 1993. The influence of rainfall and grazing on the demography of some African savanna grasses—a matrix modeling approach. *J. Appl. Ecol.* 30:119–32

26. D'Antonio CM, Vitousek PM. 1992. Biological invasions by exotic grasses, the grass/fire cycle, and global change. *Annu. Rev. Ecol. Syst.* 23:63–87

27. Buffington LC, Herbel CH. 1965. Vegetational changes on a sediment grassland range from 1858 to 1963. *Ecol. Monogr.* 35:139–64

28. Mabbutt JA. 1984. A new global assessment of the status and trends of desertification. *Environ. Conserv.* 11:103–13

29. Milton SJ, Dean WRJ. 1995. South Africa's arid and semiarid rangelands: Why are they changing and can they be restored? *Environ. Monit. Assess.* 37:245–64
30. Aagesen D. 2000. Crisis and conservation at the end of the world: sheep ranching in Argentine Patagonia. *Environ. Conserv.* 27:208–15
31. van de Koppel J, Rietkerk M, van Langevelde F, Kumar L, Klausmeier CA, et al. 2002. Spatial heterogeneity and irreversible vegetation change in semiarid grazing systems. *Am. Nat.* 159:209–18
32. Gao Q, Reynolds JF. 2003. Historical shrub-grass transitions in the northern Chihuahuan Desert: modeling the effects of shifting rainfall seasonality and event size over a landscape gradient. *Glob. Change Biol.* 9:1475–93
33. Parsons JJ. 1970. Spread of African pasture grasses in the American tropics. *J. Range Manag.* 25:12–17
34. Hughes F, Vitousek PM. 1993. Barriers to shrub reestablishment following fire in the seasonal submontane zone of Hawaii. *Oecologia* 93:557–63
35. Asner GP, Beatty SW. 1996. Effects of an African grass invasion on Hawaiian shrubland nitrogen biogeochemistry. *Plant Soil* 186:205–11
36. Mack MC, D'Antonio CM, Ley RE. 2001. Alteration of ecosystem nitrogen dynamics by exotic plants: a case study of C-4 grasses in Hawaii. *Ecol. Appl.* 11:1323–35
37. Asner GP, Borghi CE, Ojeda RA. 2003. Desertification in central Argentina: Changes in ecosystem carbon and nitrogen from imaging spectroscopy. *Ecol. Appl.* 13:629–48
38. Gallardo A, Schlesinger WH. 1992. Carbon and nitrogen limitations of soil microbial biomass in desert ecosystems. *Biogeochemistry* 18:1–17
39. Schlesinger WH, Ward TJ, Anderson J. 2000. Nutrient losses in runoff from grassland and shrubland habitats in southern New Mexico: II. Field plots. *Biogeochemistry* 49:69–86
40. Hartley AE, Schlesinger WH. 2000. Environmental controls on nitric oxide emissions from northern Chihuahuan desert soils. *Biogeochemistry* 50:279–300
41. Schlesinger WH, Peterjohn WT. 1991. Processes controlling ammonia volatilization from Chihuahuan desert soils. *Soil Biol. Biochem.* 23:637–42
42. Peterjohn WT, Schlesinger WH. 1991. Factors controlling denitrification in a Chihuahuan desert ecosystem. *Soil Sci. Soc. Am. J.* 55:1694–701
43. Huenneke LF, Anderson JP, Remmenga M, Schlesinger WH. 2002. Desertification alters patterns of aboveground net primary production in Chihuahuan ecosystems. *Glob. Change Biol.* 8:247–64
44. Asner GP, Archer S, Hughes RF, Ansley RJ, Wessman CA. 2003. Net changes in regional woody vegetation cover and carbon storage in Texas drylands, 1937–1999. *Glob. Change Biol.* 9:316–35
45. Jackson RB, Banner JL, Jobbagy EG, Pockman WT, Wall DH. 2002. Ecosystem carbon loss with woody plant invasion of grasslands. *Nature* 418:623–26
46. Hughes RF, Archer S, Asner GP, Wessman CA, McMurtrie RE, et al. 2004. Changes in primary production and carbon and nitrogen pools accompanying woody encroachment in a north Texas savanna. *Ecosystems* In press
47. Hibbard KA, Archer S, Schimel DS, Valentine DW. 2001. Biogeochemical changes accompanying woody plant encroachment in a subtropical savanna. *Ecology* 82:1999–2011
48. Geesing D, Felker P, Bingham RL. 2000. Influence of mesquite (*Prosopis glandulosa*) on soil nitrogen and carbon development: Implications for global carbon sequestration. *J. Arid Environ.* 46:157–80
49. Martin RE, Asner GP. 2004. Regional nitric oxide emissions following woody

encroachment: linking imaging spectroscopy and field studies. *Ecosystems.* In press
50. Martin RE, Asner GP, Ansley RJ, Mosier AR. 2003. Effects of woody encroachment on soil nitrogen oxide emissions in a temperate savanna. *Ecol. Appl.* 13:897–910
51. Markewitz D, Davidson E, Moutinho P, Nepstad D. 2004. Nutrient loss and redistribution after forest clearing on a highly weathered soil in Amazonia. *Ecol. Appl.* In press
52. Guild LS, Kauffman JB, Ellingson LJ, Cummings DL, Castro EA. 1998. Dynamics associated with total aboveground biomass, C, nutrient pools, and biomass burning of primary forest and pasture in Rondonia, Brazil during SCAR-B. *J. Geophys. Res. Atmos.* 103:32091–100
53. Fearnside PM, Barbosa RI. 1998. Soil carbon changes from conversion of forest to pasture in Brazilian Amazonia. *For. Ecol. Manag.* 108:147–66
54. Schlesinger WH, Pilmanis AM. 1998. Plant-soil interactions in deserts. *Biogeochemistry* 42:169–87
55. Schlesinger WH, Abrahams AD, Parsons AJ, Wainwright J. 1999. Nutrient losses in runoff from grassland and shrubland habitats in southern New Mexico: I. Rainfall simulation experiments. *Biogeochemistry* 45:21–34
56. Branson FA, Gifford GF, Renard KG, Hadley RF. 1981. *Rangeland Hydrology.* Dubuque, IA: Kendall/Hunt. 339 pp.
57. Sparrow AD, Friedel MH, Tongway DJ. 2003. Degradation and recovery processes in arid grazing lands of central Australia. Part 3: Implications at landscape scale. *J. Arid Environ.* 55:349–60
58. Belnap J. 1995. Surface disturbances: their role in accelerating desertification. *Environ. Monit. Assess.* 37:39–57
59. Intergov. Panel Clim. Change. 1995. *The Science of Climate Change.* Cambridge: IPCC Working Group I
60. Mosier AR. 1998. Soil processes and global change. *Biol. Fertil. Soils* 27:221–29
61. Robertson G. 1989. *Group report, Trace gas exchange and the chemical and physical climate: critical interactions.* See Ref. 162, pp. 24–36
62. Firestone MK, Davidson EA. 1989. Microbiological basis of NO and N_2O production and consumption in soil. See Ref. 162, pp. 7–21
63. Hartley AE. 1997. *Environmental controls on nitrogen cycling in northern Chihuahan desert soils.* PhD thesis. Duke Univ., Durham, NC
64. Mosier A, Schimel D, Valentine D, Bronson K, Parton W. 1991. Methane and nitrous oxide fluxes in native, fertilized and cultivated grasslands. *Nature* 350:330–32
65. Bouwman AF, Lee DS, Asman WAH, Dentner FJ, Van Der Hoek KW, Olivier JGJ. 1997. A global high-resolution emission inventory for ammonia. *Glob. Biogeochem. Cycles* 11:561–87
66. Yamulki S, Jarvis SC, Owen P. 1998. Nitrous oxide emissions from excreta applied in a simulated grazing pattern. *Soil Biol. Biochem.* 30:491–500
67. Johnson DE, Johnson KA, Ward GM, Branine ME. 2000. Ruminant and other animals. In *Atmospheric Methane: Its Role in the Global Environment*, ed. MAK Kahill, pp. 112–33. Berlin: Springer-Verlag
68. Stephenson NL. 1990. Climatic control of vegetation distrbution: the role of the water balance. *Am. Nat.* 135:649–70
69. Parton WJ, Lauenroth WK, Smith FM. 1981. Water loss from a shortgrass steppe. *Agric. Meteorol.* 24:97–109
70. Frank DA, Inouye RS. 1994. Temporal variation in actual evapotranspiration of terrestrial ecosystems—patterns and ecological implications. *J. Biogeogr.* 21:401–11
71. Bremer DJ, Auen LM, Ham JM, Owensby CE. 2001. Evapotranspiration in a prairie ecosystem: effects of grazing by cattle. *Agron. J.* 93:338–48
72. Svejcar T, Christiansen S. 1987. Grazing

effects on water relations of Caucasian bluestem. *J. Range Manag.* 40:15–18
73. Wraith JM, Johnson DA, Hanks RJ, Sisson DV. 1987. Soil and plant water relations in a crested wheatgrass pasture: response to spring grazing by cattle. *Oecologia* 73:573–78
74. Naeth MA, Chanasyk DS. 1995. Grazing effects on soil-water in Alberta foothills fescue grasslands. *J. Range Manag.* 48:528–34
75. Naeth MA, Chanasyk DS, Rothwell RL, Bailey AW. 1991. Grazing impacts on soil-water in mixed prairie and fescue grassland ecosystems of Alberta. *Can. J. Soil Sci.* 71:313–25
76. Trimble SW, Mendel AC. 1995. The cow as a geomorphic agent—a critical review. *Geomorphology* 13:233–53
77. Marshall JK. 1973. Drought, land use and soil erosion. In *The Environmental, Economic, and Social Significance of Drought*, ed. JV Lovett, pp. 55–77. Sydney, Aust.: Angus & Robertson
78. Hendricks BA. 1942. Effect of grass litter on infiltration of rainfall on granitic soils in a semidesert shrub grass area. *Rep. Note 96*, USDA, For. Serv., Southwest For. Range Exp. Station, Albuquerque, NM
79. Fiedler FR, Frasier GW, Ramirez JA, Ahuja LR. 2002. Hydrologic response of grasslands: effects of grazing, interactive infiltration, and scale. *J. Hydrol. Eng.* 7:293–301
80. Pickup G, Bastin GN, Chewings VH. 1994. Remote-sensing-based condition assessment for nonequilibrium rangelands under large-scale commercial grazing. *Ecol. Appl.* 4:497–517
81. HilleRisLambers R, Rietkerk M, van den Bosch F, Prins HHT, de Kroon H. 2001. Vegetation pattern formation in semi-arid grazing systems. *Ecology* 82:50–61
82. Charney J, Stone PH, Quirk WJ. 1975. Drought in the Sahara: a biogeophysical feedback mechanism. *Science* 187:434–35

83. Dirmeyer PA, Shukla J. 1994. Albedo as a modulator of climate response to tropical deforestation. *J. Geophys. Res.* 99:20863–77
84. Bryant AD, Johnson LF, Brazel AJ, Balling RC, Hutchinson CF, Beck LR. 1990. Measuring the effect of overgrazing in the Sonoran Desert. *Clim. Chang.* 17:243–64
85. Michalek JL, Colwell JE, Roller NEG, Miller NA, Kasischke ES, Schlesinger WH. 2001. Satellite measurements of albedo and radiant temperature from semi-desert grassland along the Arizona/Sonora border. *Clim. Chang.* 48:417–25
86. Archer S. 1994. Woody plant encroachment into southwestern grasslands and savannas: rates, patterns, and proximate causes. In *Ecological Implications of Livestock Herbivory in the West*, ed. M Vavra, WA Laycock, RD Pieper, pp. 13–68. Denver, CO: Soc. Range Manag.
87. van Auken WO. 2000. Shrub invasions of North American semi-arid grasslands. *Annu. Rev. Ecol. Syst.* 31:197–216
88. Archer S, Scifres C, Bassham CR. 1988. Autogenic succession in a subtropical savanna: conversion of grassland to thorn woodland. *Ecol. Monogr.* 58:111–27
89. Brown JR, Archer S. 1989. Woody plant invasion of grasslands: establishment of honey mesquite (*Prosopis glandulosa* var. *glandulosa*) on sites differing in herbaceous biomass and grazing history. *Oecologia* 80:19–26
90. Hughes RF, Archer S, Asner GP, Wessman CA. 1999. *Ecosystem-scale implications of woody encroachment: storage and production of mesquite woodlands and their impact on C and N dynamics of mixed prairie ecosystems in North Texas*. Presented at Ecol. Soc. Am. Annu. Meet., Tucson, AZ
91. Asner GP, Wessman CA, Archer S. 1998. Scale dependence of absorption of photosynthetically active radiation in terrestrial ecosystems. *Ecol. Appl.* 8:1003–21
92. Tobler MW, Cochard R, Edwards PJ.

2003. The impact of cattle ranching on large-scale vegetation patterns in a coastal savanna in Tanzania. *J. Appl. Ecol.* 40:430–44
93. Harris AT, Asner GP, Miller ME. 2003. Changes in vegetation structure after long-term grazing in pinyon-juniper ecosystems: integrating imaging spectroscopy and field studies. *Ecosystems* 6:368–83
94. Mapfumo E, Chanasyk DS, Naeth MA, Baron VS. 1999. Soil compaction under grazing of annual and perennial forages. *Can. J. Soil Sci.* 79:191–99
95. Friedel MH, Sparrow AD, Kinloch JE, Tongway DJ. 2003. Degradation and recovery processes in and grazing lands of central Australia. Part 2: Vegetation. *J. Arid Environ.* 55:327–48
96. Cingolani AM, Cabido MR, Renison D, Solis VN. 2003. Combined effects of environment and grazing on vegetation structure in Argentine granite grasslands. *J. Veg. Sci.* 14:223–32
97. Fuhlendorf SD, Briske DD, Smeins FE. 2001. Herbaceous vegetation change in variable rangeland environments: the relative contribution of grazing and climatic variability. *Appl. Veg. Sci.* 4:177–88
98. Pettit NE, Froend RH. 2001. Long-term changes in the vegetation after the cessation of livestock grazing in *Eucalyptus marginata* (jarrah) woodland remnants. *Austral Ecol.* 26:22–31
99. Boutton TW, Archer SR, Midwood AJ, Zitzer SF, Bol R. 1998. Delta C-13 values of soil organic carbon and their use in documenting vegetation change in a subtropical savanna ecosystem. *Geoderma* 82:5–41
100. Walker H. 1971. Natural savannahs as a transition to the arid zone. In *Ecology of Tropical and Subtropical Vegetation*, ed. JH Burnett, pp. 238–65. New York: Van Nostrand Reinhold
101. Sala OE, Lauenroth WK, Golluscio RA. 1997. Plant functional types in temperate semi-arid regions. In *Plant Functional Types: Their Relevance to Ecosystem Properties and Global Change*, ed. TM Smith, HH Shugart, FI Woodward, pp. 217–33. New York: Cambridge Univ. Press
102. Breshears DD, Barnes FJ. 1999. Interrelationships between plant functional types and soil moisture heterogeneity for semiarid landscapes within the grassland/forest continuum: a unified conceptual model. *Landsc. Ecol.* 14:465–78
103. Twerdoff DA, Chanasyk DS, Naeth MA, Baron VS, Mapfumo E. 1999. Soil water regimes of rotationally grazed perennial and annual forages. *Can. J. Soil Sci.* 79:627–37
104. Breshears DD, Nyhan JW, Heil CE, Wilcox BP. 1998. Effects of woody plants on microclimate in a semiarid woodland: soil temperature and evaporation in canopy and intercanopy patches. *Int. J. Plant Sci.* 159:1010–17
105. Breshears DD, Rich PM, Barnes FJ, Campbell K. 1997. Overstory-imposed heterogeneity in solar radiation and soil moisture in a semiarid woodland. *Ecol. Appl.* 7:1201–16
106. Grover HD, Musik HB. 1990. Shrubland encroachment in southern New Mexico, U.S.A.: an analysis of desertification processes in the American Southwest. *Climat. Chang.* 17:305–30
107. Hoffman WA, Jackson RB. 2000. Vegetation-climate feedbacks in the conversion of tropical savanna to grassland. *J. Clim.* 13:1593–602
108. Weaver CP, Avissar R. 2001. Atmospheric disturbances caused by human modification of the landscape. *Bull. Am. Meteorol. Soc.* 82:269–81
109. Uhl C, Buschbacher R, Serrão EAS. 1988. Abandoned pastures in eastern Amazonia. I. Patterns of plant succession. *J. Ecol.* 76:663–81
110. Asner GP, Bustamante MMC, Townsend AR. 2003. Scale dependence of biophysical structure in deforested areas bordering

the Tapajos National Forest, Central Amazon. *Remote Sens. Environ.* 87:507–20
111. Kauffman JB, Sanford RL Jr., Cummings DL, Salcedo IH, Sampaio EVSB. 1993. Biomass and nutrient dynamics associated with slash fires in neotropical dry forests. *Ecology* 74:140–51
112. Gimeno-Garcia E, Andreu V, Rubio J. 2000. Changes in organic matter, nitrogen, phosphorus, and cations in soil as a result of fire and water erosion in a Mediterranean landscape. *Eur. J. Soil Sci.* 51:201–10
113. Belillus CM, Roda F. 1993. The effects of fire on water-quality, dissolved nutrient losses and the export of particulate matter from dry heathland catchments. *J. Hydrol.* 150:1–17
114. Ellingson LJ, Kauffman JB, Cummings DL, Sanford RL Jr., Jaramillo VJ. 2000. Soil N dynamics associated with deforestation, biomass burning, and pasture conversion in a Mexican tropical dry forest. *For. Ecol. Manag.* 137:41–51
115. Emmerich WE. 1999. Nutrient dynamics of rangeland burns in southeast Arizona. *J. Range Manag.* 52:606–14
116. Sanchez PA. 1976. *Properties and Management of Soils in the Tropics*. New York: John Wiley
117. Vitousek PM, Chadwick OA, Crews TE, Fownes JH, Hendricks DM, Herbert D. 1997. Soil and ecosystem development across the Hawaiian Islands. *GSA Today* 7:1–8
118. Fernandes ECM, Biot Y, Castilla C, Canto AC, Matos JC, et al. 1997. The impact of selective logging and forest conservation for subsistence agriculture and pastures on terrestrial nutrient dynamics in the Amazon. *Ciencia e Cultura: J. Braz. Assoc. Adv. Sci.* 49:37–47
119. Murty D, Kirschbaum MUF, McMurtrie RE, McGilvray A. 2002. Does conversion of forest to agricultural land change soil carbon and nitrogen? A review of the literature. *Glob. Change Biol.* 8:105–23
120. Kauffman JB, Cummings DL, Ward DE. 1998. Fire in the Brazilian Amazon 2. Biomass, nutrient pools and losses in cattle pastures. *Oecologia* 113:415–27
121. Davidson EA, de Carvalho CJR, Vieira ICG, Figueiredo RO, Moutinho P, et al. 2004. Nutrient limitation of biomass growth in a tropical secondary forest: early results of a nitrogen and phosphorus amendment experiment. *Ecol. Appl.* In press
122. Guggenberger G, Haumaier L, Thomas RJ, Zech W. 1996. Assessing the organic phosphorus status of an oxisol under tropical pastures following native savanna using 31P NMR spectroscopy. *Biol. Fertil. Soils* 23:332–39
123. Garcia-Montiel DC, Neill C, Melillo J, Thomas S, Steudler PA, Cerri CC. 2000. Soil phosphorus transformations following forest clearing for pasture in the Brazilian Amazon. *Soil Sci. Soc. Am. J.* 64:1792–804
124. Townsend AR, Asner GP, Cleveland CC, Lefer ME, Bustamante MMC. 2002. Unexpected changes in soil phosphorus dynamics along pasture chronosequences in the humid tropics. *J. Geophys. Res.* 107(D20):8067–76
125. Asner GP, Townsend AR, Bustamante MMC. 1999. Spectrometry of pasture condition and biogeochemistry in the central Amazon. *Geophys. Res. Lett.* 26:2769–72
126. Gehring C, Denich M, Kanashiro M, Vlek PLG. 1999. Response of secondary vegetation in eastern Amazonia to relaxed nutrient availability constraints. *Biogeochemistry* 45:223–41
127. Davidson EA, Kingerlee W. 1997. A global inventory of nitric oxide emissions from soils. *Nutr. Cycl. Agroecosyst.* 48:37–50
128. Keller M, Reiners WA. 1994. Soil-atmosphere exchange of nitrous oxide, nitric oxide, and methane under secondary succession of pasture to forest in the Atlantic lowlands of Costa Rica. *Glob. Biogeochem. Cycles* 8:399–409

129. Davidson EA, Keller MK, Erickson HE, Verchot LV, Veldkamp E. 2000. Testing a conceptual model of soil emissions of nitrous and nitric oxides. *BioScience* 50:667–80
130. Crutzen PJ, Andreae MO. 1990. Biomass burning in the tropics: impact on atmospheric chemistry and biogeochemical cycles. *Science* 250:1669–78
131. Reich PB, Peterson DW, Wedin DA, Wrage K. 2001. Fire and vegetation effects on productivity and nitrogen cycling across a forest-grassland continuum. *Ecology* 82:1703–19
132. Scholes M, Andreae MO. 2000. Biogenic and pyrogenic emissions from Africa and their impact on the global atmosphere. *Ambio* 29:23–29
133. Thompson AM, Witte JC, Hudson RD, Guo H, Herman JR, Fujiwara M. 2001. Tropical tropospheric ozone and biomass burning. *Science* 291:2128–32
134. Artaxo P, Martins JV, Yamasoe MA, Procopio AS, Pauliquevis TM, et al. 2002. Physical and chemical properties of aerosols in the wet and dry seasons in Rondonia, Amazonia. *J. Geophys. Res.* 107:8081–95
135. Andreae MO, Crutzen PJ. 1997. Atmospheric aerosols: biogeochemical sources and roles in atmospheric chemistry. *Science* 276:1052–57
136. Hobbs PT, Reid JS, Kotchenruther RA, Ferek RJ, Weiss R. 1997. Direct radiative forcing by smoke from biomass burning. *Science* 275:1776–78
137. Giambelluca TW. 2002. Hydrology of altered tropical forest. *Hydrol. Process.* 16:1665–69
138. Moreira MZ, Sternberg LDL, Martinelli LA, Victoria RL, Barbosa EM, et al. 1997. Contribution of transpiration to forest ambient vapour based on isotopic measurements. *Glob. Change Biol.* 3:439–50
139. Bruijnzeel LA. 1990. *Hydrology of Moist Forests and the Effects of Conversion: A State of Knowledge Review*. Amsterdam, Neth.: Free Univ. 224 pp.
140. Costa MH, Botta A, Cardille JA. 2003. Effects of large-scale changes in land cover on the discharge of the Tocantins River, southeastern Amazonia. *J. Hydrol.* 283:206–17
141. Calder I. 1999. *The Blue Revolution, Land Use and Integrated Water Resources Management*. London, UK: Earthscan
142. Bruijnzeel LA. 2001. Forest hydrology. In *The Forests Handbook*, ed. JC Evans, pp. 56–78. Oxford, UK: Blackwell Scientific
143. Nobre CA, Sellers PJ, Shukla J. 1991. Amazon deforestation and regional climate change. *J. Clim.* 4:957–88
144. Silva Dias MAF, Rutledge S, Kabat P, Silva Dias PL, Nobre C, et al. 2002. Cloud and rain processes in a biosphere-atmosphere interaction context in the Amazon Region. *J. Geophy. Res.* 107:8072–92
145. Werth D, Avissar R. 2002. The local and global effects of Amazon deforestation. *J. Geophys. Res.* 107:8087–95
146. Gedney N, Valdes PJ. 2000. The effect of Amazonian deforestation on the Northern Hemisphere circulation and climate. *Geophys. Res. Lett.* 27:2052–56
147. Bahre CJ. 1995. Human impacts on the grasslands of southeastern Arizona. In *The Desert Grassland*, ed. MP McClaran, TR Van Devender, pp. 230–64. Tucson, AZ: Univ. Ariz. Press
148. Holmgren M, Scheffer M. 2001. El Niño as a window of opportunity for the restoration of degraded arid ecosystems. *Ecosystems* 4:151–59
149. Bachelet D, Lenihan JM, Daly C, Neilson RP. 2000. Interactions between fire, grazing and climate change at Wind Cave National Park, SD. *Ecol. Model.* 134:229–44
150. Hecht S, Cockburn A. 1990. *The Fate of the Forest*. New York: Harper Perennial. 357 pp.
151. de Haan C, Steinfeld H, Blackburn H. 1997. *Livestock and the environment. Rep.*

UN Food Agric. Organ. Fressingfield, Neth.
152. Steinfeld H, de Haan C, Blackburn H. 1997. Options to address livestock-environment interactions. *World Animal Rev.* 88:15–20
153. UN Food Agric. Organ. 2002. http://www.agrifood-forum.net/practices/sector/livestock/21systems.asp
154. Carpenter SR, Caraco NF, Correll DL, Howarth RW, Sharpley AN, Smith VH. 1998. Nonpoint pollution of surface waters with phosphorus and nitrogen. *Ecol. Appl.* 8:559–68
155. Townsend AR, Howarth RW, Bazzaz FA, Booth MS, Cleveland CC, et al. 2003. Human health effects of a changing global nitrogen cycle. *Front. Ecol. Environ.* 1:240–46
156. Vitousek PM, Aber JD, Howarth RW, Likens GE, Matson PA, et al. 1997. Human alteration of the global nitrogen cycle: sources and consequences. *Ecol. Appl.* 7:737–50
157. Matson PA, Naylor R, Ortiz-Monasterio I. 1998. Integration of environmental, agronomic, and economic aspects of fertilizer management. *Science* 280:112–14
158. Goldreich Y. 1995. Climate studies in Israel—a review. *Atmos. Environ.* 29:467–78
159. Stafford Smith DM, Reynolds JF. 2002. The Dahlem desertification paradigm: a new approach to an old problem. See Ref. 163, pp. 403–24
160. Ramankutty N, Foley JA. 1999. Estimating historical changes in global land cover: croplands from 1700 to 1992. *Glob. Biogeochem. Cycles* 13:997–1027
161. Los SO, Collatz GJ, Sellers PJ, Malmström CM, Pollack NH, et al. 2000. A global 9-year biophysical land surface dataset from NOAA AVHRR data. *J. Hydrometeorol.* 1:183–99
162. Andreae MO, Schimel DS, eds. 1989. *Exchange of Trace Gases between Terrestrial Ecosystems and the Atmosphere.* Chichester, UK: John Wiley
163. Reynolds JF, Stafford Smith DM, eds. 2002. *Global Desertification: Do Humans Cause Deserts?* Berlin: Dahlem Univ. Press

ASSESSING THE COSTS OF ELECTRICITY

Daniel M. Kammen[1,2] and Sergio Pacca[3]

[1]Energy and Resources Group and the [2]Goldman School of Public Policy, University of California, Berkeley, California 94720-3050; email: kammen@berkeley.edu
[3]Center for Sustainable Systems, School of Natural Resources & Environment, University of Michigan, Ann Arbor, MI 48109-1115; email: spacca@umich.edu

Key Words electricity costs, life-cycle methods, subsidies, externalities, energy markets, energy efficiency, carbon taxes

■ **Abstract** We review the economics of electricity generated, or conserved, from a diverse range of fossil-fuel, nuclear, and renewable energy sources and energy efficiency options. At the same time, we survey the methods used to compute the costs of generated and delivered electricity and power, including bus bar costs; wholesale and retail marketplace costs; life-cycle accounting systems; premiums associated with political, social, and environmental risks; costs that reflect explicit and implicit subsidies; costs inclusive of externalities calculated by a variety of means; and net costs, including a range of proposed and potential environmental tax regimes. These diverse and at times conflicting analytic methods reflect a wide range of assumptions and biases in how the inputs for energy generation as well as how the subsidies and social and environmental costs are computed or, is often the case, neglected. This review and tutorial provides side-by-side comparisons of these methods, international cost comparisons, as well as analysis of the magnitude and effects of a range of technological, market-based, and subsidy-driven costs on the final price of electricity. Comparability of costs between supply and conservation technologies and methods in the energy sector has consistently been a problem, and the diversity of energy cost accounting schemes provides significant opportunity for very different arguments to be made for specific technologies, regulatory and market regimes, and a wide range of social and environmental taxes. We provide a review of the tools and a commentary on how these methods are used to determine the cost of energy services. The conclusion contains an analysis of how these methods of energy valuation are similar, how they differ, as well as an analysis of the explicit and implicit assumptions that underlie each approach.

CONTENTS

INTRODUCTION: ANALYTIC METHODS FOR ENERGY COST
   COMPARISONS 302
METHOD I: BUS BAR COSTS 303
METHOD II: MARKET-BASED COSTS, RISK PREMIUMS,
   AND COST VARIABILITY 309
METHOD III: MARKET COSTS INCLUDING SUBSIDIES 314
   Direct Subsidies 315

Indirect Subsidies 316
Assessing Subsidies 316
Subsidies to Nuclear Power 320
Renewable Energy Subsidies 322
Fossil-Fuel Subsidies 324
METHOD IV: EXTERNALITIES AND ENERGY COSTS 325
Hydroelectric Plant Environmental Externalities 325
Fossil-Fuel Environmental Externalities 326
Full-Cost Accounting of Environmental Externalities of Power Plants:
 Life-Cycle Assessment and Life-Cycle Costing 327
Costs and Value Judgments 332
Valuation Strategies 333
METHOD IV: CLIMATE CHANGE AND ENERGY COSTS 335
CONCLUSION 339

INTRODUCTION: ANALYTIC METHODS FOR ENERGY COST COMPARISONS

Energy is the most significant international commodity in terms of material flows, financial transfers, and arguably in both sociopolitical and environmental impact. Eight of the largest ten global companies are involved in energy discovery or acquisition, refining, or the provision of energy services. At the same time, the methods used to assess costs of energy resources and services not only differ greatly in terms of the theoretical and philosophical perspectives employed and emphasized, but also because they are frequently used to highlight radically different assumptions about the economic, social, security, and environmental value of renewable and nonrenewable resources.

Independent of which agent sets or imposes the market price of electricity (e.g., market equilibrium methods, auctions, regulatory authorities), energy accounting is fundamental to assessments of the feasibility of proposed power generation or conservation projects. Traditional electricity costing combines capital and operating costs, resource and conversion equipment characteristics, and regulatory and financial constraints. Over the past decades, the importance of hidden costs and environmental externalities in the development of energy projects has evolved, and although the methods used to monetize these values are still debated, their influence on our thinking about cost-benefit analysis for decision making is indisputable.

This review represents a departure in form from many past *Annual Review of Energy and the Environment* chapters. As part of the new series format, we will undertake a series of periodic updates on the basics of energy and resource issues. The goal of *Annual Review of Environment and Resources* is to regularly publish updated reviews and tutorials covering the costs, values, and impacts of the uses of energy services. As a result, this review provides an assessment of the methods employed in the form of a tutorial in energy economics and finance as well as quantitative material on the actual costs of different energy technologies, resources, and delivered energy.

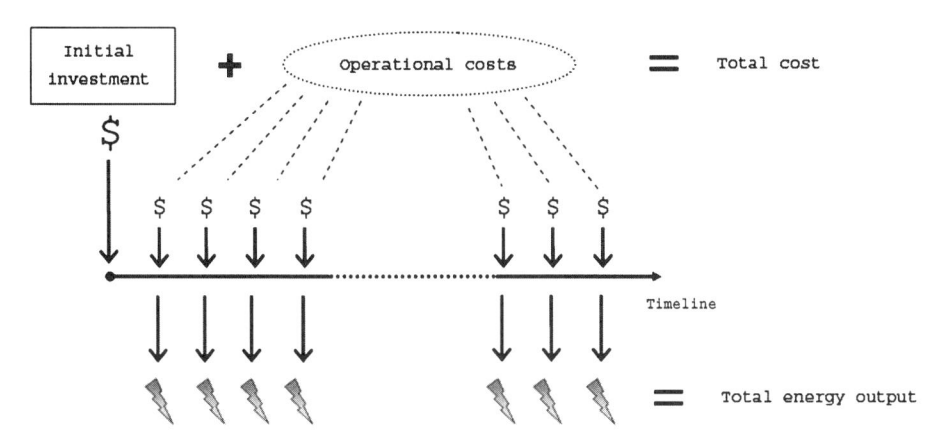

Figure 1 Simplified cash flow of a power plant.

METHOD I: BUS BAR COSTS

The break-even cost at which all expenses necessary to generate electricity are met is known as the levelized bus bar cost. Such cost is computed using cash flows throughout the facility's life cycle and includes initial expenses (design, licensing, installation), operating expenses, maintenance expenses, taxes, and decommissioning expenses. A simplified cash flow of a natural gas–fueled power plant, for example, consists of an initial investment to install the infrastructure plus a series of future operational costs, which include expenses with fuel purchases over the life cycle of the facility (Figure 1).

Ideally, each year the power plant produces the same amount of energy and consumes the same amount of fuel at a fixed cost, and the total life-cycle cost of a power plant combined with its total life-cycle energy output yields the electricity cost, which is usually expressed in terms of mills/kWh (one mill is a tenth of a cent). This value is the ratio between the annualized cost of the power plant and the energy output during one year. The calculation of the annualized cost involves the adoption of an annual discount rate (1). An annual discount rate is used to simplify the example in Figure 1, but discount rates based on shorter periods (months) may be also used. In order to convert from a fixed monthly discount rate (r_m) to a annual discount rate, (r_y): $r_y = (1 + r_m)^{12} - 1$.

Initially it is necessary to determine the present value of a stream of periodic costs to operate the power plant. The present value cost (*PVC*) aggregates future costs weighted by discounting factors, d_i, (Equation 1), where

$$PVC = C_0 + d_1 C_1 + d_2 C_2 + \ldots d_n C_n. \qquad 1.$$

The nth year is the final year of the period of analysis that does not necessarily coincide with the end of life of the facility because power plants can have their lifetime extended through retrofits. Retrofits can, of course, be incorporated in the stream of costs on a one-time or regular basis so that the lifetime of the power plant is extended, and the period of analysis is longer.

Equation 1 is used to calculate the present value of fuel, including changes in future prices, such as natural gas price escalation, used in the operation of thermal power plants. Fuel price escalation affects the value of C, and whenever a constant price escalation rate is expected, it may be added to the discount rate present in Equation 2. The discounting weight for a year in the future is a function of the annual discount rate (r) and the time elapsed in years (t) (Equation 2), where

$$d_t = \frac{1}{(1+r)^t}. \qquad 2.$$

Discounting adjusts costs in the future to render them comparable to values placed on current costs. A positive discount rate reflects that a given amount of future consumption is worth less than the same amount of consumption today. Real market discount rates represent the opportunity cost of capital or the rate of return of the best available investment option (1). Although discounting is a simple matter, analytically, important philosophical as well as economic arguments exist behind many of the numeric choices used in the literature.

Because the cost calculation is computed using an annual interval, it is necessary to know the annual energy output (AEO) and the annualized cost (AC) of the power plant. The AC is the amount one would have to pay at the end of each year, which equals the same cost in present value terms as the stream of costs being annualized (PVC), including discounting adjustments, where

$$AC = PVC \frac{r}{1-(1+r)^{-t}}. \qquad 3.$$

The annual energy output is typically assumed to be constant and reflects the installed power of the power plant in watts times the number of hours the power plant operates. Alternatively, the number of operating hours can be calculated using the capacity factor (CF) for the power plant. The CF is just a ratio expressed as a percentage between the number of hours a power plant operates and the total number of hours in the period considered, where

$$CF = \frac{\text{hours power plant is running}}{\text{total amount of hours in the period}} \times 100. \qquad 4.$$

In a fossil-fueled power plant the CF is driven by the periods of actual energy demand, whereas in the case of renewable energy it is associated with resource availability. Finally, the electricity cost, which may be reported in units of mills per kWh, is

$$\frac{AC}{AEO} (=) \frac{\text{mills}}{\text{kWh}}. \qquad 5.$$

Although a power plant is simply an energy converter, each technology demands the knowledge of different parameters to carry on an economic assessment. For example, the cost of a geothermal power plant involves estimates about the cost of studies to quantify the resource, drilling wells, power conversion equipment, and so forth (2). The cost of electricity produced by natural gas–fueled power plants involves hedging against fuel price volatility (3). Access to transmission lines to transport electricity should also be part of installation costs of a new facility. Transmission lines pose a physical limit to the amount of electricity carried (congestion), and part of the energy is lost during transmission (4). With the cost of transmission between two locations set as the difference between the cost of the energy at the two extremes of the transmission line, a comparative assessment between electricity supply options would logically account for the avoided transmission cost as a credit for decentralized systems.

Economists classify costs as fixed or variable. Fixed costs are independent of the output of the power plant, whereas variable costs are scalable depending on the output of the power plant. However, energy cost data are commonly reported in a peculiar way that includes the overnight costs, which represent the cost of the installed capacity in $/kW, the fixed and the variable operation and maintenance (O&M) costs in $/kWh, and the heat rate in MJ/kWh or Btu/kWh in the United States (5), which is a proxy for the electric efficiency of the power plant and indicates how much fuel is consumed to generate a given energy output.

At the present time, it is common to find power plants that not only produce electricity but also other services. This complicates the calculation of the electricity costs because it is often difficult to quantify the benefits arising from the provisioning of other services, and there is no consensual way to allocate the costs among different services. For example, a dam that is constructed for irrigation, water supply, and leisure may be also used to produce power (6). In the case of other forms of energy, which are by products of an electric generator, such as heat and power, the cost may be calculated for the total output using a common energy unit as a weighting factor for cost allocation.

In addition to electricity, combined heat and power (CHP) systems produce heat that is used for other purposes. The use of CHP can be compared with other energy sources that provide both power generation and another service. The electricity cost calculation for CHP involves the definition of the revenues from the steam supply, which may be included as a credit in the life-cycle cost calculations. Thus, the overall efficiency accounts for the electric output expressed in joules (0.293 J/Wh) added to the thermal output divided by the energy input. Accordingly, the net heat for electricity production is the fuel input minus the fraction of fuel attributable to produce steam that is being sold separately. Table 1 presents cost and efficiency calculations of various CHP systems. These alternatives may reduce cost and emissions through a more efficient primary energy use. (Fewer emissions do not always reduce environment and health problems because of the location of the emission source.) CHP systems have been recognized to be an opportunity for tremendous energy and economic savings. In some cases, efficient heat recovery and use can increase the overall efficiency of a power plant—now an electricity-heat facility—from from the 30% to 35% range to over 80%.

TABLE 1 Data for cost calculation of various combined heat and power (CHP) systems (7)

Size	Type	Cost ($/kWh)	O&M ($/kWh)[a]	Electric efficiency (%)[b]	Heat rate (Btu/kWh)	Thermal output (MMBtu/h)	Overall efficiency (%)[c]	Net heat rate (Btu/kWh)[d]
45–75 kW	Recip.	770	0.01	31	11,000	0.27	80	6,500
	MT	800	0.01	27.1	12,600	0.36	85	6,500
75–150 kW	Recip.	730	0.009	31.7	10,800	0.54	82	6,100
	MT	800	0.01	27.1	12,600	0.73	85	6,200
150–350 kW	Recip.	690	0.009	32.5	10,500	1.1	84	5,300
	MT	700	0.009	27.1	12,600	1.5	85	5,500
	Fuel cell	3,300	0.015	39.6	8,620	0.75	83.1	5,100
350–750 kW	Recip.	640	0.008	35	9,750	2.5	87	4,800
	MT	700	0.009	27.1	12,600	3.7	85	5,300
	Fuel cell	3,300	0.015	39.6	8,620	1.9	83.1	4,900
0.75–5 MW	Recip.	600	0.008	38	8,980	11	85	4,700
	Turbine	600	0.004	25.5	13,400	20	85	5,600
5–10 MW	Recip.	550	0.007	42	8,120	28	87.5	4,500
	Turbine	480	0.004	31	11,000	47	87.5	4,900
10–20 MW	Turbine	480	0.004	33	10,300	88	90	4,900
20–50 MW	Turbine	400	0.004	36.5	9,350	180	90	4,600
	CC	860	0.005	47	7,260	110	90	4,400
50–100 MW	Turbine	340	0.004	36.5	9,350	380	90	4,600
	CC	770	0.005	49.5	6,890	210	90	4,300
100+ MW	Turbine	270	0.004	36.5	9,350	500	90	4,400

[a]Abbreviations used include O&M, operation and maintenance; Recip., reciprocating engine; MT, microturbine—less than 750 kW; and CC, combined cycle.
[b]Electrical efficiency, overall efficiency, thermal output, and heat rates are based on lower heating value and for CHP operation at full load.
[c]Overall efficiency is based on electrical output (expressed as Btu equivalent) plus useful thermal output, divided by total energy input.
[d]Net heat rate is based on the fuel input minus the fuel required to produce the thermal output using a boiler (assuming a boiler efficiency of 85%), then divided by the full load electricity generated by the unit.

A similar approach can be applied to end use energy conservation investments. The final use of the energy, which is the energy service, may also be factored in cost calculations. Energy consumption is necessary because a service is demanded; therefore, if there is a technology that offers the same level of service but requires less energy, the annualized investment needed to install and maintain such technology (Equation 3) divided by the energy savings produces the cost of the conserved energy (CCE). Whenever the CCE is less than the marginal cost of electricity, which measures the cost to supply one unit of extra energy and deliver it to the consumer, it is better to invest in energy conservation than in supply. Figure 2 shows the CCE for different end uses in the residential and commercial sectors.

The calculation of CCE associated with different technologies and comparable energy services yields energy conservation supply curves (ECSCs) for use in the evaluation of the economic feasibility of energy conservation projects. The ECSC is assembled through the estimation of the potential energy savings and the CCE of several energy conservation measures (usually normalized to one year), and these are ranked based on their CCE. The curve is plotted in a graph where the vertical axis shows the CCE, and the horizontal axis measures the cumulative annual energy savings possible due to the incremental adoption of each technology (Figure 3). The cost of the (grid) energy supplied to the industry, which is also plotted on the conserved energy cost axis, determines the economic feasibility of projects (9, 10). Conservation supply curves were initially slow to win acceptance as a result of debates between neoclassical economists and energy conservation proponents over the value of conserved energy relative to purchased power. Thankfully, the debate over the value of "negawatts" as coined by Amory Lovins (10a), although not entirely resolved, has evolved to the point that energy savings are routinely evaluated and included in project assessments. Forecasts of energy savings and conservation have become central to evaluations of future needs and opportunities. The often dramatic savings possible for the U.S. economy are reflected in the cost of conserved energy curves produced as part of the widely cited Five Labs study (11) (Figure 4). A great many additional opportunities exist, such as the use of construction and building operation contracts in which the revenue is tied to energy efficiency performance.

There are at least two different methods to determine the total energy saved by the implementation of efficient technologies. One way is uses the baseline energy intensity, whereas the other one uses incremental savings.

Energy intensity measures the ratio between the output of a given commodity and the energy input needed to produce such output. For example, the introduction of technological changes reduced the energy intensity in the American cement industry from 7.9 GJ/Mg to 5.6 GJ/Mg ($\sim$30%) between 1970 and 1997. Currently, there is a potential for a 40% savings in the industry, which corresponds to 180 PJ (12); however, at present the actual real savings are likely to be limited to roughly one quarter of that total. Technological change has affected the American steel industry as well. In this industry the energy intensity dropped 27% between 1958 and 1994, corresponding to an energy intenstity of 9.7 GJ/Mg (13).

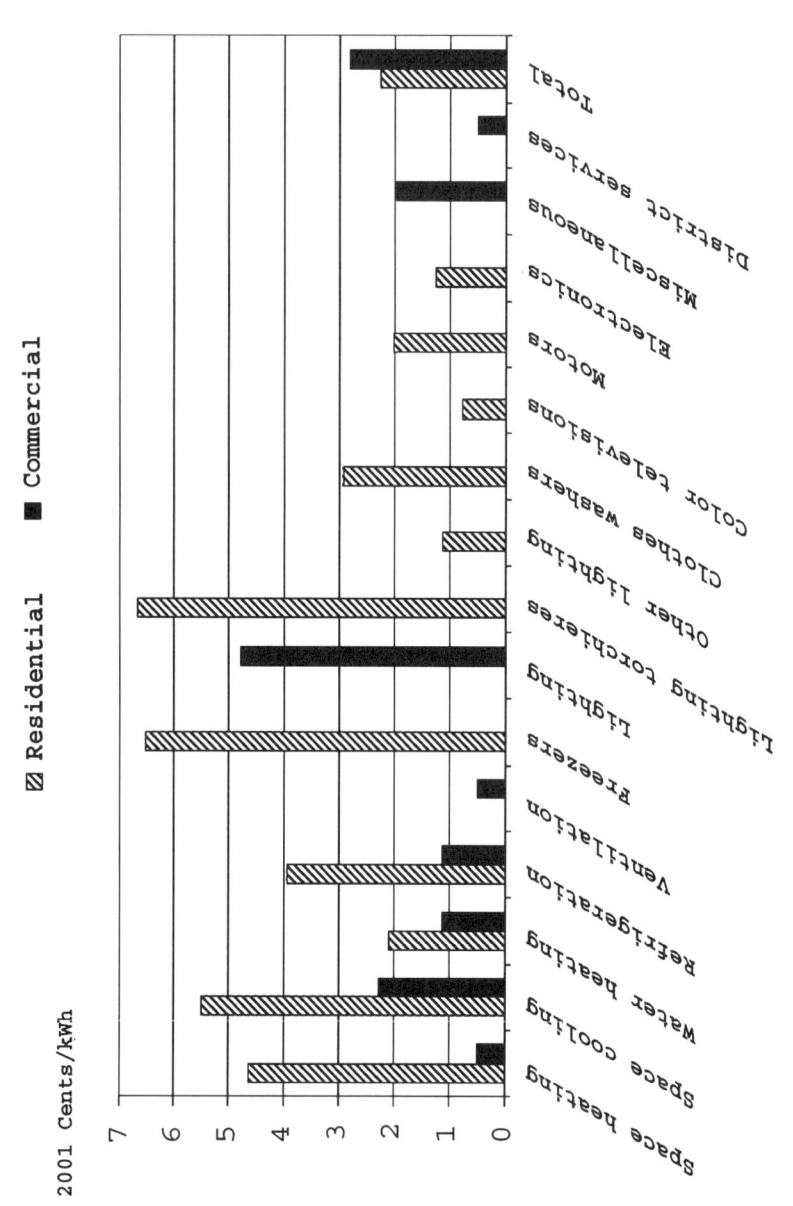

Figure 2 Cost of conserved energy for different end uses in the residential and commercial sectors (8).

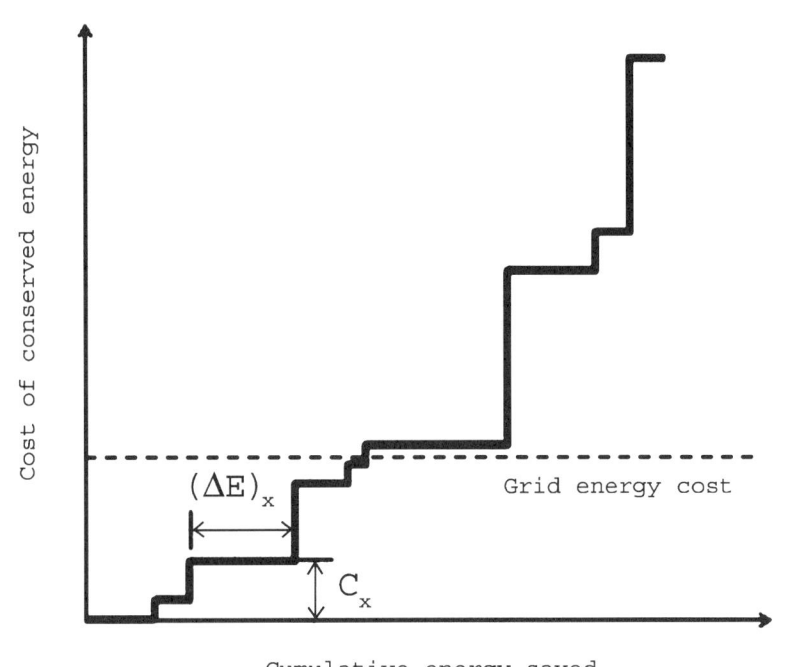

Figure 3 Energy conservation supply curve (ECSC) (10).

The ECSC based on incremental savings compares the marginal CCE versus the total amount of energy conserved. In this case, the benchmark to determine how much energy is conserved by a given technology is dynamic; that is, it is computed using the energy intensity of the previously implemented technology (14). In this case, the marginal CCE measures the investment needed to save one extra unit of energy.

Electricity costs for various current electricity generation technologies can be calculated using the equations presented herein, combined with values from Table 2, an appropriate discount rate, and fuel cost information. The differences between fossil-fuel systems, with relatively low capital costs yet sustained, sometimes volatile, fuel costs, and renewables with higher up-front costs and then both lower and more predicatable operation and maintenance costs can be striking, not only in terms of life-cycle impacts, but also in terms of revenue and expense cash flow.

METHOD II: MARKET-BASED COSTS, RISK PREMIUMS, AND COST VARIABILITY

By definition, power plants burning fuels for which there is a market are naturally subject to price fluctuations, which in turn impact the generation cost. Spot prices for both fuels (e.g., natural gas) and electricity have proved to be quite volatile,

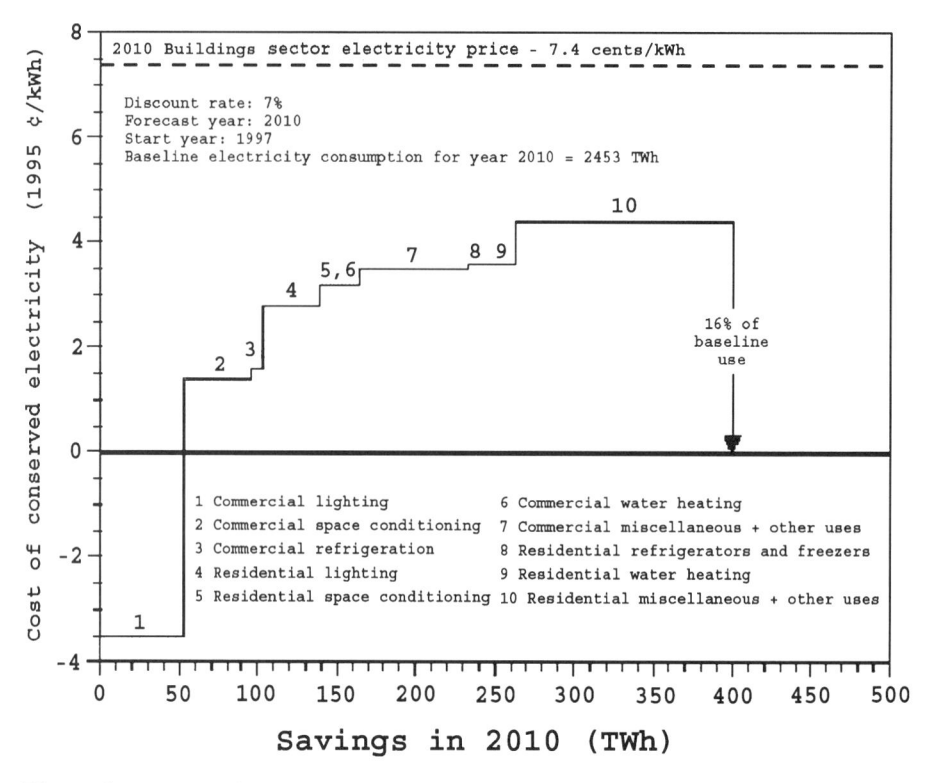

Figure 4 Conservation supply curve: forecast to 2010 (11).

largely as a result of market participants taking advantage of these vulnerabilities. A long-term economic assessment will tend to smooth out these price fluctuations. Whenever a comparison between the price of a commodity in the past and its current price is needed, values may be expressed either in nominal values, which reflect the absolute price of the commodity, or in real prices, which are also known as constant dollar prices. Real prices adjust nominal prices on the basis of inflation and measure the price of the commodity relative to the overall price level, which is measured through a basket of unchanged goods. The real price of a commodity is obtained through adjustments using the consumer price index (CPI). Monthly CPI values for the United States are available from the Bureau of Labor Statistics (15). The following example illustrates the conversion of $200 in 1995 to the corresponding 2001 value. First, the conversion factor is obtained by using Equation 6, in which

$$\frac{\text{annual average CPI for 2001}}{\text{annual average CPI for 1995}} = \frac{177.10}{152.4} = 1.16. \qquad 6.$$

The conversion factor is multiplied by the 1995 value to obtain the 2001 value. For example, $200 in 1995 corresponds to $232 in 2001 (1.16 × $200.00 = $232.00).

TABLE 2 Cost components for various current electricity technologies[a]

Technology	Overnight costs in 2003 ($2002/kW)[b]	Fixed O&M ($2002/kW)[c]	Variable O&M ($2002 mills/kWh)[c]	Heat rate in 2003 (MJ/kWh)[d]
Scrubbed coal new technology	1,168	24.81	3.1	9.5
Integrated coal-gasification combined cycle (IGCC)	1,383	34.11	2.07	8.4
IGCC with carbon sequestration	2,088	40.47	2.53	10.1
Conventional gas/oil combined cycle	542	12.4	2.07	7.9
Advanced gas/oil combined cycle (ADVCC)	615	10.34	2.07	7.3
ADVCC with carbon sequestration	1,088	14.93	2.58	9.1
Conventional combustion turbine	413	10.34	4.14	11.5
Advanced combustion turbine	466	8.27	3.1	9.8
Fuel cells	2,162	7.23	20.67	7.9
Advanced nuclear	1,928	59.17	0.43	11.0
Distributed generation, base	813	13.95	6.2	9.9
Distributed generation, peak	977	13.95	6.2	11.0
Biomass	1,731	46.47	2.96	9.4
Municipal solid waste landfill gas	1,477	99.57	0.01	14.4
Geothermal[e,f]	2,203	79.28	0	39.3
Wind	1,015	26.41	0	10.9
Solar thermal[f]	2,916	49.48	0	10.9
Solar photovoltaic[f]	4,401	10.08	0	10.9

[a]Values in this table are from Reference 5, table 38, p.71. They are not based on any specific technology, but rather are meant to represent the cost and performance of typical plants under normal operating conditions for each plant type. Key sources reviewed are listed on p. 86.

[b]Costs reflect market status and penetration as of 2002.

[c]O&M represents operation and maintenance.

[d]Conversion factor applied: 1 Btu = 1,055.87 J (5).

[e]Because geothermal cost and performance characteristics are specific for each site, the table entries represent the cost of the least expensive plant that could be built in the Northwest Power Pool region, where most of the proposed sites are located.

[f]Capital costs for geothermal and solar technologies are net of (reduced by) the 10% investment tax credit.

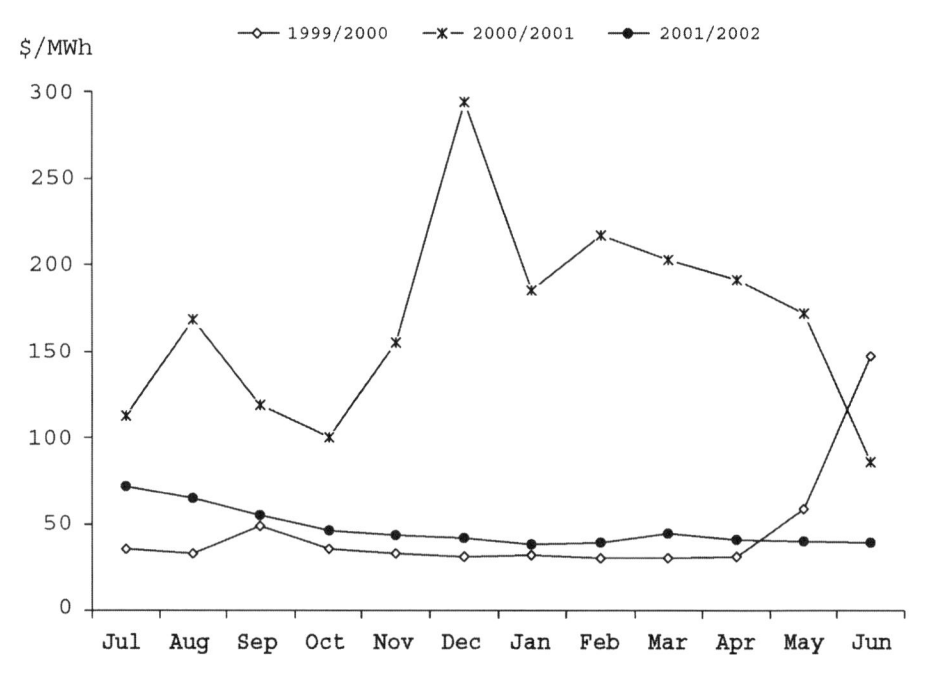

Figure 5 Average electricity cost in California of a megawatt hour (17).

The prediction of future price fluctuations is also important in calculating energy costs. For example, in January 2001, natural gas prices in California rose from values between $2 to $3 per GJ to $97 per GJ (16). The recent price volatility in both electricity (Figure 5) and natural gas (Figure 6) prices during the California energy crisis, which has been extensively discussed in the literature, is now seen largely as the result of faulty market oversight and design as well as active market manipulation by power suppliers (19, 20).

Rapid and unpredictable price fluctuations are expected to increase in the future. According to the official energy statistics from the U.S. government, natural gas prices, which in 2002 averaged $2.5/GJ (1.0825 GJ per 1000 ft^3), are projected to reach about $3.4/GJ by 2020 and $3.6/GJ by 2025 (equivalent to more than $6.5/GJ in nominal dollars) (18). Thus in 2025, natural gas costs would lead to an electricity cost of $0.05/kWh (1,025 Btu/1 ft^3 and 7000 Btu/kWh).

Different mechanisms are used by power producers to protect against fuel price changes. Hedging against natural gas prices includes both financial hedges, such as futures, swaps, and options, and investment in storage facilities, which allow withdrawal at high market prices and injection at low prices.

- *Futures* are traded in the New York Mercantile Exchange and guarantee a fixed price for a commodity for up to 6 years.
- *Swaps* allow two parties to exchange uncertain market prices for a fixed price over a shorter term than usually is considered by futures. The party selling

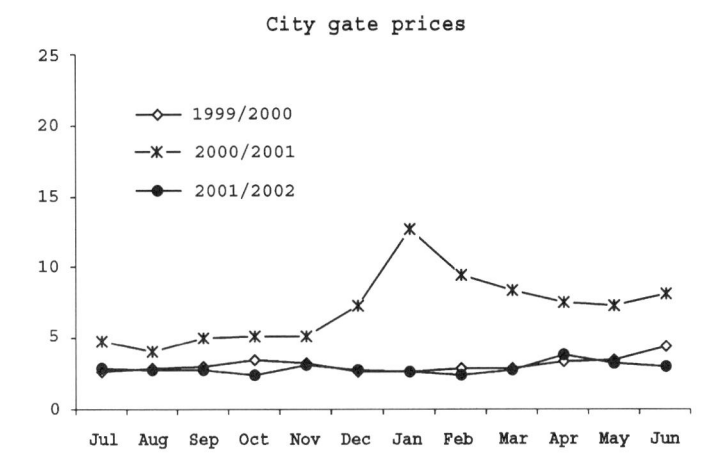

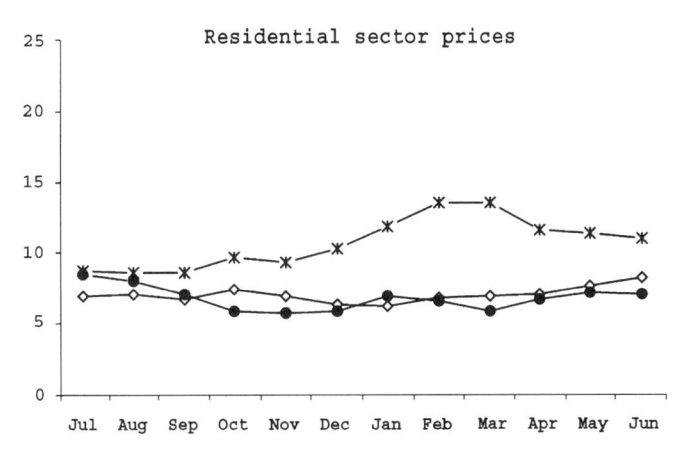

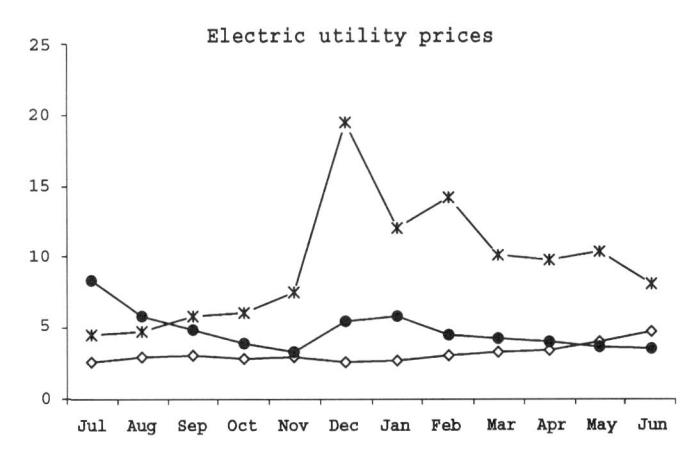

Figure 6 Nominal natural gas prices in California ($/million cubic feet) (18).

the swap is responsible for purchasing the commodity at actual prices and reselling at the agreed price level. The value of a swap can be calculated on the basis of the commodity's future series of prices and the appropriate discount rate using Equations 1, 2, and 3.

- *Options* refer to contracts that give the holder the right, but not the obligation, to buy or to sell the commodity at a specified price within a specified period in exchange for a premium payment (21).

- *Storage* corresponds to investments in physical infrastructure to control the supply of a commodity. The marginal benefit of storage, which is the amount in dollars that an investor gains in expanding her storage capacity by one unit, corresponds to the difference between the expected price of the commodity and its current price (22).

All options tend to agree in terms of actual costs, and a recent study concluded that electricity consumers have to pay $0.005/kWh ($0.50/GJ, or 0.35 ¢/kWh assuming an aggressive heat rate of 7.4 MJ/kWh) over market prices to secure natural gas prices for the next 10 years (3).

Alternatively, utilities that value stable electricity generation costs may invest in renewable generation options to hedge their vulnerability to future natural gas prices. Renewable energy technologies can contribute to a more reliable system through supply diversity, increased reliability, and predicatable and generally low O&M costs. For example, Hewlett-Packard estimates that a 20 minute blackout represents $30 million loss for a circuit fabrication plant. Overall, it is estimated that power outages cost the U.S. economy $80 billion per year (23).

In summary, when calculating electricity costs based on fossil-fueled power plants the analyst might usefully factor in the instability of future fuel prices and the risks and consequences of blackouts. A broadened definition of risk premiums also reflects the national economic cost of oil imports, and it includes costs associated with vulnerabilities to interruptions and price swings, increases in inflation, and deterioration of the balance of payments (24). This definition may be treated as a form of subsidies, which are discussed in the next section.

METHOD III: MARKET COSTS INCLUDING SUBSIDIES

A subsidy lowers producer costs or consumer prices below the preexisting market level. Sometimes they are difficult to identify, but usually, they tend to reduce production costs and intensify activity levels through financial benefits. There are different sorts of financial benefits that can be considered as subsidies. Examples include (*a*) a transfer of resources that both reduces prices paid for products or services and increases prices received for products or services and (*b*) market expansion.

The U.S. Department of Energy (DOE) quantifies federal energy subsidies by calculating the cost of the programs to the federal budget using, to the greatest

TABLE 3 Classification of subsidies

Direct	Indirect
Payment from government to producers or consumers	Insurance
	Loans or loan guarantees

Tax expenditures:
  Tax credits
  Measures that reduce taxable income
  Preferential tax rates
  Tax deferrals
	Provision of services:
	  Environmental and health safety
	  Regulatory framework
	  Energy services below market price
	  Defense

Excise taxes	Research and development:
	  Basic research
	  Applied research—existing technologies
	Trust funds

extent possible, federal government outlays and/or near equivalents, including the outlay equivalent value of tax expenditures.[1] Subsidies are classified into two major categories: direct and indirect.

Direct Subsidies

Direct subsidies involve direct payments to producers and tax policies. Indirect subsidies do not involve direct payment but rather investments in research and development or the provision of various ancillary services to support energy production (Table 3).

Examples of direct payments at the federal level are investments in energy conservation projects, and the Renewable Energy Production Incentive (REPI). In the case of REPI, money transfers simulate a reduction in the generation costs of electricity from specified sources. The goal of the program, which in 1999 had a $4 million budget, is to promote the development of renewable energy, and on a larger scale, it is essentially the program currently used in Germany to promote the generation of electricity from solar photovoltaics, which receive a price premium.

Subsidies classified as tax expenditures are provisions that reduce the tax liability for individuals and firms that generate electricity in a way that is perceived as beneficial for the public interest. Table 3 lists a series of tax expenditures. Such tax expenditures are considered direct subsidies whenever they discriminate between energy activities controlled by specific individuals or firms.

Subsidies in the form of excise taxes and trust funds aim to internalize social costs of energy production and consumption or to offset the financial or environmental risks associated with a specific technology. The burden of pollution resulting from fuel combustion is widely cited as a social cost of our energy

---

[1]An outlay equivalent is the amount of the outlay that would be required to provide the taxpayer with the same after-tax income as would be received through the tax preference.

economy, yet the extent of this social subsidy is also widely disputed, so that it is rarely, if ever, addressed quantitatively by producers and consumers involved in transactions in energy markets (25). Limits on private sector liability for accidents or remediating the adverse environmental or health impacts of pollution are also important subsidies for energy producers.

Indirect Subsidies

Indirect subsidies include financial and institutional aids, which do not imply direct or explicit monetary transfers to the producers, and public sector production of infrastructure needed to make an energy source economic. A classic example is construction of the U.S. railroad system that was, of course, built for multiple reasons, but it provided an invaluable subsidy to the coal industry. A list of indirect subsidies is presented on Table 3.

Insurance constitutes one example of indirect subsidy that is important, for example, for the nuclear power sector and is discussed in detail in the next section. Special loans can be offered to energy producers at below market interest rates, such as the ones provided to rural utilities.

The provision of market and safety oversight services may be also characterized as an indirect subsidy. Among these services are those offered by health and environmental agencies, regulatory agencies, and energy services that are provided at below market costs. Finally, expenses for defense of energy infrastructure—such as pipelines, refineries, and transmission and distribution assets—are important subsidies.

Another class of subsidies employs price discrimination between different sectors or consumers. Electricity prices vary across consumer sectors. For example, if in the same region industrial consumers pay less than residential consumers per kilowatt hour, they are being subsidized by the residential sector (26). A cross subsidy requires that some customers pay more for a good or service than it would otherwise cost so that others can pay less. Distinct delivery costs, which account for power losses and economics of scale, explain only part of price differences between residential and industrial costumers (26). Electricity price discrimination between residential and industrial consumers is a common practice around the world (8), and it has become an increasingly contentious issue as classes of "preferred" and "low value" customers emerge in deregulated energy markets (Figure 7).

Assessing Subsidies

The definition and valuation of subsidies, particulary indirect ones, is difficult, frequently subjective, and rarely done. Evaluating subsidies consists of either measuring the value of an outlay or measuring the variance between market prices with and without the subsidy. In the case of oil, for example, the impact of security expenses play a significant role. Both the costs of defending oil shipments through the Persian Gulf and the cost of building and maintaining a desirable oil reserve

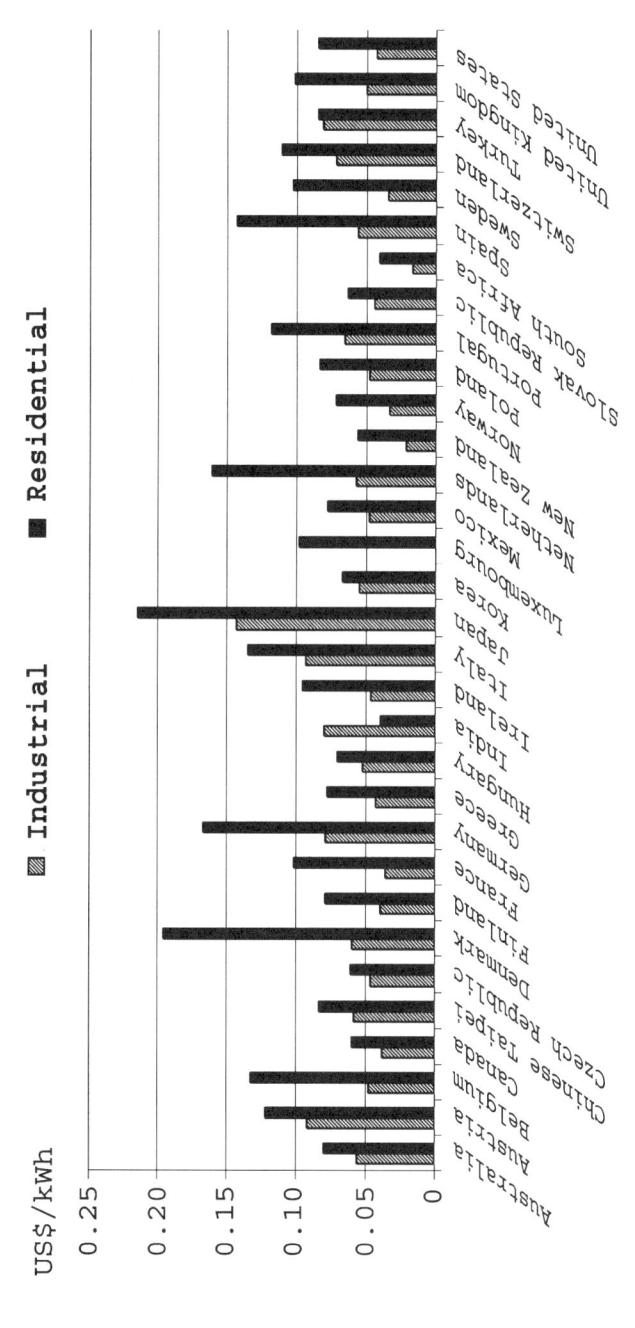

Figure 7 Electricity price discrimination between residential and industrial sectors (8).

might reasonably be included in a summation of the indirect subsidies (27). The inclusion or exclusion of energy security premiums and environmental externalities, for example, result in published estimates spanning almost four orders of magnitude for the subsidies afforded to fossil fuels (Figure 8, see color insert).

A recent review found that fossil-based energy receives the majority of federal subsidies followed by nuclear power (27). The characterization of subsidies is fundamental for energy policy and has implications for our economic security, the environment, welfare, and trade. Analysis by the U.S. Energy Information Administration found that from 1% to over 7% of total U.S. carbon emissions could be attributed to the structure of the subsidies provided to the energy industry.

A politically charged and controversial example of the oil-security linkage is that of the cost of the Gulf Wars. The cost of the first Persian Gulf war was $76.1 billion (2002 dollars) and the 2003 Iraq war is expected to cost up to $478 billion (2002 dollars) (28). The Iraqi invasion of Kuwait on August 2, 1990, resulted in the immediate reduction of 4.3 million barrels per day of crude oil normally supplied to the world oil market from the two countries, or nearly 18% of the Organization of Petroleum Exporting Countries' exports and nearly 10% of the total world supply. The spot price of crude oil in United States and world markets rose from $21 per barrel the day before the invasion to $28 per barrel within a week afterward (an increase of 33%) (29). Currently budgeted by the White House at $20 billion, the cost for reconstruction of Iraq after the 2003 war has also been counted by some analysts as an oil subsidy (30).

It is difficult to allocate investments in research and development (R&D) as part of the cost of a final product or service. For instance, two thirds of the $2.8 billion invested by DOE in 1999 was allocated to basic energy production research, which cannot be directly tied to production or consumption at the time of the investment because of the lag of the effect of R&D on production. Nonetheless, R&D investments are also energy subsidies and may be significant for many technologies, with photovoltaics and nuclear power often cited as examples for which this has strongly been the case.

Since 1948, the U.S. Department of Energy has spent over US$110 billion on R&D, and over 80% of this has subsidized the nuclear and fossil-fuel sectors. In the 50-year period up to 1998, the nuclear industry received $66 billion in subsidies and fossil-fuel industries received US$26 billion. During the same period, the government spent US$8 billion on energy efficiency measures and US$12 billion on R&D programs for renewable sources of energy (31).

In developing a comparative analysis of electricity generation technologies, a breakdown of subsidies based on technology type and their respective generation share is particularly useful. After coal subsidies ($6.7 billion), the second largest apportionment of subsidies for an electricity source goes to nuclear power ($4.6 billion) (32) (Figure 9, see color insert). Quantifying the subsidies provided to a particular technology remains a subjective step, but if accomplished, or at least attempted, it does provide a basis to internalize such expenses as part of the electricity generation costs and produce a more realistic comparison between technologies (Figure 10).

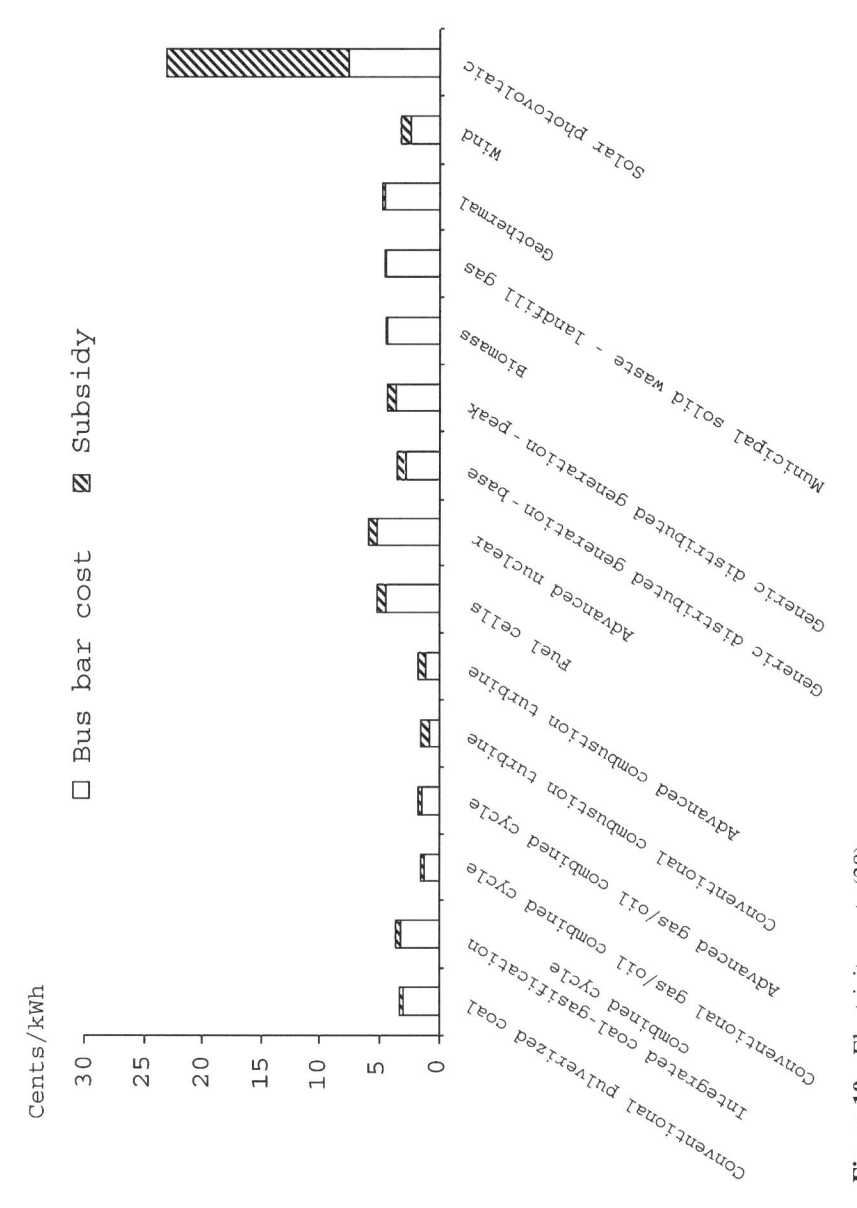

Figure 10 Electricity costs (38).

Subsidies to Nuclear Power

A high profile and often debated subsidy in the nuclear power industry is related to insurance issues, specifically the Price-Anderson Act. The act was promulgated in 1957, as an amendment to the Atomic Energy Act of 1954, to support the development of the incipient nuclear industry. Although it was originally a temporary act, it was reenacted several times (1967, 1977, 1988, 2002) following the interest of a powerful industry.

The Price-Anderson Act poses a cap on the private liability for nuclear power plants, which works as a subsidy, and reduces insurance costs for nuclear facilities. Besides offering an incentive to private investments in nuclear power plants, the act also ensures that adequate funds are available to the public to satisfy liability claims in the case of nuclear accidents. When required, resources are ultimately provided by taxpayers. The scope of the act includes fuel transportation, storage, power generation, and radioactive discharges and effluents (33).

Nuclear power facilities in the United States have two layers of insurance. A private insurer is responsible for the primary liability up to $200 million. In addition, there is an insurance pool formed by the accumulation of past deferred premiums on each nuclear facility, which currently corresponds to $94 million for each of the 110 commercial facilities. This pool of resources today amounts to $10.3 billion and serves as a self-insurance pool so that nuclear plant operators are covered in the event of a nuclear accident (34–36).

The U.S. Department of Energy is responsible for secondary indemnity under settlements of claims and judgments in lawsuits brought under the Price-Anderson Act cap. Regardless of who is legally liable for a U.S. nuclear incident, DOE facilitates a fund, to be collected through the Price-Anderson Act, which would be used to pay the indemnity.

The American Nuclear Insurers (ANI) estimates that the costs of private insurance would be prohibitive without the Price-Anderson Act because the damage of a serious nuclear incident would greatly exceed $200 million. If ANI had to provide insurance up to $200 million for each facility without the Price-Anderson Act, they would charge an annual premium from $500,000 to $2,000,000, depending on various factors, such as type and vintage of facility insured, nature of the activities performed, type and quantities of nuclear material handled, location of the facility, qualifications of site management, quality of safety-related programs, and operating history (34).

On the basis of a damage assessment, which does not take into account health effects, done by the Nuclear Regulatory Commission (NRC), it was concluded in 1990 that after the 1988 amendments the total amount of subsidy for the nuclear industry would reach $21,411,000 (1985 dollars) per facility (37). The output of 104 nuclear power plants in the year 2000 was 752 TWh (38). Dividing the total subsidy to the sector by the total energy output renders 0.5 cents/kWh of subsidy only from the Price-Anderson Act.

Besides support from the Price-Anderson Act, the nuclear power industry received in 1999 federal support for R&D as follows: $30 million for new nuclear plants, $467 million for waste management and fuel safety, and $143 million for generic investments (32). In addition, there are two more funds that support the nuclear industry. The nuclear waste fund collects user fees (1 mill/kWh in 1998) proportional to the energy output of the industry. For the fiscal year of 1999, the receipts amounted to $642 million. Second, the Uranium Enrichment Decontamination and Decommissioning Fund, which is responsible for the management of the three U.S. gaseous diffusion plants, received $171 million in 1999 from the government and commercial utilities. In the same year, the interest income for these funds corresponded to $507 million and $474 million, respectively, and the funds totaled $8.2 billion and $1.74 billion (32).

Part of the R&D funds for nuclear energy, which are categorized as "energy research and development" by the federal administration, are invested in environmental restoration and waste management of nuclear research facilities, and more than half of the R&D money to improve existing technologies is directed to nuclear activities. The investment in R&D for environment, safety, and health amounted to $47.4 million and targets the management of nuclear research facilities. In addition, $222.6 million were invested in R&D for fusion (32). An additional $53 million are spent by the NRC in nuclear R&D (32).

The suite of subsidies listed above can be totaled, adjusted to 2000 dollars, and then compared to total power output. This analysis—frequently sparred over by nuclear proponents and opponents—in many ways hinges on the the Price-Anderson Act. Proponents of nuclear power note that the insurance provided by the Act is consistent with that afforded a number of other industries, such as steel and aircraft. Opponents note that it is questionable if any nuclear plants would have been constructed in the United States without this support, and thus the value of the Price-Anderson subsidy is incalculable. This important debate aside, as of 2003 the annual subsidy totals at least $6.6 billion. Dividing the total subsidy for the sector by the total energy output (752 TWh) results in a conservative estimate of 9 mills/kWh of subsidy for nuclear power.

The 2003 Energy Bill calls for the indefinite extension of the Price-Anderson Act (39). The bill confers new authority on the U.S. secretary of energy to provide financial assistance to new nuclear projects if the secretary determines that such projects are necessary to achieve energy security, fuel or technology diversity, or attainment of clean air goals. The financial assistance can include any combination of loans, loan guarantees, lines of credit, and agreements to purchase the power from new nuclear projects. The assistance is limited to 50% of "eligible project costs," which include possible cost increases owing to regulatory or licensing delays. The legislation gives the secretary of energy 12 months to promulgate regulations implementing the new authority (40). In what has so far been a little-discussed aspect of this new bill, one section creates a nuclear parallel to the Strategic Petroleum Reserve, ensuring stability in the nuclear fuel market by specifying the amounts of uranium from the

U.S. government's stockpile that can be released into the market and the timing for such releases.

Renewable Energy Subsidies

Renewable energy technologies benefit from a range of subsidies through different programs. The introduction of the federal "million solar roofs" initiative, federal R&D programs, and the environmental regulations that encourage power generation from municipal waste combustion are all examples of subsidies that affect the economic feasibility of renewable energy. Not only are there subsidies consisting of financial assistance for the use of renewable energy, but other incentives, such as regulatory mandates, which are supported by legislation or institutional agencies, exist as well. Examples of institutional subsidies include

- Requiring utilities to purchase power from nonutilities;
- Efforts to introduce full-cost pricing that incorporates social/environmental costs of fossil fuels; and
- Requiring a minimum percentage of generation from renewables.

A milestone for the development of renewables was the National Energy Act of 1978 (NEA). In response to energy security concerns of the mid-1970s, President Carter promulgated the NEA, a compendium of five bills that sought to decrease the U.S. dependence on foreign oil and to increase domestic energy conservation and efficiency. A major regulatory mandate that has encouraged renewable energy, the Public Utility Regulatory Policies Act of 1978 (PURPA), was established as a result of the NEA.

PURPA requires utilities to buy electricity from qualifying facilities (QFs) controlled by independent power producers. The maximum installed capacity of a QF was set at 80 MW. In addition to renewable sources, cogeneration is also accepted as an energy source; however, to qualify the facility, at least 5% of the output from a cogeneration facility must be dedicated to thermal applications.

In California, QFs have relied on on 15 to 30 year contract terms that guarantee fixed payments based on future short-run avoided costs. Avoided costs represent utility power generation costs, including fuel escalation costs. Depending on future fossil-fuel cost forecasts, the rates are attractive; however, the rate is only guaranteed for the first 10 years. After that period, the price is adjusted to the new utility's short-term avoided cost, which sometimes compromises the survival of the project (41). The attractiveness of the scheme depends on the expected cost of fossil fuels at the moment the contract is signed.

A significant source of financial support for renewable energy technologies comes from tax credits. In 1992, the Energy Policy Act (EPACT) introduced a production tax credit, which offered 1.5 cents per kWh of incentive. EPACT also established the Renewable Energy Production Incentive (REPI). REPI is a federal program that offers direct payments to renewable energy producers. In 1999, the total amount available was $4 million (32). Finally, the Energy Policy Act of 1992

ASSESSING THE COSTS OF ELECTRICITY   C-1

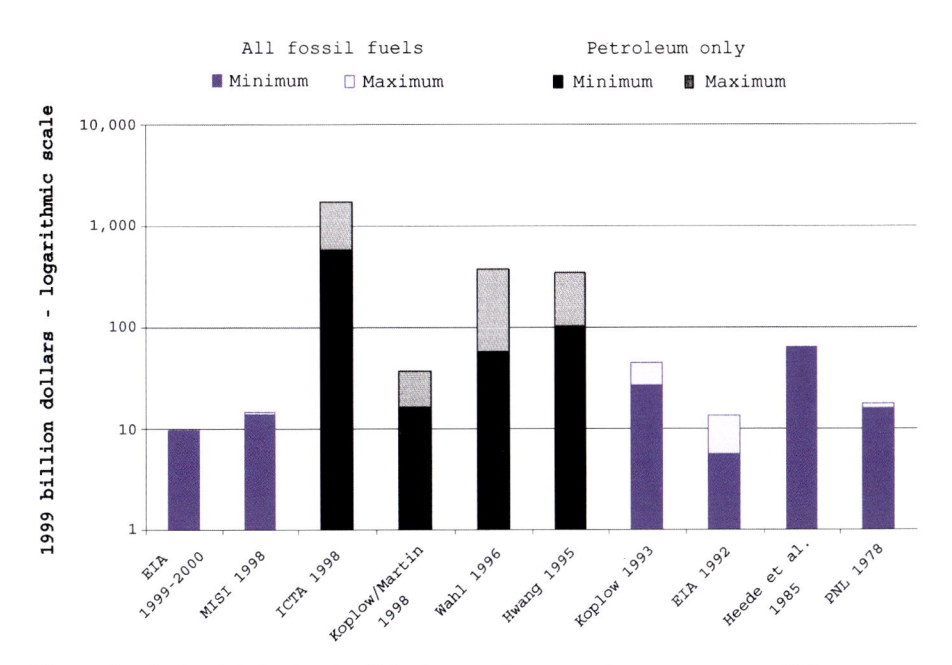

Figure 8 Total subsidies for fossil fuels according to various assessments (27).

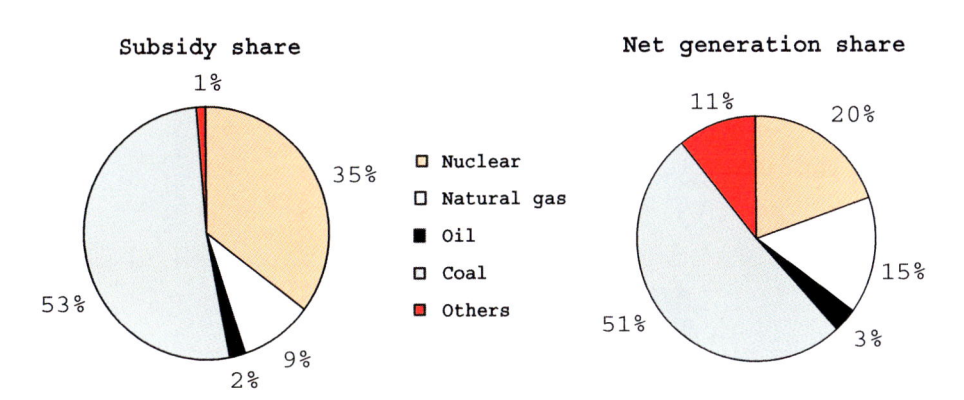

Figure 9 Share of subsidies and net generation in the United States for major electricity sources in 1999, based on (31, 32).

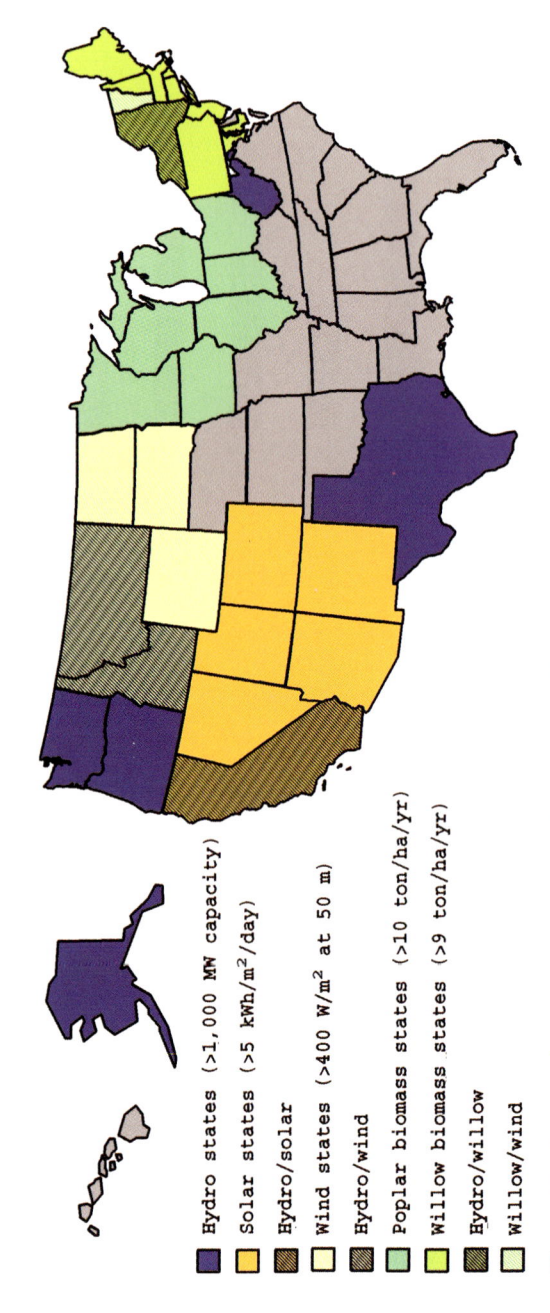

Figure 17 Renewable energy resource availability in the United States (88).

ASSESSING THE COSTS OF ELECTRICITY   C-3

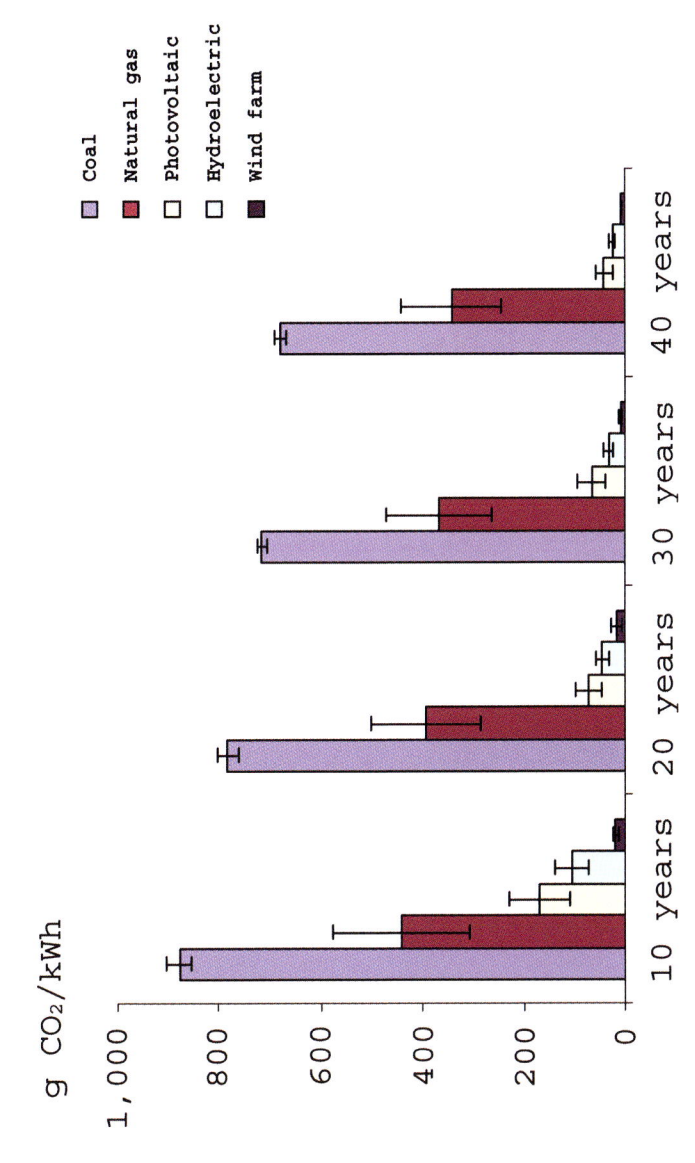

Figure 18 Life-cycle emissions for five electricity production technologies over four assessment periods (83).

offered a 10% business credit for solar and geothermal projects and $0.015/kWh for wind and biomass projects (32). Liquid fuels derived from agricultural crops receive sizeable federal support, with apportionments totaling $740 million in 1999 (32). In addition, many corn-producing states also support alcohol production. In Minnesota, for example, the Omnibus Environment, Natural Resources and Agriculture Appropriations bill (SF 3353) mandates the production of 240 million gallons of instate ethanol, and the state allocates up to $36.4 million per year for payments to producers.

Other initiatives at the regional level also support the development of renewable energy. For instance, following AB 1890, all electricity sold in California by investor owned utilities is charged a 0.7% fee that is used to support the development of renewable energy through rebates up to 1.5 cents per kWh. The Public Interest Energy Research Program supports research development and demonstration of energy projects in the public interest and makes $62.5 million available per year. In addition, solar and wind installations under 10 kW in capacity are eligible for net metering (the same rule is effective in Colorado) (41).

Initiatives in other states support renewable energy as well. In Illinois, a $0.50 monthly flat rate for commercial and residential consumers and a $37.5 flat rate for larger consumers fund the Renewable Energy Resources Trust, and wind and solar systems up to 40 MW of installed capacity are allowed to participate in net metering schemes (41). In Iowa, grants for energy efficiency and renewable energy, guaranteed buy back rates, property and sale tax incentives, net metering, research and outreach programs, and an alternative energy loan program are among the renewable energy support measures (41). In Minnesota, a 1.5 cent per kWh subsidy is offered for 10 years to wind projects up to 2 MW, and a property tax exemption excludes from taxation all or part of the value added by wind systems. Sales tax exemption for wind energy systems and net metering for renewable energy facilities up to 40 MW are also available in Minnesota (41).

Analysis of subsidies available to fossil-fuel and renewable energy technologies inevitably leads to comparisons and discussions of the playing field, i.e., the balance of incentives and disincentives in energy markets that favor certain technologies over others. In the United States, the ratio between subsidies to fossil fuels and renewable sources is at least 10:1 (42). If the analysis is confined to federal subsidies, 5% goes to renewable energy and energy conservation (43). In Australia, subsidies for renewable energy amounted to 2% of the total federal energy subsidies in 1996 (44). A UN Environment Program report finds that the allocation of subsidies between fossil fuels and renewable sources is more uneven in developing countries (43). Although interesting as a means to gauge public sector support for different energy technologies, cross-technology comparisons are arguably most directly reflections of the maturity of different energy supply systems.

In the United States, the most widely used public policy tool to promote the use of renewable energy is the "renewable energy portfolio standard" (RPS). The precise implementation of the RPS varies from state to state, but it is generally a requirement that power producers in a given service region, or state, meet a minimum content standard for energy from a set of approved technologies (often solar, wind, geothermal, wave/tidal, or biomass derived energy). California, for example, recently enacted a 20% RPS by 2017, whereas Nevada has enacted a 15% RPS (with 5% to be set aside for generally more expensive photovoltaic electricity) by 2013. The goals of RPS standards can vary dramatically, from a 30% standard for Maine that actually includes some fossil-fuel usage, to a 1.1% RPS in Arizona, although 60% of the 2007 year target is to be from solar energy. As of early 2004, 13 states have enacted RPS targets (see Figure 11).

Critical to making a RPS an economically effective tool is to couple the renewable energy generation requirement to a market for emissions permits, so that producers exceeding the local requirement can sell power, whereas those below the required level can buy permits.

Fossil-Fuel Subsidies

Fossil fuels, such as coal, receive subsidies targeting different phases of the energy production process: fuel production, operation of the plants, including technological improvements, and mitigation of health effects. For example, the royalty income of individual owners of coal leases is taxed at a 28% rate rather than at the normal tax rate of 39.6%, although this exemption is not available to corporations. This tax break amounted to $85 million in subsidies in 1999 (32). Examples exist

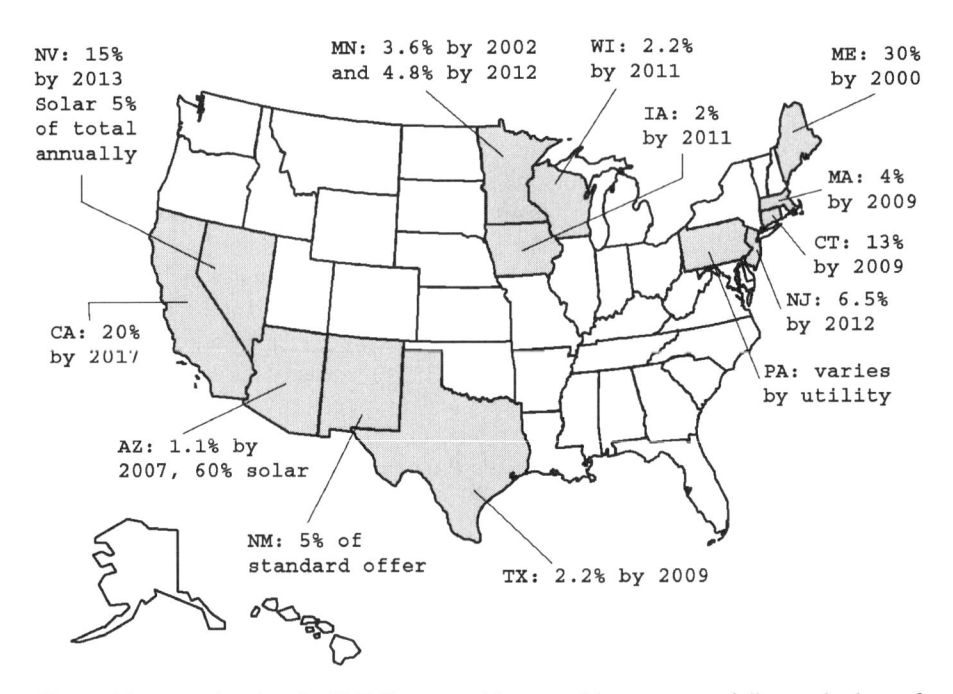

Figure 11 Map showing the 13 U.S. states with renewable energy portfolio standards as of 2003 (Staff Attorney M. Friedman, The Utility Reform Network, personal communication).

of energy taxes to address social damages as well. The Black Lung Disability Fund is a trust financed by excise taxes on coal to compensate for the health and social costs of coal production and consumption. As of 1999, this fund was in deficit, with assets of $638 million and outlays of $1021 million due to interest payments on past borrowings needed to cover outstanding claims (32).

The natural gas industry benefits from a range of subsidies. In 1999, subsidies for R&D in advanced natural gas turbine systems totaled $33 million (32), and federal subsidies for natural gas production from coalbed methane amounted to $1.2 billion. Coalbed methane accounted for 6% of all natural gas production in 1999, corresponding to natural gas sales valued at $39 billion (1999 dollars) at the wholesale level in 1998 (32).

METHOD IV: EXTERNALITIES AND ENERGY COSTS

An externality arises when the utility of an economic agent is affected by the action of another agent, and there is no control over such actions because the variables involved have no market value. External effects are not appropriately priced and allocated by the market. Efforts to quantify externalities, resulting from energy use, are not only widely debated, but when performed, they often significantly exceed fiscal subsidy levels (27).

Energy systems impact ecosystem services, including climate regulation, nutrient cycling, water distribution, soil dynamics, natural population dynamics, and others. The pressures we place on these natural systems may lead to their complete destruction, and because these life-support systems are fundamental for the operation of the economy, it is fair to claim that they have an infinite monetary value. A partial monetary valuation of the world's ecosystem services estimated the value of the aggregated world's ecosystem services to be in the range of $18 to $59 trillion with an average of $36 trillion per year (values published in 1997 were converted to 2001 dollars using CPI index) (45). Although this precise monetary valuation has been widely critiqued, the calculation has proven illustrative of the subsidy we receive from nature and of the need to put human activities into a wider ecological context. Our current energy economy is arguably the largest driver of the toll we place on the biosphere.

Hydroelectric Plant Environmental Externalities

The construction of large hydroelectric plants is usually associated with a series of social, cultural, environmental, and health externalities. Traditionally, benefits of water projects have been overestimated and costs underestimated. Hydroelectric projects have been highly controversial, with projected and real costs differing dramatically (46). For example, costs for land acquisition and resettlement for the Kayraktepe hydroelectric plant in Turkey increased from an estimate of $30 million in 1986 to more than $180 million in late 1993 (47). Assuming that the plant operates for 40 years and each year it generates 768 GWh, resettlement costs would amount to 6 mills/kWh or about 36% of the project cost (48). The World Bank estimates that between 1986 and 1993, when the construction of 300 large dams started, more than 4 million people were displaced (49). The annual incremental global energy output from hydropower in the same period was 45.5 TWh (50), and the average cost of resettling people affected by reservoirs is estimated at $3000 per capita (46). This crude estimate results in an average resettlement cost of 7 mills/kWh.

The social and environmental impacts of large dams are varied, and include population displacement, siltation in reservoirs, salinization, loss of biodiversity, and greenhouse gas emissions from flooded reservoirs. Dams are also linked to increases in diseases assocated with waterborne pests, including malaria, schistosomiasis, and dysenteries, caused by large reservoirs. The loss of cultural assets associated with sacred places and archeological sites is also of great concern and cannot be captured in economic assessments, as is true for loss of species and ecosystems.

Fossil-Fuel Environmental Externalities

The shortcomings in our abilities to measure the externalities associated with the use of energy has been a driver of efforts to develop a new set of analytic tools. The application of both epidemiological tools and methods from risk assessment have been applied to the analysis of the costs of energy services.

To quantify the impact of pollutants associated with fossil-fuel combustion, it is necessary to model the dispersion of pollutants, their transformation in the atmosphere, and the production of different compounds that affect human health and the environment. Finally, population exposure to air pollution causes morbidity and mortality, which are converted to economic values. The regional context is fundamental in this part of the analysis, which draws on air pollution modeling, atmospheric chemistry, demographics, epidemiology, and statistics in a complex analytical chain.

A recent assessment of health impacts caused by coal-fired power plants found that nine power plants in the Illinois region are linked to 300 deaths and 22,000 asthma attacks every year, two power plants in Massachusetts are linked to 100 deaths and 7,500 asthma attacks per year, and five plants in Washington are linked to 250 deaths and 20,000 asthma attacks per year.

The analysis can focus on individual plants, such as that completed for the Waukegan, Illinois, plant, which has been linked to an average of 40 deaths annually, or the Oak Creek, Wisconsin, plant, whose operation is tied to 50 annual deaths (51). Electricity generation at these two facilities in the year 2000 was 283,762 MWh and 608,118 MWh, respectively (52). If a "value of a statistical life," which represents the value of reducing a collection of individual risks, corresponding to $5 million, (53) is allocated to each death, the annual cost due to the operation of those power plants would amount to $450 million, or $0.50/kWh.

Efforts to place the human and ecological impacts of electricity generation in economic terms are clearly still evolving, but an important emerging finding is that the externalities are frequently significantly larger than the prices we associate with electricity supply options today (54–60). Figure 12 presents one such compilation, where the market prices of electricity from a range of supply options capture as little as one fifth of what an ecological or epidemiological evaluation of the costs of energy supply would dictate.

The commingling of pollutants has been a challenge to providing improved calcualtions of the full costs of electricity generation. In urban areas, in particular, it is difficult to differentiate between pollution coming from power plants and pollution coming from nonpoint sources, such as vehicles. Annual health costs associated with auto air emissions have been estimated in the range of $29.3 to $542 billion (61). Another study estimates that the same costs would be $34.2 to $79.8 billion (62); the authors find that the cost of total suspended particles is $67.9 to $114.0 billion, and the cost of impaired visibility is $10.3 to $39.9 billion. These values are based on hedonic evaluation methods, determined using willingness to pay surveys (each converted to 2001 dollars).

Full-Cost Accounting of Environmental Externalities of Power Plants: Life-Cycle Assessment and Life-Cycle Costing

Social costs of air pollution (Table 4) can be combined with emission factors (Table 5) to compute a cost per energy output associated with the operation of fossil power plants and their impacts due to emissions of criteria air pollutants (fossil-fuel power plants also emit other toxic air pollutants, such as dioxins, benzene, and mercury, which pose serious health and environmental risks). An environmental cost accounting approach that adds environmental cost information into existing energy cost accounting methods was described above. However, the comparison of externalities associated with different power sources demands the assessment of emissions over the whole life cycle of the facilities. Full-cost accounting would then involve the addition of direct and indirect environmental costs into energy costing (65).

Life-cycle assessment (LCA) has become increasingly popular as a standardized platform to compare the costs of a given technology over its lifetime. In fact, LCA of energy technologies grew out of earlier ideas of net energy analysis, a term coined after the first oil crisis to designate the assessment of the energy input-output ratio of energy supply and conservation technologies (66).

A modern LCA captures energy input and emissions during the entire production and supply chain associated with power systems, including resource extraction and materials manufacturing for construction (concrete and steel) and operation (coal, natural gas, and enriched uranium fuels), manufacturing, transportation, and installation of power plant equipment, retrofits and upgrades of power systems, waste management, and decommissioning (Figure 13). An LCA captures emissions beyond those generated during electricity production, such as those associated with the construction of the power plant.

Both process-based LCA (67) and economic input-output analysis-based LCA (68, 69) may be used to estimate emissions from supply chains. Actually, the two

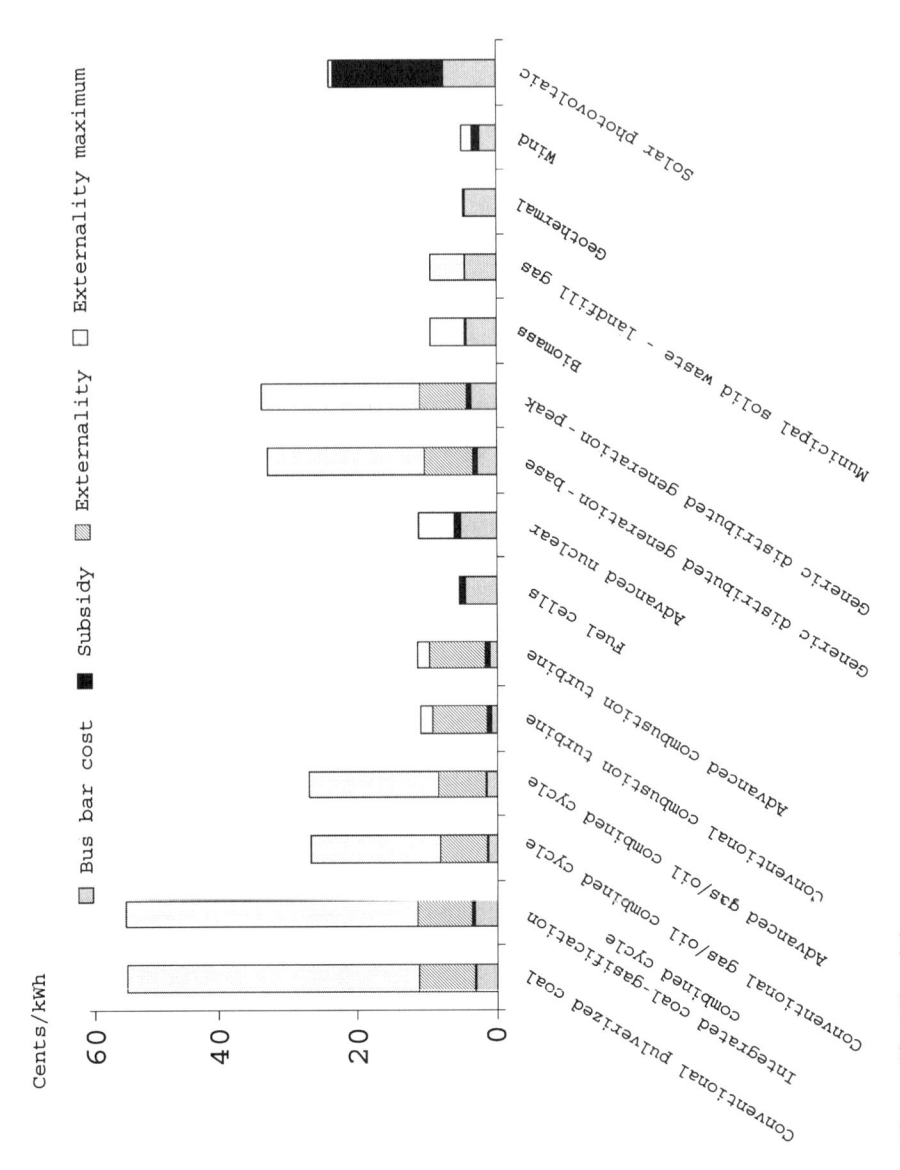

Figure 12 Electricity costs.

TABLE 4 External costs for emission of criteria pollutants in 2003 $/ton[a]

Reference and location of study	Particles	SO$_2$	NO$_x$
Ottinger et al., United States (85)	$2,958[b]	$5,258	$2,191
Alfsen et al., Norway (85)	$2,300–$30,345[b]	$548–$8,326	$1,753–$34,398
Pearce, United Kingdom (85)	$23,370[b]	$402	$136
Pearce, United Nations Economic Commission for Europe (UNECE) region (85)	$23,370[b]	$698	$537
Scheraga & Leary, United States (85)	$438–$11,941[b]	$329–$1,972	$11–$110
Hashem and Haites, United States (85)	$69,599[b]	$8,964	$17,484
European Commission, Europe (58)	$24,296[c]	NA[c]	NA
Levy et al., United States (58)	$13,252[d]	$872	$850
Levy et al., Sterling site—United States (58)	$3,092[d]	$8	$1,104
EPA (63), United States	$2,249[d]	NA	NA
Matthews (56)[e]	$5,637[e]	$2,622	$3,671

[a]All values are converted using CPI values assuming the date of publication unless specified by the author.
[b]Particles.
[c]Total suspended particles (TSP).
[d]PM$_{10}$.
[e]Mean values. The location is not available.

LCA methods differ in their boundary setting approaches. The boundary of the process-based method is flexible and is typically selected at the discretion of the analyst, whereas the boundary of input-output based LCAs is determined by the economic system that yields the data.

Process-based guidelines, developed by the Society for Environmental Toxicology and Chemistry and the U.S. Environmental Protection Agency (67), are usually adopted for process-based LCA. The framework divides each product or service into individual process flows and strives to quantify their upstream environmental effects. The assessment has the following four major components:

1. Goal and scope phase, definition of the objective of the analysis and the criteria that best represent the performance of the assessed alternatives to accomplish the objective defined;
2. Inventory phase, identification of the major material and energy inputs associated with the production of each component in the supply chain, and quantification of the stressors of interest (e.g., energy, pollution, toxic releases, water consumption, and waste generation);

TABLE 5 Emission factors for criteria pollutants and CO_2 for various fossil-fueled technologies (lb/MWh) (64)

Technology	CO_2	PM_{10}	SO_2	NO_x
Distillate oil-fired turbine	1196	0.09	0.251	4.27
Landfill gas-fired turbine	682	0.31	0.614	1.91
Digester gas-fired turbine	NA[a]	0.11	0.058	1.43
Pulverized coal	2119	2.58	0.317	7.32
Microturbine	1596	0.09	0.008	0.40
Small simple-cycle turbine	1494	0.08	0.008	1.10
Medium simple-cycle turbine	1327	0.07	0.007	0.60
Large simple-cycle turbine	1281	0.07	0.007	0.99
Large combined-cycle turbine	776	0.04	0.006	0.10
Advanced technology turbine	1154	0.07	0.006	0.30
Solid oxide fuel cell	950	0.00	0.005	0.01
Phosphoric acid fuel cell	1078	0.00	0.006	0.03
Gas-fired engine, lean burn	1108	0.03	0.006	2.20
Gas-fired engine, 3-way catalyst	1376	0.03	0.007	0.50
Diesel engine	1432	0.78	0.450	21.80
Diesel engine, selective catalytic reduction	1432	0.78	0.450	4.70

[a]NA means not applicable.

3. Impact assessment phase, quantification and aggregation of effects arising from the use of each component to yield life-cycle impacts of the object assessed; and
4. Final phase, interpretation of results by means of comparisons, rankings, sensitivity analyses, and simulations.

In contrast, one popular economic input-output analysis (EIO-LCA) utilizes a 500 × 500 commodity by commodity transaction matrix of the U.S. economy. In this model, economic transactions are used to identify interdependencies between all sectors in the economy (68). The method is more inclusive, and the boundary of the assessment is the national economy. Various commodities, such as steel, coal, and sugar, are represented by characteristic sectors. The association of the total economic output of each sector with a set of environmental indicators, such as energy consumption, water use, and pollution, produced by the respective sectors, yields environmental intensity factors that may be used in environmental analyses. The information currently available is based on transactions for 1997 (69). The environmental intensity factors have been applied to a number of product assessments (68, 70).

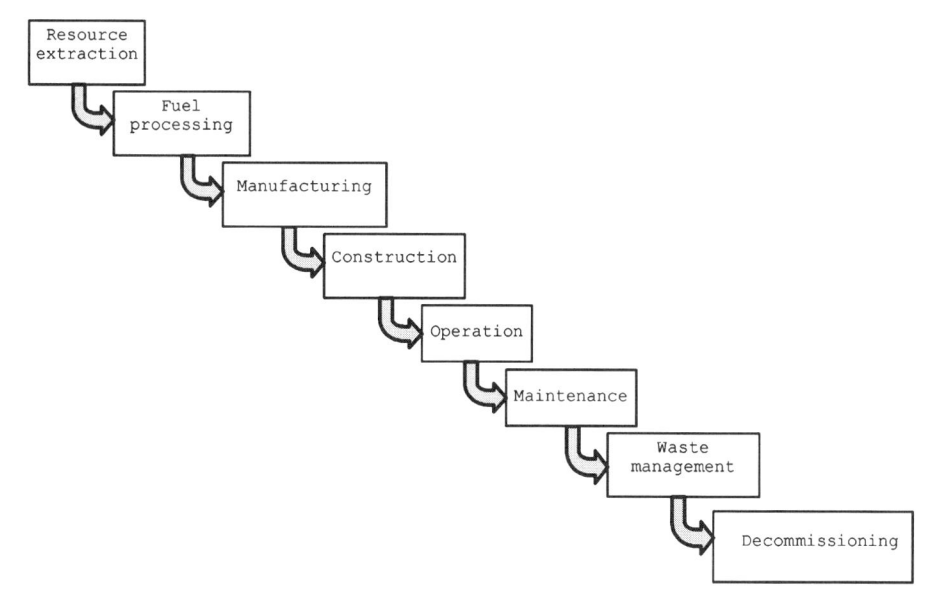

Figure 13 Life-cycle phases of a power plant.

The LCA can be a powerful tool to evaluate the performance of energy systems. In most classical economic analyses, the ratio of subsidies per energy output of different energy technologies is based on the energy output during the operation of the systems. In contrast, an LCA tracks all energy inputs over the life cycle of a power plant and includes its decommissioning and waste management. For example, in an LCA analysis of the cost of electricity from a photovoltaic system, the true cost reflects not only the bus bar cost, but also the cost of the materials and the manufacture of the panel, as well as any costs associated with the disposal of the panel at end of its operational life. In the same vein, subsidies of nuclear energy are higher if energy consumed to manage and store used fuel is taken into account. Other useful places for this type of analysis are the production of ethanol fuel and its comparison with other liquid fuels (71).

On the environmental side, LCA can be useful because different electricity generation technologies may produce a variety of impacts during different phases of their life cycle. Indeed, different life-cycle stages are dominant in the impacts of different electricity generation technologies (71, 72). The challenge is how to translate emissions that vary over spatial and temporal dimensions into meaningful dollar figures (72).

Full-cost accounting attempts to translate impacts that arise from the entire life cycle of a process or product into economic values. In the case of electricity production, the cost accounting consists of an LCA and evaluation of the resulting damage caused by pollutants and toxic releases. Next, the damages are are further aggregated, and the ratio between the total damage, which is expressed in monetary units, and the total electricity produced by the power plant renders the full environmental cost of the electricity.

Costs and Value Judgments

The comparison of the costs of externalities is further complicated because of the need to find ways to reflect human perceptions and value judgments. It is difficult to compare the "small chance of a big disaster against a persistent routine impact that is significant but not overwhelming" (72).

Nuclear accidents and global warming also share a common feature with respect to economic valuation and discounting: The impact of each could persist in the environment for centuries, well beyond the time that our conventional methods of economic valuation provide useful methods of comparison. There is a weak connection between the generation who benefits from the energy produced and the generation suffering the harm; consequently, the estimation of the present value of such impacts using market discount rates is inadequate (74, 75).

The damages caused by the operation of a power plant sometimes manifest over long time horizons, and therefore, benefit cost analysis must describe future effects in terms that help current policy makers choosing appropriate approaches for environmental protection. Global warming may remain a problem for centuries and may affect people who received little or no benefit from the electricity produced that caused the problem. That is, a power plant, which produces electricity for the current generation, also emits carbon dioxide, which accumulates in the atmosphere and has potential to trigger future environmental impacts. When time horizons associated with an environmental externality are long enough that impacts manifest over different generations, the problem is characterized as an intergenerational discounting issue. In this case, the choice of a social discount rate for practical applications requires inputs from disciplines other than economics to produce a sensible answer.

Therefore, the calculation of the present value in monetary terms of the future damage caused by CO_2 emitted today would need to include a discount rate that reflects such long-run impacts. An appropriate discount rate should at least reflect the fraction of CO_2 remaining in the atmosphere after its release. One approximation to this value is based on the pulse response function that results from a carbon cycle model used by the Intergovernmental Panel on Climate Change (76). Similarly, the costs of a nuclear accident should reflect the persistence of isotopes in the environment instead of a present value discounted by a market discount rate. Figure 14 shows the fraction of CO_2 and the fraction of strontium 90 as a function of time compared to discounting using a 4%, 7%, and a 12% discount rate.

In addition to the variability on temporal and spatial scales, who is impacted affects the way risks are perceived. Impacts from energy production have become a focus of environmental justice. Social conflicts resulting from environmental

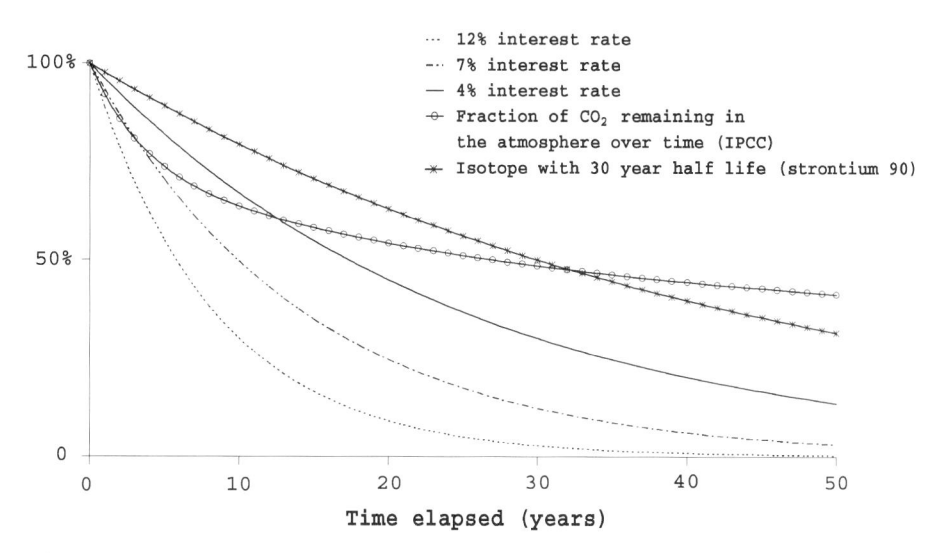

Figure 14 Decay rates for CO_2 and strontium 90 compared to discount rates. IPCC is the Intergovernmental Panel on Climate Change.

justice conflicts exist in many languages, and the economic valuation of damages is only one language. Who has the power to impose particular languages of valuation? Who rules over the ways and means of simplifying complexity, deciding that some points of view are out of order? Who has power to determine which is the bottom line in an environmental discussion (77)? Goals and values of analysts are embedded in the valuation methods. Finally, the valuation of an externality is also affected by the degree of control or adaptability for any given impact and by the degree of irreversibility of a given impact (78). Some people argue that there is an opportunity cost for climate change mitigation actions because in the future the cost to adapt to changes is going to be lower than present mitigation costs. However, if climate change leads to permanent losses, such as species extinction, this irreversible damage arguably has infinite costs.

Valuation Strategies

The cost of air pollution and greenhouse gas (GHG) emissions can be estimated either using the economic valuation of the damage caused by pollution, or they can be assessed using the cost of alternatives to reduce emissions, such as new technologies or fuel switching. Estimations based on quantification of damages are contentious because different electricity generation sources pose different forms of impacts, which vary over spatial, temporal, and social dimensions. Monetary quantification aspires to translate different impacts into a comparable and objective unit (79), but the task is not simple. The valuation of externalities draws on several components, such as emission inventory, transport and deposition modeling, environmental impact and risk assessment, and finally economic valuation. Thus, environmental costing incorporates the uncertainties of these complimentary assessments (24). Alternatively, environmental costs could be quantified on the basis of abatement costs used to mitigate health or environmental damage, e.g., control costing method.

A variety of methods is available to control air emissions from fossil-fueled power plants. For example, in the case of SO_2 emissions, which is a precursor for acid rain, reductions may be accomplished either through the installation of scrubbers or fuel switching to a lower sulfur content coal. The existence of concurrent opportunities, scattered over the United States, and the belief that a market trading scheme could achieve low cost emission reductions led to the creation of the Acid Rain Program. The program was proposed as an amendment to the 1990 U.S. Clean Air Act to reduce 1995 total air emissions of acid rain precursors from power plants back to 50% of their 1980 levels (80).

The market for SO_2 emissions, or allowances, establishes property rights on SO_2 emissions and specifies a marginal abatement cost for SO_2. This in turn allows polluters to purchase emission permits rather than implementing technologies to reduce their own emissions. Every year an emitter needs enough allowances to match his emissions over the same period. If the market operates efficiently, pollution reduction is achieved at a lower cost than through traditional command and control regulations (81, 82). Emissions control obligations of the first group of electricity generators started in 1995, but some transactions occurred prior to that year. Figure 15 shows the cost per ton of SO_2 derived from the Acid Rain Program. The same scheme is could be applied to other air emissions, such as GHGs (83).

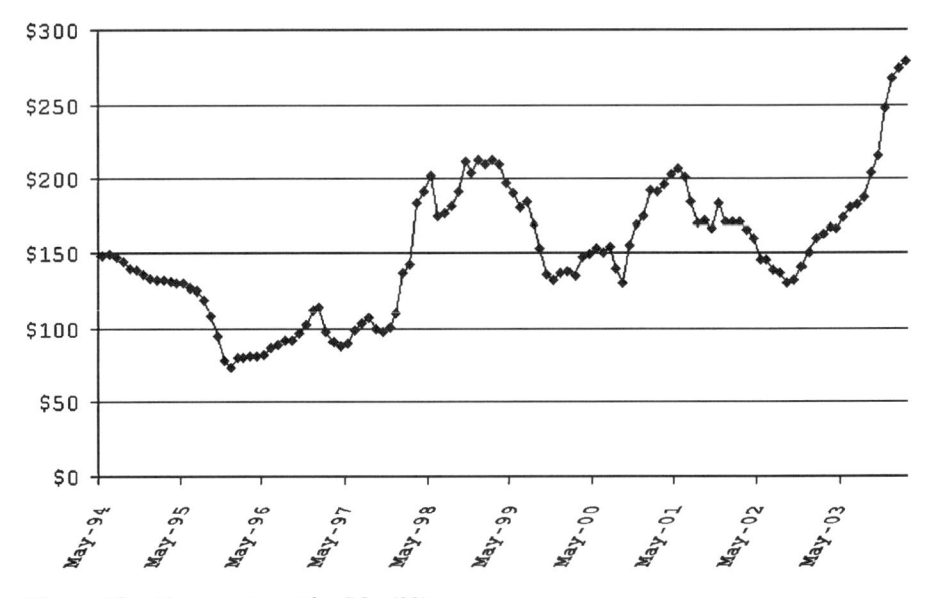

Figure 15 Abatement cost for SO_2 (82).

TABLE 6 Energy Modeling Forum marginal abatement cost of carbon emissions determined by various models in 1990 US$/tC[a]

Model	No trading United States	OECD-E[b]	Japan	CANZ	Annex I trading	Global trading
ABARE-GTEM	322	665	645	425	106	23
AIM	153	198	234	147	65	38
CETA	168	—	—	—	46	26
FUND	—	—	—	—	14	10
G-Cubed	76	227	97	157	53	20
GRAPE	—	204	304	—	70	44
MERGE3	264	218	500	250	135	86
MIT-EPPA	193	276	501	247	76	—
MS-MRT	236	179	402	213	77	27
Oxford	410	966	1074	—	224	123
RICE	132	159	251	145	62	18
SGM	188	407	357	201	84	22
WorldScan	85	20	122	46	20	5
Administration	154	—	—	—	43	18
EIA	251	—	—	—	110	57
POLES	135.8	135.3	194.6	131.4	52.9	18.4

[a]The marginal cost of carbon abatement corresponds to the cost of the last tonne of GHG reduced between 1990 and the commitment period (2008–2012) in order to meet the Kyoto target, which implies emission levels for several countries 5% below their 1990s levels (85).

[b]Abbreviations used are Organization for Economic Cooperation and Development—Europe (OECD-E), Canada, Australia, New Zealand (CANZ), Australian Bureau of Agricultural and Resource Economics (ABARE) global trade and environment model (GTEM), Asian integrated model (AIM), carbon emissions trajectory assessment model (CETA), climate framework for uncertainty negotiation and distribution model (FUND), global relationship to protect the environment (GRAPE), model for evaluating the regional and global effects of greenhouse gas reduction policies (MERGE), Massachusetts Institute of Technology emissions predictions and policy analysis (MIT-EPPA), multi-sector multi-region trade (MS-MRT), regional dynamic integrated model of climate and the economy (RICE), second generation model (SGM), U.S. administration's economic analysis—council of economic advisors (Administration), U.S. Department of Energy—Energy Information Administration (EIA), prospective outlook on long-term energy systems (POLES).

A diverse set of models have been used to examine the effects of trading on the marginal abatement cost of carbon emissions (Table 6).

METHOD IV: CLIMATE CHANGE AND ENERGY COSTS

From an economic point of view, climate change potentially affects both individual and social welfare, and its effects are measured either by means of cost-benefit frameworks or sustainability approaches. Cost-benefit analysis weighs future damages versus adaptation costs, whereas sustainability approaches attempt to prevent unacceptable harm to future generations. [However, adaptation costs would be high if an abrupt climate change occurs (84)]. One computational strategy is to use a cost-benefit analysis—assuming a set cost or benefit to reduce emissions—to then determine the financial cost of a given level of climate protection (Table 6). These values combined with CO_2 emissions may be added to the social costs of electricity as an environmental fee in the same way costs from local/regional impacts from pollution are added.

The difficulty with economic quantification of climate change impacts arises from the chain of causality between emissions and the ultimate impact valuation in monetary values. First, emissions produce changes in atmospheric GHG concentrations, which affect the radiation budget of the earth and its average temperature, which causes a myriad of global and regional impacts, which are finally subject to various evaluation methods (85). Alternative assessments of each of these analytical phases may lead to different results. For example, various studies identified different effects on the global temperature due to a doubling of the CO_2 atmospheric concentration[2] (85). These studies attempted to quantify monetary damages to various systems of the U.S. economy (Table 7).

Because climate change is a global problem, it is natural to extend the damage evaluation beyond national boundaries. For example, an estimated 160,000 persons die owing to side effects of global warming in tropical regions (86). Assuming that anthropogenic annual carbon emissions amount to 6.5 peta-grams (Pg) of C (23.8 Pg of CO_2) (87), multiplying the number of deaths by the value of a statistical life and dividing by total annual emissions render a \$33.6/Mg of CO_2 value. Interestingly, the first tradable emission permits negotiated by the Chicago Carbon Exchange were traded at \$1/Mg (83).

Alternatively, the value of CO_2 emissions may be calculated using the cost of a technology that releases fewer emissions or captures and sequesters CO_2 from the atmosphere. For example, energy conservation technologies reduce the consumption of energy without compromising the level of service. Therefore, the ratio between emissions associated with the displaced energy supply and the cost of the conservation measure yield the cost of the avoided GHG emissions (Figure 16). Because some conservation measures, such as replacing incandescent light bulbs with compact fluorescent and replacing fluorescent tubes with efficient fluorescent tubes, already yield positive revenues, the cost of the avoided carbon may be negative.

Virtually every energy technology involves some carbon release over its lifetime, even if only during the manufacturing stage. As an example, the marginal cost of renewable electricity generation may indicate the marginal abatement carbon cost. There is a considerable potential for renewable energy in the United States, and the feasibility of a particular technology varies according to its

---

[2]A doubling in CO_2 concentration means twice as much as the preindustrial level, from 270 ppmv to 540 ppmv.

TABLE 7 Monetized estimates of the effect of doubling the CO_2 concentration with respect to the preindustrial revolution level (resulting in increased average global temperature) to the present U.S. economy in billions of dollars (85)[a]

Damage category	Cline (2.5°C)	Fankhauser (2.5°C)	Nordhaus (3°C)	Titus (4°C)	Tol (2.5°C)
Agriculture	24.1	11.5	1.5	1.6	13.7
Forest loss	4.5	1.0	Small	59.9	—
Species loss	5.5	11.5	0.0	—	6.9
Sea level rise	9.6	12.4	16.8	7.8	11.7
Electricity	15.4	10.9	1.5	7.7	—
Nonelectric heating	−1.8	—		—	—
Human amenity	0.0	—		—	16.5
Human morbidity	0.0	—		—	—
Human life	8.0	15.7		12.9	51.4
Migration	0.7	0.8		—	1.4
Hurricanes	1.1	0.3		—	0.4
Construction	0.0	—	↑	—	—
Leisure activities	2.3	—	Estimated	—	—
Water supply	0.0	0.0	at 0.75%	0.0	0.0
Availability	9.6	21.4	of GDP[b]	15.7	—
Pollution	0.0	—	↓	44.8	—
Urban infrastructure	0.1	—		—	—
Air pollution	0.0	0.0		0.0	0.0
Tropospheric O_3	4.8	10.0		37.4	—
Other	0.0	—		—	—
Mobile air conditioning	—	—		3.4	—
Total	84.0	95.5	55.5	191.3	102.0
% of GDP[b] in 1990	1.5	1.3	1.0	1.0	2.5

[a]Base year 1990 converted to 2002 values using the consumer price index.
[b]GDP means U.S. gross domestic product.

location. Figure 17 (see color insert) shows the renewable energy resource availability in the United States and the technologies that are the most promising for each state (88).

An increasing arrray of options exist to reduce carbon emissions or to sequester the carbon equivalent of those emissions. For many of these options, such as as geologic sequestration, the costs are at best estimates of what they might become if the technology is scaled-up to offset megatons or gigatons of emissions.

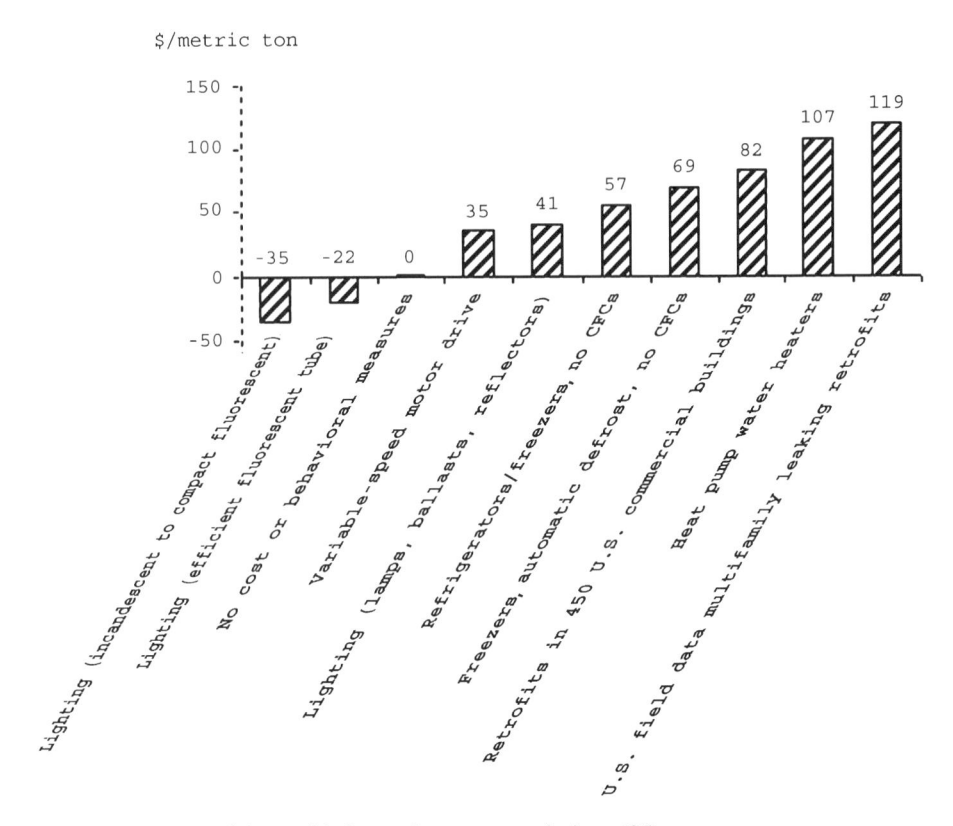

Figure 16 Cost of the avoided greenhouse gas emissions (85).

The use of top-down models is another alternative to calculate the cost of emitted carbon. These models are based on the relationship between macroeconomic parameters and the performance of economic sectors. Although top-down models present a high level of aggregation, they capture feedbacks between the energy sector and other sectors of the economy under a broad equilibrium framework at national and global scales. Table 7 presents a list of top-down models and their respective results in terms of dollars per metric ton of carbon.

The assessment of actual GHG reductions often necessitates an LCA. For example, although a photovoltaic module does not release GHGs during its operation, there is a significant contribution during manufacturing of the modules (89, 90). In contrast, the largest contribution of fossil-fueled power plants occurs during their operation (91). In the case of hydroelectric plants, an important impact is the loss of ecosystems displaced by reservoirs and the resulting loss of that ecological reservoir of carbon storage capacity (91–95). Emission factors produced from an LCA are more comprehensive than emission factors from just the operation of power plants, and thus LCA produces a more inclusive quantification of global climate change impacts. Nevertheless, monetization is not the only option to support decision making. Although the interpretation of aggregated emissions from power systems can be complex because of the spatial variations of local or regional impacts, careful application of these techniques has proven useful. In the case of global climate change, the location of GHG emissions does not affect potential impacts, which are instead more a function of the timing of the releases. The impact of emissions are then determined by the partitioning of carbon between atmospheric and other reservoirs, and the residence times. From there one can compare the airborne fraction of CO_2 emissions and the relative impacts of other GHGs over time; it is possible to compare various electricity generation options over different analytical periods and their relative impact on global climate change (Figure 18, see color insert) (91). This sustainability approach attempts to judge the technologies over time against the natural system background, e.g., the global carbon cycle.

CONCLUSION

In this review, we have provided a qualitative tutorial in the methods used to determine electricity prices. In addition, we have highlighted the impacts of price fluctuations, subsidies, concealed health, and environmental impacts that may be valued and considered by energy analysts. In the case of electricity production, costs imposed to the environment, which usually are not part of the final tariff, are often found to be of more consequence. An important finding is that, in the literature today, the social and environmental externalities associated with our present energy economy are significant—in some cases larger—than the market prices for the resulting electricity. Using the current energy mix in the United States and the inventory of subsidies outlined in this review, the real cost of electricity is arguably between $0.09/kWh and 0.28/kWh.

The environmental impacts of energy conservation are negligible, so whenever such options are available, they should be seriously considered. Because the feasibility of available conservation technologies is a function of the energy supply cost, the use of higher energy costs, which include externalities, enables economic justification for conservation measures that were previously unfeasible. The inclusion of externalities in the final energy costs encourages technological innovations on the supply side as well.

The methods available today to assess and compare the cost of energy are beginning to capture the range of social and environmental costs of energy, as well as the risk premiums that we need to pay for different supply as well as conservation options. The next important steps are, first, to utilize life-cycle and other more integrative methods in our financial analyses and, second, to bridge the gap between engineering and financial assessments of the prices of energy services, and the wider social and environmental benefits, as well as costs of different power generation options.

ACKNOWLEDGMENTS

Sergio Pacca is grateful to the University of California Toxic Substances Award, to the University of California Energy Institute, California Energy Studies Program, and to Arpad Horvath for his comments. Dan Kammen would like to thank the Energy Foundation for support and the staff of the California Public Utilities Commission for discussions and for providing internships to students working on this project.

The *Annual Review of Environment and Resources* is online at http://environ.annualreviews.org

LITERATURE CITED

1. Dorf RC. 2000. *Technology Management Handbook*. Boca Raton, FL: CRC Press
2. Edwards LM, Chilingar GV, Rieke HH III, Fertl WH. 1982. *Handbook of Geothermal Energy*. Houston, TX: Gulf
3. Bolinger M, Wiser R, Golove W. 2002. Quantifying the value that wind power provides as a edge against volatile natural gas prices. *Tech. Rep. LBNL-50484*. Environ. Energy Technol. Div., Ernest Orlando Lawrence Berkeley Natl. Lab., Berkeley, CA
4. Hogan WW. 2002. Electricity market restructuring: reforms of reforms. *J. Regul. Econ.* 21:103–32
5. DOE/EIA. 2003. Table 38. Cost and performance characteristics of new electricity generating technologies. In *Assumptions for the Annual Energy Outlook 2004 with Projections to 2025*. http://www.eia.doe.gov/oiaf/aeo/assumption/pdf/0554(2004).pdf (accessed on 10/30/2003)
6. Egre D, Milewski JC. 2002. The diversity of hydropower projects. *Energy Policy* 30:1225–30
7. Lemar PL. 2001. The potential impact of policies to promote combined heat and power in US industry. *Energy Policy* 29:1243–54
8. IEA. 2002. *Key World Statistics from the IEA 2002*. Paris: IEA
9. Meier A, Rosenfeld AH, Wright J. 1982. Supply curves of conserved energy for California's residential sector. *Energy* 7:347–58
10. Meier A, Rosenfeld AH, Wright J. 1983. *Supplying Energy Through Greater Efficiency: The Potential for Conservation in California's Residential Sector*. Berkeley: Univ. Calif. Press. 196 p.
10a. Lovins AB. 1977. *Soft Energy Paths: Toward a Durable Peace*. New York: Ballinger
11. Interlab. Work. Group. 1997. *Scenarios of U.S. Carbon Reductions: Potential Impacts of Energy-Efficient and Low-Carbon Technologies by 2010 and Beyond*. Berkeley, CA: Lawrence Berkeley Natl. Lab.
12. Worrell E, Martin N, Price L. 2000. Potentials for energy efficiency improvement in the US cement industry. *Energy* 25:1189–214
13. Worrell E, Martin N, Price L. 2001. Energy efficiency and carbon dioxide emissions reduction opportunities in the US iron and steel sector. *Energy* 26:513–36
14. Stoft S. 1995. The economics of conserved-energy 'supply' curves. *Energy J.* 16:109–37
15. US Dep. Inter. Bur. Labor Stat. 2003. *Consumer price index*. http://www.bls.gov
16. Cavanagh R. 2001. Revisiting "the genius of the marketplace": cures for the western

electricity and natural gas crises. *Electr. J.* 14(5):11–18

17. Calif. ISO. 2003. DMA Rep. http://www.caiso.com/docs/2000/07/27/2000072710233117407.html (accessed 08/09/2003)

18. DOE/EIA. 2003. *Selected national average natural gas prices, 1996–2002.* http://www.eia.doe.gov/pub/oil_gas/natural_gas/data_publications/natural_gas_monthly/current/pdf/table_04.pdf

19. Duane T. 2002. Regulation's rationale: learning from the California energy crisis. *Yale J. Regul.* 19:471–540

20. Kammen DM. 2001. Renewable energy and energy policies and the California energy crisis. In *Controller's Quarterly: Energy in California* (Office Cathleen Connell, Calif. State Controller), Summer, pp. 19–21

21. NYMEX. 2000. *New York Mercantile Exchange, Risk Management with Natural Gas Futures and Options.* New York: NYMEX

22. Considine TJ, Heo E. 2000. Price and inventory dynamics in petroleum product markets. *Energy Econ.* 22:527–47

23. Asmus P. 2003. *Climate wise; current crisis sparks innovation.* The Resour. Cent. Bus., Environ. Bottom Line. http://www.greenbiz.com/news/printer.cfm?NewsID=16034

24. Off. Technol. Assess. 1994. Studies of environmental costs of electricity. *OTA Tech. Rep. ETI-134.* Washington, DC: US GPO

25. Coase R. 1960. The problem of social cost. *J. Law Econ.* 3:1–44

26. Templet PH. 2001. Energy price disparity and public welfare. *Ecol. Econ.* 36:443–60

27. Koplow D, Dernbach D. 2001. Federal fossil fuel subsidies and greenhouse gas emissions: a case study of increasing transparency for fiscal policy. *Annu. Rev. Energy Environ.* 26:361–89

28. Nordhaus W. 2003. *The economic consequences of a war with Iraq.* http://www.econ.yale.edu/~nordhaus/iraq.pdf

29. Bohi D, Toman M. 1994. Energy security externalities and fuel cycle comparisons. In *Estimating Fuel Cycle Externalities: Analytical Methods and Issues.* Oak Ridge, TN: Oak Ridge Natl. Lab./Resour. Future

30. Pfanner E. 2003. Price of oil climbs as OPEC plans to cut output. *New York Times*, Sept. 25

31. Pye-Smith C. 2002. *The Subsidy Scandal: How Government Wastes Your Money to Wreck Your Environment.* London: Earthscan

32. US Dep. Energy. 1999. *Federal Financial Interventions and Subsidies in Energy Markets 1999: Primary Energy.* Washington, DC: US DOE

33. US Nucl. Regul. Comm. 1998. NRC's report to congress on the Price-Anderson Act. *Rep. SECY-98-160.* http://www.nrc.gov/-/reading-rm/doc-collections/commission/secys/1998/secy1998-160/1998-160scy.html

34. US Dep. Energy. 1998. *Report to Congress on the Price-Anderson Act.* Washington, DC: US Dep. Energy

35. US House Represent. 2003. *Price-Anderson Amendments Act of 2003*, HR 330 IH, 108th Congr. 1st sess. http://thomas.loc.gov/cgi-bin/query

36. US Senate. 2003. *Price-Anderson Amendments Act of 2003*, S 156 IS, 108th Congr. 1st sess.

37. Dubin JA, Rothwell GS. 1990. Subsidy to nuclear power through Price-Anderson liability limit. *Contemp. Policy Issues* 8:73–79

38. US Dep. Energy. 2001. *Annual Energy Outlook 2002.* Washington, DC: US DOE

39. Northeast States Coordinated of Air Use Manag. 2003. *Summary—Senate Energy Bill (S. 517).* http://www.nescaum.org/Greenhouse/Private/Senate_517_Summary.doc

40. US Senate. 2003. Energy Policy Act of Senate Bill 1005, 108th Congr., 1st sess. (5/6/2003). http://frwebgate.access.gpo.

gov/cgi-bin/getdoc.cgi?dbname=108_cong_bills&docid=f:s1005pcs.txt.pdf
41. US Dep. Energy. 2001. *Renewable Energy 2000: Issues and Trends.* Washington, DC: US DOE
42. Myers N, Kent J. 2001. *Perverse Subsidies: How Tax Dollars Can Undercut the Environment and the Economy.* Washington, DC: Island Press
43. UNEP 2002. *Reforming Energy Subsidies.* Oxford, UK: UNEP/IEA/AIE
44. Riedy C, Diesendorf M. 2002. Financial subsidies to the Australian fossil fuel industry. *Energy Policy* 31:125–37
45. Costanza R, d'Arge R, de Groot R, Farber S, Grasso M, et al. 1997. The value of the world's ecosystem services and natural capital. *Nature* 387:253–58
46. Scudder T. 1996. Social impacts. In *Water Resources; Environmental Planning, Management, and Development,* ed. AK Biswas. New York: McGraw-Hill
47. Cernea M. 1997. *Hydropower Dams and Social Impacts: A Sociological Perspective.* Washington, DC: The World Bank
48. Turk. Prime Ministry. 1998. Kayraktepe Dam and HEPP. *Profiles of Turkish Public Sector Projects for Foreign Funding in 1998.* http://www.dpt.gov.tr/dptweb/ekutup98/project/kayrakte.html
49. World Bank. 1996. *Involving involuntary resettlement 1986–1993.* Environ. Dep. Pap. No. 032. Washington, DC: The World Bank
50. US Dep. Energy. Energy Inf. Adm. 2003. *Hydroelectric power all countries, 1980–2001.* http://www.eia.doe.gov/pub/international/iealf/table26.xls
51. Golub R. 2003. *Racine Journal Times.* Harvard researcher links plant in Oak Creek to deaths, illness. Dec. 30:A1
52. US Dep. Energy. 2000. *Electric Power Monthly June 2000.* Washington, DC: Energy Inf. Adm.
53. US Environ. Prot. Agency. 2000. *Guidelines for Preparing Economic Analysis.* Washington, DC: US EPA
54. Hohmeyer O. 1992. Renewables and the full costs of energy. *Energy Policy* 20:365–75
55. Krupnick AJ, Burtraw D. 1996. *The social cost of electricity. Do the numbers add up?* Discuss. Pap. 96–30. Washington, DC: Resour. Future
56. Matthews S, Lave L. 2000. Applications of environmental valuation for determining externality costs. *Environ. Sci. Technol.* 34:1390–95
57. Mirasgedis S, Diakoulaki D. 1997. Multicriteria analysis vs. externalities assessment for the comparative evaluation of electricity generation systems. *Eur. J. Oper. Res.* 102:364–79
58. Levy JI, Hammitt JK, Yanagisawa Y, Spengler JK. 1999. Development of a new damage function model for power plants: methodology and applications *Environ. Sci. Technol.* 33:4364–72
59. Stirling A. 1997. Limits to the value of external costs. *Energy Policy* 25(5):517–40
60. Burtraw D, Palmer K, Bharvirkar R, Paul A. 2001. Cost-effective reduction of NO_x emissions from electricity generation. *J. Air Waste Manag. Assoc.* 51:1476–89
61. O'Rourke D, Connolly S. 2003. Just oil? The distribution of environmental and social impacts of oil production and consumption. *Annu. Rev. Environ. Resour.* 28:587–617
62. Delucchi MA, Murphy JJ, McCubbin DR. 2002. The health and visibility cost of air pollution: a comparison of estimation methods. *J. Environ. Manag.* 64:134–52
63. US Environ. Prot. Agency. 1998. *Regulatory Impact Analysis for the NO, SIP Call, FIP and Section 126 Petition.* Washington, DC: US EPA
64. US Environ. Prot. Agency. 1998. *Compilation of air pollutant emission factors, AP-42, stationary point and area sources, external combustion sources.* http://www.epa.gov/ttn/chief/ap42/Sources

65. Beaver E. 2000. LCA and total cost assessment. *Environ. Prog.* 19(2):130–39
66. Chapman PF. 1974. Energy costs: a review of methods. *Energy Policy* 2:91–103
67. Curran MA. 1996. *Environmental Life-Cycle Assessment.* New York: McGraw-Hill
68. Hendrickson CT, Horvath A, Joshi S, Lave LB. 1998. Economic input-output models for environmental life-cycle assessment. *Environ. Sci. Technol.* 32:184–91
69. Carnegie Mellon Univ., Green Design Initiat. 2002. *Economic input-output life cycle assessment 2003.* http://www.eiolca.net
70. Horvath A, Hendrickson CT. 1998. Steel-reinforced concrete bridges: environmental assessment. *J. Infrastruct. Syst.* 4(3):111–17
71. Herendeen RA. 1981. The energy embodied in the production of ecological systems: a linear programming approach. In *Energy and Ecological Modelling*, ed. WJ Mitsch, RW Bosserman, JM Klopatek, pp. 681–86. Amsterdam/New York: Elsevier. 839 p.
72. Budnitz RJ, Holdren JP. 1976. Social and environmental costs of energy systems. *Annu. Rev. Energy* 1:553–80
73. Deleted in proof
74. Lind RC, ed. 1982. *Discounting for Time and Risk in Energy Policy.* Washington, DC: Resour. Future
75. Nordhaus WD. 1997. Discounting in economics and climate change. *Clim. Change* 37(2):315–28
76. Watson RT, ed. 2000. *IPCC Special Report on Land Use, Land-Use Change and Forestry: A Special Report of the Intergovernmental Panel on Climate Change.* New York: Cambridge Univ. Press
77. Martinez-Alier J. 2001. Mining conflicts, environmental justice, and valuation *J. Hazard Mater.* 86:153–70
78. Krutilla J. 1967. Conservation reconsidered. *Am. Econ. Rev.* 57(4):777–86
79. Stirling A. 2001. Science and precaution in the appraisal of electricity supply options. *J. Hazard Mater.* 86:55–75
80. Ellerman AD, Schmalensee R, Joskow PL, Montero JP, Bailey EM. 1997. *Emission trading under the US acid rain program: evaluation of compliance costs and allowance market performance.* Cambridge, MA: Cent. Energy Environ. Policy Res., MIT
81. Carson C, Burtraw D, Cropper M, Palmer KL. 2000. Sulfur dioxide control by electric utilities: What are the gains from trade? *J. Polit. Econ.* 108:1292–326
82. Joskow PL, Schmalensee R, Bailey EM. 1998. The market for sulfur dioxide emissions. *Am. Econ. Rev.* 88(4):669–85
83. Barnaby JF. 2003. U.S. trading of emissions starts slowly. *New York Times*, Oct. 1:B1. http://www.nytimes.com/2003/10/01/business/worldbusiness/01EMIS.html?pagewanted=print&position=
84. Alley RB, Marotzke J, Nordhaus WD, Overpeck JT, Peteet DM, et al. 2003. Abrupt climate change. *Science* 299(5615):2005–10
85. Bruce JP, Lee H, Haites EF, eds. 1996. *Climate Change 1995: Economic and Social Dimensions of Climate Change.* New York: Cambridge Univ. Press http://www.grida.no/climate/ipcc_tar/wg3/341.htm
86. Doyle A. 2003. 160,000 said dying yearly from global warming. *Reuters.* http://www.alertnet.org/printable.htm?URL=/thenews/newsdesk/L30616897.htm
87. Houghton JT, Ding Y, Griggs DJ, Noguer M, van der Linden PJ, et al. 2001. *Climate Change 2001: The Scientific Basis.* New York: Cambridge Univ. Press. 881 p.
88. Spitzley D, Keoleian G. 2003. *Life cycle metrics for comparing alternative electricity generating technologies.* Presented at LCA Conf., Seattle, WA. http://www.lcacenter.org/InLCA-LCM03/Spitzley-presentation.pdf
89. Dones R, Frischknecht R. 1998. Life

cycle assessment of photovoltaic systems: results of Swiss studies on energy chains. *Prog. Photovolt.: Res. Appl.* 6:117–25

90. Alsema EA, Nieuwlaar E. 2000. Energy viability of photovoltaic systems. *Energy Policy* 28:999–1010

91. Pacca S, Horvath A. 2002. Greenhouse gas emissions from building and operating electric power plants in the upper Colorado River basin. *Environ. Sci. Technol.* 36:3194–200

92. Rudd JWM, Harris R, Kelly CA, Hecky RE. 1993. Are hydroelectric reservoirs significant sources of greenhouse gases? *Ambio* 22:246–48

93. Rosa LP, Schaeffer R. 1995. Global warming potentials: the case of emissions from dams. *Energy Policy* 23:149–58

94. Gagnon L, van de Vate J. 1997. Greenhouse gas emissions from hydropower: the state of research in 1996. *Energy Policy* 25:7–13

95. Gagnon L, Bélanger C, Uchiyama Y. 2002. Life-cycle assessment of electricity generation options: the status of research in year 2001. *Energy Policy* 30:1267–78

ADVANCES IN ENERGY FORECASTING MODELS BASED ON ENGINEERING ECONOMICS*

Ernst Worrell,[1] Stephan Ramesohl,[2] and Gale Boyd[3]

[1]*Energy Analysis Department, Lawrence Berkeley National Laboratory, Berkeley, California 94720; email: eworrell@lbl.gov*
[2]*Energy Division, Wuppertal Institute for Climate, Environment, Energy, 42103 Wuppertal, Germany; email: stephan.ramesohl@wupperinst.org*
[3]*Decision and Information Sciences Division, Argonne National Laboratory, Argonne, Illinois 60439; email: gboyd@anl.gov*

Key Words energy modeling, industry, policy, technology

■ **Abstract** New energy efficiency policies have been introduced around the world. Historically, most energy models were reasonably equipped to assess the impact of classical policies, such as a subsidy or change in taxation. However, these tools are often insufficient to assess the impact of alternative policy instruments. We evaluate the so-called engineering economic models used to assess future industrial energy use. Engineering economic models include the level of detail commonly needed to model the new types of policies considered. We explore approaches to improve the realism and policy relevance of engineering economic modeling frameworks. We also explore solutions to strengthen the policy usefulness of engineering economic analysis that can be built from a framework of multidisciplinary cooperation. The review discusses the main modeling approaches currently used and evaluates the weaknesses in current models. We focus on the needs to further improve the models. We identify research priorities for the modeling framework, technology representation in models, policy evaluation, and modeling of decision-making behavior.

CONTENTS

INTRODUCTION 346
POLICY CONTEXT AND IMPLICATIONS FOR ENGINEERING
  ECONOMIC ANALYSIS 347
    Options to Influence Energy Efficiency in Industry 347
    Policy Context and Recent Developments 348
    Implications for Policy Analysis and Modeling 348
  CONVENTIONAL ENGINEERING MODELING 351

---

*The U.S. Government has the right to retain a nonexclusive, royalty-free license in and to any copyright covering this paper.

Use of Models in Policy Development 351
Modeling Approaches 352
Approaches to Address Barriers for Implementation 355
Approaches to Model Policies 356
CHALLENGES AND REQUIREMENTS 356
Challenges 356
Directions/Issues in Modeling 361
PATHWAYS 365
Better Use of Models in Policy Analysis 368
Improving Models 369
CONCLUSIONS AND RECOMMENDATIONS 374
Research Priorities 374
Short Term Collaborative Projects 375

INTRODUCTION

In recent years, the importance of energy policy has been demonstrated around the world. Deregulation, energy security, climate change, and other environmental challenges all impact energy policy. Energy efficiency will play an important role in future energy policy. New energy efficiency policies have been developed and applied in many countries, varying from standards to voluntary or negotiated agreements to eco-taxation programs with different forms of revenue recycling that slowly shift taxation from labor to resource use.

Energy models are used in policy making to assess future energy demand, the impacts on the economy and environment, as well as the economic, environmental, and social impacts of technology and policy choices. Craig et al. (1) demonstrated the difficulties with forecasting by comparing historical forecasts for energy demand in the year 2000 against the actual trend. Although Craig et al. (1) evaluated the modeling results, this review focuses on the inner working of one group of models, the so-called bottom-up engineering economic models. We evaluate the models against the changing demands put on those models by the policy-making community.

Modelers and decision makers have distinct responsibilities in energy policy development. Policy makers rely on energy models to evaluate, *ex ante*, the potential effects of certain developments and policy choices on issues, such as energy use and economic welfare. Two main types of models have been used in energy analysis, the so-called top-down and bottom-up models. Although the line between model types has blurred, both approaches have advantages and disadvantages (2), and the applicability varies with the problem addressed. All models are an abstraction of the real world and, so by definition, have shortcomings. One of the shortcomings of many energy models is the lack of the capacity to assess the effect of nonmonetary policy instruments. Historically most tools were focused on assessing the impact of price changes and monetary policy instruments, but these tools are less well suited to assess the impact of nonmonetary policies, such as a voluntary program or that of a market transformation initiative. A critical evaluation of the models used to investigate future energy use is needed (3, 4).

We explore pathways for pursuing complementary approaches to engineering economic analysis that could help improve engineering economic modeling from a multidisciplinary background. We address three questions.

1. What are the (new) requirements for engineering economic analysis posed by nonprice energy and alternative regulation climate change policies?
2. What are the strengths and limitations of conventional engineering economic approaches in addressing nonprice and alternative regulation policy measures?
3. What are promising areas for the focus of research and model development that will help accelerate improvements in the realism and policy relevance of engineering economic analysis?

We describe the so-called engineering economic (or bottom-up) models because they include an amount of detail that appears appropriate to model nonmonetary policy scenarios that address energy end use. We further review models with comparatively high levels of detail for the industrial sector, owing to its wide variety in economic, technical, and policy characteristics. We also focus on models that have a time horizon of approximately 20 years, so many of the global, integrated assessment models used for climate change analysis are outside of the scope of this review.

POLICY CONTEXT AND IMPLICATIONS FOR ENGINEERING ECONOMIC ANALYSIS

During the past decades, the energy policy focus has ranged from concerns on supply security in the 1970s, to air pollution prevention in the 1980s, and to the challenge of global climate change mitigation during the 1990s. All aspects illustrate the vital importance of a clean, efficient, secure, and competitive energy supply to industry for society's welfare.

Options to Influence Energy Efficiency in Industry

In 1995, industry consumed 41% of global primary energy consumption, making it the largest single energy-consuming sector (5). The practical design and implementation of energy policies to improve energy efficiency in industry represents a demanding task. Measures have to account for the complex technical, economical, behavioral, and organizational structures that distinguish industry from other end-use sectors. Being a necessary input to transform and process materials into products, energy is a key element of the industrial metabolism. There are countless industrial energy technologies. As a result, the pattern of energy use can differ significantly among sectors and companies. Taking this complexity into account, there are various options to influence energy use in industry.

Although many of these options are addressed directly through energy policies, other influences are related to nonenergy policies, e.g., policies for waste management and pollution prevention affect energy use. Policy activities in different fields not only open the possibility for synergies but may also lead to conflicting demands.

Policy Context and Recent Developments

A diversification of policies influencing industrial energy is observed, challenging the standard modeling approaches. During the 1990s, a series of new policy instruments were developed that represent a changed philosophy toward policy intervention.

- There has been a growing acknowledgment of the complexity of cause-impact relationships that impede efficient policy design, especially given a situation of asymmetric information. Triggered by new public-private partnerships, different voluntary approaches emerged (6–12). Voluntary agreements have been broadly defined as "agreements between government and industry to facilitate voluntary actions with desirable social outcomes, which are encouraged by the government, to be undertaken by the participants, based on the participants' self-interest" (13, 14). These schemes are characterized by a strong involvement of industry in policy implementation and responsibility, resulting in a high degree of freedom for the companies in their response to the policy impulse.

- Secondly, there is a growing understanding of the socioeconomic dimension of industrial energy efficiency. As with any other aspect of production, energy use in industry is a result of company decision making and corporate behavior (15, 16). Energy related decisions in industry are embedded in an organizational process involving many actors. Growing empirical evidence indicates that several barriers hinder this process (5). Instruments and initiatives have been introduced to reduce these barriers.

- Often policy instruments are not applied in isolation but combined within a mix, aiming to benefit from synergies while compensating for weaknesses of individual policy instruments (17).

Implications for Policy Analysis and Modeling

Price clearly matters. It has a pronounced influence on decisions affecting energy use. However, it is not all that matters. The increasing variety (see Table 1) in policy and industry interactions and new policy approaches stresses the need for a comprehensive assessment of policy impacts and program effects, effectiveness, and efficiency. The variety also means that the standard neoclassic economic framework is insufficient for energy models aiming to explore the different dimensions of potential policy impacts. The methodological framework for policy analysis and modeling must be adapted. The three identified impact areas are

TABLE 1 The portfolio of energy policy instruments in industry

Instrument type	Availability of energy-efficient technologies	Incentives for decision making	Increased capability of companies	Examples
Regulation standards	Controls the set of technology choices	Induces high costs for the use of outdated equipment		Motor efficiency standards in the United States and European Union (E.U.)
Subsidies, direct public spending, R&D[a] support	R&D support enhances technical progress and innovation	Investment grants increase the economic attractiveness of options		Found in many OECD countries[b]
Pricing	Indirect incentive for R&D	Affects price relations in favor of energy efficiency measures	Contributes to higher awareness	Carbon taxes, fuel (excise) taxes, technology adoption tax credits, depletion allowances
Emission trading	Indirect incentive for R&D	Creates a price and market for energy efficiency/emission reduction	Contributes to higher awareness	United Kingdom, Canada
Negotiated agreements		Can create an environment for energy efficiency and innovation	Increases energy awareness, communication & dissemination	Dutch Long-term Agreement, Danish CO_2 agreement, German Voluntary Agreement scheme

(*Continued*)

TABLE 1 (Continued)

Instrument type	Availability of energy-efficient technologies	Incentives for decision making	Increased capability of companies	Examples
Public voluntary programs	Stimulates R&D		Provides information, know-how, and management support	U.S. Green lights and Energy Star, Industries of the Future U.S. Motor Challenge Voluntary Challenge & Registry (Canada)
Management tools		Lowers (in long term) transaction costs for efficiency action	Increased information Strengthened staff capacities Induced learning effects	Eco-Management and Audit Scheme ISO 14001 Eco-Energy Sweden
Labeling		Better communication of cost parameters	Increases information Higher market transparency	E.U. labels U.S. Energy Star® labels
Technology procurement	Stimulates R&D and innovation		Dissemination of information and know-how Qualification and training	Sweden E.U. energy+ initiative
Best practice dissemination			Increases awareness and information	United Kingdom E.U. initiative
Education, qualification, training			Provision of information and know-how	Austrian Ecoprofit U.S. Industrial Assessment Center Program
Agency networks			Networking of actors	Allied Partners, Energy Star®

[a]R&D, research and development.
[b]Organisation for Economic Co-operation and Development.

- Enhanced availability of energy-efficient technologies and measures to improve efficiency [e.g., public support for research and design (R&D)];
- Incentives to influence efficiency-related decision making (e.g., energy price signals); and
- Improved capability of companies to respond to technical opportunities and economic incentives (e.g., education programs).

From the perspective of policy analysis, the first area can be interpreted as the set of technology opportunities provided in engineering economic models, whereas the second area corresponds to the economic decision criteria used in the decision making process. The third dimension is often described by an exogenously fixed penetration rate that incorporates the response function of the target group. These behavioral patterns are increasingly addressed as a policy variable. Important implications for policy analysis include the following:

- Many of the new instruments do not result in a direct effect on energy consumption but contribute to an indirect impact that materializes gradually over time.
- Implementation processes within organizations take time and cause a delay that adds to technical restrictions resulting from stock turnover and investment cycles.
- Policy measures can contribute to accelerated diffusion of energy-efficient technologies. Such a market take-off can follow a nonlinear trajectory that is partially technology specific but can be influenced by the policy environment.
- The combination of policy instruments within a portfolio opens the possibility to increase the effectiveness and efficiency by exploiting synergies.

CONVENTIONAL ENGINEERING MODELING

Policy makers today are facing new challenges in the design of energy policies. More and more, forecasting models are used to evaluate the potential impact of policies. However, the traditional modeling approaches may not suffice within the changing policy environment. This section discusses the approaches commonly used in the models.

Use of Models in Policy Development

Energy models are used in policy making to assess *ex ante* the economic, environmental, and social impacts of technology and policy choices. Energy models are not the sole tool used by policy makers but are used more and more to support decision making processes. The main goals of using modeling tools in energy policy include the following (18):

- Define target levels of greenhouse gas (GHG) emission reductions;

- Find the least social cost response to GHG reduction targets;
- Identify the best technology opportunities for action;
- Assess the effects and costs of proposed public policies and programs (standards, taxes and subsidies, voluntary programs);
- Assess the distribution of costs and benefits of policy choices; and
- Assess the ancillary benefits of improving energy efficiency, such as reduced air pollution and productivity benefits.

Other goals are to

- Estimate (or at least define more clearly) sectoral and subsectoral (industry) costs, including assessments of consumers' surplus, i.e., the benefits that accrue to consumers who are willing to pay more than the market prices;
- Assess the interactive effects of various policies, one on another; and
- Assess the impacts of policies focused on one sector that spread to other sectors (e.g., impact of a policy affecting motor stock on the electricity supply sector).

The role of energy modeling in decision making and policy design has increased in recent years, especially in the debate on climate change and GHG emission mitigation. Simplistic models with limited technology representation are replaced with more complex models with more comprehensive representation of technology and economic feedbacks. Previously, engineering economic models focused on estimating the technical potential for cost-effective energy savings, whereas current models are challenged to better estimate what is achievable given behavioral and policy constraints. Policy modeling has focused on price-based and regulatory policies and is challenged to include nonprice policy instruments (18). The models need to build on interdisciplinary empirical analysis. The increased role of climate change in the energy debate also leads to the need to model a longer time horizon. This is exemplified through attempts to include technological change in models and the extension of scenario periods up to the year 2050. At the same time, policy makers need improved information at low aggregation levels to assess the distribution of costs and benefits across society.

Modeling Approaches

The so-called engineering economic (or bottom-up) approach is rooted in engineering principles that account for physical flows of energy capital equipment. This is coupled with economic information to account for energy expenses and investment that is processed through decision-making rules. The form of the decision making and the way to represent the activities vary among the various modeling approaches. Differences can be found with regard to the degree of activity representation, technology representation, and technology choice (stylistic or explicit), the goal (simulation or optimization), and degree of macroeconomic integration.

TABLE 2 Characterization of selected energy engineering models. The wide variety of models makes it impossible to include them all

Model	Country of origin	Technology representation	Goal of model	Macroeconomic integration
AMIGA[a]	United States	Explicit/stylistic	Equilibrium	Yes
CIMS	Canada	Explicit	Simulation	Yes
EERA	New Zealand	—	Simulation	No
EFOM	European Union	Explicit	Optimization	No
ENUSIM	United Kingdom	Explicit	Simulation	No
ENPEP	United States	Explicit/stylistic	Simulation	No
EPPA	United States	Stylistic	Equilibrium	Yes
ICARUS	Netherlands	Explicit	Simulation	No
IKARUS	Germany	Explicit	Optimization	Yes
ISTUM (ITEMS)	Canada/United States	Explicit	Simulation	No
LEAP	United States	Explicit/stylistic	Simulation	No
LIEF	United States	Stylistic	Simulation	No
MARKAL	OECD/IEA	Explicit	Optimization	No
MARKAL-MACRO	OECD/IEA	Explicit/stylistic	Optimization	Yes
NEMS	United States	Explicit/stylistic	Simulation	Yes

[a]Abbreviations used are AMIGA, All Modular Industry Growth Assessment; CIMS, Canadian Integrated Modeling System; EERA, Energy Efficiency Resource Assessment; EFOM, Energy Flow Optimisation Model; ENUSIM, Energy Simulation Model; ENPEP, Energy and Power Evaluation Program; EPPA, Emissions Prediction and Policy Analysis; ICARUS, Information System on Conservation and Application of Resources Using a Sector approach; IKARUS, Instrumente für Klimagas-Reduktionsstrategien; ISTUM, Industrial Sector Technology Use Model; LEAP, Long-range Energy Alternatives Planning System; LIEF, Long-term Industrial Energy Forecasting; MARKAL, Market Allocation; OECD, Organisation for Economic Co-operation and Development; IEA, International Energy Agency; and NEMS, National Energy Modeling System.

Explicit technology representation describes the actual characteristics of individual technologies. Stylistic technology representation captures the characteristics of a group of technologies through a mathematical function. The mathematical function may be derived from actual technologies represented by, for example, a supply curve. Table 2 provides a rough characterization of selected models.

One key distinction is the activity representation. To account for the differences across industries in the uses of energy and within industries for the structure of production, a simplification is employed to reduce complexity. For example, the Information System on Conservation and Application of Resources Using a Sector approach (ICARUS) model contains a lot of sector and technology detail, but it is basically a static model with exogenously assumed penetration rates. The level of activity representation varies in models, such as Energy and Power Evaluation Program (ENPEP) and Market Allocation (MARKAL), depending on the country and analysis group that are running the model. For example, the Los Alamos-U.S.

MARKAL model has 10 industrial subsectors and over 2400 technologies, although most of these technologies are not industrial. The National Energy Modeling System (NEMS) and Canadian Integrated Modelling System (CIMS) models include 12 subsectors. The Long-term Industrial Energy Forecasting model (LIEF) includes 18 manufacturing sectors. Generally, most models contain sufficient detail in the energy intensive industries and less detail for the light industries. Often, light industries are lumped together, and the technological detail is limited.

The second differentiating factor is that technology representation and technology choice are handled differently in engineering economic models. In the engineering economic framework, the model must allow for some mechanism through which choices about energy use are made. In the most generic form, the model accounts for economic conditions, such as energy prices, discount rates, and technological information, driving choices on energy-using equipment. The degree to which the technology information is explicitly modeled differs and can be a defining trait of the approach. Many models use explicitly modeled technologies (e.g., All Modular Industry Growth Assessment (AMIGA), Instrumente für Klimagas-Reduktionsstrategien (IKARUS), Industrial Sector Technology Use Model (ISTUM), and CIMS). Other models do not explicitly describe technologies but have a parametric description. For example, the LIEF model uses a set of conservation supply curves. Conservation supply curves (19) depict the relationship between cost-effective savings and energy prices for each industry. These curves are parameterized by the percent of energy use that could be reduced cost effectively in the base year and an elasticity parameter, showing how industry energy use changes in response to changes in energy prices. The values of these parameters are estimated from historical observations. For most sectors, NEMS models include explicit technologies, but for the industrial sector, NEMS has a stylistic representation of technologies, so cost-benefit analyses have to be done exogenous to the model.

Regardless of how technology is represented in the model, there are three factors that influence technology choice in the models. They include the following:

1. The state and availability of the current and emerging technology;
2. Economic costs, i.e., energy prices and equipment costs feed into technology choices as the model looks at life-cycle costs for various equipment choices; and
3. Operational decision rules, which are expressed as a rate at which an ideal energy intensity is approached, embedded in discount rates, or is reflected in the way cost calculations are done.

If these are the only "handles" available, energy technology choices can only be explicitly modeled as functions of energy prices, operating and maintenance costs, and capital costs. Although these directly affect energy technology choice, in reality, there are many other factors that influence the investment decision. Moreover, many of the socioeconomic decision variables addressed by nonmonetary policy instruments are not explicitly incorporated into decision rules but included in an aggregated representation of a penetration rate. The penetration rates are most often modeled exogenous to the model. Various approaches to modeling market variations and other intangibles are emerging, e.g., CIMS introduces monetized conditions to reflect these factors.

Third, models differ in their general modeling philosophy with regard to their ultimate goal and scope. *Optimization models* are used to find the optimal set of technology choices to achieve a specified target at the lowest costs. A well-known optimization model is MARKAL, although other linear-programming models are used as well. Sector and technology representation varies widely in the different MARKAL models used around the world. The MARKAL community (20) has started to include technical learning (for energy conversion technologies) in their models, as well as material flows (21), multiple greenhouse gases, and macroeconomic links. *Simulation models* provide a quantitative illustration of exogenously defined scenario strategies. Because of the technical and structural information incorporated, they allow evaluation of impacts and interrelations of different policies in a systematic manner. Cost information plays a central role, but strategies can follow other priorities (such as supply security). *Integrated models* (e.g., AMIGA, NEMS, MARKAL-MACRO, and CIMS) include the interaction between changes in energy use and the economy instead of using a preset economic development scenario. The modeling approach for the energy sector may be a simulation or optimization, i.e., either type of model above may be integrated into an overall economic model. The macroeconomic system is often designed on the basis of a general equilibrium model. The link to the economy helps to estimate the full costs and benefits of different scenarios.

Approaches to Address Barriers for Implementation

The implementation and transfer of energy-efficient technologies and practices is often hampered by barriers that slow their market penetration (5) or by the lack of sufficient incentives. Among the multitude of hindering factors, many barriers offer the opportunity to improve energy efficiency by removing or modifying these obstacles to the spread of technology, such as lack of information.

Barriers for energy efficiency improvement are generally not captured in the models. The movement toward considering these aspects contributes to the discussion of creating appropriate energy scenario definitions, but at the present time, there is little understanding of how to translate these factors quantitatively into the analytical framework. In some models (e.g., LIEF), it is argued that these factors are implicitly considered because they exist in the historical data or in an assumed high discount rate. This approach, however, is part of the problem itself. Decision parameters that used to be fixed through aggregated factors, such as hurdle rates or elasticities, are now target variables of policies. The scope for decision making and patterns of adoption behavior change over time, and historical data may be of limited value for an assessment of future developments—especially under changing policy conditions. The decision-making process around investment is not yet well understood, and further research to understand the mechanism and represent it in a modeling framework is needed. Moreover, a better understanding of mechanisms to reduce or overcome barriers helps to improve the design of policy tools and strategies as well as the methodological foundations of policy evaluation.

Approaches to Model Policies

Most models have historically addressed policy through addressing the implementation costs of measures for energy efficiency improvement. The relatively simple modeling approaches included the effect of subsidies and energy taxes on the costs and the degree of implementation. Some models have included the effect of research, development, and demonstration policies by including learning-by-doing curves for energy conversion technologies. The latter modeling approach has not yet been used extensively for energy-efficient technologies; however, CIMS has included this function in its modeling set and used it in its latest round of analyses assessing the cost of GHG-emission reduction for Canada. Endogenous (or induced) technological change has also been included in some of the more aggregate models. However, the extent of endogenous technological change and the policy impact on this change remains an emerging research area, and studies to date reflect an emerging, rather than comprehensive, understanding of the interactions between policy, technological change, and energy efficiency (22). This demonstrates the need for a better representation of the effects of energy efficiency policies (23). Comprehensive evaluations of energy efficiency policies are necessary to improve modeling approaches. Especially, modeling of new policy developments, such as voluntary programs and nonfiscal policies, remain a challenge for the energy modeling community (24). When they are modeled, models may mimic voluntary approaches by lowering the discount rate from the normal (based on hurdle rates or the literature on ex post analyses of discount) as an approximation for voluntary initiatives. This supposes that we can represent voluntary initiatives using economic criteria as the primary driver for decision making.

CHALLENGES AND REQUIREMENTS

The previous section discussed the issues that need further attention in the future development of engineering economic models. In this section, we outline the main challenges faced by modelers as well as the model requirements.

Challenges

SCENARIO CONSTRUCTION AND BASIC ASSUMPTIONS In scenario construction, the reference scenario assumptions are critical (10, 25). These include all major variables, including the level of activity (i.e., economic growth), structural effects, and assumptions, concerning technology availability and progress. The choice of available technology under business-as-usual (BAU) conditions is critical (25, 26).

In studies focusing on longer-term scenarios, the assumptions about technology development under future policy conditions are even more important.

Structural change has been recognized as another major driver for change in overall energy intensity (27). Structural change can be separated into intersectoral (e.g., a change to a larger fraction of light industry in the economy) and intrasectoral (e.g., a change in feedstocks without a substantial effect on product quality). Most energy modeling efforts start with an economic scenario that incorporates elements of intersector structural change for the reference scenario. Generally, the same structural development pattern is assumed for all policy scenarios, even when the modeled policy changes may have a profound effect on the energy system (such as long-term GHG concentration stabilization scenarios). Although this makes it possible to compare the results of the policy scenarios in a systematic way, it underestimates the flexibility of economic responses to important challenges to the energy and economic system (28) and, hence, may overestimate the costs of policy scenarios. This latter one can be, in part, compensated for by integration with an equilibrium model. But even an equilibrium model cannot forecast the appearance or development of new industries or sectors that may not exist today.

TECHNOLOGY AND OPPORTUNITY REPRESENTATION   Modelers try to capture the achievable potential for energy efficiency improvement given the economic and policy assumptions of each scenario. Many engineering economic models start with a database of options and a selection of economic criteria to estimate the achievable potential under different scenario conditions. One challenge faced by many modelers is the time-intensive construction of a sufficient database of energy-efficient measures, and another is to combine this with a more sophisticated method to estimate the share of measures that is implemented under different scenario conditions. The selection to estimate the achievable potential, however, is often done in a simplified way using a discount rate, varying from a social discount rate to one that closely matches hurdle rates. This method over simplifies the complexity of investment decision-making behavior in industry because it does not account for market, institutional, and cultural barriers (5) that affect the achievable potential. The problem faced by modelers is that there are limited experience and empirical data on how to translate qualitative knowledge on decision-making behavior for energy efficiency into quantitative parameters (29, 30).

Industry uses energy in myriad ways, making end-use classifications more complex than in other sectors. Energy-consuming equipment may be industry specific, process specific, and even site specific, and crosscutting technologies, such as motors, vary widely in application, size, and output. It is therefore not easy to classify industrial energy use by service demand nor to group technologies or equipment that can provide the services. However, it is important to capture the differences in production in the analysis (31). Some studies build on very detailed and well-researched databases [e.g., IKARUS and Materials Technologies for Greenhouse Gas Emission Reduction (MATTER)]. CIMS, Los Alamos U.S. MARKAL, and, to a lesser extent, NEMS determine the level of services a major process technology would require and can supply the service from a separate service node. The service, for example, pumping, requires motor drive and picks it up from the motor node. Each node is subject to competition to provide the services.

Although cogeneration [Combined Heat and Power (CHP)] is recognized in many countries as an important energy efficiency option and is the subject of specific policies in many countries, often the integration of CHP in the models is limited. Sometimes, CHP is an afterthought because models first assume implementation of cost-effective end-use measures before evaluating the use of CHP. Other models did not allow expansion of CHP due to modeling structure and limitations. Modelers need to find ways to reflect that CHP investments compete with end-use measures in the economic evaluation.

The assumptions regarding the actual performance of existing capacity and stock turnover are of equal importance. Some industrial technologies have long economic and technical lifetimes. Because relatively large energy efficiency improvements can be achieved when existing capacity is replaced by new technology, the assumptions on lifetime, age distribution, and turnover rate are essential (32). In reality, this may result in nonlinear retirement patterns without a direct relationship with the age of the equipment. A conceptual problem here is that, in practice, the distinction between retrofit and replacement is not always clear. In long-term models (>50 years), it may be assumed that a large part of energy-consuming production equipment will be replaced over the modeling period.

Furthermore, market penetration patterns of energy-efficient technologies may not be as smooth as the typical S curve may suggest. Market penetration patterns may vary because of differences in potential adopter characteristics. Mutual dependency between technologies at individual plants, technical lock in, or path dependency may limit the uptake of a technology over a certain period. This also implies that critical mass effects accelerate the uptake of technology. A few studies have addressed the learning-by-doing effects by incorporating cost-development curves for power generation equipment (33–36). Speed of adoption estimates using diffusion models have been made (37, 38), but these have not yet made much impact on energy models.

ECONOMIC EVALUATION OF ENERGY-EFFICIENT TECHNOLOGIES Tied in closely to decision-making behavior is the economic evaluation of energy-efficient technologies. Most models do not include a full description of the costs and benefits of energy efficiency measures but rely on limited economic information, such as average energy prices and stylized technology costs (see Table 2). The energy modeling community has recently given more attention to the roles of transaction and opportunity costs as some of the factors explaining the differences in results of top-down and bottom-up models (39). Definitions of transaction costs, however, vary in the literature, and it often remains difficult to tie these transaction and opportunity costs to technologies. Transaction costs are likely to decrease owing to learning effects, growing knowledge, and policy measures.

On the other hand, one key factor, not usually captured by models, is the effect of the investment on the company's profitability. It is generally believed that most firms are capital constrained and do not have the internal resources, e.g., cash flow, to make investments even when payback periods are short (40–42). Ancillary benefits for the firm's productivity make energy efficiency investments a much better sell. Some technologies have benefits that include increased productivity, capacity utilization, and product quality, accompanied by the energy efficiency benefits (33, 44). As a consequence most engineering economic models do not fully account for the nonenergy benefits in the financial accounting, which contributes to a systematic underestimation of the economic potential.

Finally, it is difficult to represent external costs of energy use in models. Despite many fuel-cycle studies there is no clear direction whether and how to incorporate external costs in a model.

POLICY MODELING   Representation of policies and policy impacts remains a challenge for the models. Most standard economic models simulate price-based policies. By definition, this limits the modeling of nonprice-based policies, which have been introduced in many industrialized countries over the past years. Policy impacts on energy-related decision making and barrier removal need to be analyzed and underline the importance of a sound representation of company behavior. In addition, several other issues are

- Special attention is needed for the modeling of R&D policies because R&D investments will likely lead to improved performance of existing and new technologies. For example, in the steel industry, scrap preheating dramatically reduces electricity use and is available for existing and new electric arc furnaces. Challenges are the link between (current) R&D expenditures and the speed of R&D progress as well as future technology availability and performance. Some modelers have tied the benefits of R&D policies into technical learning curves, but only for energy supply technologies. Comparable work on end-use technologies is still missing. Increased empirical analysis of R&D investments, technology, and management performance is essential to improve modeling of the relations.

- Economic feedbacks can impact the effectiveness of energy efficiency policy (27). Most studies of the rebound effect have focused on nonindustrial energy use and show a limited impact on the achieved savings. Recycling of energy tax revenue through tax relief in other areas is a relatively new phenomenon and used in a few taxation schemes in Europe. Revenue recycling can take various forms with different impacts. Models have difficulty in estimating the potential impacts of these feedbacks unless they have a detailed representation of the macroeconomy and taxation.

- In policy scenarios, the program costs are often not fully considered because data on the effectiveness and efficiency of industrial energy policies are difficult to find (23). The costs of classical policies, such as investment subsidies, were relatively easy to estimate, but this is more difficult for information dissemination programs or the new set of voluntary or negotiated agreements. Some studies (e.g., 25) have included an average estimate of program costs based on the evaluation of program costs of selected programs. The simultaneous and parallel implementation of different programs may increase the overall effectiveness through synergies but makes it difficult to evaluate and model individual programs.

Pandey (45) addresses the additional needs of energy policy modeling for developing countries. Pandey makes the case that the policy priorities in developing countries, existing barriers to technology diffusion, uncertainties in the policy regime, and other characteristics specific to developing countries make meaningful policy modeling in these countries even more difficult.

OVERALL CHALLENGES   Foremost is the uncertainty in data and data quality. Cost cutting in statistical data collection on energy use patterns has resulted in higher aggregation levels for available information. This is especially unfortunate at times when the energy policy challenges are driving a need for detailed information on energy consumption and emission patterns. Although many studies acknowledge problems with data quality, there seems to be no systematic analysis of the impact of uncertainties on the scenario results other than of the costs of the policy scenarios. Another aspect of uncertainty is in the model structure itself, i.e., the decision algorithms of simulation models. If they are created using statistical analysis, then the statistical properties of the parameters provide measures of uncertainty. Uncertainty in modeling is also implemented in the optimization approaches as evidenced by the stochastic versions of MARKAL. The computational challenges often do limit the types of uncertainty that can be included.

The problems of data quality and data use in the model are also related to the transparency of the model. A transparent model makes it easy for the user and policy maker to evaluate and value the quality of the scenario results. However, the increasing complexity of the relationships between energy use, environment, and economy makes it difficult to maintain transparency. The trade-off between transparency and complexity remains essential to evaluate the results.

Typically, models focus on regions or countries, whereas a few integrated models include the global economy (subdivided in a varying number of regions). With the changing dynamics of energy policy the system boundaries of these studies may not be sufficient. For example, emission trading or the clean development mechanism under the Kyoto Protocol will likely affect the costs of emission reduction for different regions, as demonstrated by many models.[1] Still, energy efficiency policy may only affect a specific region, and hence the user/policy maker may only be interested in the specific country or region for the assessment.

---

[1] It should be noted, that often the reduction in emission mitigation costs due to (international) emission trade or other flexible mechanisms, as defined under the Kyoto Protocol, is the result of simplified or uncertain assumptions on the costs of emission reduction opportunities in the other regions.

Directions/Issues in Modeling

In this section we focus on the main issues that need further attention in modeling efforts. We discuss the state-of-the-art models as well as promising directions taken by various modelers.

TECHNOLOGICAL FLEXIBILITY   Early energy models estimate the costs of GHG emission reductions to be quite high. Often this was the result of a limited menu of technology options included in the models or the reliance on a (expensive) backstop technology. Edmonds et al. (46) demonstrated the importance of good representation of technology in models to estimate the potential of GHG emission reduction and the costs. Roop & Dahowski (26) used a model with a rich technology representation to assess the Annual Energy Outlook 2000 baseline scenario developed by the U.S. Energy Information Administration. They found that a technology-rich model produced a baseline scenario with lower energy use.

TECHNICAL LEARNING   Several groups have started to incorporate mechanisms to simulate changes in technology performance as a function of development and deployment (47, 48). However, most engineering economic models have a static representation of technology, i.e., the costs of a technology do not change over the modeling period. Some studies (e.g., 48, 49) tried to address this by using exogenous assumptions for technology parameters based on expectations of future technology performance changes because of R&D and learning by doing effects. The notion of induced (endogenous) technical change, i.e., the response of technology performance to changing market and policy environments, is important. Different groups have tried to capture endogenous technological change in models (46, 50, 51). MARKAL modelers in the United States and Switzerland (52) have used a progress-ratio function to estimate the impact of increased production volumes on costs of renewable energy technologies.[2] Like MARKAL, CIMS uses a progress ratio to reduce the costs of new or upcoming technologies on the basis of their market penetration (53). Newell & Jaffe (54) provide an analysis focusing on residential energy technology. The assumed progress ratio is critical. Recent International Energy Agency reports (55, 56) found that only a few measurements of experience curves for energy technologies are publicly recorded, and those are concentrated in a few supply technologies. Laitner & Sanstad (57) demonstrated significantly different results when learning was limited to supply-side technologies compared to scenarios that included learning for both end-use and supply-side technologies. Although, experience curve studies of manufacturing sectors are numerous (e.g., 43, 59–64), none are related to energy-efficient technologies in industry. Some empirical work on price-induced change in industry

---

[2]The use of progress ratios or learning curves is especially important for modular technologies, such as renewable energy technologies and many energy efficiency technologies, in which mass production is an important factor in bringing down the costs.

is emerging. Celikkol & Stefanou (58) examined induced change in the food processing industry, but not for energy efficiency.

Zwaan et al. (51) incorporated endogenous technological change as a function of cumulative capacity and showed that this reduced the costs for CO_2 emission reduction considerably. Similarly, R&D is supposed to lead to reduced costs and improved performance of technology. R&D is generally seen as an investment with a high payback (65), but the risk of incomplete appropriation of the benefits leads to underinvestment in R&D (66). Although some modelers assume certain cost reductions or performance improvement, the modeling of R&D policies and effects is still uncharted territory (46). Goulder & Schneider (67) as well as Messner (68) have tried to include the effects of R&D in their model calculations by assuming a certain cost reduction as a function of public and private R&D investments. Few case studies exist of the development of industrial technologies and the assessment of R&D investments on technology performance (69). Similarly, studies (70, 71) that assess future technologies, their performance, and costs are needed.

MATERIAL FLOWS   Product and material demand are the important drivers for industrial energy use. So far, these interrelations are often predetermined through scenario definition, limiting the system's flexibility to respond. Modelers have tried to incorporate the material system in energy models to include changes in material flows in the development of policy scenarios. The strong interaction between climate change, energy use, and materials use will likely drive climate change policy development to include materials in the set of policy instruments. Pioneered by groups in Canada and the Netherlands, several MARKAL models are available that include a representation of the materials system (in some form) (72). Generally, the models demonstrate that including material efficiency options in the models will lead to reduced costs of GHG emission reduction and increased potential. This corresponds to a form of economic flexibility that changes the characteristics of the product mix and economic structure of industry in response to policy changes.

ECONOMIC FLEXIBILITY   In almost all studies, the model work starts from a reference scenario. The reference scenario assumes a certain economic development with a given structure. Policy scenarios are developed to achieve the same economic development pattern. However, assuming that climate change will have a profound effect on the future of the energy system and the related fundamental energy price patterns, society is likely to change economic development toward different paths. Jorgenson et al. (28) modeled the opportunities for substitution between economic sectors to provide a given level of welfare to simulate economic responsiveness of society. As a result of including the flexibility, they found that the costs for GHG emission reduction decreased compared to a scenario that assumed a rigid economic development path.

DISCOUNT RATES AND HURDLE RATES   Discount rates are used in engineering economic models to reflect the (risk) preferences of consumers or society when evaluating (energy efficiency) investments. Typically, earlier engineering economic models used social discount rates (e.g., 4% to 8%) in the studies. The choice of discount rate depends on the approach (prescriptive versus descriptive) used. A prescriptive approach typically uses lower discount rates, especially for long-term issues like climate change. Lower discount rates (4% to 8%) may also be used to appraise public sector projects. A descriptive approach uses relatively high rates (5). Other studies use a descriptive approach by using discount rates between 10% and 30%. Howarth & Sanstad (73) have challenged the common belief of economists that high discount rates reflect a rational evaluation of risk associated with an investment and of efficient markets. Instead, the use of high discount rates may be a function of asymmetric information, bounded rationality, and transaction costs. As such, it is reasonable to assume that efficient policies may affect the implicit discount rate used by consumers. For example, the LIEF model (74) allows change in the capital recovery factor used by the model, which is a reflection of the used discount (or hurdle) rate, to mimic the effect of reduced barriers.

PROGRAM COST ESTIMATES The program costs may be an important variable in policy analysis. Program costs may vary widely, depending on the type of program, the success rate, and the efficiency with which it is administered. The Clean Energy Futures study (25) uses the average specific (administrative) program costs (i.e., dollars/unit of energy saved), based on a small number of policy evaluations. This average is used to estimate all program costs. It would be desirable to be able to estimate program costs for different types of policy programs or instruments to get a better understanding of the cost-effectiveness of policy measures (75). However, it is hard to estimate these costs on a disaggregated basis owing to a lack of evaluations, especially for industry.

INTEGRATION WITH ECONOMIC SYSTEM (EQUILIBRIUM OR PARTIAL EQUILIBRIUM) The desire to integrate engineering economic models into a macroeconomic forecasting model has important implications for policy modeling. This integration has been conducted at varying levels of detail, and the manner in which this integration occurs is under examination (76, 77). NEMS, MARKAL-MACRO, and more recently Netherlands Energy Demand Model (NEMO) and AMIGA all approach the integration in different ways. NEMS uses various engineering economic submodules within a detailed energy market partial equilibrium, which is embedded in a macroeconomic response surface model. The response surface model is derived from a more detailed commercially available econometric macromodel. MARKAL-MACRO combines a detailed energy optimization model with a neoclassical growth model. NEMO (78) uses ICARUS data to parameterize a simple computable general equilibrium model. AMIGA is a computable general equilibrium model, but it has a very high degree of sectoral and technology detail (79, 80). The more recent approaches to integration directly incorporate technology models into the equilibrium framework, rather than merge preexisting technology and economic system models.

Stochastic models Engineering economic models may treat costs and energy savings as known, but they may also be viewed as unknown, random variables. Howarth & Andersson (81) illustrate how uncertainty in the form of imperfect information regarding the performance of a technology results in suboptimal adoption. Models may represent this uncertainty regarding technology adoption explicitly with Monte Carlo simulations or with probability based diffusion models. Stochastic behavior reflected in the difference in costs and/or characteristics of adopter is conveniently modeled by discrete choice models. ENPEP, Industrial Technology and Energy Modeling System (ITEMS), CIMS, and ISTUM all use a logit function to apply market shares. Discrete choice models do not model the underlying process, but only the outcome. More direct treatments of stochastic costs can be implemented in optimization models such as MARKAL, but with substantial computational challenges. Option value models that account for uncertain future outcomes have been proposed as a justification for high discount rates, but detailed models or studies have been few and conclusions are mixed (73). Explicit treatment of uncertainty would substantially improve realism in engineering economic models.

Frontier production function models   Many engineering economic models summarize the detailed technology information in the form of conservation supply curves (CSC). A CSC can be derived from parametric frontier production functions as a conditional factor of demand (82–84). The LIEF model can be viewed in this context because its CSCs are parametric. This approach reduces the burden imposed by collection of technology specific data and has the benefit of implicitly incorporating nonenergy benefits. However, the authors are not aware of any empirical CSCs derived from frontier production functions.

INCLUDING DIFFERENT DISCIPLINES IN MODELING   Scientific disciplines look differently at complex problems, such as energy modeling. For example, although an engineer understands technology as being hardware, an economist typically sees technology as part of a mathematical production function. More and more, multidisciplinary teams are used in designing models, and scientific results from different disciplines are used in modeling. There are still many lessons to be learned from the varied disciplines, which include the following:

- Social psychology investigates individual behavior and the underlying determinants of action, including values, attitudes, and norms (85, 86). Together with empirical experience from *social marketing initiatives* that aim at influencing these parameters, results on individual preferences and decisions can be expected that may challenge traditional assumptions on economic behavior and technology transfer (87). Moreover, the same actor appears several times (e.g., as employee and driver or household member) in a model of the energy system, and the actors are subject to various policy interventions.
- Management science and organizational research have accumulated considerable knowledge on change processes in companies and institutions (88–91). For energy modeling, the impact of improved management skills on the rate of technology adoption is of special importance. In this regard, many positive synergies and benefits can be found between competitiveness, economic

performance, innovation strength, and ecological performance. This field has embraced the frontier production function framework for measuring efficiency. One principle tool developed in this literature is Data Envelopment Analysis (92).

- Marketing research offers know-how on possibilities and restrictions for opening up markets. This can contribute to a more appropriate segmentation of target groups or modeling market transformation processes.

- Innovation and diffusion research analyzes the conditions for the generation and diffusion of new solutions that model penetration rates more realistically (93). Related to this, *technology foresight studies* provide methodologies and information on how to assess future technology options that play an important role in long-term scenario analyses (e.g., 70, 71).

- Bayesian economics is now applied to technology choice and learning, market leaders, and imitators (94, 95). Insights into market structure and productivity behavior could generate new directions for energy modeling. The CIMS model tries to include Bayesian economic principles in the model structure.

- Evolutionary economics in the tradition of Nelson (65) and related work in systems theory/systems analysis provide insight into dynamic processes within complex nondeterministic systems (96). Putting special emphasis on the time dependency of developments, the work on technological trajectories and path dependency, for example, provides an understanding of the constraints for technical progress and structural change in industrial systems (97, 98).

- Agent-based model (ABM) simulations have emerged as important new social science and economics simulation tools to investigate the behavior of complex adaptive systems. By simulation, the behavior and interaction of individual agents provides insight into the behavior of organizations, and the associated implications for technology adoption and integrated assessments are revealed (99, 100). ABMs have been developed to study the U.K. (101) and the U.S. (102) deregulated electric markets, and there are also ABMs for natural gas markets and infrastructure interdependencies (102, 103).

PATHWAYS

Although the current work on models and methodologies offers some interesting results, practical advances in engineering economic modeling still remain. In this section, we identify and distill the directions and trends that can enhance the contribution of engineering economic models to energy analysis in order to meet the challenges depicted in the previous section (see Table 3). The diversity of challenges can be condensed to two problems.

- The first is the complex, dynamic nature of decision-making behavior, the related transformation effects in the market systems, as well as the impact of policy on the behavior.

TABLE 3 Matrix of challenges, recent advances in modeling and remaining open questions[a]

New approaches from research	Enhanced technological flexibility	Endogenous technical learning	Incorporation of material flows	Enhanced economic flexibility	Adaptation of discount/ hurdle rates	Estimation of program costs	Macro- economic integration	Integration of stochastic elements	Integration of other disciplines	Open issues
Challenges to modeling: scenario construction and basic assumptions										
Definition of business as usual		+	+	++					+	How much change/ flexibility is already in scenario?
Choice of available technology	++	++	+							What is the future set of options?
Representation of structural change	+		++	++			+		+	What are the drivers, trends, directions, and interdependencies?
Technology and opportunity representation										
Degree of technology specification	++		++							What degree is appropriate?
Cogeneration	+		+							How to give a complete picture of a business practice?
Market and institutional barriers	+	+	+		+				+	How do market actors interact?
Socioeconomic barriers	+	+			+				++	Why, when, and under what conditions is behavior changed?
Assumptions about actual performance	+	+			+			+	+	Actual treatment of technologies in business practice?

(*Continued*)

	Treatment of technical complexity	Learning with energy efficient technologies	Modeling material flows	Representing economic behavior	Evaluation methodology	Transfer of knowledge	
Market penetration patterns	+	+		+		+	How to aggregate individual adoption behavior?
Definition of costs and benefits	+	+	+	++		+	Nature, dimension, and persistence of costs/benefits?
Representation of policies and instruments							
Barrier related instruments	+	+	+	+	+	++	What are the impacts, synergies, and persistence of effects?
Research & development	+	++	+	+	+	+	What are impacts, synergies, and persistence of effects?
Economic feedbacks		+	++	+	+	+	Role of energy efficiency as a source of economic change?
Program costs		+		+	++	+	Nature, dimension, and persistence of costs/benefits?
General aspects							
Data uncertainty	+		−	−	−		Scope and limits for better data?
Transparency	−	−	−	−		+	Trade-off between accuracy, complexity and simplification?
System boundaries	−		−		+		Appropriate choice of questions and tools?
Open issues							

^aThe meanings of the symbols used are as follows: +, a potential contribution; ++, a direct contribution; −, a problem or possible negative effect.

- The second is coping with the technical diversity and complexity of the industrial production system.

With regard to both challenges, new modeling approaches can mitigate existing deficiencies of economic-engineering modeling but cannot fully overcome conceptual limitations of modeling per se. Given this perspective, models will hardly be able to fully cover all relevant aspects of industrial energy policy, and important missing parameters need to be addressed by other tools. Accordingly, policy analysis needs to be grounded on a kind of heuristic competence that allows it to master a methodological diversity of tools with a limited scope (a network/cluster of micromodels) rather than striving toward even bigger megamodels that aim at integrating as many dimensions as possible. Moreover, the analysis process, the development of parameters, the application of the models, and the analysis of results, is at least as important as the models. Hence, the models need to be explicitly embedded in a more comprehensive analytical strategy that recognizes the limitations, strengths, and weaknesses of the tools. Two aspects are important for such a strategy.

- Sound specification of modeling tasks and system boundaries is required, i.e., an appropriate choice of analytical questions in relation to the capability of a modeling tool. Usually, models aim at a broad coverage of the economy to provide a framework for a broader policy debate. Given that the quality of sector representation differs significantly, an assessment of single policy instruments may lead to distorted results in such a model. A sound specification of policy questions and analytical tasks and the choice of a suitable modeling tool and its systems boundary are needed.

- Data quality is an essential element in any model. In certain areas, it is needed to develop the statistical foundation of modeling. At the same time, however, it has to be acknowledged that perfect data sets cannot be achieved. Given existing budget constraints, efforts need to concentrate on crucial areas. Empirical work should aim to accurately study and quantify the parameters that are of greatest relevance to sensitivity analysis. This will identify possible biases and prevent systematic over- and underestimation of parameters. Examples of such sensitive parameters are variables affecting the flexibility of policies and the representation of emerging technologies. Still, it will not be possible to reduce all uncertainties (104), and hence, presentation of modeling results that acknowledge the uncertainties is essential.

Better Use of Models in Policy Analysis

A critical assessment of the models, both by the modelers and the users of the results, will underline that not one single model is sufficiently equipped to answer all policy questions. Instead, modelers and users should try to jointly find ways to develop the right tools to answer the questions being asked. The development of new modeling approaches starts with a critical assessment of the policy needs and the impacts of these needs on the modeling tools. Also, the scenario design or definition of the policy background in the model is an essential starting point for each modeling exercise. The lessons learned of an improved interface between user and modeler include the following:

- The choice of an appropriate model structure and careful analysis of inputs and assumptions are essential. Focus on the interfaces of appropriate inputs, assumptions, and model structure, instead on the model itself. Model assumptions are often more important than the structure.
- There should be less emphasis on normative approaches in terms of optimization, owing to a relatively weak foundation for a strong message. Optimization model results are often based on the result of uncertain assumptions and inputs.
- More emphasis on simulation through quantitative assessment of impacts and interdependencies is required. Thorough analysis of diffusion patterns and policies will provide improved inputs for models and better simulate the effects of policies.
- Improved modeling of interaction mechanisms between scenario development and technology is needed. Policy scenarios reflect not only changes in energy demand and supply but also changes in the relationships with other scenario parameters. Increased energy efficiency policies driven by environmental concerns, for example, will affect purchases and production patterns and change development in directions other than BAU scenarios.
- Focus should not only be on the technical aspects of model improvement. A greater investment is needed in efforts to strengthen the "interpretative intelligence" of models through increased transparency and by relating results to questions, inputs, and assumptions.
- A multidisciplinary view of technology and its implementation mechanism in modeling will improve understanding of technology diffusion patterns and, hence, of the role that policy plays in shaping energy use.
- A more dynamic representation of technology, with an emphasis on technological learning and the side effects of technology, is another reflection of the policy environment of the scenarios assumed.

Improving Models

The results from new research fields will hardly fit directly into existing models. Moreover, adding more and more information to the models deteriorates the transparency, underlining the need for targeted exercises, e.g., based on micromodels suited to answer specific questions. The results of the different micromodels can be used to improve larger macromodels or integrated in megamodels using innovative computing techniques. Below, we discuss three pathways to improve modeling efforts.

TECHNOLOGY AND OPPORTUNITY REPRESENTATION   To make better use of the technical diversity in industrial production models, a suggested research agenda includes

- Conducting empirical studies that investigate technical and economic aspects of energy efficiency to provide data to improve modeling assumptions and improve the basis for estimating more realistic model parameters;
- Emphasizing crosscutting technologies of rising importance that have been neglected so far;
- Including technological learning effects on the performance, costs, and diffusion of industrial energy technologies;
- Using detailed modeling of production functions to study the role of structural change within the economy, including the economic flexibility to respond to policy challenges; and
- Improving understanding of the assumptions in the reference scenario.

Current advances in research that hold particular promise in this area include incorporation of material flows, enhanced economic flexibility, learning effects, and integration of stochastic elements.

More transparent modeling techniques can allow the user a clear understanding of the modeling and technology assumptions. New computer techniques, for example object-oriented programming, may help improve the modularity of the model but still build on a clear understanding by the user of the limitations of the model and its assumptions (e.g., lack of opportunities, bad representation, and interrelations in the model). By designing a common framework for energy modeling, a language for linking micromodels can be developed. Such a framework could allow salvaging elements of existing models. These computing techniques have yet to be successfully implemented for energy efficiency models.

The energy-materials link   Although physical production flows are often used implicitly to model technology, the explicit modeling of physical production allows for a more transparent analysis of the assumptions for technology and scenarios, including structural change (e.g., increased recycling and impact on primary resource consumption). Linking energy use with material flows, i.e., integrating assumptions on physical production levels, structural change effects, and related policy measures (such as recycling quota), will allow improved interaction between technology, scenario, and policy assumptions. In turn, the impact of energy policy strategies on material consumption and structural change effects needs to be investigated. All in all, such an integration of dimensions reflects the importance of integrated policy approaches that bridge the traditional separations between policy areas and administrative responsibilities.

Functional categorization of technologies   In principle, models will benefit from more detailed information on technologies. As discussed, technology-rich models often provide different results than models with poor technology representation.

However, given the complexity of many models, there are clear practical and financial limits to incorporating a vast amount of technical information. To resolve this dilemma, more emphasis on smart categorization of technologies and target groups (i.e., users) can direct scarce resources to areas of particular importance. This will result in appropriate criteria and features for building typologies of technologies and opportunities that can be handled within modeling exercises. The challenges are to go beyond traditional sector definitions derived from statistical sector categorization and to shed light on policy-relevant distinctions, e.g., in terms of impact mechanisms and driving factors. The focus should be less on the richness of the technology options and more on qualities of those technologies and their potential to effect future energy use. For example, crosscutting technologies (e.g., a motor) are often selected and installed under different conditions than process-specific technologies (e.g., a distillation tower). Strategic investments, such as CHP, are evaluated differently than auxiliaries. However, in current models, technology choice and competition are often represented in a similar way, leading to potential misrepresentation of the role of technologies and the prospects for change. The technology groups must be established exogenous to the model on the basis of detailed policy-relevant technology assessments. For example, the Canadian iron and steel industry says it will never build a coke-based steel mill again. All future mills producing steel from ore will use direct reduced-iron processes. Others will focus on recycling and the use of electric arc mills. This suggests that a policy-relevant model (at least for the Canadian steel industry) should have only short lists of coke-based steel producing technologies, even though this is currently a significant energy consumer.

Multiple technology benefits Owing to the importance of cost information for modeling, sound definitions and comprehensive representations of cost variables are needed. Traditional flaws of current models include insufficient specification of cost-benefit ratios of energy-saving technologies, overlooking the multiple benefits of a technology, and biasing the representation of the economic performance of technology. Although discussed for years (44), this aspect has hardly been considered in models. Empirical work is needed to investigate the nature and dimension of the broad range of synergetic benefits of energy-efficient technology. The same holds for changes in energy management practice that may lead to better business performance, e.g., through higher motivation and better quality control.

Transaction and opportunity costs Engineering economic models are often criticized for the underestimation of transaction and opportunity costs. A thorough analysis of transaction costs and adoption of a common terminology will result in an improved model. A better understanding of opportunity and transaction costs may help explain the varied results of different models.

Learning curves of energy-efficient technology There is a strong need to account for learning effects in end-use energy-efficient technology modeling. New information is needed to get a realistic estimate of the future costs as well as an estimate of the trajectories of technical progress. Although there is an extensive body of literature on learning effects for energy supply technologies, empirical studies are specifically needed for end-use equipment.

BEHAVIORAL REPRESENTATION   With regard to the behavior of decision makers and the development of markets, more insight is needed from (*a*) qualitative and quantitative studies on decision behavior, (*b*) the sociocultural background that determines the effectiveness of instruments and (*c*) improved understanding of technology diffusion and penetration patterns as a function of firm behavior. Advances in research to improve the understanding of decision-making behavior in firms, and modeling thereof, adaptation of discount rates and hurdle rates, analysis of technology diffusion patterns, evaluation of energy efficiency and other policies on technology diffusion, evaluation of the effectiveness and efficiency of energy policies, as well as estimating program costs contribute to this pathway.

Basic understanding of investment situation   Energy models tend to describe the decision to invest in energy-efficient technology primarily as a choice driven by energy cost savings and financial gain. In reality, however, there is a permanent turnover of production equipment, i.e., the technology stock is already in motion. For the most part, investment decisions are mainly the result of technical reasons, market prospects, and productivity gains. With regard to energy efficiency, the question is often not whether to invest or not but what version of technology to choose (standard versus high efficiency). Developing a more dynamic understanding of decision-making behavior is likely to better model the direction of an investment decision toward a more energy-efficient alternative.

The diversity of socioeconomic interactions that determine corporate behavior should be condensed into a set of model parameters. This translation, however, must not distort the dynamics of real processes that take place in company social systems. Attention must be given to the representation of change in behavior through the spread of information, evolution of awareness, and organizational learning. New approaches must be found to model the parameters that describe the adoption of technologies by a company, considering the economic, social, and political context. At the same time, we acknowledge that any quantitative simulation of firm behavior is very difficult (105).

Diffusion processes   A better understanding of the diffusion of innovations over time is needed. Starting from the rich body of innovation research (93), different methodologies have been developed to study the diffusion patterns of technology. Even if these achievements appear to be insufficient, most energy models do not include state-of-the-art features. To better model the impact of policy on diffusion processes, we need better knowledge concerning the interaction between policy incentives and the process of technology adoption (see below). Better understanding of the diffusion patterns is directly related to the discussions above, which recommend improvements in the characterization of technology by categorizing the technologies into functional groups.

POLICY REPRESENTATION   A sufficient representation of policies and instruments demands a proper definition of policy instruments and a sound analysis of the features of policy implementation, including the following:

Realistic representation of the practice of implementation   In energy models, policy instruments tend to be described in an idealistic, textbook-like manner. Real implementation practice, however, can vary significantly from the theoretical concept. In addition, the same instrument can work differently under different circumstances or with other target groups. Empirical research is needed to provide background information for the development of improved modeling assumptions on policy instruments and on their effectiveness.

Policy and program effects   Research is needed to derive indicators concerning the degree of impact (i.e., to what extent are the target groups affected by the measure) and the response time, (i.e., the time lag between the policy intervention and the time when results can be observed). The last aspect may include a "cumulative impact curve" to represent the acceleration and accumulated dissemination of energy efficiency improvement because of a policy change. The typology of policy instruments is determined on the basis of different intervention modes and moments in the typical S-curve technology diffusion. This will also model nonmonetary policies.

Program costs   To assess strategies for climate change abatement, better data on policy effectiveness and efficiency is needed. Generally, there is a lack of evaluation of (industrial) energy policies. This is a promising area for empirical research and should also include side effects (i.e., programs can suffer from a free-rider effect but can also have positive spillover effects).

Assessment of policy mixes   In reality, programs are not implemented in isolation but as part of a larger set of policies and programs. The effect of single instruments within a portfolio cannot simply be added. Synergetic effects may improve the efficiency and effectiveness of one policy instrument or program, whereas other policy developments may reduce the effectiveness. On the basis of a series of empirical studies, it is important to better understand the synergies between programs to advance the modeling of policy mixes.

Representation of nonenergy policy background in scenario definition   Most energy modeling efforts focus on energy policies, yet other policies will affect energy use patterns and diffusion of energy-efficient technologies. We need a more comprehensive representation of the policy landscape in which industry and energy policy is placed. Energy models tend to link investments to energy alone, and many other policies are not included. In reality, energy may play a minor role for strategic investments. Therefore, for example, the general investment-friendliness of the nonenergy scenario setting needs more attention because it is a major parameter for industry's response flexibility. The same holds for environmental requirements as a driver for replacement of older polluting (and often energy inefficient) technologies. Environmental (and regulatory) side benefits are also an important aspect of the model.

CONCLUSIONS AND RECOMMENDATIONS

The discussion of challenges and new requirements to engineering economic modeling revealed a fundamental shift needed in research priorities. In the past, models have been constructed principally as forecasting tools focused on energy market questions of what quantity and type of energy will be consumed in the future. Having origins in the economics of resource depletion and having grown in substantial use after the oil price shocks of the seventies, these models have price (costs) as their principle drivers. However, nonmonetary policies are becoming more and more important in the current policy debate. Formerly static parameters turn into policy variables that should change over time. Conventional modeling approaches designed for different tasks appear to be ill equipped to serve the new demand of policy analysis. At the same time, we acknowledge that models remain limited in scope and analytical power. Rather than aiming at a silver bullet, it appears to be more fruitful to strengthen the overarching framework of policy analysis in which models designed for specific tasks are placed.

Research Priorities

The development of a uniform but public modeling framework to integrate existing and future modules and models would be a major step forward. Similar to an open software development environment, it would allow for innovation in different parts (e.g., policy modeling) of the total model and allow easy integration in existing models. We propose to base this framework on object-oriented programming and modeling, allowing transparency and flexibility in modeling approaches. Research should determine a common structure and the information needed to facilitate communication between the different objects (or modules). At the same time, interaction with policy analysis can be strengthened by better linking specific modeling exercises with related research.

Technology representation has shown to be a key area in which short-term efforts can make an important impact. At issue are the full nature and the dynamics of the technology, including (*a*) nonenergy benefits in the quantitative description of a technology, (*b*) research in the learning effect of energy-efficient end-use technologies to accurately reflect the dynamics of technology development, (*c*) the level of disaggregation, and (*d*) smart categorization of technologies and target groups. With an increase in the number of technologies, there is increased need to derive appropriate criteria and features for technology typologies that can be handled by the models.

Research should aim to improve the understanding of the diffusion of technologies to better link technologies to the decision making and implementation trajectory. Current models apply a similar diffusion model to most energy-efficient technologies. In reality, other benefits than energy may drive implementation. This is linked to a proper quantification of the nonenergy benefits, but it is also linked to other nonenergy related regulation that may affect implementation of a specific technology. Improved understanding should lead to categories or groups of technologies with specific characteristics, allowing improved modeling of technology diffusion.

As the counterpart to the assessment of efficiency options, there is a need for policy evaluation of the effectiveness and efficiency of policy instruments. Full policy evaluations are rare in the field of industrial energy policy. Innovative ways are needed to translate the impact of policies on the micro- (or firm-) level to macrolevels of the technology diffusion process. It is important to account for synergies or unintended consequences of energy policy mixes and other policies. The efficiency of a policy instrument has to include the costs of implementing a policy (instrument) and potential synergies or rebound effects. This item is a plea to policy makers to include policy evaluation as an integral part of new policy development.

New modeling approaches for the decision-making framework (or behavioral representation) and process are needed that can be used in the economic-engineering models. These approaches need to include barrier representation (e.g., lack of information), decision-making behavior, as well as the effect of policies. The impact of nonmonetary policies and policies aiming to reduce barriers are especially important. Such modeling approaches need to translate behavior of individual firms to the larger model and economy. Innovative economic research may offer different potentially successful approaches, and the contribution of social sciences in the debate on firm behavior is needed to develop successful modeling approaches.

Short Term Collaborative Projects

On the basis of the research priorities and modeling directions discussed above, we identified three major areas in which collaborative projects are essential to warrant successful development of a commonly accepted modeling approach. The three areas focus on the modeling framework, technology representation, and policy evaluation. We stress that the projects should be the result of an international and multidisciplinary collaboration.

The framework should include the different modules, communication between modules, as well as outputs. It should allow for transparency and flexibility. An interdisciplinary workshop of key people is the preferred start for developing the framework.

Technology representation needs international and interdisciplinary collaboration on technology representation, typologies to categorize technologies (e.g., implementation trajectories and characteristics), the building and maintaince of databases on technologies, and the assessment of emerging technologies. The International Energy Agency (IEA) has led an effort to improve the understanding of experience curves for energy supply technologies. A similar effort is urgently needed for demand-side technologies.

We have stressed the lack of policy evaluations, which are essential to improve modeling of policies and policy impacts. Several workshops have been organized in this area, but generally there is lack of attention for policy evaluation in the design and implementation of energy policies. Besides refinement of methods and increased attention and discussion among analysts, there is a strong need for increased attention on the policy front. This is a key area where a concerted effort by international agencies is essential for success.

ACKNOWLEDGMENTS

This work was supported by the U.S. Department of Energy under Contract No. DE-AC03-76SF00098 and W-31-109-Eng-38. The review does not necessarily reflect the opinion of the U.S. Department of Energy or any other U.S. government agency. This review is based on an earlier contribution invited by the professional network for Engineering Economic Technology Analysis (EETA), and a summary presented at the 2003 ACEEE Summer Study on Energy Efficiency in Industry. EETA is coordinated by the IEA. EETA is a multidisciplinary worldwide network of professionals who use engineering economic analysis to investigate energy and climate change technologies and policies. EETA aims to improve the quality, relevance, and visibility of engineering economic assessments for energy and climate change policy making. Currently, representatives from over 20 leading institutions from around the world actively participate in EETA. The authors were chosen to represent a varied background in the economic, technical, and social sciences. Modelers represented in EETA have reviewed an earlier draft. A draft of this paper was reviewed by Kornelis Blok (Utrecht University, The Netherlands), Richard Cirillo (Argonne National Laboratory, United States), Jeff Dowd (U.S. Department of Energy), Ken Friedman (U.S. Department of Energy), Lorna Greening (New Mexico, United States), Susan Holte (U.S. Department of Energy), Skip Laitner (U.S. Environmental Protection Agency), John Nyboer (Simon Fraser University, Canada), Joe Roop (Pacific Northwest National Laboratory, United States), Leo Schrattenholzer (International Institute for Applied Systems Analysis, Austria), and Fridtjof Unander (IEA, France). Despite their efforts, the authors are solely responsible for any remaining errors.

The *Annual Review of Environment and Resources* is online at
http://environ.annualreviews.org

LITERATURE CITED

1. Craig PP, Gadgil A, Koomey JG. 2002. What can history teach us? A retrospective examination of long-term energy forecasts for the United States. *Annu. Rev. Energy Environ.* 27:83–118

2. Zhang ZX, Folmer H. 1998. Economic modeling approaches to cost estimates for the control of carbon dioxide emissions. *Energy Econ.* 20:101–20

3. Laitner JA, DeCanio SJ, Koomey JG,

Sanstad AH. 2003. Room for improvement: increasing the value of energy modeling for policy analysis. *Util. Policy* 11:87–94
4. DeCanio SJ. 2003. *Economic Models of Climate Change—A Critique*. New York, NY: Palgrave Macmillan
5. Intergov. Panel Clim. Change. 2001. *Climate Change 2001: Mitigation*. Cambridge, UK: Cambridge Univ. Press
6. Bertoldi P. 1999. The use of long-term agreements to improve energy efficiency in the industrial sector: overview of the European experiences and proposal for a common framework. In *Proc. 1999 Am. Council Energy-Efficient Econ. Summer Study Energy Effic. Ind.* pp. 287–98. Washington, DC: Am. Council Energy-Efficient Econ.
7. Börkey P, Lévêque F. 1998. *Voluntary approaches for environmental protection in the European Union*. OECD Work. Doc. ENV/EPOC/GEEI(98)29/Final, Organ. Econ. Co-op. Dev., Paris, Fr.
8. Chidiak M. 1999. Voluntary agreements for energy efficiency in five EU countries. In *Proc. 1999 European Council for an Energy-Efficient Economy Summer Study*, May 31–June 4, Mandelieu, Fr.
9. Hansen K, Larsen A. 1999. Voluntary agreements in industry: a comparative description of the process and a normative analysis. *Proc. 1999 Am. Council Energy-Efficient Econ. Summer Study Energy Effic. Ind.* pp. 311–24. Washington, DC: Am. Council Energy-Efficient Econ.
10. Krarup S, Ramesohl S. 2000. *Voluntary Agreements in Energy Policy—Implementation and Efficiency: Final Report*. Inst. Local Gov. Studies (AKF), Copenhagen, Den.
11. Mazurek J, Lehman B. 1999. Monitoring and verification of long-term voluntary approaches in the industrial sector: an initial survey. *Proc. 1999 Am. Council Energy-Efficient Econ. Summer Study Energy Effic. Ind.*, pp. 299–310. Washington, DC: Am. Council Energy-Efficient Econ.
12. Newman J. 1998. Evaluation of energy-related voluntary agreements. *Proc. Workshop Int. Netw. Energy Demand Anal. Ind. Sect.*, pp. 53–62. (LBNL-42368.) Berkeley, CA: Lawrence Berkeley Natl. Lab.
13. Storey M. 1996. *Demand Side Efficiency: Voluntary Agreements with Industry, Policy and Measures for Common Action*. Paris, Fr.: Organ. Econ. Co-op. Dev.
14. Boyd G. 1996. *Impact of Voluntary Agreements on Greenhouse Gas Emission in US Industry*. Paris, Fr.: Organ. Econ. Co-op. Dev.
15. Ramesohl S. 2000. Social interactions and conditions for change in energy-related decision-making in SMCs—an empirical socio-economic analysis. See Ref. 106, pp. 207–28
16. Laitner JA, DeCanio SJ, Peters I. 2000. Incorporating behavioural, social and organizational phenomena in the assessment of climate change mitigation options. See Ref. 106, pp. 1–64
17. Neij L. 1999. *Dynamics of energy systems—methods of analysing technology change*. PhD thesis, Lund Univ., Lund, Swed.
18. Dowd J, Newman J. 1999. Challenges and opportunities for advancing engineering-economic policy analysis. *Proc. IEA Int. Workshop Technol. Reduce Greenh. Gas Emissions: Eng.-Econ. Analyses of Conserved Energy Carbon*, May 5–7. Washington, DC. http://www.iea.org/workshop/engecon
19. Lovins AB, Lovins LH. 1991. Least-cost climatic stabilization. *Annu. Rev. Energy Environ.* 16:433–531
20. Energy Technol. Syst. Anal. Programme (ETSAP). 1997. *New Directions in Energy Modeling, Summary of Annex V (1993–1995)*. Petten, Neth.: Energy Research Cent. Neth.
21. Gielen DJ. 1995. Toward integrated energy and materials policies? A case study on CO_2 reduction in Netherlands. *Energy Policy* 23:1049–62
22. Grübler A, Nakicenovic N, Nordhaus

W, eds. 2002. *Technological Change and the Environment*. Laxenburg, Austria/Washington, DC: IIASA/RFF
23. Martin N, Worrell E, Sandoval A, Bode JW, Phylipsen D. 1998. Industrial energy efficiency policies: understanding success and failure. *Proc. Workshop Int. Netw. Energy Demand Anal. Ind. Sect.*, pp. 1–203 Berkeley, CA: Lawrence Berkeley Natl. Lab.
24. Worrell E, Price L, Ruth M. 2001. Policy modeling for energy efficiency improvement in US industry. *Annu. Rev. Energy Environ.* 26:117–43
25. Interlab. Working Group Energy-Effic. Clean-Energy Technol. 2000. *Scenarios for a Clean Energy Future*. Oak Ridge, TN/Berkeley, CA: Oak Ridge Natl. Lab./Lawrence Berkeley Natl. Lab.
26. Roop JM, Dahowski RT. 2000. Comparison of bottom-up and top-down forecasts: vision industry forecasts with ITEMS and NEMS. *Proc. 22nd Natl. Ind. Energy Technol. Conf. Apr. 5–6*, pp. 84–88. Houston, TX
27. Schipper L, ed. 2000. On the rebound: the interaction of energy efficiency, energy use and economic activity. *Energy Policy* 28:351–501
28. Jorgenson DW, Goettle RJ, Wilcoxen PJ, Ho MS. 2000. *The Role of Substitution in Understanding the Costs of Climate Change Policy*. Washington, DC: Pew Cent. Glob. Clim. Change
29. Velthuijsen JW. 1995. *Determinants of investment in energy conservation*. PhD thesis. Univ. Amsterdam, Amsterdam, Neth.
30. De Groot HLF, Verhoef ET, Nijkamp P. 2001. Energy saving by firms: decision-making, barriers and policies. *Energy Econ.* 23:717–40
31. Farla JCM. 2000. *Physical indicators of energy efficiency*. PhD thesis. Utrecht Univ., Utrecht, Neth.
32. Worrell E, Biermans G. 2004. Move over! Stock turnover, retrofit and industrial energy efficiency. *Energy Policy*. In press
33. Joskow PL, Rose NL. 1985. The effects of technology change, experience, and environmental regulation on the construction cost of coal-burning generating units. *RAND J. Econ.* 16:1–26
34. Zimmerman M. 1982. Learning effects and the commercialization of new energy technologies: the case of nuclear power. *Bell J. Econ.* 13:297–310
35. Lester R, McCabe M. 1993. The effect of industrial structure on learning by doing in nuclear power plant operation. *RAND J. Econ.* 24:418–38
36. Boyd GA, Molburg JC, Cavallo JD. 2002. Estimates of learning by doing in gas turbine electric power systems. *Energy Stud. Rev.* 10(2):85–99
37. Boyd GA. 2001. A Probit Model of Energy Efficiency Technology Decision Making. *Proc. 2001 ACEEE Summer Study Energy Effic. Ind.*, Tarrytown, NY, pp. 521–34. Washington, DC: Am. Council Energy-Efficient Econ.
38. Harrington W, Kopp R. 1999. *Public Policy, Technology Adoption, and Aggregate Energy Efficiency*. Washington, DC: Resour. Future
39. Jaffe A, Stavins R. 1994. The energy paradox and the diffusion of conservation technology. *Resour. Energy Econ.* 16:91–122
40. Ellsworth RR. 1983. Subordinate financial policy to corporate strategy. *Harv. Bus. Rev.* 61:170–82
41. Ross M. 1986. Capital budgeting practices of twelve large manufacturers. *Financ. Manag.* (Winter):15–22
42. Fazzari SM, Petersen BC. 1993. Working capital and fixed investment: new evidence on financing constraints. *RAND J. Econ.* 24:328–42
43. Boyd GA, Pang JX. 2000. Estimating the linkage between energy efficiency and productivity. *Energy Policy* 28:289–96
44. Worrell E, Laitner JA, Ruth MB, Finman H. 2003. Productivity benefits of industrial energy efficiency measures. *Energy* 28:1081–98
45. Pandey R. 2002. Energy policy modeling:

agenda for developing countries. *Energy Policy* 30:87–106
46. Edmonds J, Roop JM, Scott MJ. 2000. *Technology and the Economics of Climate Change Policy*. Washington, DC: Pew Cent. Glob. Clim. Change
47. Clarke LE, Weyant, JP. 2002. Modeling induced technological change: an overview. See Ref. 22, pp. 41–92
48. Löschel A. 2002. Technological change in economic models of environmental policy: a Survey. *Ecol. Econ.* 43:105–26
49. Worrell E, Bode JW, De Beer J. 1997. *Analysing Research and Technology Development Strategies: The 'ATLAS' Project, Energy Efficient Technologies in Industry*. Utrecht, Neth.: Dept. Sci. Technol. Soc. Utrecht Univ.
50. Van Vuuren DP, de Vries HJM. 2001. Mitigation scenarios in a world at sustainable development: the role of technology, efficiency and timing. *Clim. Policy* 1:189–210
51. van der Zwaan BCC, Gerlagh R, Klaassen G, Schrattenholzer L. 2002. Endogenous technological change in climate change modeling. *Energy Econ.* 24:1–19
52. Tseng P, Lee J, Kypreos S, Barreto L. 1999. Technology learning and the role of renewable energy in reducing carbon emissions. *Proc. IEA Int. Workshop Technol. Reduce Greenh. Gas Emissions: Eng. Econ. Anal. Conserv. Energy Carbon*, Washington, DC, May 5–7
53. Luciuk D. 1999. *The Price-Independent Trend in Energy Efficiency in Canada and the Potential Influence of Non-Price Policies*. Burnaby, BC: Simon Fraser Univ.
54. Newell R, Jaffe A, Stavins RA. 1999. The induced innovation hypothesis and energy saving technological change. *Q. J. Economics* 114(3):941–75
55. Int. Energy Agency. 2000. *Experience Curves for Energy Technology Policy*. Paris, Fr.: IEA
56. Int. Energy Agency. 2003. Experience curves: a tool for energy policy analysis and design. *Proc. Workshop Exp. Curves: Tool Energy Policy Anal. Design*, Jan. 22–24. Paris, Fr.: IEA
57. Laitner JS, Sanstad AH. 2003. Learning to capture progress on both the demand and the supply side: implications for electric utility investments. *Proc. Workshop Exp. Curves: Tool Energy Policy Anal. Design*, Jan. 22–24. Paris, Fr.: IEA
58. Celikkol P, Stefanou S. 1999. Measuring the impact of price-induced innovation on technological progress: application to the US food processing and distribution sector. *J. Prod. Anal.* 12:135–51
59. Lieberman MB. 1984. The learning curve and pricing in the chemical processing industries. *RAND J. Econ.* 15:213–28
60. Landau R, Rosenberg N. 1994. Innovation in the chemical procession industry. In *Exploring the Black Box: Technology, Economics, and History*, ed. N Rosenberg, pp. 190–202. Cambridge, Cambridge Univ. Press
61. Jarmin RS. 1994. Learning by doing and competition in early rayon industry. *RAND J. Econ.* 25:441–54
62. Yin JZ. 1994. Managing process innovation through incremental improvements: empirical evidence in the petroleum refining industry. *Technol. Forecast. Soc. Change* 47:265–76
63. Gruber H. 1992. The learning curve in the production of semiconductor memory chips. *Appl. Econ.* 24:885–94
64. Bahk BH, Gort M. 1993. Decomposing learning by doing in new plants. *J. Polit. Econ.* 101:561–83
65. Nelson RR, ed. 1982. *Government and Technical Progress*. New York, NY: Pergamon
66. Cohen LR, Noll RG. 1994. Privatizing public research. *Sci. Am.* 271(3):72–77
67. Goulder LH, Schneider SH. 1999. Induced technological change and the attractiveness of CO_2 abatement policies. *Resour. Energy Econ.* 21:211–53
68. Messner S. 1997. Endogenized technological learning in energy systems models. *J. Evol. Econ.* 7:291–313

69. Luiten EEM. 2001. *Beyond energy efficiency*. PhD thesis. Utrecht Univ. Utrecht, Neth.
70. De Beer J, Worrell E, Blok K. 1998. Future technologies for energy efficient iron and steelmaking. *Annu. Rev. Energy Environ.* 23:123–205
71. Martin N, Worrell E, Ruth M, Price L, Elliott RN, et al. 2000. *Emerging Energy-Efficient Industrial Technologies*. Berkeley, CA/Washington, DC: Lawrence Berkeley Natl. Lab./Am. Council Energy-Efficient Econ. (LBNL-46990)
72. Gielen DJ. 1999. *Materialising dematerialisation—integrated energy and materials system engineering for greenhouse gas emission mitigation*. PhD thesis. Delft Univ. Technol. Delft, Neth.
73. Howarth RB, Sanstad AH. 1995. Discount rates and energy efficiency. *Contemp. Econ. Policy* 13:101–9
74. Ross MH, Thimmapuram P, Fisher RE, Maciorowski W. 1993. *Long-term Industrial Energy Forecasting (LIEF) Model (18-Sector Version)*. (ANL/EIAS/TM-95.) Argonne, IL: Argonne Natl. Lab.
75. Blok K, de Groot H, Luiten EEM, Rietbergen MG. 2002. *The Effectiveness of Policy Instruments for Energy Efficiency Improvement in Firms*, Utrecht, Neth.: Dept. Sci. Technol. Soc., Utrecht Univ.
76. Bernow S, Rudkevich A, Ruth M, Peters I. 1998. *A Pragmatic CGE Model for Assessing the Influence of Model Structure and Assumptions in Climate Change Policy Analysis*. Boston, MA: Tellus Inst.
77. Peters I, Bernow S, Cleetus R, Laitner J, Rudkevich A, Ruth M. 2002. The Influence of Model Structure and Assumptions in Climate Change Policy Analysis: Explorations with a Pragmatic CGE Model. In *Critical Issues In International Environmental Taxation*, LA Kreiser, ed, pp. 503–22. Riverwoods, IL: CCH Inc.
78. Koopmans C, Velde D. 2001. Bridging the energy efficiency gap: using bottom-up information in a top-down energy demand model. *Energy Econ.* 23:57–75
79. Hanson D, Laitner J. 2000. An economic growth model of investment, energy savings, and CO_2 reductions. *Proc. Air Waste Manag. Assoc. 93rd Annu. Meet.*, Salt Lake City, UT. June
80. Hanson D, Laitner J. 2000. Energy-economy interactions revisited within a comprehensive sectoral model. In *Energy 2000: The Beginning of a New Millennium*, ed. P. Catania, B Golchert, C Zhou, pp. 742–46. Lancaster, PA: Balaban/Technomic
81. Howarth RB, Andersson B. 1993. Market barriers to energy efficiency. *Energy Econ.* 15:262–72
82. Stoft SE. 1995. The economics of conserved-energy "supply" curves. *Energy J.* 16:109–37
83. Blumstein C, Stoft S. 1995. Technical efficiency, production functions, and conservation supply curves. *Energy Policy* 23:765–68
84. Huntington HG. 1994. Been top down so long it looks like bottom up. *Energy Policy* 22:833–39
85. Banks N. 1999. Causal models of household decisions to choose the energy efficient alternative: the role of values, knowledge, attitudes and identity. In *Energy Efficiency and CO_2 reduction: the Dimensions of the Social Challenge. Proc. 1999 Summer Study of the European Council for an Energy Efficient Economy*, Part 2, Pap. (III. 24). Paris, Fr.: Agence Environ. Maitrise Energy (ADEME)
86. Bandura A. 1986. *Social Foundations of Thought and Action—A Social Cognitive Theory*. Englewood Cliffs, NJ: Prentice-Hall
87. Shove E. 1998. Gaps, barriers and conceptual chasms: theories of technology transfer and energy in buildings. *Energy Policy* 26:1105–12
88. Malik F. 1992. *Strategie des Managements Komplexer Systeme—Ein Beitrag zur Management-Kybernetik Evolutionärer Systeme*. Bern, Switz.: Haupt. 4th ed.

89. Dar-El E. 2000. *Human Learning: From learning Curves to Learning Organizations*. Dordrecht, Neth.: Kluwer Acad.
90. Senge P. 1994. *The Fifth Discipline—The Art and Practice of the Learning Organization*. New York, NY: Currency Doubleday
91. Argyris C. 1977. Double loop learning in organizations. *Harv. Bus. Rev.* 55(5):115–25
92. Cooper W, Seiford L. 1999. *Data Envelopment Analysis: A Comprehensive Text with Models, Applications, References, and DEA-Solver Software*. Dordrecht, Neth.: Kluwer Acad.
93. Rogers EM. 1995. *The Diffusion of Innovations*. New York, NY: Free Press
94. Jovanovic B, Nyarko Y. 1996. Learning by doing and the choice of technology. *Econometrica* 64:1299–1310
95. Kleit A, Terrell D. 2001. Measuring potential efficiency gains from deregulation of electricity generation: a Bayesian approach. *Rev. Econ. Stat.* 83:523–30
96. Weidlich W, Braun M. 1992. The master equation approach to nonlinear economics. *J. Evol. Econ.* 2:233–65
97. Erdmann G. 1990. Evolutionäre Ökonomik als Theorie ungleichgewichtiger Phasenübergänge. In *Studien zur Evolutorischen Ökonomik*, ed. U Witt, 195:135–61. Berlin, Ger.: Schriften Vereins Socialpolitik
98. Dosi G. 1988. The nature of the innovative process. In *Technical Change and Economic Theory*, ed. G. Dosi, C. Freeman, R. Nelson, G. Silverberg, L. Soete, pp. 77–93. London, UK: Pinter
99. DeCanio S, Dibble C, Amir-Atefi K. 2000. The importance of organizational structure for the adoption of innovations. *Manag. Sci.* 46:1285–99
100. DeCanio S, Dibble C, Amir-Atefi K. 2001. Organizational structure and the behavior of firms: implications for integrated assessment. *Clim. Change* 48:487–514
101. Bower J, Bunn DW. 2000. A model-based comparison of pool and bilateral market mechanisms for electricity trading. *Energy J.* 3:1–29
102. North MJ. 2002. Multi-agent social and organizational modeling of electric power and natural gas markets. *Comput. Math. Organ. Theory J.* 7:331–37
103. North MJ. 2001. Agent-based infrastructure modeling. *Soc. Sci. Comput. Rev.* 20:307–21
104. Beck MB, Ed. 2002. *Environmental Foresight and Models: A Manifesto*. Amsterdam, Neth./New York, NY: Elsevier
105. Gillissen M, Opschoor JB, Farla JCM, Blok K. 1995. *Energy Conservation and Investment Behaviour of Firms*. Amsterdam, Neth.: Dep. Environ. Econ., Free Univ.
106. Jochem E, Sathaye J, Bouille D, eds. *Society, Behaviour, and Climate Change Mitigation*. Dordrecht, Neth.: Kluwer Acad.

ENERGY MANAGEMENT AND GLOBAL HEALTH*

Majid Ezzati,[1] Robert Bailis,[2] Daniel M. Kammen,[2] Tracey Holloway,[3] Lynn Price,[4] Luis A. Cifuentes,[5] Brendon Barnes,[6] Akanksha Chaurey,[7] and Kiran N. Dhanapala[8]

[1]*Harvard School of Public Health, Harvard University, Boston, Massachusetts 02115; email: mezzati@hsph.harvard.edu*
[2]*Energy and Resources Group, University of California, Berkeley, California 94720; email: rbailis@socrates.berkeley.edu, kammen@berkeley.edu*
[3]*Center for Sustainability and the Global Environment, Gaylord Nelson Institute for Environmental Studies, University of Wisconsin, Madison, Wisconsin 53726; email: taholloway@wisc.edu*
[4]*E.O. Lawrence Berkeley National Laboratory, Berkeley, California 94720; email: lkprice@lbl.gov*
[5]*Industrial and Systems Engineering Department, P. Universidad Catolica de Chile, Santiago 6904411, Chile; email: lac@ing.puc.cl*
[6]*Medical Research Council of South Africa, Houghton 2041, South Africa; email: bbarnes@mrc.ac.za*
[7]*Energy-Environment Technology Division, The Energy and Resources Institute, New Delhi 110003, India; email: akanksha@teri.res.in*
[8]*Environmental & Natural Resource Economics, Division of Resource Management, West Virginia University, Morgantown, West Virginia 26506; email: kdhanapa@wvu.edu*

■ **Abstract** Energy and energy technologies have a central role in social and economic development at all scales, from household and community to regional and national. Among its welfare effects, energy is closely linked with public health both positively and negatively, the latter through environmental pollution and degradation. We review the current research on how energy use and energy technologies influence public health, emphasizing the risks associated with indoor and ambient air pollution from energy use, and the links between the local and global environmental health impacts of energy use. This review illustrates that, despite their large public health implications, most energy policies and programs in the developing world are fundamentally treated as components of overall economic development, without explicit assessment of their health benefits or hazards. Closer integration of health in energy management can facilitate the development of policies and programs that increase welfare and minimize negative health outcomes. Renewable energy technologies are used as an example of how an integrated energy-health approach can be used in policy analysis and formulation.

---

*The U.S. Government has the right to retain a nonexclusive, royalty-free license in and to any copyright covering this paper.

CONTENTS

INTRODUCTION	384
THE ENVIRONMENTAL HEALTH IMPLICATIONS OF ENERGY SOURCE AND TECHNOLOGY	387
Ambient Air Pollution	387
Indoor Air Pollution	390
Local-Global Linkages	396
SOCIAL DIMENSIONS OF ENERGY-HEALTH LINKAGES	399
Energy, Poverty, and Health	399
Energy, Gender, and Health	402
ENERGY MANAGEMENT AND PUBLIC HEALTH	403
Technology Options	403
Policy Instruments	404
CONCLUSIONS	407
APPENDIX 1	408
Integrated Environmental Strategies for Air Pollution and GHG Reduction in Chile	408
APPENDIX 2	411
Integrating Energy, Environment, and Public Health Policies: Charcoal in Kenya	411

INTRODUCTION

Energy and energy systems have a central role in social and economic development and human welfare at all scales, from household and community to regional and national (1). Among its various welfare effects, energy is closely linked with public health. Some of the effects of energy on health and welfare are direct: With abundant energy, more food or more frequent meals can be prepared; food can be refrigerated, increasing the types of food items that are consumed and reducing food contamination; water pumps can provide more water and eliminate the need for water storage leading to contamination or increased exposure to disease vectors such as mosquitoes and snails; and water can be disinfected by boiling or by using technologies such as radiation. Other effects of energy on public health are mediated through more proximal determinants of health and disease. Abundant energy can lead to increased irrigation, agricultural productivity, and access to food and nutrition. Access to energy can also increase small-scale income generation activities, such as processing of agricultural commodities (e.g., producing refined oil from oil seeds, roasting coffee, and drying and preserving fruits and meats) and production of crafts. The ability to control lighting and heating allows education or economic activities to be shielded from daily or seasonal environmental constraints such as light (Figure 1), temperature, precipitation, or wind. Time and other economic resources spent on collecting and/or transporting fuel can be used for other household needs if energy infrastructure and access is improved. Energy availability for transportation increases access to health and education facilities and allows increased economic

Figure 1 Energy is essential for many aspects of development, such as education, with important public health implications. (Photograph by A. Fayemi, Nigeria.)

activity by facilitating the transportation of goods and services to and from markets. Energy for telecommunications technology (radio, television, telephone, or internet) provides increased access to information useful for health, education, or economic purposes. Provision of energy to rural and urban health facilities allows increased delivery and coverage of various health services and interventions, such as tests and treatments, better storage of medicine and vaccines, disinfection of medical equipment by boiling or radiation, and more frequent and efficient health system encounters through mobile clinics or longer working hours. In fact, although the dominant view of development-energy-health linkages has been that improvements in energy and health are outcomes of socioeconomic development (e.g., the "energy ladder" framework discussed below), it has even been argued that access to higher quality energy sources and technologies can initiate a chain of demographic, health, and development outcomes by changing the household structure and socioeconomic relationships. For example, in addition to increased opportunities for food and income production, reduced infant mortality—as a result of transition to cleaner fuels or increased coverage of vaccination with availability of refrigerators in rural clinics—may initiate a process of "demographic transition" to low-mortality and low-fertility populations (2). Such a transition has historically been followed with further improvements in maternal and child health and increased female participation in the labor markets and other economic activities.

The effects of energy on public welfare and health are also closely related to the source of energy and type of conversion technology utilized (3). Harvesting energy from hydropower and biomass resources can affect the local environment through soil erosion and disruption of the water system or soil nutrient cycle. This may reduce agricultural productivity, limit access to water and energy, change local vegetation, and alter disease vector dynamics—all with important health consequences. Energy generation from combustion of biomass or fossil fuels, even using best currently available technologies, results in a large number of pollutants that are known or potential hazards to human health and ecological systems. Fuel extraction and combustion both contribute to the stock of atmospheric greenhouse gases (GHGs) that lead to climate change, with potential health implications (4). Nuclear energy, which does not have combustion byproducts, raises concerns about reactor safety as well as transport and storage of nuclear waste. Therefore, although energy has numerous benefits for social and economic development and public health, the process of energy production can result in short- and long-term negative effects on environmental determinants of health (1, 5–9). We review the current research on how energy use and energy technologies influence public health, with emphasis on the risks associated with indoor and ambient air pollution, which are two important routes for the negative effects of energy use on health (Figure 2, see color insert). We also consider the links between local and global environmental impacts of energy use.

Currently, approximately 65% of all global primary energy is consumed in the industrialized countries that make up the Organization for Economic Cooperation and Development (OECD) and the former Soviet Union (FSU), with per capita consumption averaging five times that of developing countries (13). Contributions to GHG emissions follow a similar pattern. Per capita energy consumption in North America is more than 25 times that of the poorest nations in sub-Saharan Africa, 20 times the per capita consumption in India, and 10 times that in China (13). Global carbon emissions are approximately one metric ton of carbon per year per person (tC/person-year). Per capita emissions in the United States are more than 5 tC/year compared to approximately 0.6 tC/year in developing countries as a whole, and they are less than 0.2 tC/year in the 50 developing nations with lowest emissions (14). Coupled with low levels of per capita energy consumption, fuels and energy conversion technologies currently used in developing nations result in much higher exposure to local pollution (15). Therefore, from an environmental health perspective, energy options in developing countries are of notable importance because of lack of access to clean energy sources and technologies. Further, the most rapid future growth in energy consumption is expected to take place in developing countries, as a result of both population growth and economic development (5, 8, 16). This review primarily focuses on developing countries, where much of negative health consequences arising from limited access to clean energy are concentrated. We nonetheless emphasize that many aspects of energy use and its environmental consequences are linked between the developing and industrialized worlds.

Although we describe energy as a source of pollution and disease in detail, we emphasize that energy is an instrument for development and for improving public health as described above. The challenge of sustainable development policy is therefore two sided: providing energy for human development and minimizing its negative effects. Throughout the review, we also identify knowledge gaps that should motivate new data collection and research. The next section discusses energy-environment-health linkages, including ambient and indoor air pollution with emphasis on the linkages between household or local and global impacts of energy use. The third section focuses on two important social dimensions of energy and health linkages: poverty and gender. We then use renewable energy technologies as an example of how an integrated energy-health approach may be used in policy analysis and formulations to reduce energy poverty while minimizing the negative consequences of energy use.

THE ENVIRONMENTAL HEALTH IMPLICATIONS OF ENERGY SOURCE AND TECHNOLOGY

This section discusses energy-environment-health linkages, with emphasis on the risks associated with indoor and ambient air pollution, which are two important routes for the negetaive effects of energy use on health (Figure 2). We also consider the linkages between household or local and global impacts of energy use, including global climate change. The ecological effects of energy extraction, including change in soil and vegetation dynamics as a result of biomass harvesting, construction of dams, or pollution, are also important effects of energy use but are not reviewed because of the central focus on public health.

Ambient Air Pollution

The burning of oil, coal, natural gas, and biomass results in emissions of complex mixtures of gases and particles, which spread in the atmosphere from the original emissions source. These combustion products can reduce visibility, produce acid rain (which can damage plants and erode buildings and other objects), and cause or exacerbate multiple diseases over short and long time periods. Although urban biomass use is still significant in many regions of the world, globally urban air pollution is largely and increasingly the result of the combustion of fossil fuels for transport, electricity generation, and domestic use (17–19). It is likely that the health effects of ambient air pollution are a result of the complex mixture of combustion products. Negative health effects have nonetheless been most closely correlated with three species of pollutants in epidemiological studies: fine particulate matter, sulfur dioxide, and tropospheric ozone (18, 20). Toxic chemicals, such as lead and other metals, which are present in some fuels, also have significant health effects (Figure 2).

Particulate matter (PM, also known as aerosols) is produced as a primary product of combustion processes (such as diesel soot) as well as a "secondary species" when gases react to form particles (e.g., sulfate particles formed from the burning of coal and other sulfur-containing fuels). Aerosols are commonly placed in several categories, including black carbon, organic carbon, sulfates, nitrates, dust, and even sea salt. The composition of PM depends strongly on its source, and a single particle may contain a combination of species. Although the role of the chemical composition and physical characteristics of PM in disease causation and exacerbation are the subjects of ongoing research, there is general agreement that particle size is a strong determinant in its health impact (21). The class of PM below 2.5 microns in aerodynamic diameter ($PM_{2.5}$) is the focus of much health-related inquiry because these small particles can penetrate deep into the lung (18, 20, 22, 23).

The consequences of exposure to high levels of ambient air pollution were observed in the mid-twentieth century when cities in Europe and the United States experienced air pollution episodes, such as the 1952 London fog, that resulted in many excess deaths and hospital admissions (24). Subsequent clean air legislation, regulation, and technological advances have reduced ambient air pollution in many cities, especially in higher-income countries.[1] Recent epidemiological studies, using sensitive designs and analyses, have identified health effects of combustion-derived air pollution even at the low ambient concentrations typical of western European and North American cities (21, 27). At the same time, the populations of the rapidly expanding megacities of Asia and Latin America are increasingly exposed to levels of ambient air pollution that rival and often exceed those experienced in industrialized countries in the first half of the twentieth century (18, 28) (Figure 3).

Although urban ambient air pollution has been commonly defined at the level of a city in most epidemiological studies, recent research has illustrated the variation of exposure to this risk and the associated health effects in considerably smaller microenvironments (27, 29–32). This variability occurs because (*a*) the ambient concentrations, composition, and dispersion of pollutants depend on the type and location of pollution source(s) (e.g., use of diesel fuels and mobile or stationary sources), meteorological factors (e.g., wind direction and speed), and urban physical characteristics; (*b*) indoor concentrations in buildings and vehicles as a result of ambient pollution depend on the location, type, and structure of indoor environments; and (*c*) individuals and groups spend various amounts of time in different indoor and outdoor urban microenvironments because of the location of residential neighborhoods and occupational and commercial activities (33). Exposure patterns may also differ by pollutant type. For example, fine particles ($PM_{2.5}$) and ozone tend to be more homogenously distributed over large urban or regional areas than ultrafine particles, nitrogen dioxide and polycyclic aromatic hydrocarbons (PAH), emitted from mobile sources (29).

---

[1]The relationship between economic development and air pollution in many societies has followed a pattern of initial increase in pollution followed by subsequent decline at higher income levels. This inverted-U relationship, referred to as an Environmental Kuznets Curve (EKC), has been used for policy formulation (25), although a number of methodological and conceptual questions have been raised about its validity and generalizability (26).

ENERGY MANAGEMENT AND GLOBAL HEALTH   389

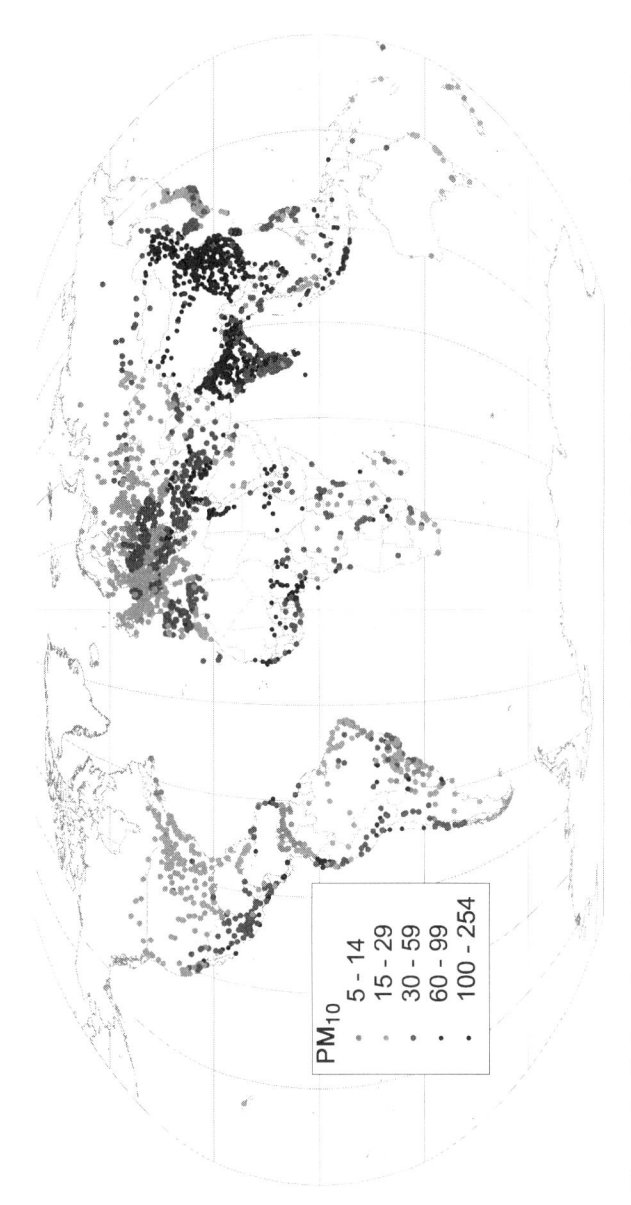

Figure 3 Estimated annual average concentrations of PM$_{10}$ (particulates below 10 microns in aerodynamic diameter) in cities with populations of 100,000 or more and national capitals in 2000. [Figure from (18).]

TABLE 1 Mortality and burden of disease as a result of exposure to ambient air pollution in 2000 (10, 11)

Regional level of development (defined by the World Health Organization)	Death in children under 5 years of age	Adult deaths	Burden of diseases (thousands of DALYs)[a]
High-mortality developing (38% of global population)	18,000	202,000	2,346
Lower-mortality developing (40% of global population)	7,000	419,000	3,095
Demographically and economically developed (22% of global population)	1,000	153,000	961

[a]Burden of disease is a measure of loss of healthy life caused by premature mortality and morbidity. It is expressed in disability-adjusted life years (DALYs) (12). In the year 2000, there were a total of 1.46 billion DALYs lost in the world from premature mortality and nonfatal health outcomes.

Many of the epidemiological studies on the relationship between ambient air pollution and health, especially studies on effects of long-term exposure, have been conducted at the relatively low concentrations observed in North American and European cities. In addition to difficulties in measuring or estimating exposure, quantifying health effects at high pollution levels in many developing country cities has required extrapolation of the concentration-response relationship beyond its observed range, resulting in significant uncertainty (18). Estimates of global mortality as a result of exposure to ambient urban air pollution are provided in Table 1.

Important research themes that would allow more systematic use of technological and regulatory instruments for reducing the health consequences of ambient air pollution include

- the role of particle composition and size distribution on the incidence or severity of various diseases;
- models and data to estimate the spatial distribution of pollution within individual cities or regions and its effects on population exposure;
- the health effects of sustained exposure at high concentrations typical of many cities in developing countries; and
- the interactions of ambient air pollution and other risk factors, such as indoor air pollution, smoking, occupational exposures, and nutrition.

Indoor Air Pollution

The relationship between household energy, indoor air pollution, and health has been reviewed in a number of recent works (34, 36, 37, 39, 46). Globally, almost three billion people rely on biomass (wood, charcoal, crop residues, and dung) and coal as their primary source of domestic energy (8, 19) (Figure 4). Biomass

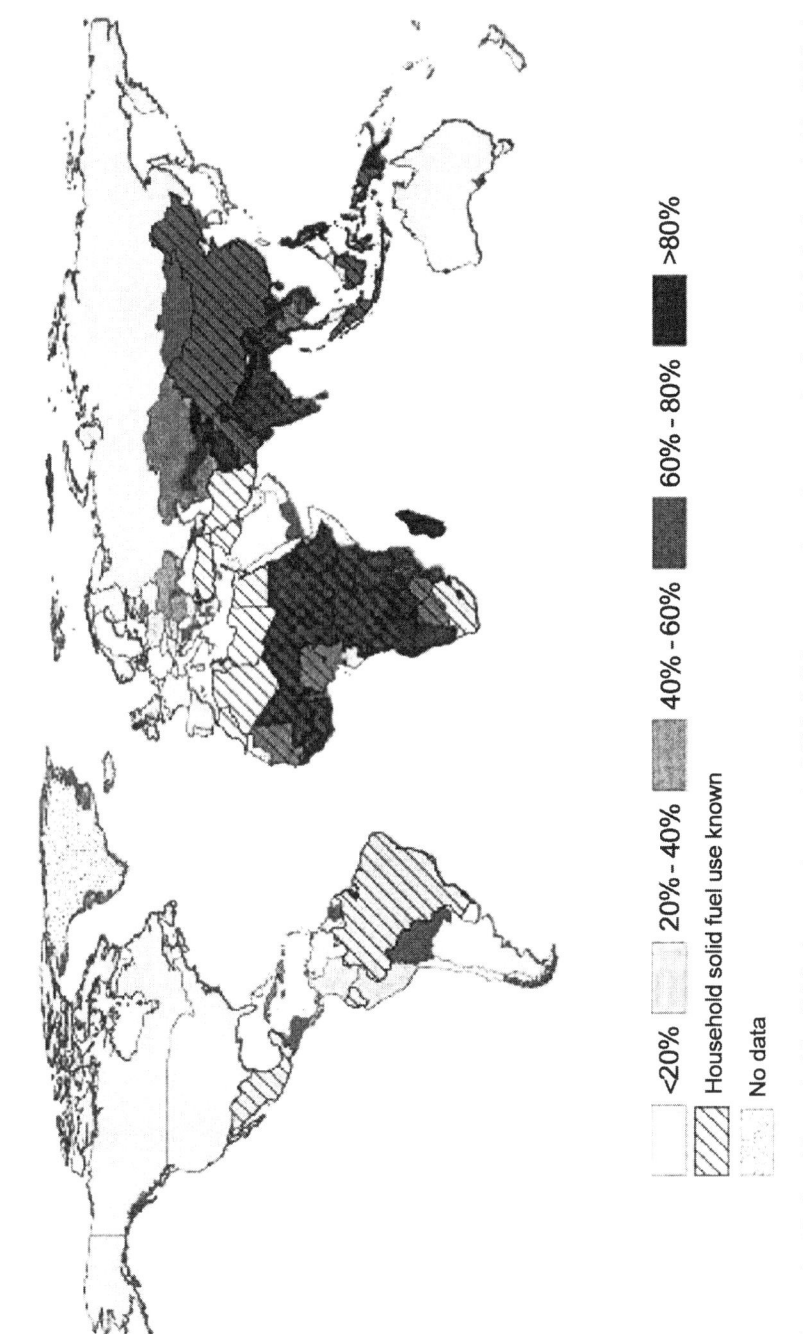

Figure 4 National household solid fuel use estimates in 2000. Solid patterns show the countries for which the household solid fuel use estimates are predictions from a model. [From (39).]

accounts for more than 50% of domestic energy in many developing countries and for as much as 95% in some lower income ones (8, 38).

Hundreds of harmful substances, in the form of gases, liquids (suspended droplets), or solids (suspended particulates), are emitted during the burning of biomass or coal in particularly large quantities when burned in open or poorly ventilated stoves. These pollutants include carbon monoxide (CO), nitrogen dioxide, particles in the respirable range (2 to 10 microns in aerodynamic diameter), and other organic matter (predominantly composed of polycyclic aromatic hydrocarbons and other volatile organic compounds, such as benzene and formaldehyde) (9, 40, 41). Combustion of coal may release oxides of sulfur, arsenic, and fluoride in addition to the above pollutants (42). Monitoring pollution and personal exposures in biomass-burning households has shown concentrations many times higher than those in industrialized countries. The latest National Ambient Air Quality Standards of the U.S. Environmental Protection Agency, for instance, required the daily average concentration of PM_{10} to be below 150 $\mu g/m^3$ (annual average below 50 $\mu g/m^3$). In contrast, typical 24-hour average concentration of PM_{10} in homes using biofuels may range from 200 to 5000 $\mu g/m^3$ or more throughout the year, depending on the type of fuel, stove, and housing (9, 15, 43–46). It has been estimated that approximately 80% of total global population exposure to airborne particulate matter occurs indoors in developing nations (15, 43).

Exposure to indoor air pollution from the combustion of solid fuels has been implicated, with varying degrees of evidence, as a causal agent of several diseases including acute respiratory infections, chronic obstructive pulmonary disease, lung cancer (from coal smoke), asthma, nasopharyngeal and laryngeal cancer, tuberculosis, low birth weight, and diseases of the eye, such as cataract and blindness (34, 46–48). Most current epidemiological studies on the health effects of indoor air pollution exposure in developing countries have focused on the first three of the above diseases (34, 46). Although detailed epidemiological and toxicological research on the health effects of exposure to indoor smoke from solid fuels has only recently begun, there is increasing consensus of its important role in burden of disease, especially among the poor and marginalized groups. Estimates of global mortality from exposure to indoor solid fuel smoke are shown in Table 2.

As a result of the magnitude of the burden of disease associated with indoor smoke and its unequal global distribution, attention of the research and policy communities has shifted to design and dissemination of interventions (36, 37, 49). The concentrations of different pollutants at locations inside the house depend on energy technology (stove-fuel combination), house design (e.g., the size and construction materials of the house, the arrangement of rooms, and the number of windows) (50, 51), and stove use behavior (e.g., whether fuel is dried before combustion). In addition to pollution levels, exposure depends on time-activity budgets of individual household members (e.g., time spent inside or near the stove and direct participation in cooking tasks) (50, 51). Therefore, reducing exposure to indoor air pollution from solid fuels can be achieved through modifications in fuel

TABLE 2 Mortality and burden of disease as a result of exposure to indoor air pollution from solid fuels in 2000 for acute respiratory infections, chronic obstructive pulmonary disease, and lung cancer (10, 11)

Regional level of development (defined by the World Health Organization)	Death in children under 5 years of age	Adult deaths	Burden of diseases (thousands of DALYs)[a]
High-mortality developing (38% of global population)	808,000	232,000	30,392
Lower-mortality developing (40% of global population)	89,000	468,000	7,595
Demographically and economically developed (22% of global population)	13,000	9,000	550

[a]Burden of disease is a measure of loss of healthy life from premature mortality and morbidity. It is expressed in disability-adjusted life years (DALYs) (12).

type and energy conversion technology, housing and ventilation, and behavioral factors, such as fuel preparation and individual time-activity budgets (36, 49).

Recent analyses have shown a complex range of energy-environment-behavior interactions in determining exposure to indoor air pollution (36), including whether energy is used for cooking versus heating. Cooking is often done in shorter time intervals and possibly in confined areas, with a subset of household members consistently close to the source of pollution. Further, emissions from open biomass stoves fluctuate over short time intervals, with emission peaks occurring when fuel is added or moved, the stove is lit, the cooking pot is placed on or removed from the fire, or food is stirred (45, 50) (Figure 5a, see color insert). Because household members who cook—typically females—are closest to the stove at such times, peak emissions contribute significantly to the exposure of female household members (Figure 5b) (50). With such exposure patterns, people who cook gain disproportionately small benefits from improved housing ventilation compared to those who are further away from the stove (51, 52). Interventions using cleaner fuels or stoves that reduce peak emissions, on the other hand, would provide comparably larger benefits to female household members (52). Heating, on the other hand, by definition involves longer hours of energy use for a larger area and a relatively similar distance to the energy source for most household members. In contrast to direct inhalation during cooking and heating, bioaccumulation of trace elements (e.g., arsenic and fluorine) in food dried and stored over the stove for long durations is an important route of exposure to these pollutants in parts of China (Figures 6a, see color insert, and 6b) (42). In this case, alternative food drying techniques and behavioral change (e.g., washing food before consumption) can reduce exposure and health hazards, such as arsenic poisoning and dental or skeletal fluorosis.

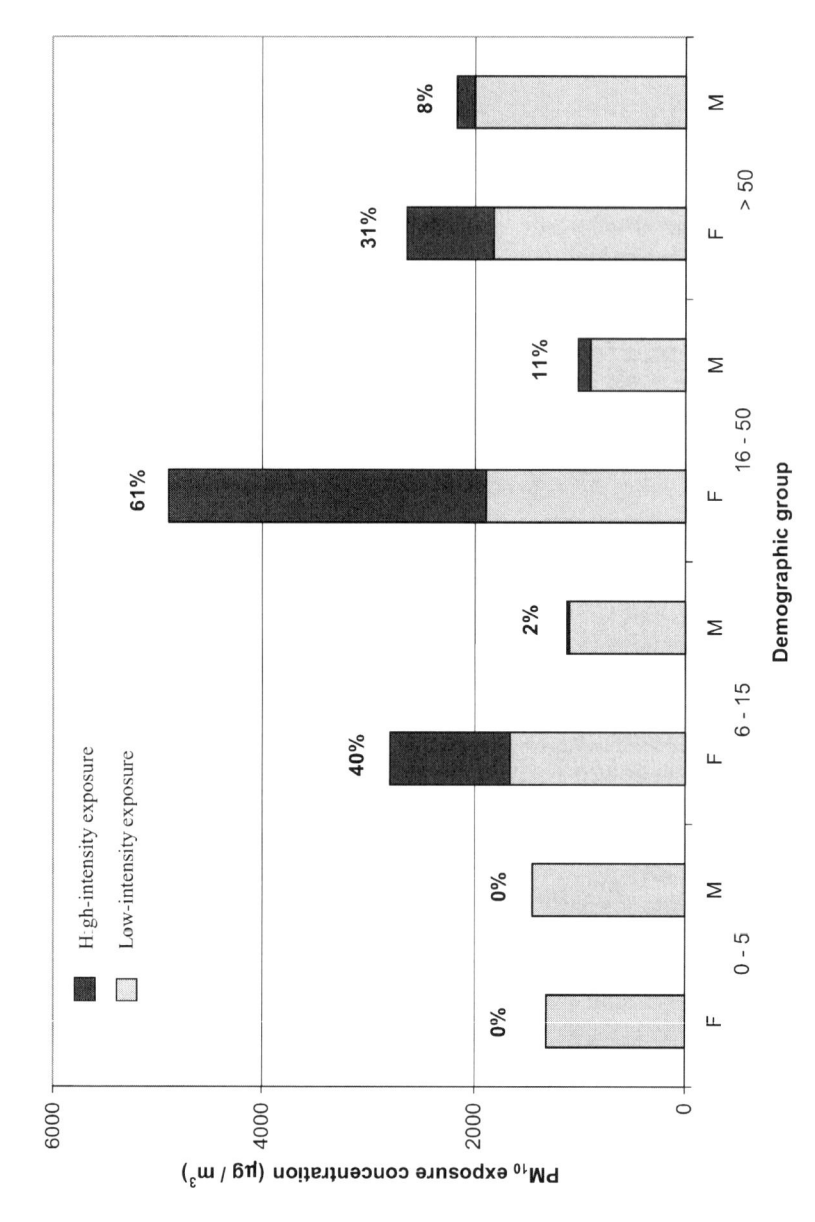

Figure 5b For each demographic group the total height of the column is the group's average exposure concentration, divided into average for high- and low-intensity components. The high-intensity component is a result of exposure to peak emissions when household members are close to the stove. [Figure from (50).]

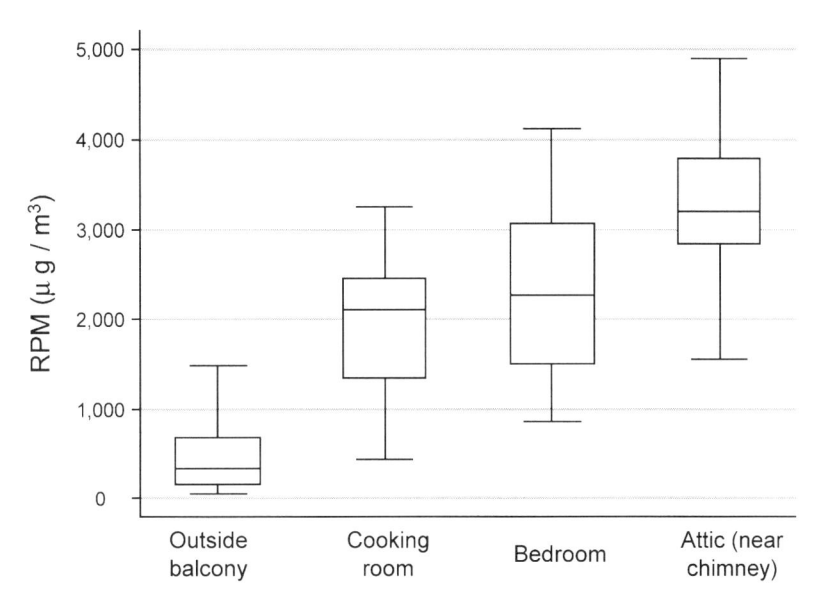

Figure 6b Pollution levels are highest near the chimney where food is dried (42). The box plot shows a summary of the distribution of the measurements of respirable particles (RPM) for different households and measurement days. The lower and upper sides of the rectangle show the 25th and 75th percentiles and therefore enclose the middle half of the distribution. The middle line, which divides the rectangle into two, is the median. [Figure from (53).]

To date, most research on indoor air pollution interventions has focused on the energy source with emphasis on improved stoves and fuels, which are believed to provide more affordable options in the near term than a complete shift to nonsolid fuels. Initial improved stove efforts, however, were often marked by a lack of detailed data on stove performance.[2] Efficiencies and emissions, for example, were often measured in controlled environments with technical experts using the stoves under conditions very dissimilar to those in the field (44, 57, 58). Beyond technical performance, some of the issues surrounding successful implementation of programs for technology dissemination have been discussed using a limited number of available case studies (49, 58–63). Some important areas for future research include the following:

---

[2]The initial emphasis of research on household energy in developing countries was on environmental impacts of biomass use, such as impacts on deforestation and desertification, resulting in a level of zeal for increased efficiency with expert perspectives often disconnected from the local perceptions of fuel scarcity and improved efficiency (44, 54–58). The public health benefits from reduction in exposure to indoor smoke as well as the reduction in carbon emissions became the subject of attention soon after. This double-dividend—improving public health while reducing adverse environmental impacts—focused a great deal of effort on the design and dissemination of improved stoves (55, 59, 60).

- The relative contributions of energy technology (stove-fuel combination, including multi-stove and multi-fuel scenarios), housing characteristics (such as the size and material of the house, the number of windows, and arrangement of rooms), and behavioral factors (such as the amount of time spent indoors or near the cooking area) affecting exposure. This should also include an assessment of the differential roles of cooking and heating to exposure and their seasonal variations.
- The exposure-response relationship, along a continuum of exposure levels for diseases affected by indoor air pollution. This would allow the health benefits of interventions with partial exposure reduction to be evaluated.
- Longitudinal monitoring of both technical performance of interventions and the socioeconomic and behavioral determinants of their adoption and continued use.

Local-Global Linkages

Air pollution transport on regional to intercontinental scales is emerging as an important component of air quality and health (68). Sophisticated atmospheric models allow estimating the flow of pollution between different countries or regions (69, 70), and satellite, aircraft, and ground-based measurement systems have tracked plumes of particles and gases moving across the Pacific and Atlantic. Figure 7, see color insert, presents model estimates of ozone dispersal from North America, Europe, and Asia (71), illustrating the extent of regional impacts even for a single pollutant.

GHGs and pollutants that affect health are both an outcome of processes of incomplete combustion, creating close linkages among the health and global environmental consequences of energy use.[3] A number of works have also considered environmental effects, including GHG emissions, from household energy use in developing countries (72–78). Under optimal conditions, combustion of biomass, which is essentially a hydrocarbon fuel with a few trace elements, results almost entirely in the emission of water vapor and carbon dioxide (CO_2). As a result, if biomass is harvested in a sustainable way so that long-term stocks of biomass are not depleted and if biomass is burned under ideal combustion conditions, it is effectively GHG neutral.[4] We can therefore identify two critical factors that

---

[3]Global climate change and the associated shifts in both the mean and variance of meteorological variables, such as temperature and precipitation, will undoubtedly affect public health in many societies and geographical areas (4). Treating climate change as a risk factor in the same way as ambient and indoor air pollution described above, however, masks the complex socioeconomic, physical, and ecological determinants of health that mediate and modulate the climate-health relationship, especially as these other factors also change over long timescales due to economic and demographic development and technological innovation (64–67).

[4]This is not the case for coal, which is a fossil fuel with extensive GHG implications because its stock cannot be replaced in the same way as biomass.

affect the extent of GHG emissions from biomass energy: the sustainability of the biomass harvest and the mode of biomass combustion.

The issue of sustainable biomass harvesting is important both from the perspective of carbon stocks and flows and more importantly from the perspective of welfare of those households that rely on biomass for their energy purposes, as discussed elsewhere (54, 73, 75, 76, 79). Under conditions of incomplete combustion typical of most household level technologies in developing countries, hundreds of gaseous and aerosolized compounds are emitted in addition to CO_2 and water vapor (1, 9). Although CO_2 is the most commonly discussed GHG, particularly in fossil-fuel-based systems, it is the non-CO_2 GHGs that are more relevant in assessing GHG emissions from biomass combustion. This is because under a system of sustainable fuel use, CO_2 released by combustion is removed from the atmosphere by future plant growth. However, non-CO_2 GHGs are not absorbed by photosynthesis and remain in the atmosphere despite new biomass growth (80). These non-CO_2 GHGs (e.g., methane) have a greater warming effect than CO_2 on a molar basis (81).

Emissions of GHGs for a number of developing country household energy technologies (stove-fuel combinations) have been calculated using measurements or estimates of various pollutants (CO_2, methane, CO, and nonmethane hydrocarbons), with examples presented in Figure 8. In Figure 8, the height of each bar shows the average emissions of each pollutant per unit of energy. The lines show the sum of non-CO_2 GHGs (squares) and sum of all GHGs, including CO_2 (circles). For biomass fuels, the former represents fuels that are harvested in a sustainable bioenergy cycle, so that biomass stocks are not depleted over time, and CO_2 may be omitted from the calculation of net global warming effect, whereas the latter is applicable if stocks of biomass are fully depleted. Because fossil fuels do not allow for CO_2 replacement, the accounting of GHGs must always include CO_2 and the non-CO_2 line is omitted for these fuels. As seen in Figure 8, both liquified petroleum gas (LPG) and kerosene have energy-based emissions that are comparable to, if not lower than, the emissions from renewable biofuels, and these emmissions are far lower than the emissions from biofuels when they are not used renewably. This result implies that, given current combustion technology and user behavior, a shift to kerosene and LPG can reduce exposure to indoor air pollution without additional GHG emissions (82). Significant increase in the usage of kerosene and LPG as interventions for reducing the health hazards of indoor air pollution would, however, necessitate considerably larger supplies than are currently accessible by most developing countries and an infrastructure for their delivery (see also Table 3).

The linkages between exposure to air pollution at household and community levels on the one hand and global environmental impacts of energy use on the other may provide an opportunity to simultaneously address multiple energy-environment-health issues (83) (Appendix 1). At the same time, given the lower historical and current per capita emissions of GHGs in developing countries and the prominence of diseases that are affected by poverty and lack of access to clean energy and water, any attempt to reduce global environmental impacts should not jeopardize welfare gains from increased energy used in developing countries (84).

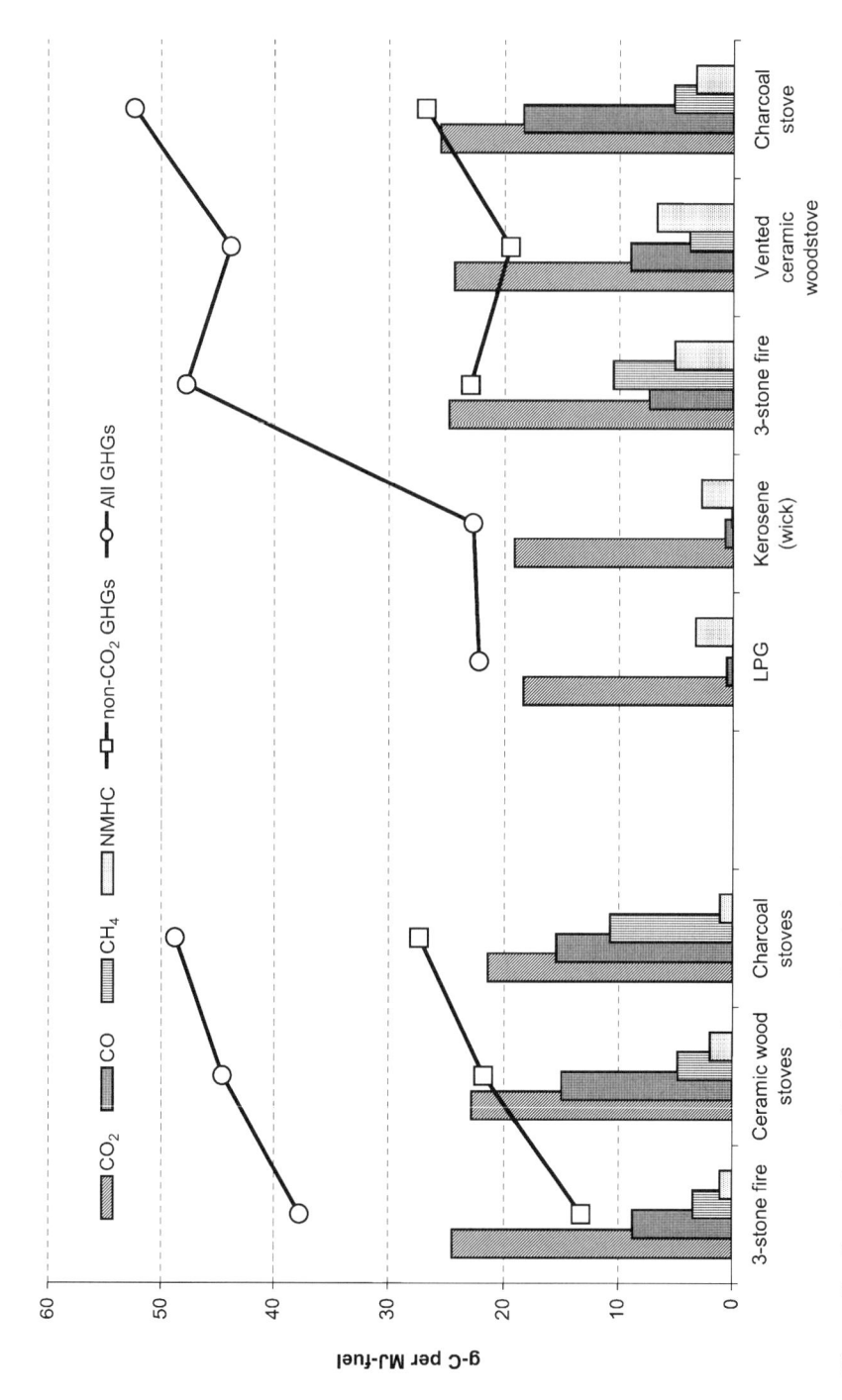

Figure 8 Comparison of energy-based emission factors (weighted by 20-year global warming potential) by stove-fuel category for India and Kenya. The first three stoves (*left*) are estimates from Kenya (78), and the last five (*right*) are estimates from India (77). All biomass stoves used acacia wood or charcoal made from acacia in these measurements. LPG is liquified petroleum gas.

TABLE 3 Household energy choices and barriers [adapted from (94, 102)]

Energy source	Equipment costs	Nature of payments	Nature of Access[a]
Electricity	Very high	Lump sum	Restricted
Bottled gas (liquified petroleum gas, butane, natural gas)	High	Lump sum	Often restricted; bulky and specialized transport
Kerosene	Medium	Small	Often restricted in low income areas
Charcoal	Low	Small	Good; dispersed markets and reliable supplies though prices and supplies can vary seasonally
Fuelwood	Low or zero	Small; zero if gathered	Good; dispersed markets and reliable supplies though prices and supplies can vary seasonally
Crop residues, animal dung	Low or zero	Small; zero if gathered	Variable; depends on local crops and livestock holding; high opportunity cost where residues are used as fodder and/or dung is used as fertilizer

[a]Nature of access refers to ease with which households can choose the fuel if they are willing to pay for it and is determined by physical and institutional infrastructure.

Further, the complex development-energy-environment-health interactions often require more integrated policy analysis than a simple double-dividend approach, including joint implementation of multiple policies (Appendix 2).

SOCIAL DIMENSIONS OF ENERGY-HEALTH LINKAGES

Energy and health both have complex socioeconomic determinants. This section focuses on two important social dimensions of energy and health linkages: poverty and gender. Although considered in separate sections, poverty, gender, and resource use are also interrelated, and women in households of differing socioeconomic status experience the health and welfare implications of energy and energy technology in different forms (85).

Energy, Poverty, and Health

Although the poor in industrialized nations spend a larger fraction of household budget on energy, the poverty-energy links are strongest in low-income countries.

It is well-known that poor households in developing countries have limited access to clean and secure sources of energy, owing to lack of resources and infrastructure (86). For example, in a participatory poverty assessment in South Africa, which aimed to provide an understanding of poverty from the perspective of those who experience it, limited access to clean energy and energy insecurity were identified as indicators of poverty and ill-being by the poor themselves (87).

Figure 9 shows the fraction of households using solid fuels among those living on less than 1 dollar ($) per day, between $1 and $2, and greater than $2 per day in various regions. As seen, except in the two (sub-Saharan) African regions, where solid fuels are by far the dominant source of domestic energy and common among all socioeconomic groups, the poor are considerably more likely to depend on more polluting fuel sources.[5] The poor are also likely to live in parts of cities that are more affected by urban ambient air pollution, such as near highways and industrial sites (88–91). High exposure to pollution as a result of restricted access to clean energy coupled with increased susceptibility from simultaneous exposure to malnutrition, poor water and sanitation, and other risk factors mean that the health consequences of energy are often disproportionately greater on the poor than those in higher income strata (92).

The correlation between poverty and energy source (i.e., fuel) has been considered in a number of works, often formalized in the energy ladder framework (8, 16, 63, 94). The energy ladder framework hypothesizes that households switch to cleaner sources of energy with increasing income. Since the formulation of this framework, a number of works have confirmed this hypothesis but have illustrated that use of multiple fuels is common across income levels (95, 96). More broadly, although the energy ladder is a convenient qualitative representation of the correlation between household energy supply and household socioeconomic status, its simplification of the social dimensions of energy use motivates a more systematic approach to evaluating the choices of household energy technology for policy purposes. In its simplest form, the energy ladder framework would imply a deterministic view of economic development and energy that need not hold if the circumstances—including the cultural context, policy, and infrastructure—are different from those of the original formulation. This deterministic formulation can also hinder innovative technological and policy approaches to addressing the energy issues of the poor that bypass the energy ladder. The energy ladder construct is also unable to account for the amount of energy (versus its form) and uncertainty in access to energy, both of which are important determinants of the welfare effects of energy.[6]

---

[5]If considered across, rather than within, regions, the higher solid fuel use in sub-Saharan Africa would strengthen the poverty-fuel correlation because incomes are generally lower in sub-Saharan Africa than other regions.

[6]Empirical examples of the importance of technology access and uncertainty can be found in the experience of diffusion of agricultural technologies (97–101). Because the outcome of technology is different (crop production versus energy consumption and health), the results may not be directly transferable to energy technologies.

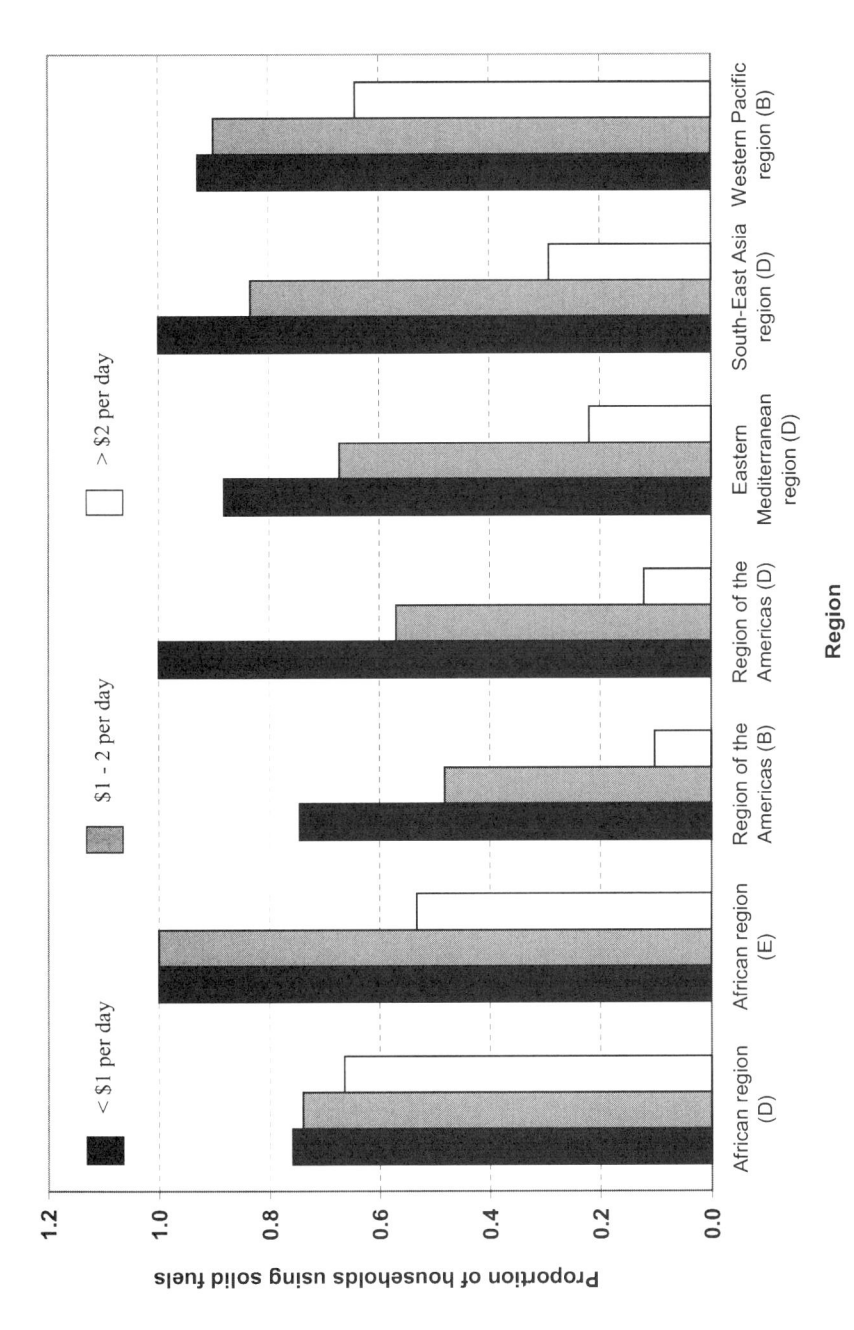

Figure 9 Decreasing prevalence of solid fuel use with increasing household income (93). The regions are the World Health Organization regions divided by their levels of child and adult mortality: B, low child mortality and low adult mortality; D, high child mortality and high adult mortality; and E, high child mortality and very high adult mortality.

The above discussion does not imply that income is not a crucial determinant of household energy choice. Rather it is important to treat income not as a deterministic cause of energy transition but rather as a source of additional freedom to choose certain types and quantities of fuel or the technology for fuel utilization. What the household actually does with the extra income will be decided by household members—influenced by differentiated gender-based priorities, community and cultural factors, energy and economic infrastructure and barriers, regulatory and political determinants of energy access, and a number of other factors (Table 3) (94, 102). Households may spend extra income on nonenergy commodities or services, such as health or education. Even within the energy realm, a household may decide to consume more energy (e.g., purchase more charcoal), switch to a different form of energy (e.g., switch to kerosene or LPG from biomass), switch its source of energy access (e.g., purchase biomass instead of collecting it), or use a mix of energy sources for different purposes (e.g., continue to use biomass for cooking and heating and purchase a photovoltaic unit for lighting).

Energy, Gender, and Health

International development research and policy have considered intrahousehold allocations of resources in addition to household level welfare effects. Energy is the aspect of development in which gender differentials in access to resources and its consequences are possibly most observable (see Reference 103 for a review). At the broadest level, cooking and heating—the most common uses of energy—are handled by women in most households in developing countries. In meeting the energy needs of the household, women allocate part of the limited household budget of cash and/or labor to procuring energy resources. When fuels are collected, which can involve walking many kilometers and carrying in excess of 20 kg of wood, the burden of work falls disproportionately on women, who may expend a significant fraction of their daily caloric needs gathering fuel (Figure 10, see color insert) (104). Therefore, energy scarcity and insecurity, often caused by joint effects of economic and environmental factors, affect the tasks and decisions of female household members and often lead to the use of less energy or more inferior energy sources (105).

Women, who gather or purchase fuel, cook, and handle fire considerably more frequently than men, also have much higher exposure to the hazards of energy use (36, 51, 106), including respiratory or eye diseases from indoor smoke, burns, or back pain and injuries from carrying heavy loads. For example, 75% of adult deaths attributable to exposure to indoor air pollution (Table 2) were among women (10, 11).

Increased access to clean energy sources can improve the day-to-day as well as long-term welfare of female household members. Health improvements, time, and/or money saved from energy needs may be used for leisure, participation in formal labor force, education, and community or commercial activities (see Table 2.4 in Reference 8 for a list of such activities). This transfer of resources could be

ENERGY MANAGEMENT AND GLOBAL HEALTH C-1

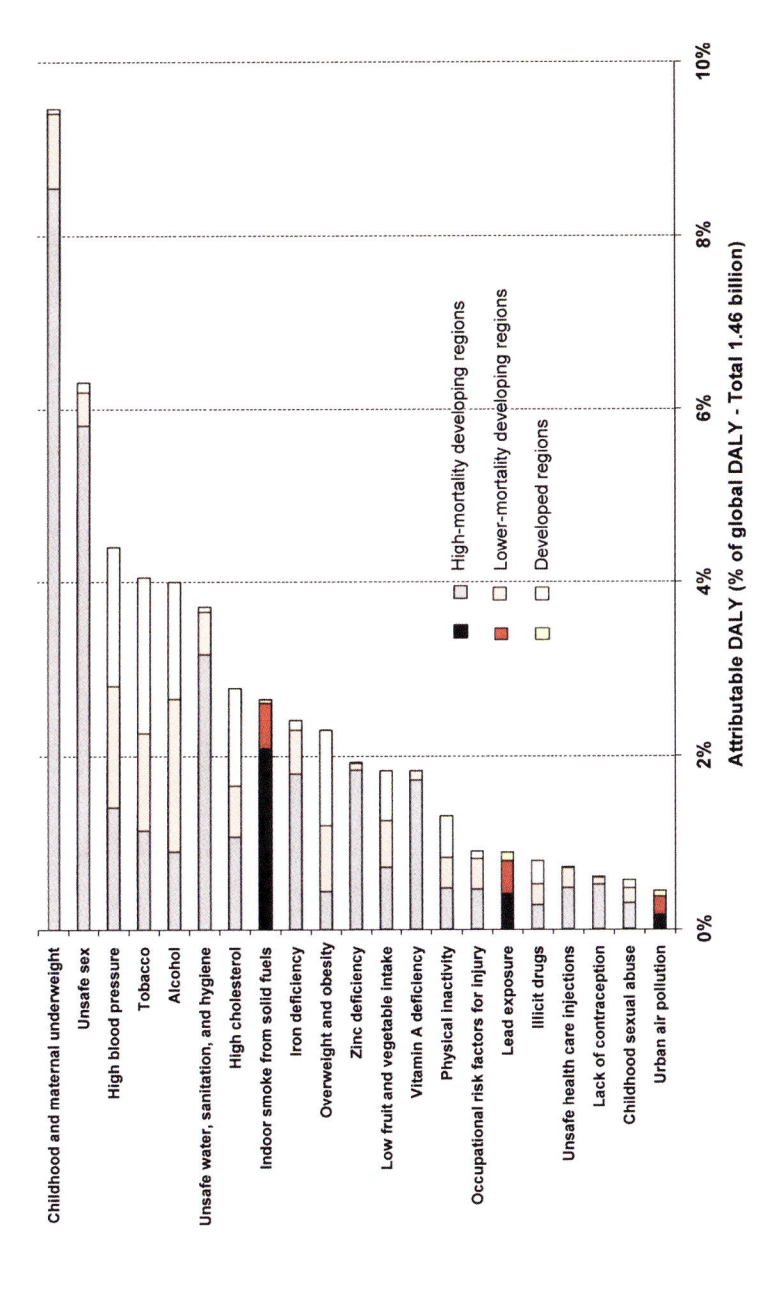

Figure 2 Burden of disease for some of the direct effects of energy systems (highlighted in black, red, and yellow) relative to other major global risk factors [see (10, 11) for a description of methods]. Burden of disease is a measure of loss of healthy life due to premature mortality and morbidity. It is expressed in disability-adjusted life years (DALYs), an aggregate measure of loss of life to premature mortality and time lived with nonfatal health outcomes (12). In the year 2000, there were a total of 1.46 billion DALYs lost in the world from premature mortality and nonfatal health outcomes.

C-2   EZZATI ET AL.

Figure 6a An important route of exposure to fluorine and arsenic from stove use in southern China is bioaccumulation in food (corn and chili), dried near a chimney. (Photograph by J. Arnold, China.)

Figure 5a In central Kenya, household members who cook are exposed to episodes of high pollution when they work directly above the fire. [Photograph by M. Ezzati, from (50).]

ENERGY MANAGEMENT AND GLOBAL HEALTH C-3

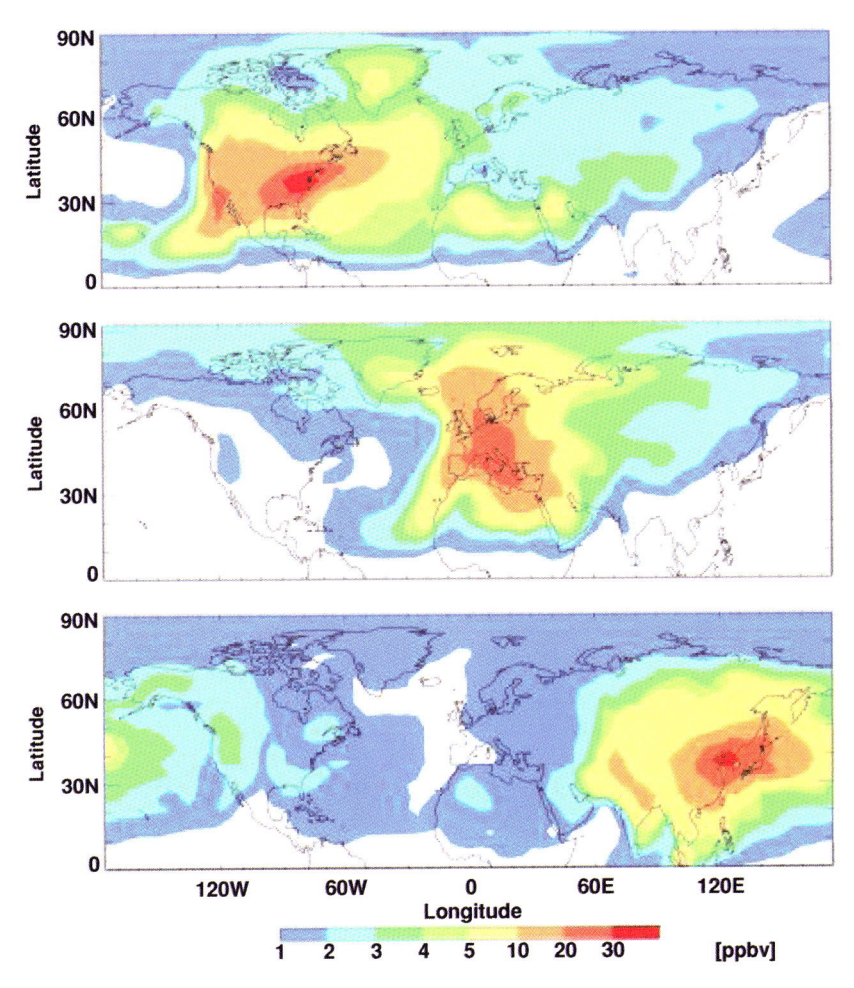

Figure 7 Model estimates of surface ozone attributable to anthropogenic emissions from North America (*top panel*), Europe (*middle panel*), and Asia (*lower panel*) during June, July, and August 1997. Units are in parts per billion volume (ppbv). [From (71).]

Figure 10 In many developing countries, female household members carry in excess of 20 kg of wood for many kilometers and hours each day. (Photograph by M. Ezzati, Kenya.)

an important mechanism to improve the status of women in developing countries. When considering energy as a tool for improving the status of women, it is essential to note that the inter- and intrahousehold economic and social institutions that hinder female access to adequate clean sources of energy are often the same that create other gender-based inequalities. In fact, it has been argued that the increased prominence of biomass as an economic and commercial commodity (e.g., as a source of energy for small-scale manufacturing) has attracted local entrepreneurs and business actors—mostly men—driving women to assume more marginal social roles and depend on inferior sources of energy (54, 79). Therefore, for improved energy access and technology to become a tool for increasing social and economic welfare of women, other institutions are also needed, including access to credit, labor and product markets, land, and education (107). Further, access to these opportunities can be sustained only if coupled with increased female participation in the social decision making and policy process (108, 109).

ENERGY MANAGEMENT AND PUBLIC HEALTH

Technology Options

Conventional energy sources based on oil, coal, and natural gas have proven to be highly effective drivers of economic development but at the same time damaging to the environment and to human health as described above (3). Over decades of development aid and lending, bilateral and multilateral development agencies have financed numerous conventional fossil-fuel-based energy projects and large-scale hydroelectric power in developing countries, which resulted in large burden of debts, had significant impacts on local environment and health, and provided only a small fraction of population with adequate energy services (110). The use of fossil-fuel-based energy as the sole or main driver of development appears increasingly problematic for many reasons, including uncertainty in price and reliability of international energy markets as well as their environmental and health consequences (see Reference 3 for a discussion).

The potential role of renewable energy technologies (RETs) in transforming global energy use, with a focus on sustainable development and increasing the welfare and health of the global poor, is enormous. Renewable energy sources, such as biomass,[7] wind, solar, hydropower, and geothermal, can provide sustainable energy services, using a mix of readily available, indigenous resources with potential to result in minimal local environmental damage or net emissions of

---

[7]In this context, biomass energy can be distinguished from traditional household biomass use in developing countries, described above. In these applications solid biomass feedstock is either burned in high-efficiency combustion devices so that potentially harmful combustion emissions can be minimized, or it is converted to a more convenient and cleaner energy carrier, such as solid briquettes or pellets, liquid or gaseous fuels, or electricity before final consumption.

GHGs. A transition to renewables-based energy systems looks increasingly desirable and possible because the costs of solar and wind power systems have dropped substantially in the past 30 years. Most forecasts indicate that costs of renewably produced electricity should continue to decline (Figure 11), while the price of oil and gas continues to fluctuate. If social and environmental costs are included in the estimation of electricity costs, RETs become still more attractive (111–113).

Renewable energy systems are usually implemented in a small-scale decentralized model that is inherently conducive to, rather than at odds with, many welfare and public health goals of energy distribution. These systems can have dramatically reduced as well as spatially dispersed environmental impacts, compared to larger and more localized effects of conventional energy sources, such as local ambient air pollution, acid rain, and ecological degradation. Although evaluation of RETs is currently on the basis of evidence from industrialized countries, the issues concerning conventional fossil-fuel-based energy systems are equally, if not more, important for developing countries. Heavy reliance on imported fossil fuels places a huge burden on the financial resources of developing countries in addition to the environmental and public health issues raised above. Supply constraints and exchange rate fluctuations affect reliability in the energy sector, which inhibits investment and retards economic activity.

Renewable energy sources currently supply between 15% and 20% of the world's total energy demand (17). The supply is dominated by traditional biomass, mostly fuelwood used for household energy needs in developing countries. A major contribution is also from the use of large hydropower with nearly 20% of the global electricity supply provided by this source. New renewable energy sources (solar energy, wind energy, modern bioenergy, geothermal energy, and small hydropower) are currently contributing about two percent of the global energy mix. In developing nations, RETs are increasingly used to address energy shortages and to expand the range of services in both rural and urban areas. In Kenya, for example, over 150,000 small [20 to 100 watt peak (Wp)] solar photovoltaic systems have been commercially financed and installed in homes, battery charging stations, and other small enterprises (115); a government program in Mexico has disseminated over 40,000 such systems; and in the Inner Mongolia autonomous region of China over 130,000 small-scale windmills provide electricity to about one third of the nongrid-connected households in this region (116, 117). Just as some developing countries are bypassing construction of telephone wires by leaping directly to cellular-based systems, so too might they avoid building large, centralized power plants and instead develop decentralized RET systems. This strategy can also reduce the need for the construction of large power grids, further mitigating the environmental and health costs of electrification.

Policy Instruments

A number of future energy scenario studies have investigated the potential contribution of RETs to global energy supplies, indicating that in the second half of

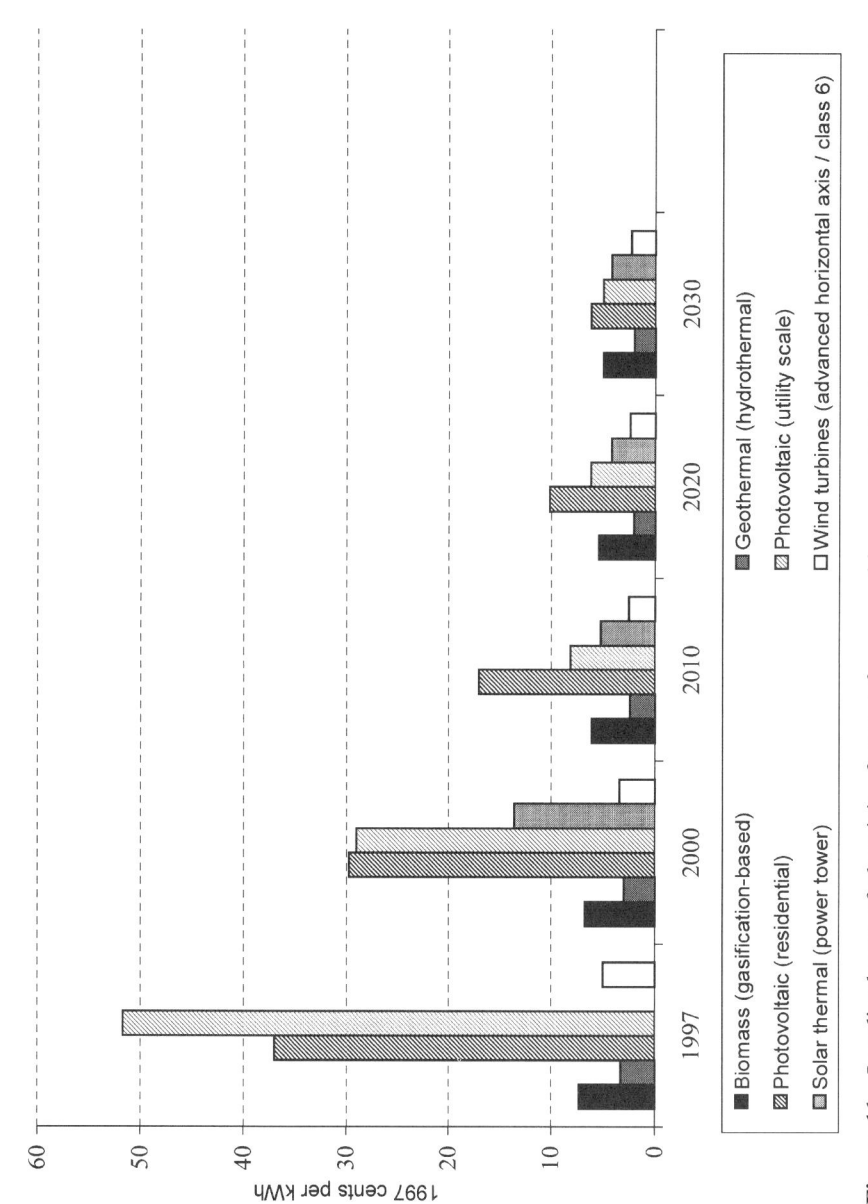

Figure 11 Levelized cost of electricity forecast for renewable energy technologies (112, 114). Levelized costs account for capital costs, operation, and maintenance.

the twenty-first century their contribution might range from the present figure of nearly 20% to more than 50%. In essence, however, RETs face a situation similar to one confronting any new technology that attempts to dislodge an entrenched technology. For many years, industrialized countries have been locked in to a suite of fossil-fuel and nuclear-based technologies, and many secondary systems and networks have been designed and constructed to accommodate these. The transition to RETs will only be realized if energy projects and policies are evaluated and implemented based on their overall social, economic, environmental, and public health merits. See References 102 and 112 for more detailed discussion.

The economic and policy mechanisms needed to support the widespread dissemination of sustainable markets for renewable energy systems have rapidly evolved. In particular, financial markets are realizing the future growth potential of renewable and other new energy technologies, a likely harbinger of the economic reality of truly competitive renewable energy systems. At the same time, important policy gaps for fully utilizing the potential of RETs as a tool for sustainable development remain as described below.[8]

LEVELING THE PLAYING FIELD   Despite their limited recent success, renewable energy sources have historically had a difficult time breaking into markets that have been dominated by traditional large-scale fossil-fuel-based systems. This is partly because renewable and other new energy technologies have previously had high capital costs relative to more conventional systems and are only now being mass produced. At the same time, coal, oil, and gas-powered systems have benefited from a range of subtle subsidies over the years. These include expenditures to protect oil exploration and production interests overseas, the costs of railway construction that have enabled low-cost delivery of coal to power plants, and a wide range of other subsidies.

RETs tend to be characterized by relatively low environmental costs. Many of these environmental costs are, however, externalities that are not priced in the market. The international effort to limit GHG emissions through the Kyoto Protocol may lead to some form of carbon-based tax, which would internalize some of these costs and benefit the spread of RETs. It is perhaps more likely that concern about local air pollution from fossil-fuel power plants will lead to pollution mitigation efforts because of more immediate and localized benefits, which will promote cleaner renewable systems and potentially also lead to GHG emission reductions (Appendixes 1 and 2).

---

[8]One limitation for increased use has been the intermittent nature of some renewable energy sources, such as wind and solar. A solution to this issue is to develop diversified systems that maximize the contribution of renewable energy sources and that also use clean natural gas and/or biomass-based power generation to provide base-load power when the sun is not shining and the wind is not blowing.

INVESTMENT IN INNOVATION   Recent efforts targeting a variety of small-scale traditional, fossil-fuel and RETs have resulted in dramatic improvements in performance, marketing, sales, and leasing opportunities, and end-user satisfaction in industrialized and developing nations. Examples include the growth of local mini-grids using renewable energy sources, improved efficiency cookstoves, photovoltaic solar home systems, wind turbines for household and microenterprise applications, microhydro generators, and advanced biomass energy systems. Some of these technologies have already had a significant impact on local patterns of energy use, economic activity, and the environment (118). The options for promoting the sustainable introduction of clean energy technologies are tightly connected with the capacity for energy research, development, demonstration, and deployment in developing countries.

Despite the widely acknowledged benefits of energy research and development, national systems of innovation, particularly in the energy sector, have proven difficult to maintain. Among the problems that plague the institutions that support research and implementation of small-scale and decentralized energy technologies and management methods is lack of steady funding. Equally critical, however, are the paucity of training venues, technology and information exchange, and technology standards for these often overlooked energy systems (119, 120). There is also a systematic lack of microcredit available to foster locally designed and implemented commercialization efforts. In some areas the governments may even see stand-alone and or mini-grid systems as unwelcome competitors to national utilities. An area that particularly suffers from the lack of research is analysis of the relationship between renewable energy projects and the social and economic contexts in which they are embedded. Finally, all too often projects are planned, implemented, or evaluated on the basis of unexamined assumptions about local conditions and the social and economic consequences of the project (61).

Research and development (R&D) requires long-term commitment because the timescale to develop both new technologies and, more critically, generations of innovators takes years or decades. The results are often diffuse, with both specific innovations and individuals moving freely about, on occasion leaving the nurturing nation. These features, particularly in poorer nations, make R&D capacity seem largely a luxury, rarely supported against the other and often more apparently pressing needs of energy development. As seen with similar experiences in agriculture and in health, local R&D is crucial to technology development and dissemination.

CONCLUSIONS

We have described some of the linkages between public health and energy. In spite of its close linkages with health, most energy policies and programs in the developing world fundamentally remain in the realm of social and economic development policies. The challenge to both energy and public health researchers and practitioners is therefore to incorporate the close links between the two sectors in the design of energy policies and programs, such as those discussed for RETs, that increase welfare and minimize the negative health consequences that those activities might entail (121).

In particular, the neglect of energy R&D capacity to meet global and national energy needs without significant public health consequences is the result of the combination of two powerful forces: the vulnerable and often neglected domestic capacity for innovation in developing nations and the lack of sustained support for energy R&D capacity by industrialized nations (122). The commitments made during the World Summit on Sustainable Development in Johannesburg should provide a critical opportunity to bring attention to this underinvestment and to build a full understanding of the need and importance of energy R&D and its public health implications.

ACKNOWLEDGMENT

This work was supported by the World Health Organization, the Energy Foundation, and the National Institutes of Health (Grant PO1-AG17625).

APPENDIX 1

Integrated Environmental Strategies for Air Pollution and GHG Reduction in Chile

The integrated environmental strategies in Chile provide an example of the interaction of measures to abate air pollution and measures to mitigate GHG emissions. Two types of analysis were conducted: a global analysis, in which the health benefits associated with a GHG mitigation scenario were estimated, and a detailed intervention analysis, in which both GHG and local air pollution reductions were estimated for specific interventions.

For the first analysis, a moderate climate policy scenario was considered. This scenario has been developed for the Chilean National Environmental Commission, and it considered only nonpositive costs measures, such as efficiency improvements in the industrial and residential sectors. The level of carbon abatement of this scenario is modest, 13% from the business-as-usual scenario. Emission reductions of local air pollutants (CO, SO_2, VOCs, NO_X, resuspended dust and PM_{10}) were estimated from emission factors recommended by the Intergovernmental Panel on Climate Change. The proportional reductions were applied uniformly to major urban areas of Chile that had data on particulate matter concentrations. The health benefits due to air pollution abatement were estimated using figures derived previously for the cost-benefit analysis of Santiago's Decontamination Plan, transferred to different cities taking into consideration local demographic and economic data.

The Santiago estimates were made on the basis of local epidemiological studies and local health and demographic data. Unit social values for the effects were estimated locally (for cost of treatment and lost productivity values) or extrapolated from U.S. values (mainly for willingness-to-pay values) using the ratio of per capita income and an income elasticity of 1. The average benefits of emission abatement (in 1997 US$ per ton) were an estimated 1800 [95% confidence interval (CI) 1200–2300] for NO_X; 3000 (95% CI 2100–3900) for SO_2; 31,900 (95% CI 21,900–41,900) for PM; and 630 (430–830) for resuspended dust. These benefits were extrapolated over time using the expected population and per capita income growth. Dividing the health benefits accrued from the local air pollutant emissions reductions by the amount of carbon abated, average ancillary benefits of 69 (95% CI 30–260) and 104 (95% CI 50–380) US$ per ton of carbon abated were estimated for the years 2010 and 2020.

The second analysis involved detailed examination of specific mitigation measures in Santiago. Most of the measures considered were primarily aimed at local air pollution abatement (e.g., technology changes in public transport buses), but some were energy efficiency measures. The emissions reductions of both GHG and local air pollutants were estimated from emission factors (some derived locally) and changes in activity levels. Figure 12 shows the relationship between reductions in carbon equivalent and $PM_{2.5}$ precursors (the percentage change was calculated on the relative contribution of unit pollutant emissions to ambient concentrations during Santiago's winter). As seen in the figure, most measures have a bigger local air pollution reduction than carbon reduction. Two measures [conversion of existing diesel buses (EPA 91) to compressed natural gas (CNG) and extended life span of existing diesel buses] have zero or negative air pollution reductions, whereas particulate traps for diesel buses have negative carbon reductions.

Next, the benefits from local air pollution abatement and carbon reduction were compared. Values of 20 and 50 US$/tCe (tons of carbon equivalent) were considered for valuing the carbon reductions, whereas the previously described values were considered for local air pollutant reductions. A comparison of the benefits shows that health benefits are generally larger than carbon benefits. For the fuel switching measures, carbon benefits were estimated as 9% to 28% of the health benefits (the latter figure for the 50 US$/tCe case for diesel to natural gas switch in boilers). In the transportation sector, the ratio was estimated from 0% to 13% for hybrid-electric buses. The electricity savings measures varied from 5% to 12%. In terms of offsetting some of the costs of the measures in the transport sector, at 20US$/tCe, carbon credits would account for just 0.6% of the annual costs of CNG buses, for 2.6% for the CNG conversion of existing buses, and for 15% of those of hybrid-electric buses. The figures increased to 1.5%, 6%, and 37% if carbon reductions were valued at 50 US$/tCe.

These results show that the local pollution health benefits of interventions that simultaneously reduce GHG emissions are significant, both for the scenario analysis and for the mitigation measure analysis. The public health benefits of carbon reduction measures can offset most of the cost of GHG reduction. However, for

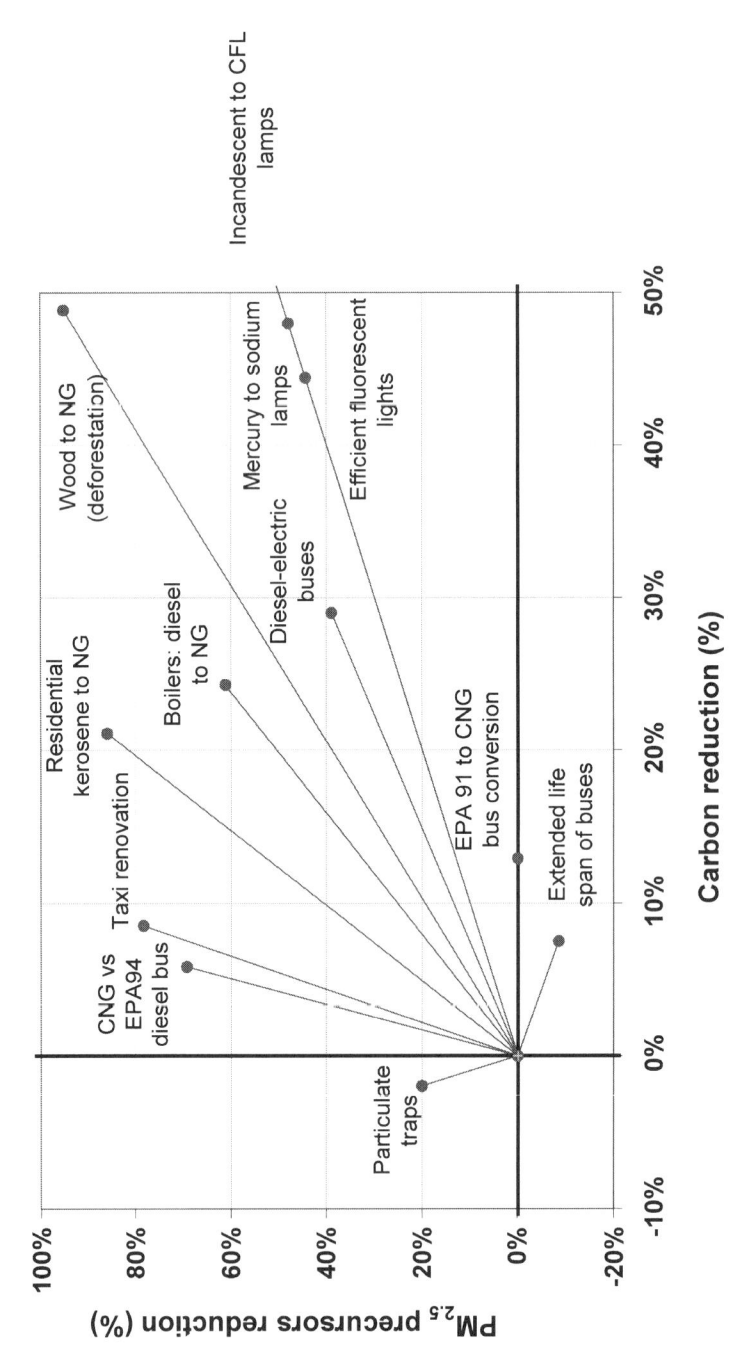

Figure 12 Percentage reductions in CO_2 equivalent and in local air pollutants for selected interventions in Santiago, Chile. The intervention incandescent to CFL lamps is on the same line as mercury to sodium lamps with a CO_2 reduction of about 80% (i.e., outside the scale of current figure). Abbreviations are CNG, compressed natural gas; CFL, compact fluorescent lights; and NG, natural gas. EPA 91 and EPA 94 are emission standards set by the U.S. Environmental Protection Agency (EPA).

most measures analyzed, the public health benefits were an order of magnitude greater than the benefits from carbon reduction. Also, the cost offsets due to potential carbon credits were limited from a few percent to 36% in the best case. This suggests that the main driver for air pollution policy is likely to remain local concerns, such as public health issues.

APPENDIX 2

Integrating Energy, Environment, and Public Health Policies: Charcoal in Kenya

The results in Figure 8 show that, on average, charcoal stoves have higher GHG emissions than woodstoves when the radiative forcing of the emitted gases is included in the calculation. The GHG picture becomes still bleaker for charcoal when one considers the entire life cycle of the fuel. Unlike woodfuel, which involves few, if any, GHG emissions prior to its use in the stove, charcoal end use only represents a fraction of the net GHG emissions from the charcoal life cycle. Charcoal production, particularly in developing countries where it is practiced with minimal technical inputs, is essentially combustion starved of sufficient oxygen, which results in very high emissions of multiple pollutants (123–125).

Although GHG emissions from charcoal production and end use are much higher than firewood, charcoal consumption can offer public health benefits over fuelwood, especially when clean-burning cooking fuels, such as kerosene and natural gas, are inaccessible or unaffordable. In rural Kenya, for example, a transition from using wood in an open (3-stone) fire to charcoal would reduce PM_{10} exposure by 75% to 95% on average for different demographic groups resulting in a 21% to 44% decrease in childhood acute lower respiratory infections as well as significant adult health benefits (52).

FUEL SWITCHING AND CHARCOAL MARKETS Nations like Kenya, which contribute very little to the total global release of GHGs (much less than 0.1%), probably stand to gain more from the immediate health benefits associated with fuel substitution from wood to charcoal than they do from discouraging its use because it carries a heavy GHG burden. This is particularly important with the increasing realization of the central role of health in meeting the development goals of poor nations (126). In Kenya, as in many other sub-Saharan African countries, charcoal is often readily available, can be purchased in small quantities, and requires no expensive equipment to use. For these reasons, and because it is relatively clean, safe, affordable, and storable, charcoal is the preferred fuel for most urban households as well as an increasing number of rural families. Charcoal has few direct substitutes in poor urban and peri-urban areas of many sub-Saharan African countries (127). In Kenya for example, over 80% of the urban population, some 1.4 million households, use charcoal as their primary cooking fuel (128). Therefore, despite the local (and global) environmental effects described above, attempts to curtail charcoal consumption are likely to be met with stiff public resistance in the absence of policies that are specifically designed to increase access to alternative household fuels, such as kerosene and LPG. However, if the decision is made to promote charcoal consumption because of its public health benefits, steps must also be taken to ensure a sustainable supply of wood or an alternative biomass feedstock.

Charcoal markets in many sub-Saharan African countries operate within a complex political economy that is hard to characterize and still more difficult to regulate. Even where regulations have been put forth, as in some West African countries, they are often poorly enforced and/or circumvented by powerful interest groups who control one or more parts of the commodity chain (see References 29 and 130 for a description of Senegal's charcoal supply chain and the ways in which regulations have been circumvented by wealthy merchants). In Kenya, which has one of the highest rates of per capita charcoal consumption in Africa, charcoal production has very ambiguous legal status that discourages investment in efficiency and conservation. The legality of charcoal production depends on the tenure relations of the land on which it is produced, varying across public, private, and communal landholdings. Transportation of charcoal requires a permit, but the process of accessing permits is inconsistent and poorly enforced. Despite these barriers, tens of thousands of people make their living by participating in one or more aspects of the charcoal supply chain, and revenues from the charcoal trade are thought to exceed US$300 million (131).

Sustainable charcoal production will be difficult to ensure where, like Kenya, the regulatory structure is poorly articulated and inconsistently enforced. In such situations, trees are undervalued, and the cost of tree replacement is not internalized in the price of the commodity; charcoal is made from natural forests or woodlands, which are slow to recover, or from woodland cleared for agriculture so that the tree cover is permanently removed. Without coherent land management policies promoting sustainable production, the public health benefits from charcoal will come at large environmental costs. In order to take advantage of the potential benefits that increased charcoal consumption can bring while minimizing the negative impacts associated with its production and use, a much more coherent policy framework is required. Such a framework would legalize and regulate charcoal production, ensure sustainable levels and methods (74) of production are maintained, and ensure consumer needs are met with prices that reflect the true cost of production, including harvesting and regeneration, conversion, transportation, and sales.

CARBON CREDITS TO MITIGATE GHG EMISSIONS   Although charcoal consumption carries a larger burden of GHG emissions than firewood use, it also has more potential to attract investment in GHG mitigation activities. Emissions from charcoal can be reduced at both the production and consumption components of its life cycle. Emission reductions in charcoal end use can be achieved by disseminating improved (high-efficiency and low-emission) charcoal stoves, which reduce emissions by improving combustion efficiency. Also, users generally see substantial fuel savings. Such charcoal stoves have been widely disseminated and adopted in urban Kenya, for example, although they are still short of saturation levels and offer potential for wider dissemination in rural areas (62). In addition, very little research has been done to assess field performance of stoves currently on the market for household use, and there are some fears that substandard stoves have crept into the market since donors and nongovernmental groups have stopped participating in stove design and dissemination projects (132).

Some research has addressed charcoal consumption in developing countries. Researchers are only now beginning to consider charcoal production in sub-Saharan Africa and elsewhere. Most charcoal production in sub-Saharan Africa occurs in earth mounds, which vent the products of incomplete combustion directly to the atmosphere. Arguably, larger GHG emission reductions and energy conversion efficiency improvements can be achieved by changing charcoal production practices than by focusing on charcoal consumption both because the activity is more centralized and because roughly 70% of non-CO_2 GHG emissions attributable to the charcoal life cycle result from the production process. To our knowledge, no attempt has been made to assess the costs, benefits, and institutional requirements of these GHG emissions reduction activities.

The *Annual Review of Environment and Resources* is online at
http://environ.annualreviews.org

LITERATURE CITED

1. Goldemberg J, ed. 2000. *World Energy Assessment: Energy and the Challenge of Sustainability.* New York: UN Dev. Programme. http://www.undp.org/seed/eap/activities/wea/drafts-frame.html
2. Filmer D, Pritchett LH. 2002. Environmental degradation and the demand for children: searching for the vicious circle in Pakistan. *Environ. Dev. Econ.* 7:123–46
3. Hall C, Tharakan P, Hallock J, Cleveland C, Jefferson M. 2003. Hydrocarbons and the evolution of human culture. *Nature* 426:318–22
4. Patz JA, McGeehin MA, Bernard SM, Ebi KL, Epstein PR, et al. 2000. The potential health impacts of climate variability and change for the United States: executive summary of the report of the health sector of the US national assessment. *Environ. Health Perspect.* 108:367–76
5. Goldemberg J, Johansson TB, Reddy AKN, Williams RH. 1985. Basic needs and more with one kilowatt per capita. *Ambio* 14:190–200
6. Goldemberg J, Johansson TB, eds. 1995. *Energy as an Instrument for Social Change.* New York: UN Dev. Programme
7. Goldemberg J, Johansson TB, eds. 2002. *Energy for Sustainable Development: A Policy Action Agenda.* New York: UN Dev. Programme
8. Reddy AKN, Williams RH, Johansson TB, eds. 1996. *Energy after Rio: Prospects and Challenges.* New York: UN Publ.
9. Smith KR. 1987. *Biofuels, Air Pollution, and Health: A Global Review.* New York: Plenum
10. World Health Organ. 2002. *World Health Report 2002: Reducing Risks, Promoting Healthy Life.* Geneva, Switz.: WHO
11. Ezzati M, Lopez AD, Rodgers A, Vander

Hoorn S, Murray CJL, Comp. Risk Assess. Collab. Group. 2002. Selected major risk factors and global and regional burden of disease. *Lancet* 360:1347–60
12. Murray CJL, Lopez AD, eds. 1996. *The Global Burden of Disease.* Cambridge, MA: Harv. School Public Health
13. World Resour. Inst./UNEP/UNDP/World Bank. 2001. *World Resources 2000–2001: People and Ecosystems: The Fraying Web of Life.* New York: Oxford Univ. Press
14. Baer P, Harte J, Haya B, Herzog AV, Holdren J, et al. 2000. Equity and greenhouse gas responsibility. *Science* 289:2287
15. Smith KR. 1988. Air pollution: assessing total exposure in developing countries. *Environment* 30:16–34
16. Reddy AKN. 2000. Energy and social issues. See Ref. 1, Chapter 2. http://www.undp.org/seed/eap/activities/wea/draftsframe.html
17. Int. Energy Agency. 2002. *World Energy Outlook 2002.* Paris: IEA
18. Cohen A, Anderson R, Gutschmidt K, Krzyzanowski M, Künzli N, et al. 2004. Urban ambient air pollution. See Ref. 133, pp. 1353–433
19. World Resour. Inst./UNEP/UNDP/World Bank. 1999. *World Resources 1998–1999: A Guide to the Global Environment.* New York: Oxford Univ. Press
20. Holgate ST, Samet JM, Koren HS, Maynard RL, eds. 1999. *Air Pollution and Health.* London: Academic
21. Pope CA III, Burnett RT, Thun MJ, Calle EE, Krewski D, et al. 2002. Lung cancer, cardiopulmonary mortality, and long-term exposure to fine particulate air pollution. *J. Am. Med. Assoc.* 287:1132–41
22. Sarangapani R, Wexler AS. 1999. Modeling aerosol bolus dispersion in human airways. *J. Aerosol Sci.* 30:1345–62
23. Wilson R, Spengler JD, eds. 1996. *Particles in Our Air: Concentrations and Health Effects.* Cambridge, MA: Harv. Univ. Press
24. Bell ML, Davis DL, Fletcher T. 2004. A retrospective assessment of mortality from the London smog episode of 1952: the role of influenza and pollution. *Environ. Health Perspect.* 112:6–8
25. World Bank. 1992. *World Development Report: Development and the Environment.* New York: Oxford Univ. Press
26. Ezzati M, Singer BH, Kammen DM. 2001. Towards an integrated framework for development and environment: the dynamics of Environmental Kuznets Curves. *World Dev.* 29:1421–34
27. Hoek G, Brunekreef B, Goldbohm S, Fischer P, van den Brandt PA. 2002. Association between mortality and indicators of traffic-related air pollution in the Netherlands: a cohort study. *Lancet* 360:1203–09
28. Krzyzanowski M, Schwela D. 1999. Patterns of air pollution in developing countries. See Ref. 20, pp. 105–13
29. Brauer M, Saksena S. 2002. Accessible tools for classification of exposure to particles. *Chemosphere* 49:1151–62
30. Levy JI, Houseman EA, Ryan L, Richardson D, Stud. 1998 Summer Program Biostat., Spengler JD. 2000. Particle concentrations in urban microenvironments. *Environ. Health Perspect.* 108:1051–57
31. Hoek G, Fischer P, Van Den Brandt P, Goldbohm S, Brunekreef B. 2001. Estimation of long-term average exposure to outdoor air pollution for a cohort study on mortality. *J. Expo. Anal. Environ. Epidemiol.* 11:459–69
32. Jerrett M, Burnett RT, Kanaroglou P, Eyles J, Finkelstein N, et al. 2001. A GIS—environmental justice analysis of particulate air pollution in Hamilton, Canada. *Environ. Plan. A* 33:955–73
33. Ozkaynak H, Spengler J. 1996. The role of outdoor particulate matter in assessing total human exposure. In *Particles in Our Air: Concentrations and Health Effects*, ed. R Wilson, JD Spengler, pp. 63–84. Cambridge, MA: Harv. Univ. Press
34. Bruce N, Perez-Padilla R, Albalak R. 2000. Indoor air pollution in developing countries: a major environmental and

public health challenge. *Bull. World Health Organ.* 78:1078–92
35. Deleted in proof
36. Ezzati M, Kammen DM. 2002. The health impacts of exposure to indoor air pollution from solid fuels in developing countries: knowledge, gaps, and data needs. *Environ. Health Perspect.* 110:1057–68
37. Ezzati M, Kammen DM. 2002. Household energy, indoor air pollution and health in developing countries: knowledge base for effective intervention. *Annu. Rev. Energy Environ.* 27:233–70
38. Arungu-Olende S. 1984. Rural energy. *Nat. Resour. Forum* 8:117–26
39. Smith KR, Mehta S, Feuz M. 2004. Indoor air pollution from household use of solid fuels. See Ref. 133, pp. 1435–93
40. De Koning HW, Smith KR, Last JM. 1985. Biomass fuel combustion and health. *Bull. World Health Organ.* 63:11–26
41. Zhang J, Smith KR. 1996. Indoor air pollution: formaldehyde and other carbonyls emitted from various cookstoves. Proc. Indoor Air 96: 7th Int. Confer. Indoor Air Qual. Clim., Nagoya, Jpn.
42. Finkelman RB, Belkin HE, Zheng B. 1999. Health impacts of domestic coal use in China. *Proc. Natl. Acad. Sci. USA* 96:3427–31
43. Smith KR. 1993. Fuel combustion, air pollution exposure, and health: situation in developing countries. *Annu. Rev. Energy Environ.* 18:529–66
44. Kammen DM. 1995. Cookstoves for the developing world. *Sci. Am.* 273:63–67
45. Ezzati M, Mbinda BM, Kammen DM. 2000. Comparison of emissions and residential exposure from traditional and improved biofuel stoves in rural Kenya. *Environ. Sci. Technol.* 34:578–83
46. Smith KR, Samet JM, Romieu I, Bruce N. 2000. Indoor air pollution in developing countries and acute lower respiratory infections in children. *Thorax* 55:518–32
47. Ezzati M, Kammen DM. 2001. Indoor air pollution from biomass combustion as a risk factor for acute respiratory infections in Kenya: an exposure-response study. *Lancet* 358:619–24
48. Boy E, Bruce N, Delgado H. 2002. Birth weight and exposure to kitchen wood smoke during pregnancy in rural Guatemala. *Environ. Health Perspect.* 110:109–14
49. von Schirnding Y, Bruce N, Smith KR, Ballard-Tremeer G, Ezzati M, Lvovsky K. 2001. Addressing the impact of household energy and indoor air pollution on the health of the poor—implications for policy action and intervention measures. In *Working Group 5, Rep. Improving the Health Outcomes of the Poor*, Comm. Macroecon. Health. http://www.cmhealth.org/wg5.htm
50. Ezzati M, Saleh H, Kammen DM. 2000. The contributions of emissions and spatial microenvironments to exposure to indoor air pollution from biomass combustion in Kenya. *Environ. Health Perspect.* 108:833–39
51. Balakrishnan K, Sankar S, Parikh J, Padmavathi R, Srividya K, et al. 2002. Daily average exposures to respirable particulate matter from combustion of biomass fuels in rural households of southern India. *Environ. Health Perspect.* 110:1069–75
52. Ezzati M, Kammen DM. 2002. Evaluating the health benefits of transitions in household energy technology in Kenya. *Energy Policy* 30:815–26
53. Ezzati M, Utzinger J, Cairncross S, Cohen A, Singer BH. 2004. Environmental risks in the developing world: exposure indicators for evaluating interventions, programs and policies. *J. Epidemiol. Community Health.* In press
54. Agarwal B. 1986. Cold hearths and barren slopes: the woodfuel crisis in the Third World. London: Zed Books
55. Kammen DM. 1995. From energy efficiency to social utility: improved cookstoves and the small is beautiful model of development. See Ref. 6, pp. 50–62

56. Karekezi S. 1994. Disseminating renewable energy technologies in sub-Saharan Africa. *Annu. Rev. Energy Environ.* 19:387–421
57. Krugmann H. 1987. Review of issues and research relating to improved cookstoves *Rep. IDRC-MR152e.* Int. Dev. Research Cent., Ottawa, Can.
58. Manibog FR. 1984. Improved cooking stoves in developing countries: problems and opportunities. *Annu. Rev. Energy* 9:199–227
59. Barnes DF, Openshaw K, Smith KR, van der Plas R. 1994. What makes people cook with improved biomass stoves? A comparative international review of stove programs. Washington, DC: World Bank
60. Smith KR, Shuhua G, Kun H, Daxiong Q. 1993. One hundred million improved cookstoves in China: How was it done? *World Dev.* 21:941–61
61. Agarwal B. 1983. Diffusion of rural innovations: some analytical issues and the case of wood-burning stoves. *World Dev.* 11:359–76
62. Kammen DM. 2001. Research, development, and commercialization of the Kenya ceramic jiko. In *Technology, Humans, and Society: Toward a Sustainable World*, ed RC Dorf, pp. 310–21. San Diego, CA: Academic
63. Hosier RH, Dowd J. 1987. Household fuel choice in Zimbabwe. *Resour. Energy* 9:347–61
64. Reiter P. 2001. Climate change and mosquito-borne diseases. *Environ. Health Perspect.* 109:141–61
65. Casman E, Dowlatabadi H, eds. 2002. *The Contextual Determinants of Malaria.* Washington, DC: Resour. Future
66. Hay SI, Cox J, Rogers DJ, Randolph SE, Stern DI, et al. 2002. Climate change and the resurgence of malaria in the East African highlands. *Nature* 415:905–9
67. Reiter P, Lathrop S, Bunning M, Biggerstaff B, Singer D, et al. 2003. Texas lifestyle limits transmission of dengue virus. *Emerg. Infect. Disease* 9:86–89
68. Ahmad K. 2002. Pollution cloud over south Asia is increasing ill health. *Lancet* 360:549
69. Jacob DJ, Logan JA, Murti PP. 1999. Effect of rising Asian emissions on surface ozone in the United States. *Geophys. Res. Lett.* 26:2175–78
70. Stohl A, Eckhardt S, Forster C, James P, Spichtinger N. 2002. On the pathways and timescales of intercontinental air pollution transport. *J. Geophys. Res.* 107(D23): 4684; doi:10.1029/2001 JD001396
71. Li Q, Jacob DJ, Bey I, Palmer PI, Duncan BN, et al. 2002. Transatlantic transport of pollution and its effects on surface ozone in Europe and North America. *J. Geophys. Res.* 107(D13); doi:10.1029/2001JD001422
72. Bradley PN, Campbell BM. 1998. Who plugged the gap? Re-examining the woodfuel crisis in Zimbabwe. *Energy Environ.* 9:235–55
73. Hall DO, Rosillo-Calle F, Williams RH, Woods J. 1993. Biomass for energy: supply prospects. See Ref. 134, pp. 594–651
74. Hosier RH. 1993. Charcoal production and environmental degradation: environmental history, selective harvesting, and post-harvest management. *Energy Policy* 21:491–509
75. Kartha S. 2001. Biomass sinks and biomass energy: key issues in using biomass to protect the global climate. *Energy Sustain. Dev.* 5:10–16
76. Leach G, Mearns R. 1988. *Beyond the Woodfuel Crisis: People, Land, and Trees in Africa.* London: Earthscan
77. Smith KR, Uma R, Kishore VVN. 2000. Greenhouse implications of household stoves: an analysis from India. *Annu. Rev. Energy Environ.* 25:741–763
78. Bailis R, Ezzati M, Kammen DM. 2003. Greenhouse gas implications of household energy technology in Kenya. *Environ. Sci. Technol.* 37:2051–59
79. Naughton-Treves L, Chapman CA. 2002. Fuelwood resources and forest

regeneration on fallow land in Uganda. *J. Sustain. For.* 14:19–32
80. Levine JS, Cofer WR, Cahoon DR, Winstead EL. 1995. Biomass burning: a driver for global change. *Environ. Sci. Technol.* 29:A120–25
81. Intergov. Panel Clim. Change. 2001. *Climate Change 2001: The Scientific Basis.* Cambridge, UK/New York, NY: Cambridge Univ. Press
82. Smith KR. 2002. In praise of petroleum? *Science* 298:1847
83. Green C, Vimmerstedt L, Renne J, Benioff R, eds. 2000. *Developing Country Case-Studies: Integrated Strategies for Air Pollution and Greenhouse Gas Mitigation.* Washington, DC: US EPA (Prepared by NREL for Off. Atmos. Programs)
84. Smith KR. 1991. Alocating responsibility for global warming: the natural debt index. *Ambio* 20:95–96
85. Agarwal B. 1997. Gender, environment, and poverty interlinks: regional variations and temporal shifts in rural India. *World Dev.* 25:23–52
86. World Bank. 2000. *Energy and Development Report 2000: Energy Services for the World's Poor.* Washington, DC: World Bank
87. May J, Norton A. 1997. A difficult life: the experiences and perceptions of poverty in South Africa. *Soc. Indic. Research* 41:95–118
88. Sexton K, Adgate JL. 1999. Looking at environmental justice from an environmental health perspective. *J. Expo. Anal. Environ. Epidemiol.* 9:3–8
89. Perlin SA, Wong D, Sexton K. 2001. Residential proximity to industrial sources of air pollution: interrelationships among race, poverty, and age. *J. Air Waste Manag. Assoc.* 51:406–21
90. Sexton K, Gong H Jr., Bailar JC 3rd, Ford JG, Gold DR, et al. 1993. Air pollution health risks: Do class and race matter? *Toxicol. Ind. Health* 9:843–78
91. O'Neill MS, Jerrett M, Kawachi I, Levy JI, Cohen AJ, et al. 2003. Health, wealth and air pollution: advancing theory and methods. *Environ. Health Perspect.* 111:1861–70
92. Ezzati M, Vander Hoorn S, Rodgers A, Lopez AD, Mathers CD, Murray CJL. 2003. Comparative risk assessment collaborative group. Estimates of global and regional potential health gains from reducing multiple major risk factors. *Lancet* 362:271–80
93. Blakely T, Hales S, Kieft, Wilson N, Woodward A. 2004. Distribution of risk factors by poverty. See Ref. 133, pp. 1949–2136
94. Leach G. 1992. The energy transition. *Energy Policy* 20:116–23
95. Davis M. 1998. Rural household energy consumption: the effects of access to electricity—evidence from South Africa. *Energy Policy* 26:207–17
96. Masera OR, Saatkamp BD, Kammen DM. 2000. From linear fuel switching to multiple cooking strategies: a critique and alternative to the energy ladder model. *World Dev.* 28:2083–103
97. Antle JM, Crissman CC. 1990. Risk, efficiency, and the adoption of modern crop varieties: evidence from the Philippines. *Econ. Dev. Cult. Change* 38:517–37
98. Conley T, Udry C. 2001. Social learning through networks: the adoption of new agricultural technologies in Ghana. *Am. J. Agric. Econ.* 83:668–73
99. Feder G, Umali DL. 1993. The adoption of agricultural innovations. *Technol. Forecast. Soc. Change* 43:215–39
100. Barnett V, Payne R, Steiner JR, eds. 1995. *Agricultural Sustainability in Economic, Environmental, and Statistical Terms.* London: Wiley
101. Frossard D. 1994. *Peasant science: farmer research and Philippine rice development.* PhD thesis. Univ. Calif., Irvine
102. Kammen DM, Bailis R, Herzog AV. 2001. *Clean Energy for Development and Economic Growth: Biomass and Other Renewable Energy Options to Meet Energy*

and Development Needs in Poor Nations. New York: UN Dev. Programme
103. Cecelski EW. 1995. From Rio to Beijing. *Energy Policy* 23:561–75
104. Levine JA, Weisell R, Chevassus S, Martinez CD, Burlingame B, Coward WA. 2001. The work burden of women. *Science* 294:812
105. Brouwer ID, Hoorweg JC, van Liere MJ. 1997. When households run out of fuel: responses of rural households to decreasing fuelwood availability, Ntcheu District, Malawi. *World Dev.* 25:255–66
106. Saksena S, Prasad R, Pal RC, Joshi V. 1992. Patterns of daily exposure to TSP and CO in the Garhwal Himalaya. *Atmos. Environ.* 26:A2125–34
107. Safilios-Rothschild C. 1985. The persistence of women's invisibility in agriculture: theoretical and policy lessons from Lesotho and Sierra Leone. *Econ. Dev. Cult. Change* 33:298–317
108. Bourque SC, Warren KB. 1990. Access is not enough: gender perspectives on technology and education. In *Persistent Inequalities*, ed. I Tinker, pp. 83–100. Oxford, UK: Oxford Univ. Press
109. Agarwal B. 2001. Participatory exclusions, community forestry, and gender: an analysis for south Asia and a conceptual framework. *World Dev.* 29:1623–48
110. Rich B. 1994. *Mortgaging the Earth: The World Bank, Environmental Impoverishment, and the Crisis of Development.* Boston, MA: Beacon
111. Ottinger RL. 1991. *Environmental Costs of Electricity.* New York: Oceana
112. Herzog AV, Lipman TE, Edwards JL, Kammen DM. 2001. Renewable energy: a viable choice. *Environment* 43:8–20
113. US Dep. Energy. 2000. Annual Energy Outlook 2000, DOE/EIA-0383. Washington, DC: Energy Inf. Adm.
114. US Dep. Energy. 1997. Renewable energy technology characterization. *Off. Util. Technol./EPRI Topical rep.*, *TR-109496*, DOE, Washington, DC
115. Duke RD, Jacobson A, Kammen DM. 2002. Photovoltaic module quality in the Kenyan solar home systems market. *Energy Policy* 30:477–99
116. Lew D. 2000. Alternatives to coal and candles: wind power in China. *Energy Policy* 28:271–86
117. Intergov. Panel Clim. Change. 2000. *Methodological and Technological Issues in Technology Transfer.* Cambridge, UK/New York: Cambridge Univ. Press
118. Kammen DM. 1999. Bringing power to the people: promoting appropriate energy technologies in the developing world. *Environment* 41:10–15, 34–41
119. Kozloff KL. 1995. Rethinking development assistance for renewable electricity sources. *Environment* 37:6–15, 32–38
120. Tata Energy Research Inst. 1998. *Climate Change: Post-Kyoto Perspectives from the South.* New Delhi, India: TERI
121. Ezzati M. 2003. Complexity and rigour in assessing the health dimensions of sectoral policies and programs. *Bull. World Health Organ.* 81:458–59
122. Margolis RM, Kammen DM. 1999. Underinvestment: the energy technology and R&D policy challenge. *Science* 285:690–93
123. Brocard D, Lacaux C, Lacaux JP, Kouadio G, Yoboue V. 1996. Emissions from the combustion of biofuels in Western Africa. In *Biomass Burning and Global Change.* Vol. 1, ed. JS Levine, pp. 350–60. Cambridge, MA: MIT Press
124. Pennise D, Smith KR, Kithinji JP, Rezende ME, Raad TJ, et al. 2001. Emissions of greenhouse gases and other airborne pollutants from charcoal-making in Kenya and Brazil. *J. Geophys. Res. Atmos.* 106:24143–55
125. Dutt GS, Ravindranath NH. 1993. Bioenergy: direct applications in cooking. See Ref. 134, pp. 653–97
126. World Health Organ. 2001. Macroeconomics and health: investing in health for economic development. *Comm. Macroecon. Health Rep.*, WHO, Geneva, Switz. http://www.cmhealth.org

127. Milukas V. 1993. Energy for secondary cities: the case of Nakuru, Kenya. *Energy Policy* 21:543–58
128. Kenya Minist. Energy. 2002. Study on Kenya's energy demand, supply and policy strategy for households, small scale industries and service establishments: final report. KAMFOR Comp. Ltd., Nairobi
129. Ribot JC. 1993. Forestry policy and charcoal production in Senegal. *Energy Policy* 21:559–85
130. Ribot JC. 1995. From exclusion to participation: turning Senegal's forestry policy around? *World Dev.* 23:1587–99
131. Anonymous. 2002. Hot and Dirty: Inside Kenya's 23 Billion Shilling Charcoal Industry. *EcoForum* (Nairobi) 25:16–22
132. Karekezi S, Ranja T. 1997. *Renewable Energy Technologies in Africa.* London: Zed Books
133. Ezzati M, Lopez AD, Rodgers A, Murray CJL, eds. 2004. *Comparative Quantification of Health Risks: Global and Regional Burden of Disease Attributable to Selected Major Risk Factors.* Geneva, Switz.: WHO
134. Johansson TB, Kelly H, Reddy AKN, Williams RH, eds. 1993. *Renewable Energy: Sources for Fuels and Electricity.* Washington, DC: Island

ENERGY INFRASTRUCTURE AND SECURITY

Alexander E. Farrell,[1] Hisham Zerriffi,[2] and Hadi Dowlatabadi[3]

[1]*Energy and Resources Group, University of California, Berkeley, California 94720-3050; email: afarrell@socrates.berkeley.edu*
[2]*Department of Engineering and Public Policy, Carnegie Mellon University, Pittsburgh, Pennsylvania 15213-3890; email: hisham@cmu.edu*
[3]*Sustainable Development Research Initiative, University of British Columbia, Vancouver, BC Canada V6T 1Z2; email: hadi@sdri.ubc.ca*

Key Words energy security, critical infrastructure protection, terrorism

■ **Abstract** Concerns about safeguarding key infrastructures (such as energy, communications, banking, and roads) from deliberate attack are long-standing, but since the end to the cold war, emphasis has turned to the possible impacts of terrorism. Activities to address these concerns are sometimes called critical infrastructure protection (CIP), a concept that is somewhat different from the one of "energy security," which focuses on politically and economically motivated supply interruptions. Different elements of the energy infrastructure are characterized by distinct vulnerabilities. Breaches of security in nuclear plants can lead to large-scale environmental disasters—but the infrastructure is concentrated and relatively easy to guard. Oil and gas production, transportation, and refining infrastructures are often spatially concentrated, and disruptions can lead to shortages if supply is not restored before stockpiles are exhausted. Traditional electricity infrastructures suffer from the need for system-wide integrity to ensure supply reliability, having critical facilities spatially concentrated (substations), and insignificant storage capacity for emergency supply. This review discusses how energy infrastructure and security are related, how this relationship differs from traditional energy security concepts, and what it may mean for private and policy decisions. Key concepts include redundancy, diversity, resilience, storage, decentralization, and interdependence. The concept of CIP is still relatively new and is likely to evolve over time, possibly away from a "guards, gates, and guns" defensive approach and toward a design approach that yields systems that are inherently harder to successfully attack. Such survivable systems may feature distributed intelligence, control, and operations.

CONTENTS

INTRODUCTION 422
   Background 423
   Early Analyses 424
CONCEPTS 427
   Routine Security 427

Expected Failures 428
　　　Attack Modes 429
　　　Diversity 431
　　　Storage 432
　　　Redundancy 433
　　　Cyber Security 433
　　　Interdependency 434
　　　Stress 434
　　　Survivability 435
　　　Centralization 436
　CRITICAL INFRASTRUCTURE PROTECTION 438
　　　Definitions 439
　　　Practice 440
　　　Research 443
　OIL AND GAS 444
　ELECTRICITY 448
　　　Prior Experience with Outages 448
　　　Transformer Vulnerabilities 449
　　　Impact of an Outage 450
　　　Analyses of Power Systems Under Stress 451
　　　Fuel Supply Disruptions 452
　NUCLEAR 452
　　　Fuel 453
　　　Reactors 453
　　　Waste 454
　　　Reprocessing 455
　　　Proliferation 455
　　　Public Reactions 456
　PREVENTION AND RESPONSE 456
　　　Guards, Gates, and Guns 457
　　　Emergency Response and Restoration 457
　　　Institutions 458
　　　Efficiency and Renewables 459
　CONCLUSIONS 460

INTRODUCTION

Conflict over resources stretches far back in human history, and energy infrastructures have long been subject to deliberate attacks. For instance, the New World Liberation Front bombed assets of the Pacific Gas & Electric Company over 10 times in 1975 alone. Members of the Ku Klux Klan and San Joaquin Militia have been convicted of conspiring or attempting to attack energy infrastructure (1, pp. 5–7; 2). Organized paramilitaries have had very significant impacts in some countries. For example, the Farabundo-Marti National Liberation Front was able to interrupt service in up to 90% of El Salvador at a time and even produced manuals for attacking power systems (3). Other examples of conflicts that have resulted in significant damage to electricity systems include the civil war in Bosnia and Herzegovina and the conflicts in Lebanon. Less direct attacks have occurred as well such as the delivery of anthrax to the British Petroleum office in Ho Chi Minh City, Vietnam, in 2001 (4, pp. 5–12). Oil and natural gas infrastructures in Colombia and Nigeria have experienced numerous attacks. Recent wars have involved attacks on other energy infrastructures. For instance, the United States, operating under North Atlantic Treaty Organization (NATO) auspices, destroyed portions of the Serbian electric power infrastructure in 1999. During the Iran-Iraq war, Iran seized all of the offshore oil-production platforms of the Dorra field in the Persian Gulf. When Iran retreated at war's end in 1988, several platforms were destroyed. Several years later Iraq spectacularly set fire to the Kuwaiti oil fields during retreat in the Gulf War in 1991.

These events and especially the rise of catastrophic terrorism in industrialized countries, such as the September 11, 2001 terrorist attacks, have heightened attention on the security of energy infrastructures. Concerns include the vulnerability of energy infrastructures to deliberate attack, the consequences of such attacks, and means of preventing or mitigating their effects.

Terrorist groups have differing goals and capabilities, and it is not clear if a highly successful physical attack on an energy infrastructure would have the same social effect as terrorist attacks that claim lives or focus on symbolic targets. Responses would likely include outrage and a sense of vulnerability, but evidence from recent large-scale blackouts indicates that panic and shock do not generally ensue. Recent war game exercises have shown that in the United States, attacks on the chemical sector may pose far larger risks than those on the energy sector (5). Nonetheless, several groups have attacked energy infrastructures in the past and can be expected to do so in the future.

We consider four main energy supply infrastructures (oil, gas, electricity, and nuclear power) but also mention end use, in which efficiency and storage (e.g., batteries and backup generators) are possible responses. Clearly, vulnerability of the primary source of energy is a common concern across oil, gas, and electricity; hence renewable energy supplies are a recurring theme. In this review, we first provide some background; next present key concepts and discuss critical infrastructure protection (CIP) efforts; then discuss oil and gas, electricity, and nuclear power infrastructures individually; and address prevention and response. We close with some brief conclusions.

Background

The modern idea of "energy security" emerged in the nineteenth century as warfare became mechanized and began to require substantial fuel inputs, first as coal for warships and trains (6). The decision of the British Admiralty prior to the First World War to switch from coal-fired to oil-fired vessels marked the start of the now traditional link between petroleum and security (7, pp. 155–56; 8, pp. 2–3; 9, pp. 29–31; 10). Today, the terms energy security and oil supplies are implicitly linked. The links between energy security and resource depletion (11–13) and geographic concentration of resources (e.g., oil in the Persian Gulf region) are also important themes (9, 14–17); however this review discusses only the latter. This review focuses on the issue of intentional acts aimed at disruption of an energy infrastructure and measures to reduce their occurrence and impact, so although the concepts of scarcity and geopolitics may accentuate infrastructure security concerns, they are not central.

Early Analyses

The theme of energy infrastructure and security appears in more general studies of national security and warfare. During the Second World War, the Allies missed a significant opportunity to shorten hostilities by failing to target Germany's electricity infrastructure (18, pp. 49–55). A similar failure to attack Japan's electricity infrastructure was a smaller error because it was highly decentralized and thus would have been very difficult to damage. An analysis of strategic attack of electric power systems during the Korean, Vietnam, and First Gulf War showed that such efforts were not highly effective in affecting public morale, economic activity, or war-fighting capability (19). Moreover, this study (19) argues that the requirements for international support during the prosecution of a contemporary limited war would likely make strategic attack on energy infrastructure an unattractive option. However, there may be underlying issues for the lack of success of such attacks, such as little dependence on electricity on the parts of the Koreans and North Vietnamese and significant preparations on the part of the Iraqis. Further, the successful attacks by U.S. forces operating under NATO auspices on the Serbian electric power system during May 1999 suggest military campaigns may continue to feature attacks on electric power systems (20).

Cold war analyses focused on limited or full nuclear exchange between the United States (and its NATO allies) and the Soviet Union (and its client states) and often discussed the potential impacts of such a nuclear exchange on energy infrastructure. We can only guess that much relevant analysis remains classified, but the 1958 U.S. Department of Defense report "Emergency Plans Book" has been published in the open literature (21). Reporting the expected outcome of a large-scale nuclear war, the report predicts that much of the energy infrastructure will be destroyed but so, too, would much of the demand. Many electricity generators are expected to survive an urban-focused strike, but transmission systems are expected to be largely destroyed, as are petroleum refining and shipping facilities. Local fuel stocks are expected to be consumed relatively rapidly, and massive loss of life, widespread contamination, and destruction of transportation systems are expected to greatly delay recovery. However, the report notes that "With strict rationing, of petroleum products and allocation of coal, the surviving [civilian] fuel production ...is sufficient to meet properly time-phased military requirements and minimum essential civilian needs..." (21).

In 1979, the Office of Technology Assessment (OTA) published a study, "The Effects of Nuclear War," which emphasized the devastation and difficulty in recovering from such an attack (3). One of the cases studied in the report is a strike against oil refineries using 10 missiles with multiple warheads (3, pp. 64–80). This case was chosen because energy systems were considered to be the most vulnerable sector of the U.S. economy, and refineries best met the study criteria of criticality, vulnerability, and long recovery times. The conclusion is that most refining capacity in each country (the United States and the Soviet Union, or USSR) would be destroyed, and both would suffer extensive reductions in industrial productivity and significant changes in socioeconomic organization, although differently. For example, the already precarious Soviet agricultural sector was thought to be heavily affected, whereas in the United States the concern was the devastating impact on industrial sectors dependent on refined petroleum products and the socioeconomic changes that would result from living with scarcity (e.g., greatly restricted mobility). The OTA report generally recognizes that decentralization and redundancy could reduce the impact of any of the attack scenarios considered.

Two reports commissioned by the U.S. government greatly sharpened the focus on decentralized energy technologies to mitigate security concerns.[1] The first, later republished as a book, *Energy, Vulnerability, and War*, provides a fairly detailed examination of the existing energy infrastructure at the time and the effects of a nuclear attack on it (22, 23). After detailing current vulnerabilities, the report reviews potential options including energy efficiency, storage (e.g., superconducting magnets and hydrogen), and renewable energy sources. *Energy, Vulnerability, and War* discusses Libyan- and Soviet-sponsored terrorism and notes that from 1970 to 1980 over 250 terrorist attacks against energy infrastructures were carried out (22, 23).

The first report's final chapter ranks technology options in terms of vulnerability, on the basis of their degree of centralization, local fuel supply, local maintenance, cost, construction lead time, and other criteria. Ethanol, low- and medium-BTU gas, new domestic petroleum, and methanol receive the highest ratings. Diesel, biogas, synthetic natural gas, biomass oils, and coal-derived oil receive medium ratings. Gasoline and hydrogen receive the lowest ratings. A second ranking for decentralized energy sources was also created. Cogeneration, small fossil plants (<250 MW), small hydro, geothermal, and fossil fuel gasification all receive the highest ratings. Next are biomass steam, wind, and biomass low-BTU gas. Solar technologies (both thermal and PV) rate next to last. The lowest ratings are received by fuel cells, waves, and ocean thermal energy conversion.

This report also suggests a fundamental institutional response, the creation of defense energy districts, "which would be administratively responsible for

---

[1]The reports were commissioned by the Defense Civil Preparedness Office of the Department of Defense. While they were being prepared, that office became part of a new organization called the Federal Emergency Management Agency, a civilian agency established in 1979 that brought together many disparate federal entities that were involved in some aspect of emergency management.

categorizing, inventorying, and coordinating the implementation of dispersed, decentralized and renewable energy resources technologies" (p. 319). Although the report describes the potential for decentralized energy technologies to address security concerns, it does not provide a method for quantifying this effect. Civil defense preparedness is emphasized, not efficiency and renewable energy, per se. Political choices regarding possible trade-offs between conflicting goals (e.g., more security versus lower prices) are not addressed in *Energy, Vulnerability, and War*, which assumes a unitary decision maker with a single goal, civil defense.

The second report was reproduced as the ground-breaking book *Brittle Power: Energy Strategy for National Security* by Amory and Hunter Lovins (10, 24). It documents an amazing array of accidents, malicious attacks, and near misses on U.S. energy systems, identifying the infrastructures for electricity, natural gas, oil, and nuclear power as "Disasters Waiting To Happen" (10, Part Two, pp. 87–174). The key factors that make these centralized energy infrastructures "the root of the problem" (10, p. 218) include the use of dangerous materials (fuels); limited public acceptance of centralized energy infrastructure; centralization of fuel sources; little fuel substitutability; the length, operational requirements, and inflexibility of energy shipment systems; interactions between energy systems; high capital intensity, long lead times; and reliance on specialized skills.

Brittle Power highlights the benefits of efficiency and small-scale renewable energy technologies under routine conditions. In their work, one paper that attempts to model the effect of decentralized energy technologies in abnormally stressful situations is identified (25). Lovins and Lovins argue that the mismatch between the scale of centralized energy system components (large) and the scale of most power consumption (small) is at the core of energy system vulnerabilities, and the mismatch can be rectified by increasing end-use energy efficiency and using more decentralized renewable energy. This approach, they argue, is cheaper than the centralized approach, in addition to any security implications.

Another key concept in *Brittle Power* is resilience, which is borrowed from ecology (23, 26), and which the authors argue should be designed into energy systems. Elements of a resilient system would include a modular structure, redundancy and substitutability, diversity, possibility of decoupling, and dispersion (pp. 179–82). This discussion is remarkably similar to the concept of "survivability" that was developed independently in the computer security field in the late 1990s (27, 28). Lovins & Lovins even use a discussion of mainframe versus distributed computation as an analogy for decentralized energy systems (pp. 208–13). However, *Brittle Power* goes further, emphasizing social factors such as minimizing the need for social control to operate and protect the energy system and for understandable technology to enhance social acceptance.

Both *Energy, Vulnerability, and War* and *Brittle Power* summarize relevant literature, provide numerous relevant facts and examples, make many logical arguments, and offer compelling visions, but they do not attempt any quantitative assessment of the value of resilience or the comparative values of centralization versus decentralization. Moreover, the details of energy system design, investment, and operation are ignored, despite the many examples provided. Crucially, both books (but especially *Brittle Power*) inextricably link together the concepts of efficiency, renewability, decentralization, and security, offering little conceptual space for decentralized energy infrastructures based on fossil fuels or small (<250 MW) nuclear reactors: "Ultimately, high national levels of end-use efficiency could... allow the entire grid to depend on inherently resilient, largely local energy sources" (*Brittle Power*, p. 281). It is hard to imagine how large concentrations of people or industry could be served this way, even with significant energy efficiency improvements, yet Lovins and Lovins insist their vision does not require "social decentralization" (10, pp. 219–20).

Thus, both books offer an idealized vision with heavy reliance on decentralized renewable energy sources. Unfortunately, when larger renewable energy systems are mentioned, the problems of grids are barely mentioned (e.g., 18, pp. 171–85, 204–15; 10, pp. 264–68, 277–82). Both books generally ignore the possibility that large-scale, renewables-based energy systems (e.g., large wind farms) might be necessary for cities and industry and the associated security issues. For instance, the problems of long transport distances and resulting vulnerability of energy infrastructures are associated with all types of centralized energy systems, whether fueled by coal, uranium, or the wind. In addition, for some key distributed generation (DG) challenges, such as network coordination, backup power, and line-worker safety, no universal solutions have emerged. And because these books assume renewable energy is both more secure and less expensive, questions of how much society should be willing to pay for security and who should pay never arise. Nonetheless, some elements of the vision outlined in *Brittle Power* are being put into practice, providing the lessons and experiences necessary to make progress in resolving issues. If this vision proves accurate in the long term, it changes the nature of the debate on how much energy security a society wants, how best to obtain it, and who should pay for it.

CONCEPTS

Several key concepts can be identified with the issue of energy infrastructure and security; some of which are present to one degree or another in the early analysis, but some of which are new.

Routine Security

Like any other activity, the energy industries have secured their assets and operations against ordinary threats such as theft, low-level vandalism, and commercial espionage. To do so, relatively modest efforts were all that were required, and less-than-perfect prevention was acceptable. That is, the costs of loss prevention had to be balanced with the cost of losses themselves. Typical efforts taken by firms include the use of various methods for monitoring and control of access (e.g., surveillance, fences, and computer passwords). These firm-level security measures are embedded in a social setting where security is provided by various government measures, ranging from definition of who has control over property, through policing property against unlawful access, and protecting national borders.

Thus, economists would describe routine security as a mixture of private and public good (29).[2] O'Hanlon et al. (30, pp. 79–82) provide several reasons for government action in this area, including national sovereignty, economies of scale, and mismatches between public and private goals. Of course, the level of routine security varies from place to place, but at any level, it embodies at least an implicit agreement on adequate levels of routine security and on the means to pay for it, privately or publicly. Naturally, such agreements on the level and distribution of acceptable security costs are controversial, and politics is generally involved in reaching agreement. What is not clear, however, is if these processes have considered the possibility of achieving functional security through an alternative infrastructure designed to be fault tolerant and, hence, an unrewarding target for disruption. This approach might have higher costs during routine operation but lower overall costs when nonroutine events are considered.

Expected Failures

Engineered systems, such as energy infrastructures, require periodic maintenance and suffer occasional equipment failures. Except for unexpected systematic failures, experience is used to generate reliable expectations of failure rates, as well as other information, with which to balance the costs of failures, maintenance, and new capital. These expectations are conditional upon routine conditions, such as proper equipment operation and usage rates and the availability of trained repair personnel and supplies. These expectations yield normal outage rates for customer service in various energy infrastructures, which range from extremely rare (e.g., residential natural gas delivery) to several hours per year (e.g., residential electricity service). Similarly, labor strikes and bad weather can interfere with the transportation of fuel (e.g., coal) or electric power system operation and cause routine outages that must be part of management planning.

These issues are more important in electric power systems than in other energy infrastructures because of the inability to economically store electricity and the consequent necessity of matching supply and demand continuously. The necessity of dealing with these constraints during normal operations has resulted in a long history of *reliability* planning in the electricity sector, which includes consideration of both normal operation under reasonable expectations of intended operating conditions (adequacy) and of limited disturbances due to weather and occasional stochastic equipment failures that are expected but whose occurrence cannot be scheduled (security) (31).

---

[2]Some economists (8, 30) use the concept of externalities, but this seems a less useful approach because many aspects of security are nonexclusive and nonrival, key properties of public goods.

Furthermore, large-scale blackouts result from *cascading failures*, which occur when equipment failure or other disruption causes further failures or disruptions in large portions of the power grid (32). These events are relatively rare but very costly. Normally, reliability planning is more successfully implemented in industrialized than in less-industrialized countries. However, systematic changes in the management of power delivery have been known to overwhelm such planning, resulting in rolling blackouts (e.g., in Eastern Europe of the 1990s, when they sought hard currency and exported to the West during peak demand periods, and in California in the summer of 2000).[3]

Attack Modes

The most obvious effect from an attack on energy infrastructures is supply interruption; blackouts and oil embargos figure prominently in the popular and political interpretations of energy security. Supply interruptions are discussed below in the sections Oil and Gas as well as Electricity. However, there are a number of other possible attack modes as well. The fuel and waste of nuclear power plants are both radiologically dangerous and can (with significant processing) be used to produce nuclear weapons, as discussed below in the section Nuclear Power. Other attack modes can include releasing the stored energy in fuels [e.g., liquefied natural gas (LNG), storage vessels, or tankers] or in the water impounded behind hydroelectric dams against life and property (33, 34). We deal with this last group below.

LNG is stored at approximately 150-peak-shaving plants worldwide, and it is shipped between 40 terminals in about 150 tankers (35). There is a negligible probability that an attack on an LNG tank (whether on land or afloat) would cause an explosion, although a fierce fire would likely burn for up to an hour. Boiling liquid expanding vapor explosions are not uncommon for liquefied petroleum gas and other chemicals, but none has been observed during experiments or in the 30 years of LNG trade (36–38). Worldwide, approximately 30 tanker safety incidents have occurred since commercial shipping began in 1959, of which 12 involved LNG spillage, but none resulted in a fire or explosion. Several significant accidents on land have occurred, including a recent explosion at an LNG terminal in Skikda, Algeria, that killed about 30 people and will cost approximately $800 million to repair (39). However, even this accident caused no off-site damage and did not appear to involve stored LNG. Given the security measures currently in place, possible terrorist attacks on LNG infrastructure may present a smaller hazard to public health and safety than possible attacks on other hazardous materials shipped in large quantities and may present a greater risk to supply security than to public safety.

Cooling towers at electric power plants could conceivably be used in a deliberate attack as a means of dispersing biological or chemical agents. The magnitude of this threat is not well understood because these facilities have some physical security

---

[3]Rolling blackouts, voltage variations, and unreliable supply in many less-industrialized countries are often the result of insufficient generation capacity or fuel and demand outstripping supply, a more fundamental challenge than an issue of poor reliability planning.

and because the effectiveness of cooling towers to disperse various agents is not well studied.

Hydroelectric dams can store significant amounts of energy in the form of water retained behind them. If they were suddenly breached, both property and lives could be lost. It is not very easy to successfully attack most large dams, however, and physical access to them can be controlled relatively easily. One complicating factor is that smaller upstream facilities, such as locks or small dams, may be more vulnerable to attack. Breeching one or more of these could send a pulse of water downstream, possibly causing a larger dam downriver to fail catastrophically. Physical security (access control) is the primary means of mitigating this threat.

Finally, large electromagnetic pulses (EMP) can induce instantaneous voltages of hundreds of thousands of volts in conductors, creating very large disruptions in electric power systems and destroying electrical equipment components such as motors, backup generators, and microprocessors (18, pp. 47–49; 67). Concerns about EMP have traditionally been focused on the impact of high-altitude nuclear detonations, and there is an extensive body of literature in this area (much of it seemingly written in the 1970s and 1980s). However, relatively simple, inexpensive nonnuclear devices that can deliver an EMP have been designed and tested by the United States and other nations, raising concerns that EMP could be used by malicious groups with relatively low levels of sophistication and resources.

Recently, concerns have emerged that even crude devices could be deployed with significant localized impacts (40, 41). Such weapons could damage the electric power systems and also use the electric power systems as a conduit to attack other infrastructures (e.g., telecommunications) without physically penetrating facility perimeters. It is not clear how vulnerable the current systems are to such an assault nor what could be done to defend them. The continued vulnerability of power systems to geomagnetically induced currents as a result of solar activity indicates that power systems have not been hardened against such threats. There are a number of factors that impact how solar flares (which occur on a relatively regular cycle of 11 years) will affect a power system, but the historical evidence indicates the potential for widespread outages is real. For example, a 1989 solar flare resulted in a multi-hour, widespread blackout in Quebec (42).

Currently, there is very little information from credible sources on the EMP threat from nonstate actors, so this concern is somewhat speculative. It is also unclear how similar such a threat would be to a solar flare or thermonuclear event. One study that modeled solar- and thermonuclear-induced currents showed that even these two types of fairly well known events have differing characteristics and potential impacts (43). The electromagnetic pulse from a nuclear blast is stronger but not as long-lived as the one from the solar flare event. Although both can cause the transformer to produce harmonics and become a reactive power load, potentially causing the system to try to isolate transformers (and thus possibly resulting in outages), the longer timescale of the solar events can provide enough time for transformer cores to overheat and lead to greater equipment damage. Possible damage to sensitive electronics at the end use is not discussed.

Diversity

One of the key methods for achieving a reliable energy supply and secure energy infrastructures has been through diversity, even if accidentally achieved. This concept was imported to some degree from ecology (10, pp. 195–98; 23, 26). Vulnerability due to a lack of diversity was well demonstrated in the first oil crisis. The price hikes in 1973 led to an active and successful search for oil reserves outside the Middle East and especially outside the Organization of Petroleum Exporting Countries (OPEC). The resulting diversity of supply reduced the power of OPEC as an oligopoly (120). However, non-OPEC production seems to be peaking, renewing concerns about the concentration of reserves in the Middle East and about oil supply vulnerabilities (44–47).

Another form of diversity is not across suppliers of one fuel, but across types of fuels and technologies for their utilization. Diversity of fuel mix often occurs in the production of electricity, and advocates of every fuel can use this term to support policies that could mandate minimum and maximum market shares. For instance, Porter & Steen (48) illustrate how diversity in fuel supplies is being sought through renewable energy in the United Kingdom, and Lemar (49) shows how it can be achieved in the United States through combined heat and power. Diversity in technology is also important as a means of reducing vulnerability to a design error leading to widespread failures or preemptive shutdowns in order to affect repairs. Evans & Hope (50) argue that although standardized designs in nuclear plants improve economies of production, they also increase exposure to the possibility of systematic unknown failures due to that design. They stress the need for a range of nuclear plant designs. Taking a longer-term perspective, several researchers have documented the need for diversity in energy research and development in order to assure a broad choice of technologies into the future (51, 52).

In recent times there is evidence that neither political control nor market forces can be counted on to yield diversity in energy systems. For instance, before market liberalization in the United Kingdom (U.K.) political pressure from coal miners' unions prevented coal-fired plants from being installed near ports because this would open them up to steam-coal imports at a quarter of the prevailing price from U.K. mines. At the same time, however, the public electricity monopoly in England and Wales (CEGB) included diversity of supply as an operational issue. After privatization, market forces have yielded a singular "dash to gas." A strong preference for local fuels is common in electricity generation, as is a preference for whatever the least-cost or most fashionable technology happens to be. For instance, in Spain, dirty, expensive local brown coal was used for power generation long after it was economic to do so, largely to preserve local jobs (53). In the United States, a fairly diverse set of fuels for the electricity sector has come from a century of investment decisions in generation technologies that have been relatively uniform nationwide within each cohort. Companies shifted their emphasis in new capacity investments from one technology to another with each pulse of system renewal and expansion starting with hydroelectric, then coal, nuclear, and, now, gas-fired plants. If global oil markets were strictly competitive, much more production in the ultralow-cost Middle East region might result, although risk aversion by producing firms might cause them to broaden their production portfolio to include other regions, even if a cost premium was required. However, the balance that would be struck in this way would reflect the interests of the infrastructure owners more than public interest.

Such portfolio management approaches use a probabilistic framework for quantifying the risks of various technologies and the use of utility maximization or other probabilistic techniques. It has been suggested that such techniques can fail if the uncertainty and risk cannot be adequately characterized, and in such cases, diversity may yield benefits that would not be captured by such techniques (54). There have been several efforts at formalizing the benefits of diversity, which could include mitigating technological path dependencies for the future, allowing for multiple and contradictory social choices to be met, fostering innovation and hedging against ignorance (55, 56).

Storage

The second key method for achieving reliable energy supply and secure energy infrastructures is storage, which applies most strongly to the oil and gas sectors because electricity cannot be stored readily. A key issue is the amount of storage that might be necessary, especially as compared with demand. Together, these two factors will determine how long normal operations can go on without interruption and give some indication of how much demand reduction (conservation) might be needed in an emergency to extend the period during which storage can supply vital services.

A major topic in energy policy is the creation and management of strategic petroleum reserves (SPRs), which is discussed in a subsequent section. However, SPR facilities can become a security risk themselves. Storage is expensive and consumers may not be willing to pay for it regularly, so socially optimal levels may not be achieved under purely market conditions. For natural gas, regional storage (typically in depleted oil and gas reservoirs) is an important component of the infrastructure system and helps gas utilities deal with high demands in the winter. Such storage areas can also act as buffers in the event of damage to the upstream system, allowing a utility to ride through a disturbance for days or even weeks, depending on when the incident occurs.

Opportunities to store electricity are much more limited. Hydroelectric dams offer some measure of storage capacity that can provide supplies for a short-term emergency. Pumped-storage (air and water) schemes (have storage capacity ranging from tens to hundreds of megawatt hours) are also a possibility for even shorter-term supply security. On the user side, the rapid proliferation of portable devices (e.g., local backup systems) has introduced a few hours of storage capacity embodied in the batteries and fuel of such devices. This end-user storage capacity does not extend, however, to the vast majority of end uses supported by electricity.

Redundancy

The third key method for achieving reliable energy supply redundancy builds on the concept of planning for expected failure through reserve margins and applies most strongly to the electricity sector. For example, in many locations hospitals are served directly by multiple feeder lines in order to have some measure of security against interruptions in part of the distribution networks. Redundancy in an electricity network would mean significantly larger reserve margins and multiple transmission and distribution networks. This approach is very costly because much of the infrastructure sits unused most of the time, but it makes supply disruption more difficult because all redundancy for a particular load must be simultaneously rendered inoperative. Only a subset of consumers may be willing to pay for such a system.

Cyber Security

An increasingly important topic in the security of infrastructure, and one that distinguishes current concerns from the primary concerns of the cold war era is computer, or cyber, security, especially as delivered through the Internet. Traditionally, information technology (IT) in the energy sector has been considered less vulnerable to attack (at least by outsiders) than the infrastructure itself. This is partly because these IT systems often consisted of dedicated systems without interconnection to other computer networks and with built-in redundancies.

Energy sector IT systems have traditionally relied on uncommon, often proprietary protocols and the need for considerable hard-to-obtain knowledge about operating systems. However, such measures are insufficient, particularly when one considers the insider threat problem. An employee with the proper knowledge could create serious problems and face minimal resistance from the system owing to lack of encryption and authorization requirements. Moreover, these systems are changing to standardized systems, which lower costs and increase flexibility and capabilities. Thus, concern about current and future energy sector IT systems arises because of their use of open protocols, increased use of intelligent devices, and lack of encryption (57). Remote systems receiving control signals from the control center often do not verify such signals for authenticity. Current systems may also be more vulnerable to attack because of their increasing use of dial-up modems and the Internet. For instance, in January 2003, an Internet-transmitted computer virus infected and disabled several computers at the Davis-Bessie nuclear power plant, although the plant was shut down for emergency repairs, so there were no safety concerns.

In the electricity industry, energy management systems (EMS) monitor and control the production, transmission, and distribution of electrical energy. This includes scheduling and controlling generators and monitoring and analyzing the transmission network in order to provide power while maintaining reliability of the system. Competition is leading to more and more use of electricity markets to make decisions about which power plants will be operated when. Because markets are typically open, it may be impractical (or more expensive) to verify the identity and reliability of all participants, exacerbating the problem.

A rare public admission of energy-related cyber warfare was recently described in a news column (58). The U.S. government apparently arranged for the sale of faulty natural gas pipeline operating software to a third party who it knew would illegally resell (pirate) the program to the Soviet Union. The fault was designed to overpressurize gas pipelines, which led to an explosion of nuclear proportions in an uninhabited area of Siberia in June of 1982, and more importantly, slowed Soviet scientific and engineering work that was using similarly pirated software.

Interdependency

A relatively new and crucial concept associated with the security of energy infrastructures is interdependency, which is the reliance of one infrastructure (e.g., electric power) upon another (e.g., telecommunications) or even mutual reliance of infrastructures upon one another (59, 60). Amin (61) goes so far as to argue that a new megainfrastructure is emerging. Interdependency effects have been observed numerous times, such as during the U.S. western states power outage in 1996, which very nearly led to the collapse of the telecommunications system.

Rinaldi et al. (60) identified six dimensions for understanding infrastructure systems, including infrastructure characteristics, such as spatial and organizational scope, and the legal/regulatory framework. One of those dimensions is the type of interdependency. They created a classification scheme with four types of interdependencies (physical, cyber, logical, and geographic). Other research efforts focused on developing specific tools to understand infrastructure interdependencies. Longstaff & Haimes' (62) Hierarchical Holographic Modeling technique is one example.

Another example of infrastructure interdependency is that some nations rely on petroleum products for a considerable fraction of electricity generation, such as Singapore (65%), Italy (32%), and the Philippines (28%) (63). A significant oil supply interruption could impact the electricity sector in these countries. A final example is provided by Zweifel & Bonomo (64), who show that simultaneous shortages of both oil and gas lead to different optimal strategic responses than does consideration of singular supply interruptions.

Stress

The reliability planning long used for energy infrastructure investment fairly well describes most conditions in high-income countries, but they do not describe a variety of situations now considered important in both high- and low-income countries (31, 65, 66). In this review, deviation from intended or routine operating conditions is defined as a condition of *stress*, which includes deliberate attacks, multiple failures, persistent failures or attacks, and conditions that make system restoration difficult (e.g., a lack of spare parts) (67–69). Stress differs from the modes of disturbance analyzed in typical reliability planning in several important ways, including events with one or more of the following general characteristics.

1. Coordination of attack: Unlike equipment failures or even extreme weather events, deliberate attacks are not short-term, random events. Both militaries and terrorists have the capability to coordinate attacks and intentionally maximize damage to the system. Attacks can also be repeated as system components are repaired.

2. Significant scope of impacts: The failure of distribution equipment within one-half mile of the customer accounts for about half of electricity outages in the United States. However, in conflict situations, remote transmission lines, transformer substations, pipeline pumping stations, or oil terminals can also become primary targets or be impacted by indirect damage stresses. Nonconflict stresses (e.g., poor access to spare parts) would also have a wider scope of impacts.

3. Persistence of outage: Deliberate attacks may not be single events, and they may occur under conditions (or create conditions) that make restoration of service and repair more difficult. Alternatively, conditions could be created that make even routine maintenance more difficult. When outages do occur, there are a number of factors that can lead to outages that persist for days or even longer. Such factors would include risks to personnel, impeded transportation of personnel and parts, insufficient funds for replacement parts, absence of technical expertise, and the possibility of subsequent sabotage. Although long outages, lasting from hours to days, are commonplace in less-industrialized countries, they are so abnormal in industrialized countries that a "sustained interruption" is generally classified as one that lasts more than one hour. There are no further classifications for longer outages.

Survivability

The traditional reliability planning approach does not lend itself well to responding to unexpected, deliberate, and potentially very high-impact attacks. For one thing, it is very difficult to imagine all possible attack modes or strategies. Even if this problem could be overcome, current practices in reliability analysis allow for essentially only one strategy—redundancy—a very costly solution that competitive firms are not likely to implement, and one that may divert resources from other important uses and possibly slow economic growth (70). Thus, supply-side solutions are not likely to be sufficient any longer; more attention to the economic and social implications of end-use disruptions will be needed. One concept that may link reliability and security and may also be compatible with competitive energy industries is *survivability*, also known as "the self-healing grid" or "the resilient network." Survivability is similar to the ecological concept of resilience that was applied to energy systems over 20 years ago (10 Chapt. 13; 26, 28, 62, 63, 67, 68, 71, 72).

Survivability is the ability of a system to fulfill its mission in a timely manner, despite attacks, failures, or accidents. It can be contrasted with the current fortress model of security that tries to prevent or counter all attacks but has disastrous outcomes (e.g., cascading failures) when it does inevitably fail. A fundamental assumption of survivability analysis and design is that no individual component of a system is immune from attacks, accidents, or design errors. Thus, a survivable system must be created out of inherently vulnerable subunits, making survivability an emergent property of the system rather than a design feature for individual components.

Because of the size and complexity of energy system operations, and the speed at which faults can propagate in some of them, it may be difficult to recognize attacks until there is extensive damage. Thus, ways must be found to recognize attack early and isolate the affected area in order to protect the rest of the system. Survivable systems must be able to function autonomously, maintain or restore essential services during an attack, and recover full service after the attack. Thus, the system must fail gracefully, shedding low-priority tasks, and later resume tasks in a priority order during recovery. Our current energy systems are optimized for operation in routine conditions and cannot do this. The prolonged outage (in many locations as long as five days) of power delivery in Ontario in the aftermath of the August 2003 blackout was primarily the result of system stability concerns when energizing a grid that would immediately have to meet peak demand conditions from air conditioners that could not be remotely shut down.

For example, in most cities, traffic signals are powered by the same circuits that provide service to much less critical loads like billboards. During blackouts, injury and property loss may occur because of blank traffic signals. Worsening the problem, blackouts cause gridlock that hinder police and emergency response crews from reaching their destinations. This demonstrates the fortress aspect of traditional reliability planning—it creates a system in which frequent or large-scale blackouts are not supposed to occur, but when they do, the consequences are severe. In contrast, a system designed around survivability concepts might use low-power light-emitting diode traffic lights with battery backup to ensure that a blackout does not interrupt traffic flow. However, if this approach has higher costs, it is not obvious how many should be installed, where they should be installed, or how best to pay for them.

Centralization

A key theme in the literature on energy infrastructure and security is centralization, particularly as it applies to the electricity sector. Several observers have documented how the combination of technological innovation and social (political and financial) forces throughout the twentieth century has led to ever larger centralized electricity generation plants connected by ever larger synchronized grids (73, 74, Chapt. 3; 75, Chapt. 19). Even a quadruple crisis in the late 1970s that led to fundamental change in the electric utility industry (the introduction of competition) failed to completely arrest this process.[4] Centralization also affects oil and gas infrastructures because of the number and location of key parts of the supply chain, including facilities for production, gathering, shipping, processing, and delivering raw materials and products (4, 10). Given the geographic concentration of petroleum and gas deposits in a relatively small number of locations worldwide, and the need to ship petroleum through constrained corridors (e.g., the Straits of Molucca), the potential for decentralization in this sector seems slight. In addition, it is not clear that resilient technologies for these sectors exist.

Critics of centralized energy systems argue that they are brittle and prone to failure, whereas decentralized systems can be resilient (10, 76, 77). Resilient technologies are argued to include efficiency improvements, electricity generation near point of use, responsive demand, and renewables (which require no fuel supply). Supporters of these approaches also claim other benefits, such as lower costs, lower environmental impact, and, sometimes, more decision-making power in local (not federal or corporate) hands (78). One of the main promoters of such concepts, Amory Lovins (79, p. 38), claimed that "[t]he distinction between the hard and soft energy paths rests not on how much energy is used but rather on the technical and political *structure* of the energy system."

In contrast, supporters of centralized electricity systems argue that large interconnected grids have traditionally delivered improved reliability. They focus on the need for a sufficiently large grid in which to embed higher-efficiency centralized plants and the ability of a grid to capture the time-diversity of demand, allowing the integrated system to have a higher load factor, all of which also lower costs. The reliability benefits of large, coordinated systems are visible only by looking at unexpected energy flows during partial network failures, which is uncommon outside of the electricity industry. Thus, supporters of large, centralized systems tend to support technologies that will make electric power grids connecting large, centralized plants "smarter" (increased automation and computation), more "aware" (more and better sensors and communications), and faster to react (automation and power electronics instead of manual electromechanical controls) (80–82).

For instance, the recent National Transmission Grid Study includes "targeted energy efficiency and distributed generation" as one of ten approaches to "relieving transmission bottlenecks," not as a central organizing paradigm to be applied widely. Similarly, the United States Energy Association's "National Energy Security Post 9/11" report is highly asymmetrical in the treatment of centralized energy supply compared to efficiency, renewables, and decentralized supply (82). Strong policies to support centralized supply are recommended without reservation, e.g., "Allow refiners and other energy producers to recapture the full cost of meeting new environmental regulations"; whereas policy recommendations on efficiency are limited to research and development; and policy recommendations for renewables are weak and contingent, e.g., "Encourage deployment of renewable energy

---

[4]The four elements of this crisis were technological failures, fuel price shocks, environmental control costs, and unexpected interest rate increases (75).

supplies when doing so will strengthen the energy infrastructure and/or increase U.S. energy security" (82).

Government efforts to support improved security of energy infrastructure generally ignore these issues as well, generally leaving decisions regarding technology choice to the private sector. Thus, government tends to work to improve the security of whatever infrastructure the private sector builds but often does not require the private sector to include security concerns in its investment decisions. The cost of government efforts tends to be socialized by support from general revenue, not by the infrastructures that create concerns. This approach may yield more infrastructure and more infrastructure security activities than would an efficient market outcome, and it would tend to subsidize technologies with greater security concerns over those with fewer (83). This would likely be both inefficient and unfair because those that impose security burdens are not required to pay for them (30, pp. 77–97).

More recently, von Meier (84) used the term supple electric power technologies to identify technologies that promote decentralization without regard to renewability, which characterized prior analyses from the 1980s. Supple technologies are modular, suited to dispersed siting, and fuel flexible, and they include reciprocating engines, microturbines, and fuel cells. She notes other important differences, including the fact that the current energy system can no longer be characterized as purely hard; energy efficiency improvements and smaller-scale generation are now more common and accepted.

Von Meier observes that the fundamental political changes Lovins and others sought in order to achieve widespread adoption of soft technologies have not been accomplished. Instead, technological improvements in decentralized technologies have had an effect, and more importantly, market forces have come to the fore. Von Meier argues that "the ensemble of supple technologies does not support a natural monopoly in ... electricity" (84, p. 213). This may not be strictly true; Strachan & Dowlatabadi (85) document the very successful deployment of decentralized energy technologies in the Netherlands by incumbent utility companies once proper incentives were provided. However, there may be a potentially fundamental antagonism between the interests of large, incumbent energy firms operating a centralized infrastructure under a monopoly franchise system and those who deploy decentralized energy technologies, because such a deployment may undermine the monopoly position of the incumbent. This problem may significantly limit the potential contributions of decentralized production to the security of energy infrastructures in areas with monopoly franchises. Ample evidence in the United States supports the claim that large, incumbent electricity firms tend to be antagonistic to decentralized energy (86).

CRITICAL INFRASTRUCTURE PROTECTION

As noted above, cold war concerns about the security of energy and other infrastructures faded in the late 1980s. However, the rise of catastrophic terrorism within industrialized countries (e.g., the truck bombing of the World Trade Center in 1993), the Western States power outage in 1996, and the realization in the mid-1990s that the transition from 1999 to 2000 might cause significant disruptions led to a renewed concern about the potential vulnerability of key infrastructures. The response to these developments has come to be termed critical infrastructure protection (CIP), which links energy and other infrastructures with national security (87, 88). Many nations have undertaken CIP activities in the past several years, especially the United States (89).

Definitions

Definitions of CIP vary somewhat. For instance, Section 1016(e) of the *USA Patriot Act* defines critical infrastructure as

> systems and assets, whether physical or virtual, so vital to the United States that the incapacity or destruction of such systems and assets would have a debilitating impact on security, national economic security, national public health or safety, or any combination of these matters. (158)

The White House subsequently highlighted the symbolic value of critical infrastructures, which

> provide the foundation for our national security, governance, economic vitality, and way of life. Furthermore, their continued reliability, robustness, and resiliency create a sense of confidence and form an important part of our national identity and purpose. (91, p. viii)

International agreement on a definition of CIP does not exist. For instance, some would add maintaining ecological health (87). However, despite the specific definition of critical infrastructure, all nations that use this term include energy systems (or networks) in this categorization. Other CIP sectors usually include banking and finance, communications, transportation, water supply, emergency services (e.g., police and fire), law enforcement, and public health.

Another key issue in defining CIP, and one that distinguishes it from previous analysis, is the role that cyber security plays in the operation of critical infrastructures (92). All infrastructure systems in industrialized economies are highly computerized, and cyber security is viewed as a separate and equally serious challenge as physical security. For example, the White House has released one national strategy document on physically protecting infrastructures and another on securing cyberspace (91, 93). This has occasionally resulted in the terms critical infrastructure protection and cyber security of infrastructures to be used synonymously. However, it is difficult to determine the likelihood of success or the impact of a cyber attack on an energy infrastructure because there is scant historical precedent to analyze.

In an interesting review of definitions, Moteff et al. (94) note that since Executive Order 13,010 was signed in 1996, the definition of CIP, used by the U.S. federal government, has grown broader. They note that an overly broad and overly flexible definition of CIP is problematic because this could lead to vague, ineffective policies and a growing federal government commitment. If the list of critical infrastructures continues to change, or if multiple lists of critical infrastructures are created, public and private decision makers may find it more difficult to actually protect these infrastructures. This problem raises the need for prioritization, and Moteff et al. propose five approaches for prioritizing CIP actions based on different aspects of the problem: the degree of criticality of any infrastructure element, vulnerabilities that cut across infrastructures, interdependencies among infrastructures, key geographic locations where multiple critical infrastructures coexist, or assets owned by or relied on by the federal government.

Practice

Australia and the United States were the first nations to address CIP, and we will focus on U.S. CIP efforts because they are by far the most comprehensive. The first formal CIP measure in the United States was the establishment of the President's Commission on Critical Infrastructure Protection (PCCIP) under Executive Order 13,010 (95). This commission's documents, as well as subsequent analyses, highlighted the potentially serious consequences of attacks on critical infrastructure. In 1997, the commission issued its final report, which had several key recommendations, including the creation of a national warning center, an idea that was acted on by the creation of a National Infrastructure Protection Center (NIPC, see http://www.nipc.gov) within the Federal Bureau of Investigation in 1998 (96). The PCCIP also identified a large number of gaps in existing capabilities needed for successful CIP and called for a significant research, development, and education initiative (97).

These recommendations were taken up in Presidential Decision Directive 63, which called for a range of activities (98). Among these steps was an enhancement of the NIPC as "a national focal point for gathering information on threats and facilitating government's response to computer-based incidents" and to provide "the principal means of facilitating and coordinating the Federal Government's response to incidents, mitigating attacks, investigating threats, and monitoring reconstitution efforts" (88, p. 8). Since that time, especially after the attacks on the World Trade Center on September 11, 2001, a significant CIP bureaucracy has been developed in the U.S. government, some of which has (or may have) significant impacts on the energy sector. The new Office of Energy Assurance in the U.S. Department of Energy identifies over 60 CIP organizations, ranging from the National Security Council (NSC), to the U.S. Coast Guard, to the North American Electricity Reliability Council (NERC) (99).

One of the most significant organizational developments since Presidential Decision Directive 63 has been the creation of the new Department of Homeland Security (DHS). Initially created by Executive Order as an office within the White House, it has now become a government department and has taken over several roles (and organizations) once located in various parts of the federal government (90, 100). Other new federal positions and organizations include the following:

- National Coordinator for Security, Critical Infrastructure, and Counter-Terrorism in the NSC;
- Critical Infrastructure Assurance Office;
- National Infrastructure Simulation and Analysis Center (NISAC);
- Critical Infrastructure Coordination Group;
- Department of Energy's Office of Energy Assurance; and
- Several other intergovernmental groups focused on cyber security (90, 100).

The key roles of these organizations are to coordinate public sector activities, from the federal to the local level; conduct research and development; and coordinate and encourage private sector owners of critical infrastructure to help assure its protection. (A large majority of the energy infrastructure in the United States is privately owned.)

Coordination between the federal government (through the NIPC) and the private sector is conducted through Information Sharing and Analysis Centers (ISACs), which for the energy sector are coordinated by NERC (http://www.esisac.com) and the American Petroleum Institute (http://www.energyisac.com). There is considerable disagreement about the appropriate role of legally binding CIP standards or requirements versus voluntary targets and self-regulation. Naturally, industry prefers less regulation yet the public good nature of CIP makes it unclear that wholly voluntary approaches can yield a socially optimal level of CIP. At the moment, the government has only officially called for "standardized guidelines" for risk assessment and security that would be developed in partnership with industry and other levels of government (91).

Another important issue is determining the level of control and funding for government activity at the federal, state, and local levels. O'Hanlon et al. (30, pp. 77–97) argue that activities with primarily local benefits should be decided upon and paid for locally, whereas those with national implications should be under the jurisdiction of the federal government.

The issue of financing overall homeland security measures, including critical infrastructure protection, is complex and will remain a mix of both public and private expenditures (30). In the United States, proposed public expenditures for infrastructure protection in 2005 are over $850 million out of a total nondefense homeland security budget of almost $34 billion. There is some concern over the economic impact that expenditures in these areas may have. O'Hanlon et al. (30) recommend a homeland security program that would result in $45 billion of public and $10 billion of private costs per year. Their estimate is that this would result in a 0.3% to 0.5% reduction in real output from the economy and reduce growth rates by 0.1 percentage points or less. The "National Strategy for Homeland Security" states that the federal government will set priorities on the basis of a consistent methodology and an approach that will allow it to balance costs and expected benefit, but it does not state what an appropriate methodology or approach might be (94, 101).

The key issues associated with recovering security-related costs in regulated utilities are summarized in a recent National Regulatory Research Institute (NRRI) white paper (102). Some of the most important issues include differentiating security-related from competition-related costs, applying tests of reasonableness appropriately to CIP expenditures, and devising cost recovery mechanisms (e.g., rates). A survey conducted by NRRI showed that in 2003, only 17% of state public service commissions either had or were developing guidelines for the prudence of CIP-related expenditures, even though 45% reported that utilities had filed requests for recovery of such costs (103). Of those states reporting such filings, only a small fraction (23%) reported that utility CIP-related expenditures were driven by state or federal regulations.

Some business leaders have raised concerns that the high level of security expenditures in the United States could result in a reduction in international competitiveness, requiring a balance between security and competitiveness (70). They argue that "[t]op-down, prescriptive security standards could drain productivity and dampen growth prospects, putting U.S. companies, universities and workers at a disadvantage vis-à-vis their foreign competitors. Only the private sector is able to design integrated security solutions to protect productivity and competitiveness." In contrast, O'Hanlon et al. (30) argue that "in most cases, providers and owners of the property or activity should generally pay for the costs of additional security. Furthermore, in most cases, the action should take the form of performance-oriented mandates on the private sector, perhaps coupled with insurance requirements or incentives, rather than direct subsidies or tax incentives." This approach is thought to discourage risky activities, prevent rent-seeking behavior, and promote innovation in antiterror strategies.

Another important area of disagreement is disclosure of private CIP information by infrastructure owners to the federal government (104). This debate focuses on the reconciliation of two conflicting public goals: the need to share information confidentially for CIP purposes and the need for public access to information to ensure open government. Private owners of critical infrastructure are reluctant to provide information that may have security or commercial value to the government for fear of it falling into the wrong hands under provisions like those of the federal *Freedom of Information Act* (FOIA) (104a). Advocates for civil liberties and for changes in regulation (e.g., environmental groups) are concerned that special protection of critical infrastructure information would preclude the ability to obtain information about abusive government practices, cast a veil of secrecy over central DHS activities, possibly allow industry to improperly shield information with policy implications unrelated to CIP, and are unnecessary because of existing FOIA exemptions. Some public interest groups are concerned that such protection would improperly shield infrastructure owners and operators from liability under antitrust, tort, tax, labor, and consumer protection laws (105).

Action in this area has already been taken by many regulatory agencies. In 2003, the Federal Energy Regulatory Commission (FERC) issued a rule providing definitions for Critical Energy Infrastructure Information (CEII) and procedures besides the FOIA for obtaining CEII information that has been submitted to FERC (106). In addition, the NRRI found in surveys that the percentage of state public utility commissions offering FOIA protection for sensitive information increased from 42% in 2002 to 82% in 2003 (103).

Nonetheless, concerns about secrecy have led to bills such as the Leahy-Levin-Jeffords-Lieberman-Byrd "Restore FOIA" proposal. Specific concerns include third-party liability, the lack of antitrust exemptions for industry-wide information sharing, and the release of competitively sensitive information. These issues will most likely take several years to be resolved by Congress and the courts. However, there have already been some examples identified of public-private information sharing that have been considered successful (one in telecommunications and one in health care), and these could act as models for future activities (107).

Similar, if smaller, CIP activities are underway in many other countries. The idea of a warning center and information-sharing mechanism embodied in the NIPC has been replicated in at least 11 countries (Australia, Canada, Germany, Israel, Italy, Japan, the Netherlands, New Zealand, South Korea, Sweden, and the United Kingdom) and over 12 more have investigated the concept (87, 108, 109). Many, such as New Zealand's Center for Critical Infrastructure Protection, formed in August 2001, and the United Kingdom's National Infrastructure Security Co-Ordination Center, focus on cyber attack.

Research

Research into CIP has begun to appear in the literature, although it is likely that a considerable amount of such activities will remain classified or proprietary. The U.S. National Academy of Sciences produced a comprehensive survey of, and strategy for, research and development in support of counterterrorism (110). This effort stressed the vulnerabilities of the electric power infrastructure and recommended research into tools for identifying and assessing infrastructure vulnerabilities, improving monitoring, hardening energy infrastructure from attack, enabling faster recovery, preventing cyber attack, and deploying an intelligent, adaptive power grid. Since then, significant research efforts have begun by academia, government, and private industry in these areas. Related research is also going on outside the United States, some of it oriented toward survivability concepts (111).

Several themes have emerged from this research. A fundamental goal of these efforts has been to better understand the specific vulnerabilities of infrastructure systems. A corollary to this effort has been research on robustness and survivability of current and alternative infrastructure systems. The goals of such efforts have included gaining a better understanding of the vulnerability of individual infrastructure systems, specific interdependencies between infrastructure systems, survivable systems, and the larger economic impacts of infrastructure failures.

Another major focus of research has been to develop modeling, simulation, and analysis tools to analyze infrastructures. Several of the U.S. national laboratories have taken on this role. Sandia National Laboratory recently created NISAC in order to apply the largest scale computational capabilities to model and analyze infrastructure vulnerabilities and provide support to government and industry (112). Modeling and the development of energy infrastructure test beds are under development at the Idaho National Engineering and Environmental Laboratory. One of the key strengths of modeling and simulation is that it can shed light on infrastructure interdependencies that are otherwise very hard to quantify (112, 113).

In many cases, the questions that have been asked over the past five to ten years could not be analyzed with the tools available (in some cases, simply because the problem has been posed in a slightly different manner). Improvements in computational speed have led to significant advances in modeling capabilities. This includes the improvement of traditional risk, vulnerability, and engineering methods, as well as the application of more recent modeling methods (such as agent-based models) to the infrastructure protection problem.

Another tool being used to understand the vulnerability of energy infrastructure systems are simulation exercises, similar to those used in military war games or in disaster response preparation. In the United States, these have included the Blue Cascades (focused on the Pacific Northwest) and Silent Vector (focused on national responses to terrorist strikes) exercises (5). These exercises have highlighted a number of issues related to the coordination of protection efforts, risk communication, differences between the public and private sector, and vulnerability of different infrastructure and economic sectors to disruption.

OIL AND GAS

The vast majority of the literature on energy security focuses on oil imports and on possible interruptions of petroleum supply (8, 46, 114). Figure 1, percent shares of conventional petroleum and natural gas, illustrates the reasons; the major economic powers, the United States, Europe and Japan, import huge amounts of oil, while the Middle East holds about two thirds of proved oil reserves (115, 116). Current production trends suggest production will tend to concentrate (centralize) further in the Middle East. An important counter-trend is in the discovery and production of nonconventional oil, such as deposits deep off-shore or formations like the Albertan tar sands, or even synthetic petroleum from gas or solids (117). Technological innovation tends to make these resources more economical, raising effective petroleum reserves, and decentralizing them as well. This effect is nontrivial; the Albertan tar sand deposits may hold the equivalent of over one third of Middle East conventional oil reserves.

The dependency of major oil-producing nations on the income from petroleum sales, coupled with the availability of alternative supplies at only slightly higher prices, may limit the potential for oil supply interruptions caused by national governments (14, 15, 17, 118). In addition, the flexibility demonstrated by global oil markets may limit the damage to oil-importing countries (119, 120). However,

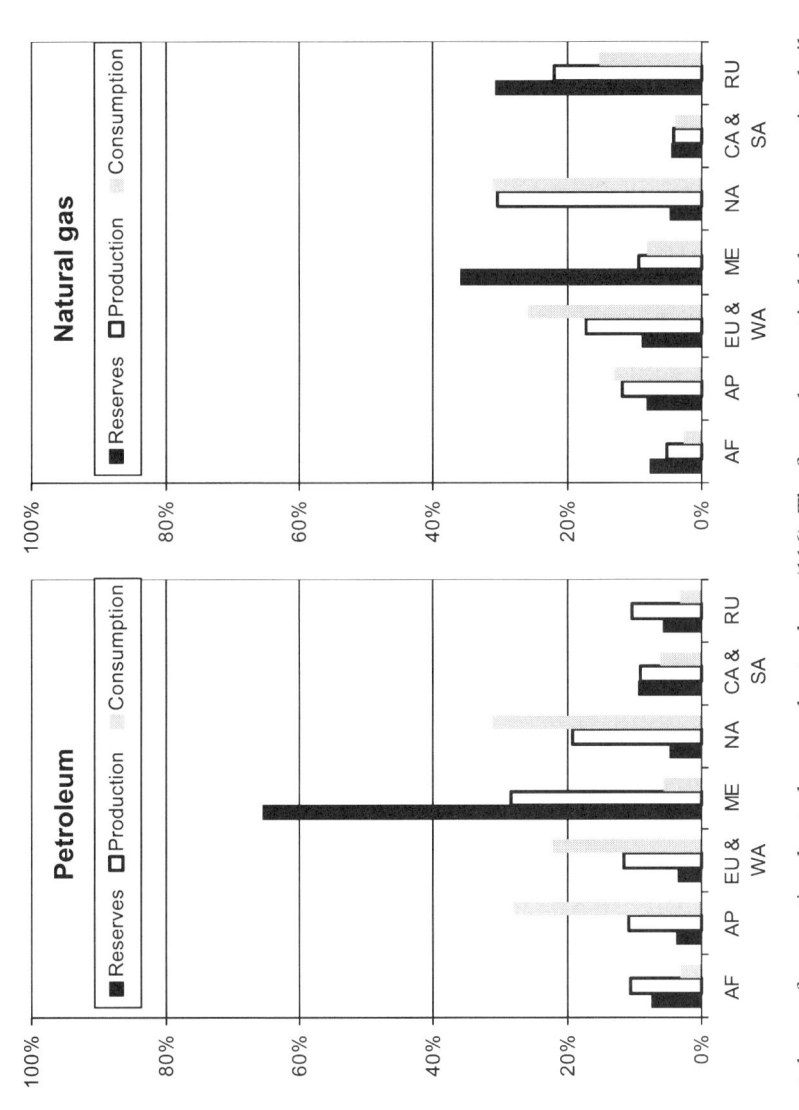

Figure 1 Percent shares of conventional petroleum and natural gas (116). The figure does not include nonconventional oil, so, for instance, Albertan tar sands and methane hydrates are excluded. Abbreviations are AF, Africa; AP, Asia Pacific; EU & WA, Europe and West Asia (e.g., Kazakhstan); ME, Middle East; NA, North America; CA & SA, Central and South America; and RU, Russia.

some terrorists may find this adds to the attractiveness of oil-production facilities as a target because destabilization of current Middle Eastern regimes may be among their goals. Thus, deliberate attack on oil supply infrastructure may be one of the more likely causes of supply interruptions. However, given market structures like those in use today, the outcome will be increased prices, not physical scarcity.

The most important vulnerabilities are in refineries and pipeline pumping stations, only a limited number of which typically supply any particular region (2, 4, 10). An additional problem is that several chokepoints vulnerable to mines or other types of attack exist on ocean petroleum shipment routes, including the Straits of Molucca, Bosporus Straits, and Straits of Hormuz. Although petroleum production (wells) and shipping (tankers) can and have been attacked, they are numerous and operate through a global market, so substitutes may be relatively readily found. One possible limitation is the time it takes to bring new petroleum production capacity on stream, especially nonconventional sources. Increasing imports of oil and gas by east Asian nations has created new concerns about energy security in these countries, which may force some of these nations to take more active roles in international affairs and heighten their interest in combating terrorism (47, 121–123).

Much of the early work on likely effects of oil supply interruptions is summarized in a report published by the Oak Ridge National Laboratory (44), which examines both the costs and benefits of petroleum imports. This and subsequent work by the same authors identified 24 oil supply shocks, averaging 8 months in length and 3.7% of global supply, from 1950 to 2003 (124). This study also characterized two types of costs associated with oil supply interruptions: increased payments for imports and macroeconomic adjustment losses (124, pp. 37–51).

The concept of increased payments for higher-priced oil imports is straightforward, but it is important to note that although futures markets and other mechanisms can hedge against the private costs, they cannot hedge against social losses (125). Thus, even improvements in oil markets will not mitigate the effects of increased prices for oil in the case of a successful attack on the supply infrastructure.

Abundant energy supplies are universally acknowledged as a key element of the modern industrial economy. However, two schools of thought have emerged on the relationship between energy prices and economic growth in the wake of the oil price shocks of 1973 and 1979. Some see high energy prices as having led to the rapid reduction in economic growth (126). Others have argued that it was not higher energy prices but restricted money supply that led to a slower pace of capital investment and technical change (127). These two perspectives lead to very different policy prescriptions. If the former analysis is correct, it is advisable to have policies that keep energy prices steady. If the latter is correct, it is advisable to have good macroeconomic policies in place to minimize the impact of energy price fluctuations. The studies discussed in the next two paragraphs assume oil prices are the main effect.

Macroeconomic adjustments are changes in labor and capital utilization to reflect the new, higher prices relative to other goods and services. These changes take time owing to, for instance, labor contracts and sunk capital. Although Bohi & Toman (119) find no stable estimates of these effects, a significant amount of subsequent research finds that they do exist in many countries (124, 128). Several key findings emerge. First, the effect is asymmetric; price increases have greater recessionary effects than decreases have expansionary effects. Second, the effect is nonlinear and may have a threshold that moves over time. Third, the best (linear) estimate of the effect of doubling the price of oil for one year on the gross domestic product for 11 countries, including the United States, France, Thailand, and others, is an average decline of 6.5% for 2 years. Generally, this research finds that the use of strategic petroleum reserves (SPRs) can be quite effective in managing short- and midterm supply interruptions, but that current policy in the United States and elsewhere does not take significant advantage of these opportunities.

In related work, LaCasse & Plourde (129) find that SPRs are more effective against random, short-term supply interruptions, not longer increases in price. This suggests that strategic oil reserves might be a reasonable precaution against possible attacks on the petroleum infrastructure. Of course, such reserves become part of the infrastructure and a potential target themselves. Greene et al. (45) model a two-year oil supply reduction similar in magnitude to those in the 1970s and find that OPEC's revenues increase substantially, paid for by the importing countries. They find strategic SPRs to be ineffective in this longer scenario, highlighting the importance of considering the duration that energy storage can meet end-use demands, as discussed above.

Figure 1 shows that the concentration (centralization) of natural gas supplies is less than that of petroleum, but this is largely the result of extensive proved reserves in one country, Russia (130). However, because a single global market (such as exists for oil) has not emerged (and may never emerge) for natural gas, this is a regional effect. And it is not a wholly security-enhancing effect. Europe is highly and increasingly dependent on Russian gas supplies. Again, nonconventional sources could dramatically change this picture. Methane hydrates may be an order of magnitude or more larger than conventional resources.

The gas supply infrastructure is more vulnerable to deliberate attack than the petroleum infrastructure, but less so than electricity. The natural gas supply infrastructure is more vulnerable to attack than the oil infrastructure for a simple reason: Gas requires compression or cryogenics to store and move. Natural gas systems consist of production facilities, transmission pipelines, storage areas, city gates and subtransmission mains, distribution vaults, and distribution pipes. High-pressure pipelines or liquefied natural gas (LNG) tankers are required to transport gas, which may make them more fragile and perhaps more vulnerable to attack, although in routine service they have been quite reliable (131). In addition, LNG facilities are much more expensive and time consuming to construct than are oil-handling and -shipping facilities, which would be disadvantageous in the case of a deliberate attack (132).

Gas supply infrastructure is less vulnerable than is the electricity infrastructure because it is mostly buried underground, it can be used to store gas (line pack), and it can use relatively secure depleted oil and gas wells for storage (63). Like the electricity industry, companies in the gas business have long recognized and effectively planned for contingencies that mitigate terrorism risks. Spare parts are generally kept on hand to effect quick repairs. However, the potential vulnerabilities in the gas supply system are illustrated by the August 2000 rupture and explosion caused by corrosion in a 30-inch gas pipe near Carlsbad, NM, killing 12 people. This explosion led to significant increases in gas prices in California, exacerbating the electricity crisis there, an example of infrastructure interdependency.

ELECTRICITY

An attack on the electric power system that led to a supply disruption would be similar to a blackout caused by more typical events, so there is much to be learned from the study of past outages (133, 134). Contingency planning, spare equipment preplacement, emergency preparedness training, and temporary personnel transfers tend to be the keys to recovery from large outages. Power companies often loan trained workers in emergencies under fairly informal arrangements, knowing that they are likely to need to make such requests themselves someday. Several aspects of successful management of electric system outages have been identified: planning, training, analysis, and communications (31). However, communication during and after an event might be difficult, especially if the attack is not on the physical part of the electricity infrastructure but on the associated information technology infrastructure. Further, privatization of and the introduction of competition to the electricity industry may diminish the application or effectiveness of the practices described above, which were common in electricity systems owned by the government or organized around monopoly franchises.

Prior Experience with Outages

The experience of several high-profile outages reinforces the need for planning and leadership, no matter the ownership structure. Although memories of the great blackout of 2003 are still fresh, 38 years earlier a similar event, in this case affecting interconnected systems owned by local monopolies, plunged New York, as well as much of Ontario and New England, into darkness following an equipment failure. New York City was blacked out for an entire night, and about 30 million people were directly affected. The National Opinion Research Center studied this event and found that:

> An outstanding aspect of public response to the blackout was the absence of widespread fear, panic, or disorder. There is probably little question that this absence is largely due to the ability of individuals to interpret their initial encounter with power loss as an ordinary event.... Of equal importance in maintaining order was the rapid dissemination of information about the blackout. (135)

A smaller outage in New York City in July 1977 was far more troubling (136, 137). Although outright panic did not emerge, there was considerable looting in some parts of the city. At the time, crime had been increasing, and there was a general sense of insecurity in New York City. Some of the looting occurred owing to poor response by the police, leaving some areas of the city more vulnerable. The 1977 blackout was frightening in ways that ordinary electricity outages are not, suggesting that there can be troubling social responses to turning out the lights.

There is some experience with widespread physical damage from natural forces. For example, in January 1998, an ice storm struck southeastern Canada, New York, and New England, felling over 700 transmission towers and thousands of distribution poles while sending many tree branches into power lines. This event left 1.6 million people without power, some for more than a month. Almost a quarter-million people had to leave their homes to take shelter, and at least a dozen people died (mostly due to loss of heat or suffocation from faulty temporary heating setups). Insurance claims reached approximately $1 billion Canadian. This event, although massively destructive, did not cause panic or shock.

It is difficult to imagine a terrorist organization amassing the capability to accomplish damage on this scale, but a terrorist attack could nonetheless be larger and more long lasting than a typical equipment- or weather-related problem, and multiple attack modes could be coordinated for maximum effect. Critical points exist in the electricity infrastructure (especially among transmission and substation assets) where attacks could cause more damage. A recent U.S. National Research Council panel found that "a coordinated attack on a selected set of key points in the system could result in a long-term, multi-state blackout" (110, p. 181). Furthermore, the ability of the electric power sector to deal with coordinated attacks on the system is lacking. As noted by NERC, "most (electricity sector) members do not have in place business recovery plans that include procedures for dealing with widespread, well-planned attacks on physical facilities. Likewise, they do not include procedures for dealing with deliberate attempts to hamper repair and restoration activities" (138, p. 36).

Transformer Vulnerabilities

High-voltage transformers have long been identified as a key vulnerability in electric power infrastructure, but owing to the cost of stockpiling, few spares are available. It might be possible to develop modular, flexible transformers, but this goal is frustrated by the tendency of different power companies to insist on unique standards and often on customized equipment for every situation. The current trend toward restructured markets may exacerbate this problem: "[d]eregulation has encouraged efficiency, invested-cost utilization and return on investment rather than redundancy, reliability and security. For the same reasons, power companies keep fewer spares on hand" (110). Other problems have also been identified. Spares are often kept at the substation site, increasing the possibility that an attack will also result in damage to the spares. If spares have to be ordered from the manufacturer, the customized nature of the transformers may mean the units could take a year or more to manufacture. Delivery could also be lengthy given that transformers are increasingly manufactured in a small number of countries where costs are low (e.g., China and India).

Impact of an Outage

Estimates of the cost of a successful attack on the electricity infrastructure could be made using estimates of the costs of longer blackouts, to which a successful attack would probably be similar, or estimates of the cost of short outages and associated estimates of the value of reliability. The duration of the disruption caused by the attack could then be associated with supply disruptions that range in their impact from merely a nuisance to interruption of work and leisure activities, to disruption of vital services (e.g., health services and water supply), to loss of life, and to permanently damaged capital infrastructure (e.g., blast furnaces).

The literature on blackout costs is sparse and appears to be based on ad hoc techniques. Generally, estimates of the costs of specific blackouts are found only in postoutage reports or articles in the popular press. The aggregate economic impacts of such events can vary widely, with the largest such blackout events having costs that reach into the billion dollar range. For instance, the 1998 blackout in Auckland, New Zealand, left some of the downtown without power for up to 2 months, with an estimated cost of approximately $50 million (1998 U.S. dollars), whereas a relatively short outage in New York in 1990 reportedly cost Citicorp $100 million (139, p. 15). In addition, estimates of the 1977 blackout in New York City are about $1 billion (137, 140, p. 23; both adjusted to 2002 U.S. dollars). The cost of the January 1998 ice storm in Canada was approximately $2 billion (U.S.) and at least 25 deaths, although not all of this is due directly to the ensuing power outage (141). The losses due to the Northeast blackout of 2003 are variously estimated in the range of $2 billion to $10 billion, as summarized in a recent report by a group representing industrial electricity consumers (142).

The literature on the value of reliability was surveyed recently by Eto et al. (139), who found over 100 studies based in the United States alone. They found multiple methods to estimate costs and that studies often focused on different aspects of the problem. Perhaps the most common method was to conduct surveys that covered different categories of losses, customer classes, and severity of reliability events (143). These surveys either elicited costs based upon experienced outages or used contingent valuation techniques to determine the willingness to pay (to avoid outages) or willingness to accept (compensation for experienced outages). Another method was to find an economic indicator that can act as a proxy for the overall cost of outages (for example, the value of lost production using sectoral economic data). A third common method was to use consumer participation in markets (e.g., for interruptible power supply) as an indicator of the value of reliability. Eto et al. also found that there were few comprehensive studies and few systematic studies of large outages. The few aggregate estimates of the annual costs to the U.S. economy of typical outages and poor power quality ranged over two orders of magnitude, from $5 billion to $400 billion. However, it is hard to interpret values in the upper half of this estimate because they are greater than the total cost of electricity in the U.S. economy.

Analyses of Power Systems Under Stress

There are few analyses of electric power systems under stress. An early analysis by Kahn (25, 144) compares two mixed systems, one with intermittent renewable generation plus hydroelectric dams that provide storage capacity and one with central station generators plus hydro. This study looks only at generation adequacy and is somewhat abstract, but it finds the excess storage capacity that the intermittent-based system needs for ordinary reliability purposes makes that system more resilient in the face of exogenous uncertainty (stress).

A more detailed study compares a centralized system (based on the reference test system of the Institute of Electrical and Electronics Engineering), which includes multiple generator types and a stylized representation of a transmission system, with a very similar system that used distributed, gas-fired engines, including the necessary gas distribution system (67, 69). This research finds the distributed system is much more reliable, requiring virtually no excess capacity to match the performance of the centralized system. It is also much less sensitive to stress. The costs of the distributed system are higher if only electricity supply under typical conditions is considered, but if heat recovery is possible, the distributed system is less expensive even under routine conditions. Under stress conditions, the distributed system is always far less costly, according to this study.

One modeling study compares two terrorist scenarios, one involving a sequence of small supply interruptions over the course of a year due to attacks on substations and the second a single, large-scale attack on generation and transmission assets (107). Although the year-long scenario involved only half the destruction, it involved significant damage to generation and subsequent damage to transmission assets that made recovery difficult. Not only was this smaller, but lengthy, scenario five times more costly than the big, one-time attack, but it had a much more significant long-term effect as well. This study showed how series of small disruptions can give a strong signal about increased risk and drive business away.

Thus, it is not surprising that in places where deliberate attacks on the power system and interruption of service are frequent, both everyday life and economic development can be damaged (63). However, it is not clear if an attempt to turn out the lights would permit terrorists to create widespread panic or the shock associated with violent attacks on symbolic objects that cause loss of human life. Electricity customers in most industrialized countries lose power for an average of a couple of hours per year. For the most part, individuals and society cope with these outages well. Power companies respond rapidly to restore service, and facilities that have special needs for reliability (e.g., hospitals and airports) typically have backup generators.

Fuel Supply Disruptions

Electric power systems vary in how vulnerable they are to fuel supply disruption. In addition to oil, gas, and nuclear fuels (discussed in separate sections), electricity can also be generated with renewable energy sources, which is discussed above in the section on Centralization and below in the section on Renewables, and with coal, which is discussed here.

Coal is the fuel least vulnerable to deliberate attacks because it is produced in many locations, can be shipped by multiple means, and can be easily stored. In addition, coal supply systems are made up of large and relatively robust capital equipment (122, 123, 145). Coal is transported by a variety of means. Rail dominates, and other major modes include river barge and truck, and there is some international marine shipment of coal. Coal-fired power plants may often have multiple supply routes available to them, although one mode will tend to domi nate and generally only that mode will have coal-handling capacity sufficient for long-term supply. Coal can be readily stored on site and coal-fired power plants typically have 4 to 12 weeks of fuel supply on hand. For power plants built at coal mines, fuel security is largely irrelevant, although these plants may require more transmission assets.

NUCLEAR

Unlike other energy sources, nuclear fuel and waste are intrinsically dangerous both in terms of their radiological and chemical hazards and as a potential resource for construction of weapons. Radiological material released by any explosion creates a "dirty bomb." Thus potential attacks against various segments of the nuclear power infrastructure (fuel production, reactors, waste handling, and reprocessing facilities) are of concern.

The consequences of an attack against a nuclear facility are considered serious enough that this sector is considered to be one of vital national security and is generally treated somewhat differently than other parts of the electric power sector (91, p. 83). This is, in some ways, simply a continuation of how the nuclear industry is treated in general, with its own regulatory bodies like the U.S. NRC, because of the highly technical nature of the required regulations and the particular risks posed by the technology (146). As a result, in this industry, there already exist numerous regulations and standards that are meant to help in both protecting these plants and operating them safely. However, one area of open inquiry is whether the existing set of regulations and standards is sufficient or properly focused to address new and changing risks.

Typically, the costs of mitigating the CIP risks of nuclear power plants and other security risks, such as proliferation, are not fully included in the cost of electric power these plants produce. For instance, after the terrorist attacks of September 11, 2001, many governors in U.S. states put National Guard troops at nuclear plants, so the taxpayer in effect subsidized electricity consumers. This was done without the sort of debate that O'Hanlon suggests is needed. As the owners of nuclear power electricity facilities have begun to face competition, and the bottom line becomes more important, the costs of security are likely to receive greater scrutiny.

Fuel

Although refueling is infrequent (every 18 months or so for most reactors), it does involve risks of deliberate attack associated with production and shipping. The top seven countries ranked in order of nuclear contribution to electricity generation have few uranium resources (e.g., France, Ukraine, Korea, Germany, Japan, Spain, and the United Kingdom). However, uranium deposits exist in many countries and are available in significant quantities in several stable democracies (e.g., Australia, Canada, and the United States). Production of nuclear fuel is typically conducted by the national government under relatively tight security arrangements, or it is closely supervised by the national government, as is trade and shipping.

Reactors

The most obvious threat is a direct attack upon nuclear reactors themselves. One possible attack mode is by airplane. Most nuclear reactor containment buildings are massive structures designed to withstand significant impacts (exceptions include plants like the Chernobyl facility in the Ukraine). Design studies for these structures typically examined massive accidents, such as earthquakes and unintentional airplane crashes. Seismic events do not appear to be relevant to understanding deliberate attacks, but airline crashes obviously are. The design studies usually considered a large commercial plane for the time, a Boeing 707 traveling at a moderate speed or a military jet (e.g., a Phantom II) traveling much faster but without weapons. In both cases, the critical factor is the ability of a turbine shaft to penetrate the multiple layers of containment that surround the reactor core. Although some questions remain regarding the effects of a deliberate aircraft attack on a nuclear power plant, these events would not likely present more severe stresses on reactor containment systems than those originally used as the design basis (147–150). Higher impact speeds tend to reduce the probability that a large aircraft could be flown into a specific point on a power plant, reducing the risk somewhat (151). However, an attack on a nuclear power plant, no matter how it was carried out, could reveal systemic flaws or common-mode failures, which could lead regulators to order an immediate shutdown of numerous reactors (50).

The possibility of an armed assault on a nuclear facility itself has also been a concern, and contingency measures are supposed to be in place to protect these facilities from being taken over by a hostile force that could damage the plant. Concerns about direct attack by truck bombs or commando squads have led to physical barriers and armed guards that protect all nuclear power plants. However, it is not clear how effective these steps are; a 1999 review by the NRC found significant weaknesses in 27 of the 57 plants evaluated (152).

Another concern is the number of relatively less well-defended research reactors. These exist in many more countries than do power reactors and are often sited at facilities such as universities and research institutes that may be in highly populated areas and may not have adequate security measures. Research reactors are low-power reactors used to study reactions, create isotopes, and carry out a variety of research projects. These reactors do not have the same amount of radioactive materials in them, but it may be easier for a terrorist to successfully attack one of these facilities and disperse radioactive materials (153).

Waste

After removal from nuclear reactors, spent fuel rods are highly radioactive. Spent fuel rods are first placed in pools to help dissipate the heat caused by radioactive decay of fission products and then are placed in "dry storage" awaiting disposal. At the moment, no country with a nuclear program has begun operation of a permanent waste repository for spent nuclear fuel, which must remain isolated from the environment for thousands of years (154). As a result, there are temporary spent nuclear fuel storage areas at reactor sites all over the world. Currently, the vast majority of these spent fuel storage facilities are special pools that are cooled to dissipate the heat. However, a growing amount of spent nuclear fuel is being stored in massive casks without cooling water.

Standards for both wet and dry storage of spent nuclear fuel vary significantly from country to country. Spent nuclear fuel storage in Germany, for instance, is either in a pool that is inside a containment vessel or in massive casks that have successfully resisted penetration by simulated turbine shafts moving at near-sonic speeds, and the casks themselves are held in massively reinforced structures to prevent damage by missile attack (155, 156).

In contrast, spent nuclear fuel in the United States is far less protected (91, 157). Lacking a final repository for spent nuclear fuel, some spent fuel pools are being packed with fuel rods at a much higher density than originally envisioned, and boron has been added to the pool water to absorb neutrons and prevent criticality accidents. These densely packed storage pools are not inside containment buildings, and many are elevated well above ground level. The concern about such sites is that they are more vulnerable than are reactors that sit inside massive containment buildings, and a loss of the coolant as a result of sabotage or terrorist act could result in a nuclear accident. A loss of coolant could cause rapid heating, and then the outside shell of the fuel rods (called the cladding) could catch fire. The result could be significant dispersal of the highly radioactive fission products, such as Cs-137. Using a variety of studies conducted for the NRC by various national laboratories and other sources, Alvarez et al. (157) argue that it would be wise to move a significant amount of spent nuclear fuel at reactor sites in the United States to something similar to the massive cask plus massive building storage now used in Germany.

As with the issue of breaching reactor containment structures, there is disagreement as to both the possibility of a problem and the potential impacts should there be an incident at a nuclear waste facility. Recently, the NRC (159) argued that the analysis by Alvarez et al. (157) was overly conservative. However, this rebuttal used classified research, and so it is impossible to evaluate (160).

Reprocessing

Reprocessing facilities are used to process spent nuclear fuel rods in order to separate plutonium from the rest of the highly radioactive fuel. These facilities have served both military purposes (and are necessary for all modern nuclear weapons) and civilian purposes in an effort to create so-called closed fuel cycles that reuse the plutonium as a reactor fuel. For both of these uses, the reprocessing is done primarily through chemical processes, resulting in large quantities of liquid waste that is highly radioactive. Reprocessing facilities pose two risks from the infrastructure security point of view. The first is that, like reactors and spent fuel storage pools, the waste facilities at reprocessing sites contain large quantities of highly radioactive material that could potentially be dispersed. The second concern is that materials from these sites could be stolen for use in either a nuclear or radiological weapon. In particular, separated plutonium for use in a nuclear weapon would make such sites attractive. However, similar to reactors, there are strict national and international standards for the protection of these sites against assault. It is not readily apparent if the testing record of these facilities is better or worse than that of power reactors.

Proliferation

Nuclear power plants also present a unique threat labeled proliferation, which is the potential for nuclear fuel (or waste) to be used in creating nuclear or radiological weapons. Materials might be obtained from fuel production, fuel storage at power plants, waste reprocessing operations, or from waste storage. One of the major impediments to the terrorist use of a nuclear or radiological weapon is both the technical skills necessary to design a weapon and access to materials. However, designing a crude nuclear device is not necessarily considered to be difficult, and material access may in fact be the main impediment (161).

There are a number of means by which one could obtain the necessary nuclear materials to build a nuclear or radiological weapon. Nuclear fission weapons require fissile materials that can sustain a chain reaction (either highly enriched uranium or plutonium), which could be obtained either in the form of a weapon or as a raw material. Separated plutonium would be the result of spent fuel reprocessing in military or civilian nuclear programs, and plutonium stockpiles are orders of magnitude larger than what is necessary for a single weapon (162). One source of highly enriched uranium to make a weapon would be the many operating and closed research reactors that are fueled with highly enriched uranium (HEU). Although the United States did replace the HEU in most domestic research reactors with low-enriched uranium and did embark on a program to replace the HEU it sent to overseas research reactors, there are still a large number of reactors in existence that use HEU (153).

A radiological weapon does not require fissile material. Instead, it relies on conventional explosives to disperse radioactive materials. Adequate radioactive materials could come either from sources such as spent fuel rods (which would contain both fissile materials and fission products) or from the reprocessing waste that follows the separation of fissile materials from spent fuel. New reactor designs that are more resistant to physical assault or require no refueling might be developed, but the cost of doing so is unclear.

Another risk that has been raised and is also the subject of debate is the transportation of the spent fuel rods from the spent fuel pools at the reactors to an eventual waste repository. There is concern that the fuel rods could be intercepted and the materials used for a radiological dispersal weapons (163). One method to deal with the threat of proliferation of nuclear materials is to improve and strengthen international standards for material accounting and protection (153).

Public Reactions

Attacks on nuclear facilities, even if there is little direct impact, could raise public alarm and lead to a variety of negative consequences. Because of the dread the public has of nuclear radiation (whether scientifically supported or not), it might be possible to create significant public distress (or even terror) with an unsuccessful attack on a nuclear power plant. The core meltdown of the Three Mile Island plant in Pennsylvania in 1976 had a devastating effect on the U.S. nuclear power industry, although no one was hurt and insignificant amounts of radioactivity were released (164, pp. 172–77). An unsuccessful attack could lead to panicked publics and political pressure for nuclear plant closures, which could have a significant impact on some electricity systems that rely heavily on nuclear power.

The degree to which this is an issue is unknown as it will depend on both government response to an incident (including how risk is communicated) and the public's response to an extreme situation. Civil defense preparedness has been an important government function for a long time, and emergency procedures are in place for a variety of contingencies. The question remains whether the radioactive nature of the incident would result in behavior that could hamper the response efforts. Panic is a widely expected behavior under those circumstances. However, evidence from response to the World Trade Center attacks and other historical events shows it may not be the overwhelming reaction (165). Surveys on responses to terrorism indicate issues with risk communication that may help in shaping an appropriate public response (166).

PREVENTION AND RESPONSE

A variety of approaches can be taken to either prevent the impacts of deliberate attack on energy infrastructure or to mitigate their impacts. Some are similar to, or extensions of, traditional and current practices, which generally limit the importance of deliberate attack, and others depart from such approaches.

Different energy infrastructures have varied combinations of the approaches described below, but it does not appear that the question of preferred combinations has been addressed.

Guards, Gates, and Guns

One approach to dealing with these issues is to assess, and if necessary and justified, improve the physical security of energy infrastructure. For instance, following the September 11, 2001, attacks, a number of energy facilities owners did increase their security (particularly nuclear power plants). Some companies have begun to hire trained counter-terrorism officers and obtained waivers from the state for their protective force to carry heavier arms. This approach also probably requires relying on surveillance technologies to detect attack, ranging from manned surveillance to automated sensors to detect intrusion. The primary purposes of such technologies are to detect an attack and mobilize the resources (i.e., private security force, local police, and military) to repel the attack and prevent damage. A secondary purpose would be to collect evidence to be used in the investigation of any attack. Improved physical security (including surveillance) is particularly important for the electricity infrastructure because of its exposure and geographic extent. Although there exists a wide variety of monitoring and surveillance technologies, they are not considered adequate for protecting the electricity infrastructure. In the case of remote facilities, such as transformers and powerlines, monitoring technologies may not be of use in preventing an attack if the response time of an intervention force is too long.

Unfortunately, any technology used for monitoring or surveillance has the risk of failure. Another problem has to do with nuisance alarms. Surveillance and monitoring systems are not always able to distinguish between an intruder and an animal or between a line being deliberately cut and one that has been struck by a falling tree. Guarding against failures and false positives may require backup systems or complementary technologies that can confirm or deny events, increasing costs (110).

Emergency Response and Restoration

Because there is no guarantee that an attack can be prevented or will be unsuccessful, emergency response and restoration plans for each energy sector must be, and are, in place. The nature of those response plans will vary quite widely depending on the particular energy infrastructure in question and the extent of the problem. In the event of a nuclear accident or radiological weapon, the immediate problem will be issues such as risk communication to avoid panic and exacerbation of the problem, possible evacuation, and medical treatment. Longer-term problems would include decontamination and repair, health monitoring, continued risk assessment, and attention to public concerns.

For the oil and gas industry, we consider supply and demand responses. Suppliers face two distinct challenges: (*a*) the immediate process of damage containment (e.g., control of spills and fires, evacuation of personnel and public) and (*b*) the process of restoration of service (e.g., repairs to affected infrastructure and resources). From an end-user perspective, the time to restoration of supply following an attack or accident is critical to their needs. On-site fuel storage can easily allow end users to experience no significant impact from a supply disruption if the disruption lasts for a period shorter than the rate at which stored fuels are depleted. However, if the resumption of supply is expected to take longer than available storage, end users need to weigh the relative costs of curtailment of activities and alternative sources of supply, even alternative energy sources.

The rich and highly technical literature on the restoration of electric power systems shows how valuable the ability to fail softly or gracefully could be (134, 167). Restoring a power system after a blackout can be a complicated process, even when the physical infrastructure itself has not been damaged. Both load and generation have to be brought back online while maintaining the various parameters of the system within prespecified bounds (e.g., voltage and frequency). A number of tools have been developed to aid in the process ranging from training simulators to computer-aided restoration, employing knowledge-based systems.

However, these analyses assume demand is fixed and cannot be controlled at all. Considering the demand side, and especially possible trade-offs between curtailment of activities and alternative energy supplies during a prolonged outage, firm level experience with these issues is more widespread that is often recognized because many electricity and gas utilities have long offered interruptible supply contracts to their larger customers.

Institutions

As noted above in the section Routine Security, the security of energy infrastructure is at least partly a public good, and so it will not be provided in socially desired quantities by market forces alone. Government action of one sort or another is needed. Most notable are government regulations and private institutions that have been established to promote reliability in the electric power sector. In the United States, voluntary coordination councils were set up by the electric utility industry, following the 1965 blackout, to avoid government regulation of reliability. State public utility commissions play a role as well. All countries have some form of electricity reliability institution. However, industry restructuring is drastically changing current institutional arrangements, leading to serious questions about whether private, voluntary approaches will be adequate to ensure reliability, let alone provide adequate security. Following the 2003 blackout in the northeastern United States, pressures to move toward regulation and mandatory reliability rules mounted.

Institutional issues also play out in apparently purely technical domains. For instance, several studies have shown that barriers are often raised to the interconnection of a distributed source to the grid (86). These barriers could come from market structure issues, the relative roles of DG owners and utilities, and standards that are developed for the interconnection of distributed resources. Similar concerns exist about the incentives for cooperation and investment in new control strategies and technologies.

One of the key challenges for the future is ensuring that institutional solutions to emerging energy infrastructure security are created for whatever new structure the electricity industry takes. This includes looking at threats that go beyond those considered in traditional contingency planning. However, the potential for creating terror through attacks on the electric power system seems limited (with the exception of an attack on a nuclear facility). Loss of power, even if large-scale and frequent, is costly and annoying and, if caused by malicious attacks, can be disconcerting, but it pales in comparison with the effect of large-scale loss of life that is often the purpose of terrorist acts. Given sufficient time, societies can adapt to energy shortages, such as occurs in the Indian electric power system, although this is not without a cost.

Efficiency and Renewables

A great deal has been made of the potential of both efficiency and renewable energy sources to reduce the vulnerability of energy infrastructures from *Brittle Power* to more recent versions of the same somewhat idealized and vague arguments (168–170). There are two related, but slightly different, arguments about energy efficiency. The first is that improved energy efficiency reduces the impact of a disturbance to the infrastructure. Higher efficiency reduces the burden on the infrastructure, according to this argument, which would be particularly important during a crisis and could allow the system to continue to function, and stored fuels would last longer during an emergency. This argument does have salience when security is defined in traditional terms of concerns about oil imports from the Middle East. However, in this new definition of security, which includes deliberate attacks on supply systems, there is no reason to presume that suppliers would not adjust to greater end-use energy efficiency by maintaining reserve margins (as a percentage of use) at previous levels in order to save money, resulting in no improvement in security.

A related concept is responsive demand, which is most applicable to the electricity sector (171, 172). Demand response, or "intelligent loads," can react automatically to signals from the energy supplier to reduce energy consumption. This can help reduce the need for peak capacity, which might typically be used to reduce costs in routine operation but could also be used to cope with supply interruptions. Thus, energy systems optimized for economical supply under normal conditions but with the inclusion of demand response might or might not be more robust in the face of deliberate attacks.

The second argument for efficiency is that energy efficiency could make the scale of fuel consumption more compatible with local production capacity and make renewable sources a more feasible alternative to large-scale, centralized fossil and nuclear energy production and distribution. For example, it may be infeasible to supply a nation's entire fleet of pickup trucks and sport utility vehicles with biofuels, but it could be possible to produce biofuels locally for small, hybrid cars.

The argument for renewables is similar to the argument for high-efficiency technologies: they reduce reliance on vulnerable fuel supplies. Small-scale renewable energy sources have little, if any, fuel supply vulnerabilities. However, large-scale systems, such as hydro and wind utilized to service distant urban centers, cannot be dissociated with risks to the transmission system. Fortunately, these issues are now beginning to be dealt with more seriously (173). However, if the challenge of energy supply security is serious enough to encourage us to probe fundamental characteristics of our current energy infrastructure, the option of combining efficiency and local renewable resources may be so persuasive as to reshape our landscape.

CONCLUSIONS

Historically, access, availability, and affordability have dominated public policy and design of energy systems. The costs of existing security measures have been implicitly divided between energy users, suppliers, and the government. In addition, past approaches to electric power system reliability could take advantage of economies of scale, of which few are still available for exploitation. Today, the security of energy infrastructures against deliberate attack has become a growing concern. Therefore, the context within which energy is supplied and used has evolved well past the paradigm that has led to the current physical energy infrastructure and associated institutional arrangements.

Concerns about deliberate attacks on the energy infrastructure have highlighted many critical questions to which no ready answers exist. For example, how much and what kind of security for energy infrastructure do we want and who will pay for it? Current government CIP efforts tend to ignore this issue entirely, focusing on preventing attacks and protecting whatever energy infrastructure the private sector creates. These decisions are being made in a context in which many of the costs of security have been socialized for decades, favoring certain risk-creating technologies over others.

Many different approaches are likely to be necessary to achieve desired levels of energy infrastructure security. Routine security and emergency planning have obvious roles, and some features seem to inherently enhance system security, including decentralization, diversity, and redundancy. Other features, such as utilization of specific energy sources and efficiency, seem to have mixed effects. In particular, there is no essential link between renewability and security; some renewable energy technologies can be deployed more securely than fossil and nuclear technologies, whereas others cannot. And highly efficient systems may have more, equal, or less capability to withstand a deliberate attack than do less efficient systems with greater reserves or more low-impact curtailment opportunities.

It is possible that survivability may eventually supplant security as a conceptual guide, but this is likely to require changes in both technology and perceptions. It is unlikely, however, that either security or survivability will be achieved without policies, incentives, and institutions to guide energy infrastructure investment and operation to achieve these goals.

Although energy security has been one of many battlefields in which advocates for various energy sources have clashed, energy security per se has never been a primary driver of the energy system evolution. At first, economics alone largely drove issues. In the late nineteenth century whale oil gave way to kerosene for lighting, after which horse fodder, wind, and coal gave way to petroleum as a transportation fuel. Throughout the late twentieth century, environmental and resource issues increasingly defined the battle lines. Today, concern about critical infrastructures have once again brought into sharp relief the diversity of perspectives on the different paths toward a socially desireable energy system.

The realization of various economic inefficiencies has already led us to revisit the public policy shaping the institutional infrastructure for energy supply. Perhaps the realization of new security concerns will also lead to the recognition that our options are bifurcated along the lines of (*a*) increasingly inefficient and ineffective security measures (paid for privately and publicly) used to protect a brittle infrastructure and (*b*) adoption of a new paradigm of security based on a soft-fail infrastructure promoted through appropriate public policies. The latter also opens the door to more innovative approaches to encouraging resource diversity, improving system management (including demand management), developing energy storage, and advancing energy conversion.

ACKNOWLEDGMENTS

The authors would like to thank the Carnegie Mellon Electricity Industry Center, the University of California Berkeley Committee on Research, and Resources for the Future for support.

The *Annual Review of Environment and Resources* is online at
http://environ.annualreviews.org

LITERATURE CITED

1. Seger KA. 2003. *Utility Security: A New Paradigm*. Tulsa, OK: PennWell. 238 pp.
2. Parfomak PW. 2004. Pipeline security: an overview of federal activites and current policy issues. *Rep. RL31990*, Congr. Res. Serv., Washington, DC
3. Off. Technol. Assess. 1979. The effects of nuclear war. *US Congress Rep., NTIS PB-296946*. US GPO, Washington, DC. http://www.wws.princeton.edu/~ota/disk3/1979/7906_n.html
4. Adams N. 2003. *Terrorism & Oil*. Tulsa, OK: Penn Well. 208 pp.
5. Anonymous. 2003. Silent vector: issues of concern and policy recommendations. *Cent. Strateg. Int. Studies, Rep.*, Washington, DC. http://www.csis.org/isp/sv/
6. Bucholz A. 1994. Armies, railroads, and

information: the birth of industrial mass war. See Ref. 174, pp. 53–70
7. Yergin D. 1991. *The Prize: The Epic Quest for Oil, Money, and Power.* New York: Simon & Schuster. 917 pp.
8. Bohi D, Toman M. 1996. *The Economics of Energy Security.* Boston, MA: Kluwer Academic
9. Klare MT. 2001. *Resouce Wars: The New Landscape of Global Conflict.* New York: Henry Holt. 289 pp.
10. Lovins AB, Lovins LH. 1982. *Brittle Power: Energy Strategy for National Security.* Andover, MA: Brick House. 486 pp.
11. Campbell CJ, Laherrere JH. 1998. The end of cheap oil. *Sci. Am.* 278(3):78–83
12. Bentley RW. 2002. Global oil & gas depletion: an overview. *Energy Policy* 30:189–205
13. Rogner HH. 1997. An assessment of world hydrocarbon resources. *Annu. Rev. Energy Environ.* 22:217–62
14. Jaffe AM, Manning RA. 2000. The shocks of a world of cheap oil. *Foreign Aff.* 79:16–29
15. Gause FG. 2000. Saudi Arabia over a barrel. *Foreign Aff.* 79:80–94
16. Gately D. 2001. How plausible is the consensus projection of oil below $25 and Persian Gulf oil capacity and output doubling by 2020? *Energy J.* 22:1–27
17. Morse EL, Richard J. 2002. The battle for energy dominance. *Foreign Aff.* 81:16–22
18. Clark W, Page J. 1981. *Energy, Vulnerability, and War.* New York: WW Norton. 251 pp.
19. Griffith TE Jr. 1994. *Strategic attack of national electrical systems*, MS thesis. Sch. Adv. Airpower Studies, Maxwell Air Force Base, AL. 64 pp.
20. Mijuskovic N. 2000. *Serbia restoration after war damages May-99.* Presented at CIGRE Session 2000, SC 39 Workshop Large Disturb. Bucharest
21. Keeney LD. 2002. *The Doomsday Scenario.* St. Paul, MN: MBI Publ. 127 pp.
22. Clark W, McCosker J. 1980. Dispersed, decentralized, and renewable energy sources: alternatives to national vulnerability and war: final report. *Contract: DCPA-01–79-C-0320*, Energy Def. Project for Fed. Emerg. Manag. Agency Work Unit #2314-F, Washington, DC
23. Clark WC, Jones DD, Holling CS. 1979. Lessons for ecological policy design—case study of ecosystem management. *Ecol. Model.* 7:1–53
24. Lovins A, Lovins LH. 1981. Energy policies for resilience and national security. Friends of the Earth, San Francisco, *for contract: DCPA01-79-C-0317*, Fed. Emerg. Manag. Agency Work Unit #4351-C, Washington, DC
25. Kahn E. 1980. Reliability planning for solar electric power generation. *Technol. Forecast. Soc. Change* 18:359–78
26. Holling CS, ed. 1978. *Adaptive Environmental Assessment and Management.* New York: Wiley. 377 pp.
27. Ellison RJ, Fisher DA, Linger RC, Lipson HF, Longstaff T, Mead NR. 1999. Survivable network systems: an emerging discipline. *Rep. CMU/SEI97-TR-013, ESC-TR-97–013*, Carnegie Mellon Softw. Eng. Inst., Pittsburgh, PA
28. Lipson HF, Fisher DA. 1999. *Survivability—a new technical and business perspective on security.* Presented at New Secur. Paradigms Workshop, Caledon Hills, Ont., Can.
29. Schlager E, Ostrom E. 1992. Property-rights regimes and natural resources: a conceptual analysis. *Land Econ.* 68:249–62
30. O'Hanlon ME, Orszag PR, Daalder IH, Destler IM, Gunter DL, et al. 2002. *Protecting the American Homeland: One Year On.* Washington, DC: Brookings Inst. 182 pp. http://www.brookings.edu/fp/projects/homeland
31. Garces FF. 2004. Electric power: transmission generation reliability and adequacy. See Ref. 175, pp. 301–8

32. Little RG. 2002. Controlling cascading failure: understanding the vulnerabilities of interconnected infrastructures. *J. Urban Technol.* 9:109–23
33. Keeney R, Kulkarni R, Nair K. 1978. Assessing the risk of an LNG terminal. *Technol. Rev.* 81:64–72
34. Fay JA. 2003. Model of spills and fires from LNG and oil tankers. *J. Hazard. Mater.* 96:171–88
35. Parfomak PW. 2003. Liquefied natural gas (LNG) infrastructure security: background and issues for Congress. *Rep. RL30153*, Congr. Res. Serv., Washington, DC
36. Tan DM, Xu J, Venart JES. 2003. Fire-induced failure of a propane tank: some lessons to be learnt. *Proc. Inst. Mech. Eng. Part E-J. Process Mech. Eng.* 217:79–91
37. Planas-Cuchi E, Vilchez JA, Perez-Alavedra FX, Casal J. 1998. Effects of fire on a container storage system—a case study. *J. Loss Prev. Process Ind.* 11:323–31
38. Leslie IRM, Birk AM. 1991. State-of-the-art review of pressure liquefied gas container failure modes and associated projectile hazards. *J. Hazard. Mater.* 28:329–65
39. Romero S. 2004. Algerian explosion stirs foes of U.S. gas projects. *New York Times*, Feb. 12, pp. W1.
40. Abrams M. 2003. The dawn of the E-bomb. *IEEE Spectr.* 40:24–30. http://www.spectrum.ieee.org/WEBONLY/publicfeature/nov03/1103ebom.html
41. Kopp C. 1998. The electromagnetic bomb—a weapon of electrical mass destruction. *Air Space Power Chron.* Maxwell Air Force Base. http://www.airpower.maxwell.af.mil/airchronicles/kopp/apjemp.html
42. Kappenman JG. 1996. Geomagnetic storms and their impacts on power systems. *IEEE Power Eng. Rev.* 16:5–8
43. Meliopoulos APS, Glytsis EN, Cokkinides GJ, Rabinowitz N. 1994. Comparison of SS-GIC and MHD-EMP-GIC effects on power systems. *IEEE Proc. Power Deliv.* 9:194–207
44. Leiby PN, Jones DW, Curlee TR, Lee R. 1997. Oil imports: an assessment of benefits and costs. *Rep. ORNL-6851*, Oak Ridge Natl. Lab., Oak Ridge, TN
45. Greene DL, Jones DW, Leiby PN. 1998. The outlook for US oil dependence. *Energy Policy* 26:55–69
46. Salameh MG. 2003. The new frontiers for the United States energy security in the 21st century. *Appl. Energy* 76:135–44
47. Salameh MG. 2003. Quest for Middle East oil: the US versus the Asia-Pacific region. *Energy Policy* 31:1085–91
48. Porter D, Steen N. 1996. Renewable energy in a competitive electricity market. *Renew. Energy* 9:1120–23
49. Lemar PL. 2001. The potential impact of policies to promote combined heat and power in US industry. *Energy Policy* 29:1243–54
50. Evans N, Hope C. 1984. *Nuclear Power: Futures, Costs and Benefits*. New York: Cambridge Univ. Press. 171 pp.
51. Margolis RM, Kammen DM. 1999. Underinvestment: the energy technology and R&D policy challenge. *Science* 285:690–92
52. Gritsevskyi A, Nakicenovic N. 2000. Modeling uncertainty of induced technological change. *Energy Policy* 28:907–21
53. Farrell AE. 2004. Local-national-international institutional linkages in environmental policy: air pollution in Spain. In *Smoke and Mirrors: Air Pollution in Culture and Politics*, ed. M Dupuis, pp. 241–60. Albany, NY: State Univ. New York Press
54. Awerbuch S. 2000. Investing in photovoltaics: risk, accounting and the value of new technology. *Energy Policy* 28:1023–35
55. Stirling A. 1998. *On the economics and analysis of diversity.* SPRU Electron.

Work. Pap. Brighton, UK: Sci. Policy Research Unit, Univ. Sussex
56. Stirling A. 1994. Diversity and ignorance in electricity supply investment—addressing the solution rather than the problem. *Energy Policy* 22:195–216
57. Shea DA. 2002. Critical infrastructure: control systems and the terrorist threat. *Rep. RL31534*, Libr. Congr., Congr. Res. Serv., Washington, DC
58. Safire W. 2004. The farewell dossier. *New York Times*, Feb. 2. pp. A25.
59. US Dep. Energy, Off. Crit. Infrastruct. Prot. 2001. Critical infrastructure interdependencies: impact of the September 11 terrorist attacks on the World Trade Center (a case study). *Rep. US Dep. Energy*, Off. Crit. Infrastruct. Prot., Washington, DC
60. Rinaldi SM, Perenboom JP, Kelly TK. 2001. Critical infrastructure interdependencies. *IEEE Control Syst. Mag.* 21:11–25
61. Amin M. 2002. Toward secure and resilient interdependent infrastructures. *J. Infrastruct. Syst.* 8:67–75
62. Longstaff TA, Haimes YY. 2002. A holistic roadmap for survivable infrastructure systems. *IEEE Trans. Syst. Man Cybern. Part A: Syst. Humans* 32:260–68
63. Farrell AE, Zerriffi H. 2004. Electric power: critical infrastructure protection. See Ref. 175, pp. 203–15
64. Zweifel P, Bonomo S. 1995. Energy security—coping with multiple supply risks. *Energy Econ.* 17:179–83
65. Karki R, Billinton R. 2001. Reliability/cost implications of PV and wind energy utilization in small isolated power systems. *IEEE Trans. Energy Convers.* 16:368–73
66. Ubeda JR, Garcia M. 1999. Reliability and production assessment of wind energy production connected to the electric network supply. *IEEE Proc. Gener. Transm. Distrib.* 146:169–75
67. Zerriffi H, Dowlatabadi H, Strachan ND. 2002. Electricity and conflict: advantages of a distributed system. *Electr. J.* 15:55–65
68. Farrell AE, Lave LB, Morgan MG. 2002. Bolstering the security of the electric power system. *Issues Sci. Technol.* 18:49–56
69. Zerriffi H, Dowlatabadi H, Farrell AE. 2005. Incorporating stress in electric power system reliability models. *Proc. IEEE: Special Issue Energy Infrastruct. Def. Syst.* In press
70. Counc. Compet. 2002. *Creating opportunity out of adversity*. Presented at Natl. Symp. Compet. Secur., Pittsburgh, PA
71. Byon I. 2000. *Survivability of the U.S. electric power industry*. MS thesis. Carnegie Mellon Univ., Pittsburgh, PA. 85 pp.
72. Strachan ND, Zerriffi H, Dowlatabadi H. 2003. System implications of distributed generation: economics and robustness. In *Critical Infrastructures: State of the Art in Research and Applications*, ed. WAH Thissen, PM Herder, pp. 39–75. Boston, MA: Kluwer Acad.
73. Hughes TP. 1983. *Networks of Power: Electrification in Western Society, 1880–1930*. Baltimore, MD: Johns Hopkins Univ. Press. 474 pp.
74. Hirsh RF. 1999. *Power Loss: The Origins of Deregulation and Restructuring in the American Utility System*. Cambridge, MA: MIT Press. 406 pp.
75. Hyman L. 2002. America's electric utilities: past, present and future. *Rep.* Public Util. Reston, VA. 297 pp.
76. Lovins A. 1976. Energy strategy: the road not taken. *Foreign Aff.* 55:65–96
77. Cowart R. 2002. Electrical energy security: policies for a resilient network. *Rep.* Regul. Assist. Proj., Montpelier, VT
78. Martin B. 1978. Soft energy, hard politics. *Undercurrents* 27:10–13
79. Lovins AB. 1978. Soft energy technologies. *Annu. Rev. Energy Environ.* 3:477–517

80. Amin M. 2001. Toward self-healing energy infrastructures. *IEEE Comput. Appl. Power.* 14:20–28. http://ieeexplore.ieee.org/xpl/tocresult.jsp?isNumber=19333&puNumber=67
81. Electr. Advis. Board. 2002. Transmission grid solutions. *Rep.* US Dep. Energy, Washington, DC. 37 pp.
82. US Energy Assoc. 2002. National energy security post 9/11. *Rep.* US Energy Assoc., Washington, DC. http://www.usea.org
83. Kunreuther H, Heal G, Orszaq PR. 2002. Interdependent security: implications for homeland security policy and other areas. *Rep. Policy Brief. 108*, Brookings Inst., Washington, DC
84. von Meier A. 1994. Integrating Supple Technologies Into Utility Power. See Ref. 174, pp. 211–30
85. Strachan ND, Dowlatabadi H. 2002. Distributed generation and distribution utilities. *Energy Policy* 30:649–61
86. Alderfer RB, Eldridge MM, Starrs TJ. 2000. Making connections: case studies of interconnection barriers and their impacts on distributed power projects. *Rep. NREL/SR-200–28053*, Natl. Renew. Energy Lab., Golden, CO. http://www.nrel.gov/docs/fy00osti/28053.pdf
87. Luiijf E, Burger HN, Klaver MH. 2003. Critical infrastructure protection in the Netherlands: a quick-scan. In *EICAR Conference Best Paper Proceedings*, ed. UE Gattiker, pp. 19. Copenhagen: EICAR. http://www.tno.nl/instit/fel/refs/pub2003/BPP-13-CIP-Luiijf&Burger&Klaver.pdf
88. US Gen. Account. Off. 2001. Critical infrastructure protection. *Rep. GAO-01–323*, US Gen. Account. Off., Washington, DC. http://www.gao.gov/cgi-bin/getrpt?GAO-01-323
89. Moteff JD. 2002. Critical infrastructures: background, policy, and implementation. *Rep. RL30153*, Libr. Congr., Congr. Res. Serv., Washington, DC. http://www.fas.org/irp/crs/RL30153.pdf
90. *Homeland Security Act of 2002*, 107th Cong., 2nd sess. PL 107-296. http://www.dhs.gov/interweb/assetlibrary/hr_5005_enr.pdf
91. Pres. US. 2003. *The National Strategy For the Physical Protection of Critical Infrastructures and Key Assets*, White House, Washington, DC. 83 pp. http://www.whitehouse.gov/pcipb/physical_strategy.pdf
92. President's Crit. Infrastruct. Prot. Board. 2002. *The National Strategy to Secure Cyberspace (Draft for Comment)*, Pres. Crit. Infrastruct. Prot. Board, Washington, DC. 65 pp. http://purl.access.gpo.gov/GPO/LPS28730
93. Pres. US. 2000. *Defending America's Cyberspace: National Plan for Information Systems Protection*. Washington, DC: Crit. Infrastruct. Assur. Off. 159 pp. http://www.fas.org/irp/offdocs/pdd/CIP-plan.pdf
94. Moteff J, Copeland C, Fischer J. 2002. Critical infrastructures: What makes an infrastructure critical? *Rep. RL31556*, Libr. Congr., Congr. Res. Serv., Washington, DC. http://www.fas.org/irp/crs/RL31556.pdf
95. Pres. US. 1996. Executive Order 13010: Critical Infrastructure Protection. *Fed. Regist.* 61:37347–50. Jul. 17. http://www.fas.org/irp/offdocs/eo/
96. President's Commission Crit. Infrastruct. Prot. 1997. Critical foundations: protecting America's infrastructures. *Rep. President's Commission Crit. Infrastruct. Prot.*, Washington, DC. 192 pp. http://permanent.access.gpo.gov/lps15260/PCCIP_Report.pdf
97. President's Commission Crit. Infrastruct. Prot. 1997. Research and development recommendations for protecting and assuring critical national infrastructure. *NTIS ADA391667*. Dep. Justice, Washington, DC
98. Pres. US. 1998. Presidential Decision Directive 63: Critical Infrastructure Protection. In *PDD-63*, pp. 12. Washington,

DC: Dep. Justice. http://www.fas.org/irp/offdocs/pdd-63.htm
99. Townsend W. 2002. *The Office of Energy Assurance*. Presented at 2002 State Heat. Oil Propane Conf., Kennebunkport, ME. http://www.naseo.org/events/shopp/2002/
100. Pres. US. 2001. Executive Order 13228: Establishing the Office of Homeland Security and the Homeland Security Council. *Fed. Regist. 66:51812–17, Oct. 8.* http://www.fas.org/irp/offdocs/eo/
101. Off. Homel. Secur. 2002. National strategy for homeland security. *Exec. Off. President, July Rep.*, Off. Homel. Secur., Washington, DC, pp. 90. http://www.dhs.gov/interweb/assetlibrary/nat_strat_hls.pdf
102. Burns RE, Wilhelm J, McGarvey J, Lehmann T. 2003. *Security-related cost recovery in utility network industries*, White pap. Natl. Regul. Research Inst., Columbus, OH
103. McGarvey J, Wilhelm J. 2003. NARUC/NRRI 2003 survey on critical infrastructure security. *Rep. 04-01*. Natl. Regul. Research Inst., Columbus, OH. http://www.nrri.ohio-state.edu
104. Stevens GM. 2003. Homeland Security Act of 2002: Critical Infrastructure Information Act. *Rep. RL31762*, Congr. Res. Serv., Washington, DC. http://www.fas.org/sgp/crs/RL31762.pdf
104a. *Freedom of Information Act.* 5 US Code § 552. http://www.usdoj.gov/oip/foia_updates/Vol_XVII_4/page2.htm
105. Moteff J, Stevens GM. 2003. Critical infrastructure information disclosure and homeland security. *Congr. Res. Serv. Rep. RL31556*, Washington, DC. http://www.fas.org/irp/crs/RL31556.pdf
106. Fed. Energy Regul. Comm. 2003. Order 630: critical energy infrastructure information. *Fed. Regist.* 68:9857–73, Feb. 21. http://www.fas.org/sgp/news/2003/04/fr041603.pdf
107. Robinson CP, Woodard JB, Varnado SG. 1998. Critical infrastructure: interlinked and vulnerable. *Issues Sci. Technol.* 15:61–67
108. Dick RL. 2001. *Statement of Ronald L. Dick, Director of the National Infrastructure Protection Center on critical infrastructure protection*. Testimony before Senate Comm. Gov. Affairs. May 8. Washington, DC. http://www.senate.gov/~gov_affairs/050802dick.htm
109. Stein W, Hammerli B, Pohl H, Posch R. 2003. *Critical infrastructure protection (CIP) workshop—introduction and goals*. Presented at Crit. Infrastruct. Prot. (CIP) Workshop—Status Perspect., Frankfurt am Main, Ger.
110. Natl. Research Counc. 2002. *Making the Nation Safer: The Role of Science and Technology in Countering Terrorism*. Washington, DC: Natl. Acad. http://www.nap.edu/books/0309084814/html/
111. Schmitz W. 2003. Comprehensive roadmap: analysis and assessment for critical infrastructure protection. *Rep. ACIP IST-2001–37257*, Eur. Union Inf. Soc. Technol. Progam. Copenhagen, Den.
112. Robinson DG, Ranade SJ, Rodriquez SB, Jungst RG, Urbina A, et al. 2001. Development of the capabilities to analyze the vulnerability of bulk power systems. *Rep. SAND2001-3188*, Sandia National Laboratory, Albuquerque, NM. http://www.osti.gov/dublincore/ecd/servlets/purl/787793-XYt5d9/native/
113. Rinaldi SM. 2004. *The role of modeling and simulation in critical infrastructure protection*. Presented at 27th Hawaii Int. Conf. System Sci., Honolulu, HI
114. Muller F. 2003. Energy security—risks of international energy supply. *Int. Politik* 58:3–10
115. Energy Inf. Adm. 2002. *International Energy Outlook*. Washington, DC: US Dep. Energy, DOE/EIA-0484 (2002). http://www.eia.doe.gov/bookshelf.html
116. Br. Pet. Co. 2003. BP statistical review of world energy. *Rep.* Br. Pet. Co., London, UK. http://www.bp.com

117. Senden MMG, Punt AD, Hoek A. 1998. Gas-to-liquids processes: current status & future prospects. *Natural Gas Convers.* 119:961–96
118. Ramcharran H. 2002. Oil production responses to price changes: an empirical application of the competitive model to OPEC and non-OPEC countries. *Energy Econ.* 24:97–106
119. Bohi D, Toman M. 1993. Energy security: externalities and policies. *Energy Policy* 93:1093–109
120. Adelman MA. 1995. *The Genie Out of the Bottle: World Oil Since 1970.* Cambridge, MA: MIT Press. 350 pp.
121. Chang HJ. 2003. New horizons for Korean energy industry—shifting paradigms and challenges ahead. *Energy Policy* 31:1073–84
122. Larson ED, Wu ZX, DeLaquil P, Chen WY, Gao PF. 2003. Future implications of China's energy-technology choices. *Energy Policy* 31:1189–204
123. ZhiDong L. 2003. An econometric study on China's economy, energy and environment to the year 2030. *Energy Policy* 31:1137–50
124. Jones DW, Leiby PN, Paik IK. 2004. Oil price shocks and the macroeconomy: What has been learned since 1996? *Energy J.* 25(2):1–32
125. Newbery DM, Stiglitz JE. 1981. *The Theory of Commodity Price Stabilization.* New York: Oxford Univ. Press
126. Jorgenson D. 1988. Productivity and economic growth in Japan and the United States. *Am. Econ. Rev.* 78:217–22
127. Denison EF. 1985. *Trends in American Economic Growth, 1929–1982.* Washington, DC: Brookings Inst. 141 pp.
128. Hamilton JD. 2003. What is an oil shock? *J. Econom.* 113:363–98
129. LaCasse C, Plourde A. 1995. On the renewal of concern for the security of oil supply. *Energy J.* 16:1–23
130. Rempel H. 2002. Natural gas for Europe—present state and predictions for a stable supply in the future. *Energy Explor. Exploit.* 20:219–37
131. Anonymous. 2000. A brief history of U.S. LNG incidents. *Rep. TD-02109,* CH-IV Corp. Millersville, MD. http://www.ch-iv.com/lng/incid1.htm
132. Jensen JT. 2003. The LNG Revolution. *Energy J.* 24:1–45
133. Friedlander GD. 1966. The northeast power failure—a blanket of darkness. *IEEE Spectr.* 3(2):54–73
134. Knight UG. 2001. *Power Systems in Emergencies: From Contingency Planning to Crisis Management.* New York: Wiley. 378 pp.
135. Anonymous. 1966. *Public Response to the Northeastern Power Blackout.* Chicago: Natl. Opin. Research Cent. http://www.norc.chicago.edu
136. Wilson GL, Zarakas P. 1978. Anatomy of a Blackout: How's and Why's of the series of events that led to the shutdown of New York's power in July 1977. *IEEE Spectr.* 15(2):39–46
137. Congr. Res. Serv. 1978. The cost of an urban blackout: the consolodated edison blackout, July 13–14, 1977. *Rep. 95-54,* US Congr., Washington, DC
138. N. Am. Electric Reliab. Council. 2001. *An approach to action for the electricity sector.* Presented at N. Am. Electric Reliab. Council. (NERC) Work. Group Forum Crit. Infrastruct. Prot., Princeton, NJ. http://www.nerc.com/~filez/cipfiles.html
139. Eto J, Koomey J, Lehman B, Martin N, Mills E, et al. 2001. Scoping study on trends in the economic value of electricity reliability to the U.S. economy. *Rep. LBNL-47911.* Energy Analysis Dep. Environ. Energy Technol. Div. Lawrence Berkeley Natl. Lab., Berkeley, CA. http://eetd.lbl.gov/ea/EMS/reports/47911.pdf
140. Off. Technol. Assess. 1990. Physical vulnerability of electric systems to natural disasters and sabotage. *Rep. OTA-E-453,* US Congr., Washington,

DC. http://www.wws.princeton.edu/cgi-bin/byteserv.prl/~ota/disk2/1990/9034/903401.PDF
141. Kerry M, Kelk G, Etkin D, Burton I, Kalhok S. 1999. Glazed over: Canada copes with the ice storm of 1998. *Environment* 41:6–11
142. Electr. Consum. Resour. Counc. 2004. The economic impacts of the August 2003 blackout. *Rep.* Electr. Consum. Resour. Counc., Washington, DC. http://www.elcon.org/Documents/EconomicImpactsOfAugust2003Blackout.pdf
143. Morgan AJ. 1987. *A quantification of the effects of electricity supply interruptions.* PhD thesis. Cavendish Lab., Cambridge Univ., Cambridge, UK
144. Kahn E. 1979. The compatibility of wind and solar technology with conventional energy systems. *Annu. Rev. Energy* 4:313–52
145. Off. Coal, Nuclear, Electric Altern. Fuels. 1998. The changing structure of the electric power industry: selected issues. *Rep. DOE/EIA-0620*, Energy Inf. Adm., Washington, DC. http://www.eia.doe.gov/bookshelf/historic.html
146. US Nuclear Regul. Comm. 1999. Briefing on existing event response procedures (including federal response plan and coordination of federal agencies in response to terrorist activities). *Proc. US Nuclear Regul. Comm. July 15*, pp. 1–56. *Rockville, MD.* http://www.nrc.gov/reading-rm/doc-collections/commission/tr/1999/19990715a.html
147. Chapin DM, Cohen KP, Davis WK, Kintner EE, Koch LJ. 2002. Nuclear safety: nuclear power plants and their fuel as terrorist targets. *Science* 297:1997–99
148. Brenner DJ. 2003. Letter: Revisiting nuclear power plant safety. *Science* 299:201–3. http://www.sciencemag.org
149. Chapin DM, Cohen KP, Davis WK, Kintner EE. 2003. Response: Revisiting nuclear power plant safety. *Science* 299:201–3
150. von Hippel FN. 2003. Letter: Revisiting nuclear power plant safety. *Science* 299:201–3
151. Swiss Fed. Nuclear Saf. Insp. 2003. Postion of the Swiss Federal Nuclear Safety Inspectorate regarding the safety of the Swiss nuclear power plants in the event of an intentional aircraft crash. *Rep. HSK-AN-4626*, Wurenlingen, Switz. http://www.hsk.psi.ch/english/files/pdf/gus_03_04_03_e.pdf
152. Travers WD. 1999. Recommendations of the safeguards performance assessment task force. *WITS 199800188*, US Nuclear Regul. Comm., Washington, DC. http://www.nrc.gov/reading-rm/doc-collections/commission/secys/1999/secy1999-024/1999-024scy.html
153. Bunn G, Braun C. 2003. Terrorism potential for research reactors compared with power reactors: nuclear weapons, "dirty bombs," and truck bombs. *Am. Behav. Sci.* 46:714–26
154. Mcfarlane A. 2001. Interim storage of spent fuel in the United States. *Annu. Rev. Energy Environ.* 26:201–35
155. Janberg K. 2002. *History and actual status of aircraft impact and anti-tank weaponry consequences on spent fuel storage installations.* Presented at MIT Workshop Spent Reactor Fuel Storage, Cambridge, MA
156. Thomauske B. 2003. *Realization of the German concept for interim storage of spent nuclear fuel—current situation and prospects.* Presented at Waste Manag. 2003, Tuscon, AZ. http://www.bfs.de/transport/publika/vortr_zwila_tuscon2/vt_thomauske_tuscon_2003.pdf
157. Alvarez R, Beyea J, Janberg K, Kang J, Lyman E, et al. 2003. Reducing the hazards from stored spent power-reactor fuel in the United States. *Sci. Global Secur.* 11:1–51. http://www.princeton.edu/~globsec/publications/pdf/11_1Alvarez.pdf
158. *USA PATRIOT Act of 2002.* 107th Cong., 1st sess. PL 107-56. http://thomas.loc.gov/cgi-bin/bdquery/z?d107:h.r.03162:

159. US Nuclear Regul. Comm. 2003. Nuclear Regulatory Commission (NRC) review of "reducing the hazards from stored spent power-reactor fuel in the United States." *Sci. Global Secur.* 11: 203–11. http://www.nrc.gov/reading-rm/doc-collections/fact-sheets/reducing-hazards-spent-fuel.html
160. Alvarez R, Beyea J, Janberg K, Kang J, Lyman E, et al. 2003. Response by the authors to the NRC review of "reducing the hazards from stored spent power-reactor fuel in the United States." *Sci. Global Secur.* 11:213–23. http://www.princeton.edu/~globsec/publications/pdf/SGS_213-223_response.pdf
161. Maerli MB, Schaper A, Barnaby F. 2003. The characteristics of nuclear terrorist weapons. *Am. Behav. Sci.* 46:727–44
162. Makhijani A. 2001. Plutonium endgame: managing global stocks of separated weapons-usable commercial and surplus nuclear weapons plutonium. *Rep.* Inst. Energy Environ. Research. http://www.ieer.org
163. Dilger F, Halstead R. 2003. The next species of trouble: spent nuclear fuel transportation in the United States, 2010–2048. *Am. Behav. Sci.* 46:796–811
164. Garwin RL, Charpak G. 2001. *Megawatts and Megatons*. Chicago: Univ. Chicago Press. 412 pp.
165. Tierney K. 2002. *Strength of a city: a disaster research perspective on the World Trade Center attack*. Soc. Sci. Research Cent. http://www.ssrc.org/sept11/essays/tierney.htm
166. Fischhoff B, Gonzalez RM, Small DA, Lerner JS. 2003. Evaluating the Success of Terror Risk Communication. *Biosecurity Bioterrorism* 1(4):255–58
167. Adibi MM, ed. 2000. *Power System Restoration: Methodologies and Implementation Strategies*. New York: IEEE Press. 690 pp.
168. Asmus P. 2001. The war against terrorism helps build the case for distributed renewables. *Electr. J.* 14:75–80
169. Dunn S. 2002. Micropower: new variable in the energy-environment-security equation. *Bull. Sci. Technol. Soc.* 22:72–86
170. Jacobson MZ, Masters GM. 2001. Exploiting wind versus coal. *Science* 293:1438
171. Staunton RH, Kueck JD, Kirby BJ, Eto J. 2001. Demand response: an overview of enabling technologies. *Public Util. Fortn.* 139:32–39
172. Hirst E, Faruqui A. 2002. Demand response: how to reach the other side. *Electr. Perspect.* 27:16–33
173. DeCarolis JF, Keith DW. 2001. Letter: The real cost of wind energy. *Science* 294:1000–3
174. Summerton J, ed. 1994. *Changing Large Technical Systems*. Boulder, CO: Westview
175. Cleveland CJ, ed. 2004. *Encyclopedia of Energy*. London: Elsevier

Subject Index

A

ABMS
  See Agent based model simulations
Acacia, 279
Access control, 430
Accumulative reservoirs, 72
ACE
  See Aerosol Characterization Experiment
Acid rain, 334
Acid rock drainage (ARD), 213, 222
Acidity of the oceans
  CO_2 emissions increasing, 127
Activism
  anti-mining, 223
Actual evapotranspiration (AET), 265, 267
Adult movement
  tagging studies of, 43–48
Advanced Very High Resolution Radiometer (AVHRR), 14–15, 20
Advances in energy forecasting models based on engineering economics, 345–81
  challenges and requirements, 356–65
  conventional engineering modeling, 351–56
  directions/issues in modeling, 361–65
  economic evaluation of energy-efficient technologies, 358–59
  implications for policy analysis and modeling, 348–51
  modeling (pathways), 365–74
  options to influence energy efficiency in industry, 347–48
  policy context and recent developments, 348
  policy modeling, 359–60
  recommendations, 374–76
  research priorities, 374–75
  short term collaborative projects, 375–76
  technology and opportunity representation, 357–58
  uncertainty in data and data quality, 360
Aegilops, 162–63
AEO
  See Annual energy output
AERONET, 7, 11
Aerosol burdens
  trends in, 4
Aerosol Characterization Experiment (ACE), 11, 18
Aerosol effects on climate, 5–14
  direct, 6–7
  indirect, 12–14
  semidirect, 11–12
  thermodynamical, 7–11
Aerosol emissions
  in deforestation, 284–85
Aerosol sources and distributions, 3–5
AET
  See Actual evapotranspiration
Agent based model simulations (ABMS), 365
Aggregates, 70
Agricola, 208
Agricultural crops
  liquid fuels from, 323
Agricultural residues
  combustion through, 74
Air pollution
  ambient, 387–90
  controlling, 334
  environmental strategies for, 408–11
  indoor, 390–96
  mortality and disease burden resulting from, 390, 396
  social costs of, 327, 333
Albedo changes, 282
Alberta Research Council, 126
Alchemy
  modern, 243–45
All Modular Industry Growth Assessment (AMIGA), 354, 363
Along Track Scanning Radiometer (ATSR), 15–16
Aluminum cycle, 103
Amazon Basin, 247
Ambient air pollution, 387–90
American Electric Power, 126
American Nuclear Insurers (ANI), 320
American Petroleum Institute, 441
AMIGA
  See All Modular Industry Growth Assessment
Anaconda, 230

471

Analytic methods for energy
    cost comparisons, 302
  method I–bus bar costs,
    303–9
  method II–market-based
    costs, risk premiums, and
    cost variability, 309–14
  method III–market costs
    including subsidies,
    314–25
  method IV–externalities
    and energy costs, 325–39
Andara, 40
Andean Highlands, 247
ANI
  See American Nuclear
    Insurers
Animal units (AUs), 262
Annual energy output (AEO),
  304
*Annual Review of Energy and
  the Environment*, 302
Anthropogenic dominance of
    mobilization flows,
    85–92, 94
  indications of degree of, 93
  versus logarithm of
    aqueous solubility, 95
Anti-mining activism, 223
Apo Island, 40
Appalachian Mountains, 235
Aquifers
  deep saline, 125
ARD
  See Acid rock drainage
Argopecten irradians, 41
Arid grazing systems, 272
Asian monsoon, 7–8
Assessing subsidies, 316–19
Assessment of policy mixes,
  373
Atomic Energy Act, 320
ATSR
  See Along Track Scanning
    Radiometer
Attack modes
  in energy infrastructure and
    security, 429–30
Attacks
  deliberate, 435
Aus
  See Animal units
Availability of germplasm
  maintained in situ, 163–66
  obstacles to, from
    genebanks users'
    perceptions, 159–60
AVHRR
  See Advanced Very High
    Resolution Radiometer

B

Backup generation capacity,
  451
Baie Mare (Romania), 246
Balancing technology with
  the environment, 104
BANANA (build absolutely
  nothing anywhere near
  anything), 182
Barriers to implementation
  approaches to addressing,
    355–56
BAT
  See Best available
    technology standards
Batelle, 126
BAU
  See Business-as-usual
    conditions
Bayesian economics, 365
BC
  See Black carbon
Behavioral representation,
  372
  basic understanding of
    investment situation, 372
  diffusion processes, 372
  improvements on, 372
Benefits
  multiple, of technology,
    371
Best available technology
  (BAT) standards, 231

Bioclimatic conditions, 270
  GIS analysis of grazing
    systems under, 263–69
Bioclimatic setting, 290
Biodiversity reporting, 224
Biofuel mineral materials,
  185
  burning, 3, 74
Biogeochemistry
  of deforestation, 283–84
  of desertification, 273–75
  of woody encroachment,
    280–81
Bioleaching techniques, 222
Biomass burning, 402–3
  mobilization through, 74,
    76
Biome area
  global, 265
  statistics on, 266
Black carbon (BC), 2–8, 11,
  16–17, 21
Black Lung Disability Fund,
  325
Black lung disease, 217
Blackouts
  costs of, 450
  in New York City,
    448–50
  in northeastern U.S., 458
  in Quebec, 430
Blue Cascades, 444
Boron
  geochemical cycle of, 76
Bosphorus Straits, 446
Bottom-up models, 347, 352
BP, 110, 423
*Brittle Power: Energy
  Strategy for National
  Security*, 426–27
Broad-scale cycles, 73
Budget, 71
Bureau of Labor Statistics,
  310
Burlington Resources, 126
Burning
  repeated, 284

SUBJECT INDEX 473

Business-as-usual (BAU)
  conditions, 356, 369

C

Calanus finmarchicus, 53
Calcium cycle, 93
Canadian Integrated
  Modeling System
  (CIMS), 354–57, 364
  Bayesian economic
    principles in, 365
Carbon
  black, 2
  organic, 2
Carbon capture
  costs of, 112
Carbon capture and storage
  (CCS) cost modeling for
  electricity generation,
  130–36
  integrated modeling,
    133–36
  plant-level modeling,
    130–33
Carbon capture and storage
  (CCS) technologies
  the energy penalty,
    reference technology, and
    model assumptions,
    113–15
  opportunities for CO_2
    capture, 115–21
  potential role of, 111–13
  prospects for, 109–42
Carbon credits
  to mitigate GHG
    emissions, 412–13
Carbon dioxide (CO_2)
  emissions
  airborne, 339
  cost of capture and storage
    of, 116
  IGCC plants with physical
    absorption of, 118
  increasing acidity of the
    oceans, 127
  injecting, 112, 126

from Lake Nyos, 123
  limiting, 111
  opportunities for
    capturing, 115–21
  stationary sources of, 115
Carbon dioxide (CO_2)
  transportation and
  storage, 121–30
  biological conversion to
    fuels, 129
  conversion to carbonates,
    129
  direct use, 128
  geologic storage, 123–26
  ocean storage, 127–28
  regulatory issues and
    leakage, 129–30
  transportation, 122–23
Carbon emissions, 318
Carbon Mitigation Initiative
  (Princeton), 111
Carbon monoxide (CO)
  in syngas, 118
Carbonaceous aerosols, 3
Carnegie Mellon University,
  133, 135
  sector model of carbon
    capture and storage, 135
Cascading failures, 429
Categorization of
  technologies
  functional, 370–71
CCE
  See Cost of conserved
    energy
CCN
  See Cloud condensation
    nuclei
CCS
  See Carbon capture and
    storage technologies
C&D
  See Construction and
    demolition waste
CDNC
  See Cloud droplet number
    concentrations

CEII
  See Critical Energy
    Infrastructure Information
Cement manufacture, 120
Cement production, 307
  stationary sources of CO_2
    emissions, 115
Center for Critical
  Infrastructure Protection
  (New Zealand), 443
Centralization
  in energy infrastructure and
    security, 436–38
Centre for Genetic Resources,
  155
CFCs
  See Chloroflurocarbons
CGIAR
  See Consultative Group on
    International Agricultural
    Research
Charcoal burning, 74
  carbon credits to mitigate
    GHG emissions, 412–13
  fuel switching and charcoal
    markets, 411–12
  in Kenya, 411–13
Charcoal life cycle, 411
Charcoal making, 74, 412–13
Charcoal markets
  fuel switching and, 411–12
Chemical absorption
  of CO_2, conventional
    power plants with, 117
  postcombustion, 117
Chemical tags of movement
  in otoliths and statoliths,
    48–53
Chemicals, 119
Chernobyl (Ukraine), 453
Chesapeake Bay watershed,
  51
Chevron, 110
Chicago Board of Trade, 195
Chicago Carbon Exchange,
  336
Chilean National

Environmental Commission, 408
Chilean nitrates, 235
China
  coal reserves in, 111
  genebanks in, 157
Chlorine
  concentrations in seawater, 77
Chloroflurocarbons (CFCs), 70, 80
  flows of, 93
CHP
  See Combined Heat and Power
Chromis punctipinnis, 45
CIMMYT
  See International Maize and Wheat Improvement Center (CIMMYT)
CIMS
  See Canadian Integrated Modeling System
CIP
  See Critical infrastructure protection
Circuit fabrication, 314
Citicorp, 450
Civil defense preparedness, 456
Clark Fork River basin, 213
Clean Air Act, 230, 334
  amendments to, 230
Cleaner production, 217–25
  eco-efficiency and environmental performance, 218–21
  innovation for pollution prevention, 221–22
  new drivers of environmental performance, 222–24
Climate-health relationships, 396n
Climate interactions
  current uncertainties in assessing aerosol effects on, 1–30
  in deforestation, 286
  in desertification, 277–78
  in woody encroachment, 282
Closed cycles, 71
  two-reservoir model of, 72
Cloud condensation nuclei (CCN), 285
Cloud droplet number concentrations (CDNC), 12–14, 18–20
Cloud lifetime, 12
Club of Rome, 208
CNG
  See Compressed natural gas
Coal-bed methane
  geologic storage of CO_2 in enhanced, 126
  recovery of, 126
Coal fly ash, 185, 196
Coal Mine Health and Safety Act, 217n
Coal plants, 326
  retrofitting existing, 117
  See also Integrated gasification combined-cycle coal plants; Natural gas combined-cycle power plants; Pulverized-coal power plants
Coal production, 93, 98
  trends in, 96–97
Coal reserves
  in developing countries, 111
Coal subsidies, 318
Cogeneration, 358
Collaborative projects
  short term, 375–76
Combined heat and power (CHP), 305–6, 358, 371
Combustion
  pure oxygen, 118–19
  through agricultural residues, 74
Command-and-control regulations, 231
Commingling
  of pollutants, 327
Community
  mining and the social environment, 216–17
Composites, 70
Compressed natural gas (CNG), 409
Comstock Lode, 244
Concentration factors, 77–80
Concepts in energy infrastructure and security, 427–38
  attack modes, 429–30
  centralization, 436–38
  cyber security, 433–34
  diversity, 431–32
  expected failures, 428–29
  interdependency, 434
  redundancy, 433
  routine security, 427–28
  storage, 432–33
  stress, 434–35
  survivability, 435–36
Conflict Diamonds campaign, 238
Conservation
  of productive capacity, 233
Conservation function
  of genebank collections, 159
Conservation International, 216
Conservation supply curves (CSC), 307, 364
Construction and demolition (C&D) waste, 194, 198
Construction materials, 206
  life-cycle assessment of, 188–90
Construction materials and designs
  comparison of, 190–92
  environmental effects

SUBJECT INDEX   475

of, 187–92
Construction materials and
    the environment,
    181–204
  end-of-life options for
    construction materials,
    194–96
  expected shortages of
    construction materials,
    192–94
  future research, 196–200
  importance of the
    construction industry in
    the U.S. economy, 183–85
  materials use in
    construction, 185–86
Consultative Group on
    International
    Agricultural Research
    (CGIAR), 156
  System-wide Information
    Network for Genetic
    Resources, 156–57, 162
Consumer Price Index (CPI),
    310, 325
Contamination
  secondary and tertiary, 215
Convention on Biological
    Diversity, 144, 164, 167
Conventional engineering
    modeling, 351–56
  addressing barriers to
    implementation, 355–56
  approaches to model
    policies, 356
  modeling approaches,
    352–55
  use of models in policy
    development, 351–52
Conventional power plants
  with chemical absorption
    of CO_2, 117
Copper
  historical production of, 93
  trends in production of,
    96–97
Copper cycle, 93

spatially-resolved, 101
Corporate environmental
    trajectories, 219
Cost of conserved energy
    (CCE), 307–9
  marginal, 309
Costs of electricity, 301–44
  analytic methods for
    energy cost comparisons,
    302
  bus bar costs, 303–9
  climate change and energy
    costs, 335–39
  externalities and energy
    costs, 325–35
  fixed vs. variable, 305
  market-based costs, risk
    premiums, and cost
    variability, 309–14
  market costs including
    subsidies, 314–25
  method I, 303–9
  method II, 309–14
  method III, 314–25
  method IV, 325–39
  predicting price
    fluctuations, 312
CPI
  See Consumer Price Index
Criteria pollutants, 329
Critical Energy Infrastructure
    Information (CEII), 443
Critical infrastructure
    protection (CIP), 421,
    423, 438–44
  definitions, 439–40
  practice, 440–43
  research, 443–44
Cross subsidies, 316
Crown Butte Resources, 242
Crown Jewel Mine, 212n
CSC
  See Conservation supply
    curves
Cultural politics of extraction,
    240–45
  modern alchemy and

  mining as transformation,
    243–45
  the underground, 242–43
*Cultural Survival
  Quarterly*, 223
Cyanide spills, 246
Cyber security
  in energy infrastructure and
    security, 433–34
Cycle analysis, 71–72, 98
  for industrial materials, 101
Cycles
  broad-scale, 73
  characterization of, 70, 73
  closed, 71
  components of, 71–72
  estimating relative
    anthropogenic dominance
    of, 74–93
  over space and time,
    93–101
  practical utility of, 101–3
  spatially-discrete, 101
  spatially-resolved, 101
  status report on human vs.
    natural dominance,
    69–107
  survey of information
    about, 73–74
  technological, 71

D

DAI
  See Dangerous
    anthropogenic
    interference levels
Dams
  See Hydroelectric dams;
    Tailings dams
Dangerous anthropogenic
    interference (DAI)
    levels, 12
Data and data quality
  uncertainty in, 360
Data Envelopment Analysis,
    365
Davis-Bessie nuclear power

plant, 433
"Decarbonization"
  of fossil fuels, 118
Decentralized energy
  technologies, 438
Deep-ocean sequestration, 128
Deep saline aquifers, 125
Defense Civil Preparedness Office, 425n
Definitions
  in critical infrastructure protection, 439–40
Deforestation, 74, 270–71, 274, 282–86
  biogeochemistry, 283–84
  climate interactions, 286
  ecosystem structure, 282–83
  hydrology, 285–86
  trace-gas and aerosol emissions, 284–85
Deindustrialization
  medium term, 228
Demographic patterns
  of grazing systems, 263
Demolition
  See Construction and demolition waste
Dependency, rights, and justice, 234–40
  extraction, governance, and the state, 236–38
  land rights, resistance, and environmental justice, 238–40
Depleted oil and gas reservoirs
  geologic storage of CO_2 in, 123–24
Desertification, 271–78
  biogeochemistry, 273–75
  climate interactions, 277–78
  ecosystem structure, 271–73
  hydrology, 276–77

of the Sahel, 277
  trace-gas emissions, 275–76
Destabilization
  of the Middle East, 446
Development of minerals and the resource curse, 225–29
Development policy, 226
DG
  See Distributed generation challenges
DHS
  See U.S. Department of Homeland Security
Diesel engine emissions, 23
Diffusion processes, 372
Diffusion research analyses, 365
Diospyros, 279
Direct effects
  of aerosols on climate, 6–7
Direct subsidies, 315–16
Direct use
  of CO_2, 128
"Dirty bombs," 452
Disciplines included in modeling, 364–65
  agent based model simulations, 365
  Bayesian economics, 365
  evolution economics, 365
  innovation and diffusion research analyses, 365
  management science and organizational research, 364–65
  marketing research, 365
  social psychology, 364
Discount rates and hurdle rates, 362–63
Discounting, 304
Dispossession
  juxtaposed with mining, 241
Disruptions
  in fuel supply, 452

Dissostichus eleginoides, 44
Distributed generation (DG) challenges, 427
Distribution
  in assessing aerosol effects on climate, 16–17
Diversity
  in energy infrastructure and security, 431–32
Donora disaster, 230
Dutch Disease, 228

E

Early analyses
  of energy infrastructure and security problems, 424–27
Earth moving
  mining as physical landscape modification, 209–10
Earth Summit, 233
Eco-efficiency, 218
  and environmental performance, 218–21
Eco-geographic surveys, 164
Economic evaluation
  of energy-efficient technologies, 358–59
Economic flexibility, 362
Economic input-output analysis (EIO), 330
Economic performance
  mineral wealth impeding, 228
Ecosystem responses, 261–99
  deforestation, 270–71, 274, 282–86
  desertification, 271–78
  the global footprint of grazing systems, 263–71
  woody encroachment, 270–71, 274, 278–82
Ecosystem responses to managed grazing, 286–91
  knowledge gaps and

research needs, 289–91
response typologies,
 286–89
Ecosystem structure
 in deforestation, 282–83
 in desertification, 271–73
 in woody encroachment,
  278–79
Ecosystems
 changes reported in, 288
 mining as a driver of
  regional and global
  environmental change,
  214–16
ECSCs
 See Energy conservation
  supply curves
Edaphic conditions, 270
 GIS analysis of grazing
  systems under, 263–69
Edmunds Underwater Park,
 35–36
Efficiency
 prevention and response in,
  459–60
EIO
 See Economic input-output
  analysis
EIR
 See Extractive Industries
  Review
EKC
 See Environmental
  Kuznets Curve
Electric power plant
 opportunities for CO_2
  capture, 115–19
 conventional power plants
  with chemical absorption
  of CO_2, 117
 IGCC plants with physical
  absorption of CO_2, 118
 pure oxygen combustion,
  118–19
Electric Power Research
 Institute, 111
Electricity

current technologies, 311
 traditional costing, 302
Electricity generation
 carbon capture and storage
  cost modeling for, 130–36
Electricity infrastructure and
 security, 448–52
 analyses of power systems
  under stress, 451
 fuel supply disruptions,
  452
 impact of an outage,
  450–51
 prior experience with
  outages, 448–49
 transformer vulnerabilities,
  449–50
Electricity prices, 312, 319,
 328, 405
Electromagnetic pulses
 (EMP), 430
El Niño Oscillation, 17
El Porco mine, 213
Emergency responses
 prevention and response in,
  457–58
Emissions
 in assessing aerosol effects
  on climate, 16–17
Emissions Prediction and
 Policy Analysis (EPPA)
 model, 134
EMP
 See Electromagnetic pulses
EMS
 See Energy management
  systems
End-of-life options
 for construction materials,
  194–96
Energy
 and public health policies
  in Kenya, 411–13
Energy Bill, 321
Energy conservation supply
 curves (ECSCs), 307,
 309

Energy converters
 power plants as, 304
Energy efficiency, 348
Energy-efficient technology
 learning curves of, 371–72
Energy forecasting models
 based on engineering
  economics
 advances in, 345–81
Energy-health linkages
 energy, gender, and health,
  402–3
 energy, poverty, and health,
  399–402
 social dimensions of,
  399–403
Energy infrastructure and
 security, 316, 421–69
 background, 423–24
 concepts, 427–38
 critical infrastructure
  protection, 438–44
 early analyses, 424–27
 electricity, 448–52
 nuclear, 452–56
 oil and gas, 444–48
 prevention and response,
  456–60
Energy intensive industries
 stationary sources of CO_2
  emissions, 115
"Energy ladder" framework,
 385, 400
Energy management and
 global health, 383–419
 charcoal in Kenya, 411–13
 energy management and
  public health, 403–7
 environmental health
  implications of energy
  source and technology,
  387–99
 integrated environmental
  strategies for air pollution
  and GHG reduction in
  Chile, 408–11
 social dimensions of

energy-health linkages, 399–403
Energy management systems (EMS), 433
Energy-materials link, 370
Energy Modeling Forum, 335
Energy penalty
  for carbon capture and storage costs, 113–15
  of carbon capture process, 113
Energy Policy Act (EPACT), 322
Energy and Power Evaluation Program (ENPEP), 353, 364
Energy source
  environmental health implications of, 387–99
Energy technologies
  decentralized, 438
Energy, Vulnerability, and War, 425–26
Engineering and management approaches to mining and environment, 217–25
  eco-efficiency and environmental performance, 218–21
  innovation for pollution prevention, 221–22
  new drivers of environmental performance, 222–24
Engineering economic models, 347
Engineering economics
  energy forecasting models based on, 345–81
Enhanced oil recovery (EOR) methods, 112, 122–24
ENPEP
  See Energy and Power Evaluation Program
Environment, 208–17

balancing with technology, 104
mining as a driver of regional and global environmental change, 214–16
mining as physical landscape modification, 209–10
mining and the social environment, 216–17
mining waste as pollution, 210–14
and public health policies in Kenya, 411–13
Environmental change
  mining as a driver of, 214–16
Environmental effects
  of construction materials and designs, 187–92
Environmental effects of construction materials and designs, 187–92
  comparison of construction materials and designs, 190–92
  life-cycle assessment of construction materials, 188–90
Environmental externalities of power plants
  full-cost accounting of, 327–32
Environmental health
  implications of energy source and technology, 387–99
  ambient air pollution, 387–90
  indoor air pollution, 390–96
  local-global linkages, 396–99
Environmental impacts
  of construction materials, 198–99

of electrical generation, 332
Environmental justice, 238–40
Environmental Kuznets Curve (EKC), 388n
Environmental performance
  eco-efficiency and, 218–21
  new drivers of, 222–24
Environmental strategies
  for air pollution and GHG reduction in Chile, 408–11
Environmental sustainability, 104
Environmental trajectories
  corporate, 219
EOR
  See Enhanced oil recovery methods
EPA
  See U.S. Environmental Protection Agency
EPACT
  See Energy Policy Act
Epinephelus striatus, 50
EPPA
  See Emissions Prediction and Policy Analysis model
Equator Principles, 223
ET
  See Evapotranspiration
Ethanol, 323
EURISCO Web catalog, 162
Evapotranspiration (ET), 276, 285
Evolution economics, 365
Executive Order #13,010, 440
Expected service life, 199
Externalities
  concept of, 428n
  internalizing, 230–33
Externalities and energy costs, 325–35
  costs and value judgments, 332–33

fossil-fuel environmental externalities, 326–27
hydroelectric plant environmental externalities, 325–26
life-cycle assessment and life-cycle costing, 327–32
valuation strategies, 333–35
Extraction and the state, 236–38
"Extractive-dependent communities," 228
Extractive Industries Review (EIR), 207n, 250
Extractive Industries Transparency Initiative, 207n, 223
ExxonMobil, 110

F

Failures
cascading, 429
expected in energy infrastructure and security, 428–29
of tailings dams, 246
FAO
See Food and Agriculture Organization
Farabundo-Marti National Liberation Front, 422
Fatal Transactions campaign, 238
Federal Bureau of Investigation, 440
Federal Emergency Management Agency, 425
Federal Energy Regulatory Commission (FERC), 442–43
Federal Highway Administration, 189
FERC
See Federal Energy Regulatory Commission

Fire suppression, 278, 287
Fish otolith microchemistry, 49–50, 52–53, 57, 60
Five Labs study, 307
Fixed costs
vs. variable, 305
Flash smelting technology, 221
Flexibility
economic, 362
technological, 361
Florida Keys National Marine Sanctuary, 37
Fluxes, 71
FOIA
See *Freedom of Information Act*
"Folk economics," 228
Food and Agriculture Organization (FAO), 145, 147, 156, 159–60
"Global Plan of Action for Conservation and Sustainable Utilization," 160, 170
Panel of Experts on Plant Exploration and Introduction, 151
World Information and Early Warning System database, 152
Ford Motor Company, 110
Fossil fuel combustion, 77
mobilization through, 74
Fossil-fuel environmental externalities, 326–27
Fossil-fuel subsidies, 318, 324–25
Fossil fuels
"decarbonization" of, 118
wealth invested in, 112
Fowler Commission, 238
Freedom of Information Act (FOIA), 442–43
bill to restore, 443
Freeport McMoran, 237

Frontier production function models, 364
Fuel minerals, 206
Fuel prices
escalation of, 304
Fuel supply disruptions, 452
Fuel switching
and charcoal markets, 411–12
Fuels
liquid, from agricultural crops, 323
nuclear, 453
Function models
frontier production, 364
Future hydrogen production, 121
Future impacts
of aerosol effects on climate, predicting, 20–21
Future recycling
reservoirs for, 101
Futures trading, 312

G

Gadus morhua, 50
Gas infrastructure and security, 444–48
Gas prices, 313
Gas reservoirs
geologic storage of CO_2 in depleted, 123–24
Gas supply infrastructure, 447
GCM cloud fields, 8, 13–14, 18–19, 21
Gender and health
energy context of, 402–3
Gender-typing
in mine jobs, 239–40
Genebank collections, 146, 149, 150–52
conservation function of, 159
cost of maintaining, 156
current, 152–56
"minor crops" in, 153
problems with, 161

480 SUBJECT INDEX

Generators
  backup capacity, 451
Genotype-by-environment
  interaction, 162
Geochemical cycles
  of boron, 76
Geographic information
  system (GIS), 262–63,
  265, 269, 290
  analysis of grazing systems
  under bioclimatic and
  edaphic conditions,
  263–69
Geologic sequestration, 337
Geologic storage of CO_2,
  123–26
  in aquifers, 124–26
  in depleted oil and gas
  reservoirs, 123–24
  from enhanced coal-bed
  methane, 126
Georges Bank, 41
Geoscience Laser Altimeter
  System (GLAS), 15
Geothermal power plants, 305
Germplasm
  flows of, 156–59
  problems of supply,
  160–63
  See also Availability of
  germplasm
Germplasm collections, 146,
  151
  historic data on, 156
GHGs
  See Greenhouse gases
GIS
  See Geographic
  information system
GISS
  See Goddard Institute for
  Space Studies
GLAS
  See Geoscience Laser
  Altimeter System
Glen Canyon hydroelectric
  plant, 192

GLI
  See Global Imager
Global biome area, 265
Global change, 261–99
  deforestation, 270–71, 274,
  282–86
  desertification, 271–78
  ecosystem responses to
  managed grazing, 286
  woody encroachment,
  270–71, 274, 278–82
Global climate change, 110
Global Climate and Energy
  Project (Stanford), 111
Global Crop Diversity Trust,
  170
Global Environment Facility,
  166
Global environmental change
  mining as a driver of,
  214–16
Global footprint of grazing
  systems, 263–71
  basic demographic
  patterns, 263
  GIS analysis of bioclimatic
  and edaphic conditions,
  263–69
  regional syndromes in the
  global grazing footprint,
  269–71
Global health
  energy management and,
  383–419
Global Imager (GLI), 16
Global-local linkages,
  396–99
Global metal flows, 70
Global Mining Initiative
  (GMI), 207n
Global warming effect
  (GWE), 192, 332
Global Witness, 238
GMI
  See Global Mining
  Initiative
Goddard Institute for Space

  Studies (GISS), 6, 8, 18,
  21
Gold Rush (California), 244
Governance and the state,
  236–38
Grasberg Mine (Irian Jaya),
  223
Grazing systems, 261–99
  arid, 272
  deforestation, 270–71, 274,
  282–86
  desertification, 271–78
  ecosystem responses to
  managed grazing, 286
  global footprint of, 263–71
  managed, 269
  woody encroachment,
  270–71, 274, 278–82
Great Barrier Reef, 52
Greenhouse Gas R&D
  Programme, 111
Greenhouse gases (GHGs), 2,
  110, 333, 336, 338–39,
  351–52, 361–62, 386,
  396–97, 404, 406, 411
  carbon credits to mitigate,
  412–13
  environmental strategies
  for reducing in Chile,
  408–11
Grids, 307
  "self-healing," 435
Guianan Shield, 239
Gulf Wars, 318
GWE
  See Global warming effect

H

Hadley circulation, 286
HEU
  See Highly-enriched
  uranium
Hewlett-Packard, 314
Hierarchical Holographic
  Modeling technique,
  434
High-pressure pipelines, 447

SUBJECT INDEX   481

High-voltage transformers, 449
Highly-enriched uranium (HEU), 455
HIV/AIDS, 216
Homestake (California), 222
Hopkins Marine Life Refuge, 35
Human action, 70
Human dominance of elemental cycles, vs. natural, 69–107
  components of cycles, 71–72
  cycles over space and time, 93–101
  estimating relative anthropogenic dominance of elemental cycles, 74–93
  the practical utility of cycles, 101–3
  survey of elemental cycle information, 73–74
Human-initiated biomass burning
  mobilization through, 74
Hydroelectric dams, 192, 305, 325–26, 432
Hydroelectric plant environmental externalities, 325–26
Hydroelectric power, 460
Hydrogen (H_2)
  future production, 121
  from natural gas for industrial uses, 120–21
  in syngas, 118
Hydrogen-based energy systems, 118
Hydrology
  of deforestation, 285–86
  of desertification, 276–77
  of woody encroachment, 281–82
Hydrometallurgical techniques, 222

I

IBPGR
  See International Board for Plant Genetic Resources
ICARDA
  See International Center for Agricultural Research in the Dry Areas
ICARUS
  See Information System on Conservation and Application of Resources Using a Sector approach model
Ice Cloud and land Elevation Satellite (ICESat), 15
Idaho National Engineering and Environmental Laboratory, 444
IEA
  See International Energy Agency
IECM
  See Integrated Environmental Control Model
IGCC
  See Integrated gasification combined-cycle coal plants
IKARUS
  See Instrumente für Klimagas-Reduktionsstrategien
Imaginary mining, 240–45
  modern alchemy and mining as transformation, 243–45
  the underground, 242–43
Imperialism
  juxtaposed with mining, 241
Implementation
  barriers for, approaches to addressing, 355–56
  realistic representation of practice of, 373

Implications for policy analysis and modeling, 348–51
Improvement of models, 369–74
  behavioral representation, 372
  policy representation, 373–74
  technology and opportunity representation, 370–72
INCO (Canada), 221
India
  coal reserves in, 111
Indian Ocean Experiment (INDOEX), 8, 14, 17
Indirect effects
  of aerosols on climate, 12–14
Indirect subsidies, 316
INDOEX
  See Indian Ocean Experiment
Indonesia, 126
Indoor air pollution, 390–96
Industrial materials cycle analysis, 101
Industrial minerals, 206
Industrial opportunities for CO_2 capture, 119–21
  cement manufacture, 120
  chemicals, 119
  future hydrogen production, 121
  hydrogen production from natural gas for industrial uses, 120–21
  iron and steel manufacture, 119–20
  natural gas production, 120
  petroleum refining, 119
Industrial Revolution, 93
Industrial Sector Technology Use Model (ISTUM), 354, 364
Industrial Technology and Energy Modeling

482   SUBJECT INDEX

System (ITEMS), 364
Industrialization
   juxtaposed with mining, 241
Information System on Conservation and Application of Resources Using a Sector approach (ICARUS) model, 353, 363
Information technology (IT), 433
Infrastructure
   interdependency, 448
Innovation in public health investment in, 406–7
Innovation research analyses, 365
Institute of Electrical and Electronics Engineering, 451
Institutional subsidies, 322
Institutions
   prevention and response in, 458–59
Instrumente für Klimagas-Reduktionsstrategien (IKARUS), 354, 357
Insurance issues, 316
Integrated Environmental Control Model (IECM), 131
Integrated environmental strategies
   for air pollution and GHG reduction in Chile, 408–11
Integrated gasification combined-cycle (IGCC) coal plants, 113–14, 118, 131, 133–35
   with physical absorption of CO_2, 118
Integrated modeling of carbon capture and storage, 133–36, 355

Carnegie Mellon Electricity sector model, 135
MIT Emissions Prediction and Policy Analysis world economy model, 134
Pacific Northwest National Laboratory world economy model, 135–36
Integrating energy, environment, and public health policies, 411–13
Integration with economic system (equilibrium or partial equilibrium), 363–64
   frontier production function models, 364
   stochastic models, 363–64
"Intelligent loads," 459
Interdependence
   and PGRFA transfers, 147–48
Interdependency
   in energy infrastructure and security, 434
   infrastructure, 448
Intergovernmental Panel on Climate Change (IPCC), 3, 17, 22, 110, 332–33, 408
Internalizing externalities, 230–33
International Board for Plant Genetic Resources (IBPGR), 144, 151
International Center for Agricultural Research in the Dry Areas (ICARDA), 155
International Center for Tropical Agriculture, 161
International Energy Agency (IEA), 375
   Greenhouse Gas R&D Programme, 111

International Labor Organization, 223
International Maize and Wheat Improvement Center (CIMMYT), 148, 161
International Organization for Standardization (ISO), 188
International Plant Genetic Resources Institute (IPGRI), 152, 160
International Rice Research Institute (IRRI), 154, 161
International Satellite Cloud Climatology Project (ISCCP), 15
International Treaty on Plant Genetic Resources for Food and Agriculture, 167, 169–70
Investment in innovation
   in public health, 406–7
Investment regimes
   liberalization of, 236
Investment situation
   basic understanding of, 372
IPCC
   See Intergovernmental Panel on Climate Change
IPGRI
   See International Plant Genetic Resources Institute
Iran-Iraq War, 423
Iron and steel manufacture, 119–20
Iron and steel manufacturing emissions, 307
   in the Netherlands, 120
   stationary sources of CO_2, 115
IRRI
   See International Rice Research Institute
ISCCP

SUBJECT INDEX **483**

See International Satellite
Cloud Climatology
Project
ISO
See International
Organization for
Standardization
ISTUM
See Industrial Sector
Technology Use Model
IT
See Information
technology
ITEMS
See Industrial Technology
and Energy Modeling
System

K

Kayraktepe hydroelectric
plant (Turkey), 325
Kennecott, 221, 244
Kerosene, 397, 402
Kimberley Process, 238
Knowledge gaps
in ecosystem responses to
managed grazing, 289–91
Kuwait
Iraqi invasion of, 318
oil fire in, 10, 423
Kyoto Protocol, 360, 406

L

LAI
See Leaf area index
Lake Nyos (Cameroon), 123
Land rights, 238–40
Landfills, 72
mining, 70
Landsat Thematic Mapper,
278
LCA
See Life-cycle assessment
Lead cycle, 99–100
Leadership in Energy and
Environmental Design
(LEED), 187

Leaf area index (LAI),
276–77, 285
Leahy-Levin-Jeffords-
Lieberman-Byrd bill,
443
Leakage of CO_2
regulatory issues and,
129–30
Learning curves
of energy-efficient
technology, 371–72
LIEF
See Long-term Industrial
Energy Forecasting model
Life-cycle assessment (LCA),
188, 192, 327, 331, 338
of construction materials,
188–90
full-cost accounting of,
327–32
process-based, 329
Limits to Growth, The, 208
Liquefied natural gas (LNG),
429, 447
Liquefied petroleum gas
(LPG), 397–98, 402
Liquid fuels
from agricultural crops,
323
Liquid water content (LWC),
12, 20
Liquid water path (LWP),
12–15
budgets predicted, 24
LNG
See Liquefied natural gas
Local-global linkages,
396–99
Long-term Industrial Energy
Forecasting (LIEF)
model, 354–55, 363–64
Los Frailes mine (Spain),
213, 246
LPG
See Liquefied petroleum
gas
Lutjanus campechanus, 44

LWC
See Liquid water content
LWP
See Liquid water path
Lycopersicon
wild, 163

M

MAAC
See Mid-Atlantic Area
Council
Mabo Decision (Australia),
238
Magnesium
mobilization of, 74–75
Managed grazing systems,
269
ecosystem responses to,
286–91
Management approaches to
mining and environment,
217–25
Management science, 364–65
Manhattan Minerals, 242
Marine Area Network, 40
Marine Protected Areas
(MPAs), 32, 37
Marine reserves and ocean
neighborhoods, 31–68
chemical tags of movement
in otoliths and statoliths,
48–53
marine reserves as
experiments in ocean
neighborhoods, 36–39
neighborhoods and
management, 58–60
population genetics and
measuring dispersal,
53–56
results from marine reserve
protection, 33–36
the spillover cloud, 39–43
tagging studies of adult
movement, 43–48
what such different types
of data tell us, 56–58

Market Allocation
 (MARKAL) model,
 353–55, 357, 362–64
 stochastic versions of, 360
Market costs of electricity,
 including subsidies,
 314–25
 assessing subsidies,
 316–19
 direct subsidies, 315–16
 fossil-fuel subsidies,
 324–25
 indirect subsidies, 316
 nuclear power subsidies,
 320–22
 renewable energy
 subsidies, 322–24
Marketing research, 365
Materials
 trends in production, 96
 used in construction,
 185–86
 See also Energy-materials
 link
Materials flows, 187, 362
Materials Technologies for
 Greenhouse Gas
 Emission Reduction
 (MATTER), 357
MATTER
 See Materials Technologies
 for Greenhouse Gas
 Emission Reduction
McLaughlin mine, 222
MEA
 See Monoethanol amine
Measuring dispersal
 population genetics and,
 53–56
Medium term
 deindustrialization, 228
Mendel's laws of heredity
 rediscovery of, 146
Mercury, 215
Metals, 206
 mining, 211
Methane, 276

recovery from coal-beds,
 126
Mid-Atlantic Area Council
 (MAAC), 135
Middle East
 destabilization of, 446
 proven oil reserves in, 444
Mie scattering calculations, 7
Militarism
 juxtaposed with mining,
 241
"Million solar roofs"
 initiative, 322
Mineral extraction, 234
Mineral law reform, 226
Mineral-rich countries, 228
Mineral wastes, 211
Mineral wealth
 cycling of, 244
Mini Climate Change
 Assessment Model
 (MiniCAM), 21, 135
Mining, 241
 as a driver of regional and
 global environmental
 change, 214–16
 investment in, 247
 legacy effects of, 232
 "a metaphor for the times,"
 242
 mobilization through, 74
 as physical landscape
 modification, 209–10
 and the social environment,
 216–17
 sustainable, 245
 as transformation, 243–45
 See also Anti-mining
 activism
Mining, Minerals and
 Sustainable
 Development (MMSD)
 Project, 207n
Mining and Environment
 Research Network, 218
Mining and the environment,
 205–59

cleaner production, 217–25
contested terrain, 205–59
cultural politics of
 extraction, 240–45
dependency, rights, and
 justice, 234–40
engineering and
 management approaches
 to, 217–25
environmental issues,
 208–17
imaginary mining, 240–45
the new reality of mineral
 development, 206–7
political ecologies of
 extraction, 234–40
sustainable development
 through public policies
 for harnessing mineral
 wealth and preventing
 pollution, 225–34
Mining code reform, 226
Mining Journal, 216
Mining waste
 as pollution, 210–14
"Minor crops"
 in genebank collections,
 153
MISR
 See Multiple Imaging
 Spectroradiometer
MIT Emissions Prediction
 and Policy Analysis
 world economy model of
 carbon capture and
 storage, 134
MMSD
 See Mining, Minerals and
 Sustainable Development
 Project
Mobility classes, 38
Mobilization factors, 74
 through fossil fuel
 combustion, 74
 through human-initiated
 biomass burning, 74
 through mining, 74

SUBJECT INDEX   485

Mobilization flows, 71
  anthropogenic, 85–92, 94
  magnitudes of, 77
  natural, 85–92
Mobilization rates
  calculation of, 81–84
Mobilization reservoirs, 71
Model assumptions
  for carbon capture and
    storage costs, 113–15
Model policies
  approaches to, 356
Model process treatments
  in assessing aerosol effects
    on climate, 17–19
Modeling, 365–74
  approaches to, 352–55
  better use of models in
    policy analysis, 368–69
  conventional, 351–56
  improving models, 369–74
Modeling directions and
    issues, 361–65
  discount rates and hurdle
    rates, 362–63
  economic flexibility, 362
  including different
    disciplines in, 364–65
  integration with economic
    system (equilibrium or
    partial equilibrium),
    363–64
  material flows, 362
  program cost estimates,
    363
  technical learning, 361–62
  technology flexibility, 361
Models, 366–67
  assumptions of, 369
  better use of in policy
    analysis, 368–69
  integrated, 355
  optimization, 355
  simulation, 355
  top-down, 338
  using in policy
    development, 351–52

Moderate Resolution Imaging
    Spectroradiometer
    (MODIS), 15
MODIS
  See Moderate Resolution
    Imaging
    Spectroradiometer
Monoethanol amine (MEA),
    117
Mount Simon sandstone
    saline formation, 126
MPAs
  See Marine Protected
    Areas
Multiple Imaging
    Spectroradiometer
    (MISR), 15
Multiple technology benefits,
    371
Mumford, Lewis, 241n, 243

N
NAICS
  See North American
    Industry Classification
    System
NASA
  See National Aeronautic
    and Space Administration
National Academy of
    Sciences, 443
National Aeronautic and
    Space Administration
    (NASA), 15
  Geoscience Laser
    Altimeter System, 15
National Ambient Air Quality
    Standards, 392
National Energy Act (NEA),
    322
National Energy Modeling
    System (NEMS), 354,
    357, 363
National Infrastructure
    Protection Center
    (NIPC), 440–41, 443
National Infrastructure

Security Co-Ordination
  Center (United
  Kingdom), 443
National Inventories
  of European countries, 162
National Marine Fisheries
  Service, 61
National Opinion Research
  Center, 448
National Regulatory Research
  Institute (NRRI), 442
National Research Council,
  144, 151, 449, 452, 454
National Security Council
  (NSC), 440
National Seed Storage
  Laboratory, 151
"National Strategy for
  Homeland Security," 441
National Transmission Grid
  Study, 437
Native American
  reservations, 235, 237
NATO
  See North Atlantic Treaty
    Organization (NATO)
Natuna natural gas field
  (Indonesia), 126
Natural gas
  for industrial uses,
    hydrogen production
    from, 120–21
  power plants fueled by,
    303, 305
  production of, 120
  reserves of, 445
  See also Liquefied natural
    gas
Natural gas combined-cycle
  (NGCC) power plants,
  113–15, 131, 133–35
Natural mobilization flows,
  85–92
NCR
  See Nuclear Regulatory
    Commission
NDVI

See Normalized difference vegetation index
NEA
  See National Energy Act
Neighborhoods
  and management, 58–60
  See also Ocean neighborhoods
Nematoscelis difficilis, 53
NEMS
  See National Energy Modeling System
Neolithic Era
  world population growth since, 168
NERCO
  See North American Electricity Reliability Council
Net primary productivity (NPR), 270
Netherlands
  decentralized energy technologies in, 438
  iron and steel emissions in, 120
  petrochemical industries in, 119
  See also Dutch Disease
Netherlands Energy Demand Model (NEMO), 363
Networks
  resilient, 435, 437
New World Liberation Front
  bombings by, 422
New York Mercantile Exchange, 312
New Zealand
  Center for Critical Infrastructure Protection, 443
NGCC
  See Natural gas combined-cycle power plants
NGOs
  See Nongovernmental organizations
NIMBI (not in my backyard), 182
NIPC
  See National Infrastructure Protection Center
NISSAN, 443–44
Nitrates, 235
Nitric and nitrous oxide emissions, 275–76, 281
Nitrogen
  gritted emissions for, 101
Nitrogen dioxide, 388
Nonconventional oil, 444
Nonenergy policy
  background representation in scenario definition, 373–74
Nongovernmental organizations (NGOs), 223–24, 237–39
Nordic Gene Bank, 157
Normalized difference vegetation index (NDVI), 267–68
North American Electricity Reliability Council (NERCO), 135, 440–41, 449
North American Industry Classification System (NAICS), 183
North Atlantic Oscillation, 17
North Atlantic Treaty Organization (NATO), 423–24
Norway
  carbon emissions tax in, 112
NPR
  See Net primary productivity
NRRI
  See National Regulatory Research Institute
NSC
  See National Security Council
Nuclear fuel production, 453
Nuclear infrastructure and security, 452–56
  fuel, 453
  proliferation, 455–56
  public reactions, 456
  reactors, 453–54
  reprocessing, 455
  waste, 454–55
Nuclear power, 318
Nuclear Regulatory Commission (NCR), 320

O

Oak Ridge National Laboratory, 446
Obligate chemolithoautotrophs, 222
Observational evidence
  of aerosol effects on climate, 14–16
OC
  See Organic carbon
Ocean neighborhoods, 32–33, 59
  marine reserves as experiments in, 36–39
Ocean storage
  of CO_2, 127–28
Oceans
  CO_2 emissions increasing acidity of, 127
OECD
  See Organization for Economic Cooperation and Development
Office of Defense Technology (OTA), 424–25
  "Effects of Nuclear War," 424
Office of Energy Assurance, 440
Ohio River Valley, 126
Oil infrastructure and

security, 444–48
Oil production, 98
  nonconventional, 444
  stationary sources of CO_2 emissions, 115
  trends in, 96–97
  See also Enhanced oil recovery methods
Oil reservoirs
  geologic storage of CO_2 in depleted, 123–24
Ok Tedi mine (Papua New Guinea), 239
Omai Mine, 213
Omnibus Environment, Natural Resources and Agriculture Appropriations bill, 323
OPEC
  See Organization of Petroleum Exporting Countries
Open systems, 72
Ophiodon elongates, 44
Opportunities for CO_2 capture, 115–21
  electric power generation, 115–19
  industry, 119–21
Opportunity costs, 371
Opportunity representation improvements on, 370–72
Optimization models, 355
  results of, 369
Options, 314
Organic carbon (OC), 2, 7, 17, 21
Organization for Economic Cooperation and Development (OECD), 386
Organization of Petroleum Exporting Countries (OPEC), 318, 431
Organizational research, 364–65
OTA

See Office of Defense Technology
Otoliths
  chemical tags of movement in, 48–53
Outages
  impact of, 450–51
  prior experience with, 448–49
Outokumpu (Finland), 221
Overseas Private Investment Corporation, 223
Oxfam America, 229
Oxisols, 267
Oxygen combustion
  pure, 118–19
Oxyjulis californica, 45
Ozone, 2

P
Pacific Northwest National Laboratory, 135
  world economy model of carbon capture and storage, 135–36
Pagrus auratus, 49, 52
PAH
  See Polycyclic aromatic hydrocarbons
Pan Canadian Resources Ltd., 123
Panel of Experts on Plant Exploration and Introduction, 151
Papua New Guinea, 237, 239, 243
Paralabrax clathratus, 45
Particulate matter (PM), 387–89, 392
  $PM_{2.5}$, 388, 409
  PM_{10}, 389, 392, 394
Patch dynamics, 273
PC
  See Pulverized-coal power plants
PCCIP

See President's Commission on Critical Infrastructure Protection
Pearson product-moment correlation analyses, 264
Pelates sexlineatus, 51
Periodic chart
  of anthropogenic dominance of mobilization flows, 94
Perkins, George, 214
Persian Gulf
  costs of defending oil shipments in, 316
Persian Gulf war, 318
Petrochemical industries
  in the Netherlands, 119
  See also Compressed natural gas; Liquefied natural gas; Liquefied petroleum gas; Natural gas; Oil production
Petroleum
  reserves of, 445
  synthetic, 444
Petroleum refining, 119
Petroleum shipment routes, 446
  Bosphorus Straits, 446
  Straits of Hormuz, 446
  Straits of Molucca, 446
Petrus rupetris, 44
PGRFA
  See Plant genetic resources for food and agriculture
Phelps Dodge Corporation, 209
Physical landscape modification
  mining as, 209–10
Physical security, 430
Placopecten magellanicus, 41
Plant genetic resources for food and agriculture (PGRFA)
  assessing global availability, 143–79

collections
  availability of
    germplasm maintained in situ, 163–66
  ex situ and in situ, 148–66
  genebanks, 150–56
  germplasm flows, 156–59
  obstacles to availability from genebanks users' perceptions, 159–60
  problems of supply, 160–63
  historical background, 145–47
  interdependence and PGRFA transfers, 147–48
  policy, law, and access, 166–68
Plant-level modeling
  of carbon capture and storage, 130–33
Plastics, 70
Plectropomus leopardus, 45
Pneumoconiosis, 217n
Polarization and Directionality of the Earth's Reflectance (POLDER), 13–15, 20
Policy
  developing, 226
  modeling, 359–60
  modifying, 103–4
Policy analysis, 351
  better use of models in, 368–69
Policy context
  and recent developments, 348
Policy development
  use of models in, 351–52
Policy instruments, 348–50
  in public health, 404–7
Policy needs
  and aerosol effects on climate, 21–23

Policy representation, 373–74
  assessment of policy mixes, 373
  improvements on, 373–74
  policy and program effects, 373
  program costs, 373
  realistic representation of practice of implementation, 373
  representation of nonenergy policy background in scenario definition, 373–74
Political ecologies of extraction, 234–40
  extraction, governance, and the state, 236–38
  land rights, resistance, and environmental justice, 238–40
Pollutants
  commingling of, 327
Pollution
  innovation in handling, 221–22
  mining waste as, 210–14
  preventing, 218, 220
Polycyclic aromatic hydrocarbons (PAH), 388
Pomacentrus amboinenis, 52
Pomatomus saltatrix, 50
Population genetics
  and measuring dispersal, 53–56
Population growth
  worldwide since Neolithic Era, 168
Postcombustion chemical absorption, 117
Poverty and health
  energy context of, 399–402
Power plants
  annualized cost of, 303
  coal-fired, 326, 452
  conventional, with

chemical absorption of CO_2, 117
  damages caused by, 332
  as energy converters, 304
  fueled by natural gas, 303
  geothermal, 305
  life-cycle phases, 331
  as stationary sources of CO_2 emissions, 115
Power systems under stress
  analyses of, 451
Presidential Decision Directive 63, 440
President's Commission on Critical Infrastructure Protection (PCCIP), 440
Prevention and response, 456–60
  efficiency and renewables, 459–60
  emergency response and restoration, 457–58
  guards, gates, and guns, 457
  institutions, 458–59
Price-Anderson Act, 320–21
Price discrimination, 316–17
Primary production
  mobilization through net, 74
Probability-based diffusion models, 364
Producer Price Index, 117
Productive capacity
  conservation of, 233
Program costs, 373
  estimating, 363
Program effects, 373
Proliferation
  nuclear, 455–56
Prosopis glandulosa var. *glandulosa*, 279, 281
Protection systems
  UPOV style, 158
Proven oil reserves
  in the Middle East, 444
Public health, 384, 403–7

SUBJECT INDEX 489

investment in innovation, 406–7
leveling the playing field, 406
policy instruments, 404–7
technology options, 403–4
Public Interest Energy Research Program, 323
Public policies for harnessing mineral wealth and preventing pollution, 225–34
  internalizing externalities, 230–33
  minerals and the resource curse, 225–29
  sustainable development, 233–34
Public policy, 461
Public reactions
  nuclear, 456
Public Utility Regulatory Policies Act (PURPA), 322
Pulverized-coal (PC) power plants, 114
Pumped-storage schemes, 432
Pure oxygen combustion, 118–19
PURPA
  See Public Utility Regulatory Policies Act

R

Radiological material
  releases of, 452
Reactors
  nuclear, 453–54
Realistic representation
  of practice of implementation, 373
Reclamation, 245
Rectisol, 118
Recycling
  of construction materials, 194, 200
  reservoirs for future, 101
Redundancy
  in energy infrastructure and security, 433
Reference technology
  for carbon capture and storage costs, 113–15
Regional environmental change
  mining as a driver of, 214–16
Regional syndromes
  in the global grazing footprint, 269–71
Regulations
  command-and-control, 231
Regulatory issues
  and leakage of CO_2, 129–30
Reliability planning, 428–29, 450
"Renewable energy portfolio standard" (RPS), 323–24
Renewable Energy Production Incentive (REPI), 315, 322
Renewable Energy Resources Trust, 323
Renewable energy sources, 111, 337
Renewable energy subsidies, 322–24
Renewable energy technologies (RETs), 403–4, 406, 408
Renewables
  prevention and response in, 459–60
Renewals, 70
Repeated burning, 284
REPI
  See Renewable Energy Production Incentive
Representation
  improvements on, 369–74
Reprocessing
  nuclear, 455
Reprocessing facilities, 455
Research analyses
  innovation and diffusion, 365
Research needed, 374–75
  in construction materials, 196–200
  in critical infrastructure protection, 443–44
  in ecosystem responses to managed grazing, 289–91
Research Scanning Polarimeter (RSP), 15
Reserve base
  estimating, 73
Reservoir-monitoring project, 124
Reservoirs, 71
  for future recycling, 101
  of materials in use, 101
  mobilization, 71
  sequestration, 71
Resilient networks, 435, 437
Resistance, 238–40
Resource Conservation and Recovery Act
  Bevill Amendment, 231
Resource curse
  development of minerals and, 225–29
Resource development
  allocating costs of, 246
  and the environment, 207
Resource violence, 238
Resources
  access to, 247
  analysis of, 103
  community control of, 239
  estimating, 74
Response typologies
  in ecosystem responses to managed grazing, 286–89
Restoration
  prevention and response in, 457–58
Retrofitting

of existing power plants,
 117, 303
RETs
 See Renewable energy
  technologies
Riverine systems, 70
Rock weathering, 70
Routine security
 in energy infrastructure and
  security, 427–28
Royal Commission Report
 (1842), 216, 241
RPS
 See "Renewable energy
  portfolio standard"
RSP
 See Research Scanning
  Polarimeter

S

Sahel, 13
 desertification of, 277
Sandia National Laboratory,
 443
San Juan basin (New
 Mexico), 126
Satellite retrievals
 in assessing aerosol effects
  on climate, 19–20
Scomberomorus munroi, 44
*Scomberomorus
 queenslandicus*, 44
Sea spray
 estimations of, 77
 mobilization through, 74,
  77
Sea surface temperature
 (SST), 13
Sebastes caurinus, 54–55
Sebastes chlorostictus, 45
Sebastes paucispinus, 45–46
Secondary contamination, 215
Security
 energy infrastructure and,
  421–69
 routine in energy
  infrastructure and

security, 427–28
Security expenses, 316
Segregative processes, 210
Selexol, 118
"Self-healing" grids, 435
Semidirect effects
 of aerosols on climate,
  11–12
Sequestration
 in deep ocean locations,
  128
 flows, 71
 geologic, 337
 reservoirs, 71
Seriola lalandi, 44
Service life
 expected, 199
Sex-segregation
 in mine jobs, 239–40
Shell International, 110
Short term collaborative
 projects, 375–76
Shortages of construction
 materials
 expected, 192–94
Sierra de Manantlan Man and
 Biosphere Reserve, 166
Silent Vector, 444
Silicosis, 217n
Sillaginodes punctata, 44
Silver cycle, 101–3
Silver Valley (Idaho), 228
Simulation exercises, 444
Simulation models, 355
Smelting technology
 flash, 221
Social costs
 of air pollution, 327
Social dimensions of
 energy-health linkages,
  399–403
 energy, gender, and health,
  402–3
 energy, poverty, and health,
  399–402
Social environment
 mining and, 216–17

Social marketing
 initiatives, 364
Social psychology, 364
Society for Environmental
 Toxicology and
 Chemistry, 329
Solanum, 163
Solar flare events, 430
Solid fuel use, 391, 400–1
Sonalika wheat cultivar, 148
Space and time
 cycles over, 93–101
Spatial scale of marine
 populations and their
 management, 31–68
Spatially-resolved cycles, 101
Spillovers
 cloud over, 39–43
SPRs
 See Strategic petroleum
  reserves
SST
 See Sea surface
  temperature
*State of the World's Plant
 Genetic Resources for
 Food and Agriculture,
 The*, 145
Statoil (Norway)
 natural gas mining
  operations, 112, 126
Statoliths
 chemical tags of movement
  in, 48–53
Steel manufacturing
 See Iron and steel
  manufacturing emissions
St. Lucia, 37
Stochastic models, 363–64
Stockpile determinations
 national, 103
Storage issues, 314
 in energy infrastructure and
  security, 432–33
Straits of Hormuz, 446
Straits of Molucca, 446
Strategic petroleum reserves

(SPRs), 321, 432, 447
Stress
　analyses of power systems under, 451
　in energy infrastructure and security, 434–35
Strombus gigas, 41
Subsidies, 314–25
　assessing, 316–19
　to coal, 318
　direct, 315–16
　to fossil-fuel, 324–25
　to fossil fuels, 318
　indirect, 316
　to institutions, 322
　to nuclear power, 320–22
　renewable energy, 322–24
Sulfates, 2
Sulfur emissions
　gridding for, 101
Summitville gold mine (Colorado), 232
Supply disruptions, 433
Surface water quality
　quality of, 246
Surinam
　gold mining boom in, 228
Survivability, 426
　in energy infrastructure and security, 435–36
Sustainable development, 225–34
　internalizing externalities, 230–33
　minerals and the resource curse, 225–29
Sustainable development through public policies for harnessing mineral wealth and preventing pollution, 225–34
Sustainable mining, 245
Swaps, 312, 314
Syngas, 118
Synthesized products, 70
Synthetic petroleum, 444

System-wide Information Network for Genetic Resources, 156

T

Tagging studies, 47
　of adult movement, 43–48
Tailings dams
　failures of, 246
Tambogrande mining project (Peru), 247n
Technical learning, 361–62
Technological cycles, 71
Technologies
　balancing with the environment, 104
　"brute force," 245
　environmental health implications of, 387–99
　flash smelting, 221
　flexibility of, 361
　foresight studies, 365
　functional categorization of, 370–71
　multiple benefits of, 371
Technology options
　in public health, 403–4
Technology representation, 357–58, 370–72
　energy-materials link, 370
　improvements on, 370–72
　learning curves of energy-efficient technology, 371–72
　transaction and opportunity costs, 371
Tenualosa ilisha, 50
Terrorism
　catastrophic, 438
Tertiary contamination, 215
Texaco, 110
Thalassoma bifasciatum, 51
Thermodynamical effects of aerosols on climate, 7–11
Thiobacillus ferrooxidans, 214

Third World
　underdevelopment in, 235
Three Mile Island, 456
TOMS
　See Total Ozone Mapping Spectrometer
Top-down models, 338
Total Ozone Mapping Spectrometer (TOMS), 15
Toxicity
　cumulative, 70
Toxics Release Inventory (TRI), 231
Trace-gas emissions
　in deforestation, 284–85
　in desertification, 275–76
　in woody encroachment, 281
Trace metals
　global flux of, 215
Transaction costs, 371
Transformer vulnerabilities, 449–50
Transmission systems, 305
　risks to, 460
Transportation
　of CO_2, 122–23
TRI
　See Toxics Release Inventory
Triticum, 162–63
Two-reservoir model
　of closed cycles, 72

U

Ultisols, 267
Ultra violet (UV)
　absorption in, 3
Uncertainties
　in data and data quality, 360
Uncertainties in assessing aerosol effects on climate, 1–30
　aerosol sources and distributions, 3–5

estimates of aerosol effects on climate, 5–14
observational evidence, 14–16
policy needs, 21–23
predicting future impacts, 20–21
understanding uncertainties, 16–20
Underground Injection Control program, 129–30
Underground matters, 242–43
United Kingdom
 National Infrastructure Security Co-Ordination Center, 443
UN Educational, Scientific, and Cultural Organization, 223
UN Environment Program, 323
UN Food and Agriculture Organization (FAO), 145, 147
U.S. Department of Agriculture, 151, 162
U.S. Department of Commerce, 188
U.S. Department of Defense, 425n
U.S. Department of Energy (DOE), 110, 118, 126, 314, 318, 320
 Defense Civil Preparedness Office, 425–26
 Office of Energy Assurance, 440
U.S. Department of Homeland Security (DHS), 440–42
 veil of secrecy over activities of, 442
U.S. Department of the Interior, 212n
U.S. economy
 importance of the construction industry in, 183–85

U.S. Energy Association "National Energy Security Post 9/11," 437
U.S. Energy Information Administration, 318, 361
U.S. Environmental Protection Agency (EPA), 129, 329
 National Ambient Air Quality Standards, 392
 Underground Injection Control program, 129–30
U.S. Forest Service, 214
U.S. genebanks, 157
U.S. General Mining Law, 212n
U.S. Interagency Working Group on Industrial Ecology, Material and Energy flows, 98
UPOV style protection systems, 158
Uranium Enrichment Decontamination and Decommissioning Fund, 321
USA Patriot Act, 439
UV
 See Ultra violet

V

Valuation strategies, 333–35
Value judgments
 costs and, 332–33
Variable costs
 vs. fixed, 305
Vicia, 165

W

Waste
 from construction and demolition, 194, 198
 nuclear, 454–55
Water
 quality of surface, 246
Weathering

of the continental crust, 74
rock, 70
Weyburn oil field, 123–24
Whitehorse Mining Initiative (Canada), 238n
Wild *Lycopersicon*, 163
Wind energy, 460
Woody encroachment, 270–71, 274, 278–82
 biogeochemistry, 280–81
 climate interactions, 282
 ecosystem structure, 278–79
 hydrology, 281–82
 trace-gas emissions, 81
World Bank, 216, 326
 Extractive Industries Review, 207n, 250
World Conservation Union, 223
World Diamond Council, 238
World Health Organization, 401
World Information and Early Warning System database, 152
World population growth since the Neolithic Era, 168
World Resources Institute, 216
World Summit on Sustainable Development, 408
World Trade Center attacks, 438, 440, 456–57
 rebuilding after, 187

Y

Yellowstone National Park, 242

Z

Zinc
 historical production of, 93
 trends in production of, 96–97
Zinc cycle
 spatially-resolved, 101

Cumulative Indexes

CONTRIBUTING AUTHORS, VOLUMES 20–29

A
Abraham MA, 28:401–28
Adelman MA, 22:13–46
Amann M, 25:339–75
Anderson D, 20:495–511, 562–73; 22:187–215; 27:271–308
Anderson J, 24:431–60
Anderson S, 29:109–42
Asner GP, 29:261–99
Aubinet M, 26:435–65
Ausubel JH, 20:463–92
Azar C, 24:513–44

B
Bacon RW, 20:119–43; 26:331–59
Bailis R, 29:383–419
Baldwin SF, 26:391–434
Barkenbus JN, 20:179–212
Barnes B, 29:383–419
Barnes DF, 21:497–530
Battle M, 23:207–23
Baumol WJ, 20:71–81
Baxter L, 22:119–54
Beck PW, 24:113–37
Bender ML, 23:207–23
Besant-Jones J, 26:331–59
Blake DR, 25:685–740
Blanchard CL, 24:329–65
Blok K, 23:123–205
Bodansky DM, 20:425–61
Bormann FH, 21:1–29
Boyd G, 29:345–81
Branch TA, 28:359–99
Bridge G, 29:205–59
Broecker WS, 25:1–19
Brooks H, 26:28, 29–48
Brown MA, 23:287–385

Brown ML, 24:487–512
Brown N, 28:59–106
Brown RE, 27:119–58
Bukharin O, 21:467–96
Bunn M, 22:403–86

C
Cairns J Jr, 21:167–89
Calwell C, 27:119–58
Cano-Ruiz JA, 23:499–536
Carbonell R, 25:115–46
Carmichael G, 25:339–75
Cassman KG, 28:315–58
Cavanagh R, 20:519–25
Chapel SW, 22:155–85
Chaurey A, 27:309–48; 29:383–419
Chávez O, 24:607–43
Chen Q, 25:567–600
Chertow MR, 25:313–37
Chua S, 24:391–430
Cicchetti CJ, 20:512–18
Cifuentes LA, 29:383–419
Connolly S, 28:587–617
Connors SR, 25:147–97
Craig PP, 24:461–86; 27:83–118
Cullicott C, 27:119–58

D
Daily GC, 21:125–44
Dargay J, 20:145–78
DeAngelo BJ, 22:75–118
Dearing A, 25:89–113
Davies JA, 28:401–28
de Beer J, 23:123–205
DeCicco J, 25:477–535
Decker EH, 25:685–740
De Laquil P III, 21:371–402

Denison RA, 21:191–237
Dernbach J, 26:361–89
DeSimone JM, 25:115–46
Dhanapala KN, 29:383–419
Dilling L, 28:521–58
Dirzo R, 28:137–67
Dobermann A, 28:315–58
Doney SC, 28:521–58
Dowlatabadi H, 24:513–44; 29:421–69
Dracker R, 21:371–402
Drake EM, 21:145–66
Driese KL, 28:107–35

E
Edmonds J, 24:487–512; 28:521–58
Ehrenfeld J, 22:487–535
Ehrlich PR, 21:125–44
Elliott S, 25:685–740
Elmore AJ, 29:261–99
Emanuel AE, 22:263–303
Erdal S, 25:765–802
Ernst B, 28:359–99
Eto JH, 27:119–58
Eyer JM, 21:347–70
Ezzati M, 27:233–70; 29:383–419

F
Farrell AE, 29:421–69
Feinstein CD, 22:155–85
Fine J, 28:59–106
Fisher RK, 24:173–88
Fisher-Vanden K, 22:589–628
Fisk WJ, 25:537–66
Floor WM, 21:497–530
Flynn J, 20:83–118

493

Foell W, 25:339–75
Forsberg C, 20:179–212
Fowler C, 29:143–79
Friedmann R, 23:225–52
Fulkerson W, 24:487–512

G
Gadgil A, 23:253–86;
   27:83–118
Galloway JN, 21:261–92
Gately D, 20:145–78
Geist HJ, 28:205–41
Gleick PH, 28:275–314
Glicksman LR, 26:83–115
Goldemberg J, 23:1–23
Goldstein BD, 25:765–802
Goodchild MF, 28:493–519
Goody R, 27:1–20
Gopalakrishnan A,
   27:369–95
Gower ST, 28:169–204
Graedel TE, 20:265–300;
   21:69–98;
   29:69–107
Greden LV, 26:83–115
Green C, 25:339–75
Greene DL, 24:487–512;
   25:477–535
Grubb M, 27:271–308
Grübler A, 24:545–69
Gurney KR, 28:521–58

H
Haddad BM, 22:357–401
Hadley S, 22:119–54
Hall SJ, 21:311–46
Harris AT, 29:261–99
Harriss R, 28:521–58
Harte J, 22:75–118
He K, 27:397–431
Heath LS, 26:435–65
Heckman JR, 21:167–89
Held IM, 25:441–75
Hendriks C, 26:303–29
Hermann F, 20:233–64
Herzog HJ, 21:145–66
Hettelingh J-P, 25:339–75

Hilborn R, 28:359–99
Hirst E, 20:535–55;
   22:119–54
Hodgkin T, 29:143–79
Holdren JP, 22:403–86;
   26:391–434
Holloway S, 26:145–66
Holloway T, 29:383–419
Hordijk L, 25:339–75
Horgan SA, 21:347–70
Horvath A, 29:181–204
Houghton RA, 21:293–310;
   24:571–605
Huo H, 27:397–431

I
Iannucci JJ, 21:347–70

J
Johnson T, 25:339–75
Joshi V, 25:741–63
Joskow PL, 20:526–34

K
Kammen DM, 27:233–70;
   29:301–44, 383–419
Kandlikar M, 25:629–84
Karjalainen T, 26:435–65
Kates RW, 26:xiv, 1–26;
   28:559–86
Kazimi MS, 24:139–71
Keeling CD, 23:25–82
Keeling RF, 23:207–23
Keith DW, 25:245–84
Khalil MAK, 24:645–61;
   25:741–63
Kheshgi HS, 25:199–244
Kicklighter DW,
   21:293–310
Kinsman J, 26:435–65
Kishore VVN, 25:741–63
Klee RJ, 29:69–107
Köhler J, 27:271–308
Koomey JG, 20:535–55;
   23:287–385;
   27:83–118, 119–58
Koplow D, 26:361–89

L
Lackner KS, 27:193–232
Laitner S, 27:119–58
Lambin EF, 28:205–41
Lashof DA, 22:75–118
Lee JJ, 26:167–200
Lepers E, 28:205–41
Levine MD, 23:287–385
Lew D, 27:309–48
Li J, 25:339–75
Lin J, 27:349–67
Linden HR, 21:31–67
Liverman DM, 24:607–43
Lukachko SP, 26:167–200
Lynd LR, 21:403–65

M
Macfarlane A, 26:201–35
MacLeod M, 28:463–92
Magnusson A, 28:359–99
Mahlman JD, 23:83–105
Malone TF, 20:1–29
March PA, 24:173–88
Marland G, 25:199–244
Marteel AE, 28:401–28
Martin N, 26:303–29
Martin PH, 26:435–65
Martin RE, 29:261–99
Martinot E, 22:357–401;
   27:309–48
Matos G, 23:107–22
Matson PA, 21:311–46
Mauzerall DL, 26:237–68
May AD, 21:239–60
McGowan JG, 25:147–97
McGranahan G, 28:243–74
McGuire AD, 21:293–310
McKone TE, 28:463–92
McMahon JE, 20:535–55
McNeill JA, 22:263–303
McRae GJ, 23:499–536
Melillo JM, 21:293–310
Menon S, 29:1–30
Minte-Vera CV, 28:359–99
Mitchell C, 25:285–312
Mitchell JV, 24:83–111
Mitchell RB, 28:429–61

Mock JE, 22:305–56
Mödl A, 20:233–64
Mooney HA, 24:1–31
Moreira JR, 27:349–67
Morgenstern RD,
 24:431–60
Morris JG Jr, 24:367–90
Mosdale R, 24:281–328
Murtishaw S, 26:49–81

N
Nabuurs G-J, 26:435–65
Nadel S, 27:159–92
Nagpal T, 25:339–75
Nakićenović N,
 24:545–69
Nash CA, 21:239–60
Nash J, 22:487–535
Naylor RL, 21:99–123
Newell R, 29:109–42
Nichols AL, 20:556–61
Norford LK, 26:83–115

O
Ogden JM, 24:227–79
Olander LP, 29:261–99
Olson WW, 28:401–28
Orans R, 22:155–85
O'Rourke D,
 28:587–617
Ozawa Meida L,
 26:303–29

P
Pacca S, 29:301–44
Pacyna JM, 20:265–300
Palumbi SR, 29:31–68
Parris TM, 28:559–86
Parson EA, 22:589–628
Patrick R, 22:1–11
Pearce D, 27:57–81
Peng C, 25:339–75
Price L, 26:117–43,
 303–29; 29:383–419
Prince RC, 25:199–244
Prinn RG, 28:29–57
Pu Y, 25:339–75

R
Rabl A, 25:601–27
Ramachandran G,
 25:629–84
Ramakrishna K,
 24:571–605
Ramankutty R, 25:339–75
Ramesohl S, 29:345–81
Raven PH, 28:137–67
Ravindranath NH,
 23:387–437
Reddy AKN, 27:23–56
Reiners WA, 28:107–35
Reynolds S, 28:59–106
Rind D, 22:47–74
Rogner H-H, 22:217–62
Romm JP, 23:287–385
Rosenfeld AH, 23:287–385;
 24:33–82
Rosenzweig C, 22:47–74
Roth P, 28:59–106
Roth PM, 21:311–46
Rowland FS, 25:685–740
Russell A, 22:537–88
Russell M, 23:439–63
Ruth M, 26:117–43

S
Sagar AD, 25:377–439
Saleska SR, 22:75–118
Sànchez R, 24:607–43
San Martin RL, 24:487–512
Sanstad AH, 20:535–55
Sathaye JA, 23:387–437
Satterthwaite D, 28:243–74
Schafer A, 26:167–200
Scheuerell MD, 28:359–99
Schimel D, 28:1–28,
 521–58
Schipper L, 20:325–86;
 26:49–81
Schock RN, 24:487–512
Schoenung SM, 21:347–70
Shah J, 25:339–75
Sheinbaum C, 23:225–52
Siddiqi TA, 20:213–32
Sinton JE, 22:357–401

Slovic P, 20:83–118
Smil V, 25:21–51, 53–88
Smith FA, 25:685–740
Smith KR, 25:741–63
Soden BJ, 25:441–75
Sørensen B, 20:387–424
Spadaro JV, 25:601–27
Spengler JD, 25:567–600
Srinivasan S, 24:281–328
Starr C, 20:31–44
Stephens B, 28:521–58
Stevens P, 24:281–328
Stieglitz M, 22:47–74
Stokes G, 28:521–58
Streets D, 25:339–75

T
Taylor DK, 25:115–46
Tester JW, 22:305–56
Themelis NJ, 23:465–97
Thomas VN, 20:301–24
Thornton J, 27:119–58
Ting M, 26:49–81
Todreas NE, 24:139–71
Toman MA, 24:431–60

U
Uma R, 25:741–63
Unander F, 26:49–81

V
Valero JL, 28:359–99
Varady RG, 24:607–43
Victor DG, 24:545–69
Vine EL, 26:435–65
Vuilleumier L,
 28:59–106

W
Wagner L, 23:107–22
Waitz IA, 26:167–200
Wallace LA, 26:269–301
Walters DT, 28:315–58
Wamukonya N, 27:309–48
Wang G, 28:1–28
Wang X, 26:237–68
Webber C, 27:119–58

Wernick IK, 20:463–92;
　23:465–97
Worrell E, 23:123–205;
　26:117–43, 303–29;
　29:345–81
Wright PM, 22:305–56

Wuebbles DJ, 20:45–70
Wyman CE, 24:189–226

Y
Yang C, 24:281–328
Yang H, 28:315–58

Z
Zerriffi H,
　29:421–69
Zhang J, 25:741–63
Zhang Q,
　27:397–431

CHAPTER TITLES, VOLUMES 20–29

Earth's Life Support Systems

CLIMATE

Weighing Functions for Ozone Depletion and Greenhouse Gas Effects on Climate	DJ Wuebbles	20:45–70
The Emerging Climate Change Regime	DM Bodansky	20:425–61
The Role of Moisture Transport Between Ground and Atmosphere in Global Change	D Rind, C Rosenzweig, M Stieglitz	22:47–74
Terrestrial Ecosystem Feedbacks to Global Climate Change	DA Lashof, BJ DeAngelo, SR Saleska, J Harte	22:75–118
International Technology Transfer for Climate Change Mitigation and the Cases of Russia and China	E Martinot, JE Sinton, BM Haddad	22:357–401
Integrated Assessment Models of Global Climate Change	EA Parson, K Fisher-Vanden	22:589–628
Science and Nonscience Concerning Human-Caused Climate Warming	JD Mahlman	23:83–105
Climate Change Mitigation in the Energy and Forestry Sectors of Developing Countries	JA Sathaye, NH Ravindranath	23:387–437
Converging Paths Leading to the Role of the Oceans in Climate Change	WS Broecker	25:1–19
Geoengineering the Climate: History and Prospect	DW Keith	25:245–84
Water Vapor Feedback and Global Warming	IM Held, BJ Soden	25:441–75
Greenhouse Implications of Household Stoves: An Analysis for India	KR Smith, R Uma, VVN Kishore, J Zhang, V Joshi, MAK Khalil	25:741–63

Climate Change, Climate Modes, and Climate Impacts	G Wang, D Schimel	28:1–28

ATMOSPHERE

Asia-Wide Emissions of Greenhouse Gases	TA Siddiqi	20:213–32
Anthropogenic Mobilization of Sulfur and Nitrogen: Immediate and Delayed Consequences	JN Galloway	21:261–92
NO_x Emissions from Soil: Implications for Air Quality Modeling in Agricultural Regions	SJ Hall, PA Matson, PM Roth	21:311–46
The O_2 Balance of the Atmosphere: A Tool for Studying the Fate of Fossil Fuel CO_2	ML Bender, M Battle, RF Keeling	23:207–23
Non-CO_2 Greenhouse Gases in the Atmosphere	MAK Khalil	24:645–61
The Causes and Consequences of Particulate Air Pollution in Urban India: A Synthesis of the Science	M Kandlikar, G Ramachandran	25:629–84
Observing and Thinking About the Atmosphere	R Goody	27:1–20
Urban Air Pollution in China: Current Status, Characteristics, and Progress	K He, H Huo, Q Zhang	27:397–431
The Cleansing Capacity of the Atmosphere	RG Prinn	28:29–57
Evaluating Uncertainties in Regional Photochemical Air Quality Modeling	J Fine, L Vuilleumier, S Reynolds, P Roth, N Brown	28:59–106
Current Uncertainties in Assessing Aerosol Effects on Climate	S Menon	29:1–30

MARINE AND TERRESTRIAL ECOSYSTEMS

Restoration Ecology: The State of an Emerging Field	J Cairns Jr, JR Heckman	21:167–89
Tropical Deforestation and the Global Carbon Budget	JM Melillo, RA Houghton, DW Kicklighter, AD McGuire	21:293–310
The Development of the Science of Aquatic Ecosystems	R Patrick	22:1–11

On the Road to Global Ecology	HA Mooney	24:1–31
Harmful Algal Blooms: An Emerging Public Health Problem with Possible Links to Human Stress on the Environment	JG Morris Jr	24:367–90
Transport of Energy, Information, and Material Through the Biosphere	WA Reiners, KL Driese	28:107–35
Global State of Biodiversity and Loss	R Dirzo, PH Raven	28:137–67
Marine Reserves and Ocean Neighborhoods: The Spatial Scale of Marine Populations and Their Management	SR Palumbi	29:31–68

BIOGEOCHEMISTRY

Phosphorus in the Environment: Natural Flows and Human Interferences	V Smil	25:53–88
Integrated Analysis for Acid Rain in Asia: Policy Implications and Results of RAINS-ASIA Model	J Shah, T Nagpal, T Johnson, M Amann, G Carmichael, W Foell, C Green, J-P Hettelingh, L Hordijk, J Li, C Peng, Y Pu, R Ramankutty, D Streets	25:339–75
Carbon Sinks in Temperate Forests	PH Martin, G-J Nabuurs, M Aubinet, T Karjalainen, EL Vine, J Kinsman, LS Heath	26:435–65
Carbonate Chemistry for Sequestering Fossil Carbon	KS Lackner	27:193–232
Patterns and Mechanisms of the Forest Carbon Cycle	ST Gower	28:169–204
The Role of Carbon Cycle Observations and Knowledge in Carbon Management	L Dilling, SC Doney, J Edmonds, KR Gurney, R Harriss, D Schimel, B Stephens, G Stokes	28:521–58

Elemental Cycles: A Status Report on Human or Natural Dominance	RJ Klee, TE Graedel	29:69–107

Human Use of Environment and Resources

ENERGY

A Personal History: Technology to Energy Strategy	C Starr	20:31–44
Yucca Mountain: A Crisis for Policy: Prospects for America's High-Level Nuclear Waste Program	J Flynn, P Slovic	20:83–118
The Response of World Energy and Oil Demand to Income Growth and Changes in Oil Prices	J Dargay, D Gately	20:145–78
Internationalizing Nuclear Safety: The Pursuit of Collective Responsibility	JN Barkenbus, C Forsberg	20:179–212
The Elimination of Lead in Gasoline	VN Thomas	20:301–24
Determinants of Automobile Use and Energy Consumption in OECD Countries	L Schipper	20:325–86
History of, and Recent Progress in, Wind-Energy Utilization	B Sørensen	20:387–424
Energy Efficiency and the Economists: The Case for a Policy Based on Economic Principles	D Anderson	20:495–511
Four Misconceptions About Demand-Side Management	CJ Cicchetti	20:512–18
Energy-Efficiency Solutions: What Commodity Prices Can't Deliver	R Cavanagh	20:519–25
Utility-Subsidized Energy-Efficiency Programs	PL Joskow	20:526–34
Energy Efficiency Policy and Market Failures	MD Levine, JG Koomey, JE McMahon, AH Sanstad, E Hirst	20:535–55
Demand-Side Management: An Nth-Best Solution?	AL Nichols	20:556–61
Roundtable on Energy Efficiency and the Economists—An Assessment	D Anderson	20:562–73
The Evolution of an Energy Contrarian	HR Linden	21:31–67
Carbon Dioxide Recovery and Disposal from Large Energy Systems	HJ Herzog, EM Drake	21:145–66

Energy Storage for a Competitive Power Market	SM Schoenung, JM Eyer, JJ Iannucci, SA Horgan	21:347–70
Progress Commercializing Solar-Electric Power Systems	R Dracker, P De Laquil III	21:371–402
Overview and Evaluation of Fuel Ethanol from Cellulosic Biomass: Technology, Economics, the Environment, and Policy	LR Lynd	21:403–65
Security of Fissile Materials in Russia	O Bukharin	21:467–96
My Education in Mineral (Especially Oil) Economics	MA Adelman	22:13–46
Transition-Cost Issues for US Electricity Utilities	E Hirst, L Baxter, S Hadley	22:119–54
The Distributed Utility: A New Electric Utility Planning and Pricing Paradigm	CD Feinstein, R Orans, SW Chapel	22:155–85
An Assessment of World Hydrocarbon Resources	H-H Rogner	22:217–62
Geothermal Energy from the Earth: Its Potential Impact as an Environmentally Sustainable Resource	JE Mock, JW Tester, PM Wright	22:305–56
Managing Military Uranium and Plutonium in the United States and the Former Soviet Union	M Bunn, JP Holdren	22:403–86
Mexican Electric End-Use Efficiency: Experiences to Date	R Friedmann, C Sheinbaum	23:225–52
The Art of Energy Efficiency: Protecting the Environment with Better Technology	AH Rosenfeld	24:33–82
Nuclear Energy in the Twenty-First Century: Examination of a Contentious Subject	PW Beck	24:113–37
Nuclear Power Economic Performance: Challenges and Opportunities	MS Kazimi, NE Todreas	24:139–71
It's Not Easy Being Green: Environmental Technologies Enhance Conventional Hydropower's Role in Sustainable Development	PA March, RK Fisher	24:173–88
Biomass Ethanol: Technical Progress, Opportunities, and Commerical Challenges	CE Wyman	24:189–226

Prospects for Building a Hydrogen Energy Infrastructure	JM Ogden	24:227–79
Fuel Cells: Reaching the Era of Clean and Efficient Power Generation in the Twenty-First Century	S Srinivasan, R Mosdale, P Stevens, C Yang	24:281–328
The Economics of "When" Flexibility in the Design of Greenhouse Gas Abatement Policies	MA Toman, RD Morgenstern, J Anderson	24:431–60
High-Level Nuclear Waste: The Status of Yucca Mountain	PP Craig	24:461–86
Energy in the Twentieth Century: Resources, Conversions, Costs, Uses, and Consequences	V Smil	25:21–51
Opportunities for Pollution Prevention and Energy Efficiency Enabled by the Carbon Dioxide Technology Platform	DK Taylor, R Carbonell, JM DeSimone	25:115–46
Windpower: A Turn of the Century Review	JG McGowan, SR Connors	25:147–97
The Potential of Biomass Fuels in the Context of Global Climate Change: Focus on Transportation Fuels	HS Kheshgi, RC Prince, G Marland	25:199–244
Engineering-Economic Analyses of Automotive Fuel Economy Potential in the United States	DL Greene, J DeCicco	25:477–535
Methyl tert-Butyl Ether as a Gasoline Oxygenate: Lessons for Environmental Public Policy	S Erdal, BD Goldstein	25:765–802
Indicators of Energy Use and Carbon Emissions: Explaining the Energy Economy Link	L Schipper, F Unander, S Murtishaw, M Ting	26:49–81
Energy Conservation in Chinese Residential Buildings: Progress and Opportunities in Design and Policy	LR Glicksman, LK Norford, LV Greden	26:83–115

Policy Modeling for Energy Efficiency Improvement in US Industry	E Worrell, L Price, M Ruth	26:117–43
Storage of Fossil Fuel-Derived Carbon Dioxide Beneath the Surface of the Earth	S Holloway	26:145–66
Historical and Future Trends in Aircraft Performance, Cost, and Emissions	JJ Lee, SP Lukachko, IA Waitz, A Schafer	26:167–200
Interim Storage of Spent Fuel in the United States	A Macfarlane	26:201–35
Global Electric Power Reform, Privatization, and Liberalization of the Electric Power Industry in Developing Countries	RW Bacon, J Besant-Jones	26:331–59
The PCAST Energy Studies: Toward a National Consensus on Energy Research, Development, Demonstration, and Deployment Policy	JP Holdren, SF Baldwin	26:391–434
The Evolution of an Energy Analyst: Some Personal Reflections	AKN Reddy	27:23–56
What Can History Teach Us? A Retrospective Examination of Long-Term Energy Forecasts for the United States	PP Craig, A Gadgil, JG Koomey	27:83–118
Appliance and Equipment Efficiency Standards	S Nadel	27:159–92
Household Energy, Indoor Air Pollution, and Health in Developing Countries: Knowledge Base for Effective Interventions	M Ezzati, DM Kammen	27:233–70
Renewable Energy Markets in Developing Countries	E Martinot, A Chaurey, D Lew, JR Moreira, N Wamukonya	27:309–48
Appliance Efficiency Standards and Labeling Programs in China	J Lin	27:349–67
Evolution of the Indian Nuclear Power Program	A Gopalakrishnan	27:369–95
Prospects for Carbon Capture and Storage Technologies	S Anderson, R Newell	29:109–42

WATER

Drinking Water in Developing Countries	A Gadgil	23:253–86
Water Use	PH Gleick	28:275–314

AGRICULTURE

Energy and Resource Constraints on Intensive Agricultural Production	RL Naylor	21:99–123
Protecting Agricultural Crops from the Effects of Tropospheric Ozone Exposure: Reconciling Science and Standard Setting in the United States, Europe, and Asia	DL Mauzerall, X Wang	26:237–68
Meeting Cereal Demand While Protecting Natural Resources and Improving Environmental Quality	KG Cassman, A Dobermann, DT Walters, H Yang	28:315–58
Plant Genetic Resources for Food and Agriculture: Assessing Global Availability	C Fowler, T Hodgkin	29:143–79

SETTLEMENTS

Urban Congestion: A European Perspective on Theory and Practice	AD May, CA Nash	21:239–60
Energy and Material Flow Through the Urban Ecosystem	EH Decker, S Elliott, FA Smith, DR Blake, FS Rowland	25:685–740
Urban Centers: An Assessment of Sustainability	G McGranahan, D Satterthwaite	28:243–74

INDUSTRY AND MANUFACTURING

Environmental Industries With Substantial Start-Up Costs as Contributors to Trade Competitiveness	WJ Baumol	20:71–81
National Materials Flows and the Environment	IK Wernick, JH Ausubel	20:463–92
On The Concept of Industrial Ecology	TE Graedel	21:69–98

Future Technologies for Energy-Efficient Iron and Steel Making	J de Beer, E Worrell, K Blok	23:123–205
Recycling Metals for the Environment	IK Wernick, NJ Themelis	23:465–97
Environmentally Conscious Chemical Process Design	JA Cano-Ruiz, GJ McRae	23:499–536
Industrial Symbiosis: Literature and Taxonomy	MR Chertow	25:313–37
Carbon Dioxide Emissions from the Global Cement Industry	E Worrell, L Price, N Martin, C Hendriks, L Ozawa Meida	26:303–29
Green Chemistry and Engineering: Drivers, Metrics, and Reduction to Practice	AE Marteel, JA Davies, WW Olson, MA Abraham	28:401–28
Construction Materials and the Environment	A Horvath	29:181–204
Contested Terrain: Mining and the Environment	G Bridge	29:205–59

LIVING RESOURCES

State of the World's Fisheries	R Hilborn, TA Branch, B Ernst, A Magnusson, CV Minte-Vera, MD Scheuerell, JL Valero	28:359–99
Grazing Systems, Ecosystem Responses, and Global Change	GP Asner, AJ Elmore, LP Olander, RE Martin, AT Harris	29:261–99

LAND USE

Dynamics of Land-Use and Land-Cover Change in Tropical Regions	EF Lambin, HJ Geist, E Lepers	28:205–41

Management and Human Dimensions

GOVERNANCE

Privatization and Reform in the Global Electricity Supply Industry	RW Bacon	20:119–43
Rural Energy in Developing Countries: A Challenge for Economic Development	DF Barnes, WM Floor	21:497–530
Renewable Energy Technology and Policy for Development	D Anderson	22:187–215
Electric Power Quality	AE Emanuel, JA McNeill	22:263–303
From Physics to Development Strategies	J Goldemberg	23:1–23
Toward a Productive Divorce: Separating DOE Cleanups from Transition Assistance	M Russell	23:439–63
Economic Growth, Liberalization, and the Environment: A Review of the Economic Evidence	S Chua	24:391–430
Environmental Issues Along the United States-Mexico Border: Drivers of Change and Responses of Citizens and Institutions	DM Liverman, RG Varady, O Chávez, R Sánchez	24:607–43
Technologies Supportive of Sustainable Transportation	A Dearing	25:89–113
The England and Wales Non-Fossil Fuel Obligation: History and Lessons	C Mitchell	25:285–312
Federal Fossil Fuel Emmissions: A Case Study of Increasing Transparency for Fiscal Policy	D Koplow, J Dernbach	26:361–89
International Environmental Agreements: A Survey of Their Features, Formation, and Effects	RB Mitchell	28:429–61

METHODS

Atmospheric Emissions Inventories: Status and Prospects	JM Pacyna, TE Graedel	20:265–300
Codes of Environmental Management Practice: Assessing Their Potential as a Tool for Change	J Nash, J Ehrenfeld	22:487–535

Regional Photochemical Air Quality Modeling: Model Formulations, History, and State of the Science	A Russell	22:537–88
Engineering-Economic Studies of Energy Technologies to Reduce Greenhouse Gas Emissions: Opportunities and Challenges	MA Brown, MD Levine, JP Romm, AH Rosenfeld, JG Koomey	23:287–385
Methods for Attributing Ambient Air Pollutants to Emission Sources	CL Blanchard	24:329–65
A Review of Technical Change in Assessment of Climate Policy	C Azar, H Dowlatabadi	24:513–44
Modeling Technological Change: Implications for the Global Environment	A Grübler, N Nakićenović, DG Victor	24:545–69
An Intellectual History of Environmental Economics	D Pearce	27:57–81
Sorry, Wrong Number: The Use and Misuse of Numerical Facts in Analysis and Media Reporting of Energy Issues	JG Koomey, C Calwell, S Laitner, J Thornton, RE Brown, JH Eto, C Webber, C Cullicott	27:119–58
Induced Technical Change in Energy and Environmental Modeling: Analytic Approaches and Policy Implications	M Grubb, J Köhler, D Anderson	27:271–308
Geographic Information Science and Systems for Environmental Management	MF Goodchild	28:493–519
Assessing the Costs of Electricity	DM Kammen, S Pacca	29:301–44
Advances in Energy Forecasting Models Based on Engineering Economics	E Worrell, S Ramesohl, G Boyd	29:345–81

OBSERVATIONS, MONITORING, INDICATORS

International Environmental Labeling	A Mödl, F Hermann	20:233–64
Ecology: A Personal History	FH Bormann	21:1–29

Environmental Life-Cycle Comparisons of Recycling, Landfilling, and Incineration: A Review of Recent Studies	RA Denison	21:191–237
Rewards and Penalties of Monitoring the Earth	CD Keeling	23:25–82
A Review of National Emissions Inventories from Select Non-Annex I Countries: Implications for Counting Sources and Sinks of Carbon	RA Houghton, K Ramakrishna	24:571–605
Characterizing and Measuring Sustainable Development	TM Parris, RW Kates	28:559–86

HEALTH AND WELL-BEING

Global Change and Human Susceptibility to Disease	GC Daily, PR Ehrlich	21:125–44
Health and Productivity Gains From Better Indoor Environments and Their Relationship with Building Energy Efficiency	WJ Fisk	25:537–66
Indoor Air Quality Factors in Designing a Healthy Building	JD Spengler, Q(Yan) Chen	25:567–600
Public Health Impact of Air Pollution and Implications for the Energy System	A Rabl, JV Spadaro	25:601–27
Human Exposure to Volatile Organic Pollutants: Implications for Indoor Air Studies	LA Wallace	26:269–301
Tracking Multiple Pathways of Human Exposure to Persistent Multimedia Pollutants: Regional, Continental, and Global Scale Models	TE McKone, M MacLeod	28:463–92
Energy Management and Global Health	M Ezzati, R Bailis, DM Kammen, T Holloway, L Price, LA Cifuentes, B Barnes, A Chaurey, KN Dhanapala	29:383–419
Energy Infrastructure and Security	AE Farrell, H Zerriffi, H Dowlatabadi	29:421–69

POPULATION AND CONSUMPTION

Consumption of Materials in the United States, 1900–1995	G Matos, L Wagner	23:107–22
Capacity Development for the Environment: A View for the South, A View for the North	AD Sagar	25:377–439
Queries on the Human Use of the Earth	RW Kates	26:1–26
Just Oil? The Distribution of Environmental and Social Impacts of Oil Production and Consumption	D O'Rourke, S Connolly	28:587–617

ETHICS, VALUES, JUSTICE

Reflections on the Human Prospect	TF Malone	20:1–29
Ethics and International Business	JV Mitchell	24:83–111
How Much Is Energy Research & Development Worth As Insurance?	RN Schock, W Fulkerson, ML Brown, RL San Martin, DL Greene, J Edmonds	24:487–512

Emerging Integrative Themes

Autonomous Science and Socially Responsive Science: A Search for Resolution	H Brooks	26:29–48

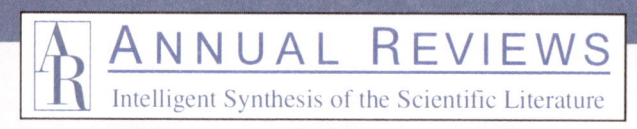

ANNUAL REVIEWS
Intelligent Synthesis of the Scientific Literature

Annual Reviews – Your Starting Point for Research Online
http://arjournals.annualreviews.org

- Over 900 Annual Reviews volumes—more than 25,000 critical, authoritative review articles in 31 disciplines spanning the Biomedical, Physical, and Social sciences—available online, including all Annual Reviews back volumes, dating to 1932
- Current individual subscriptions include seamless online access to full-text articles, PDFs, Reviews in Advance (as much as 6 months ahead of print publication), bibliographies, and other supplementary material in the current volume and the prior 4 years' volumes
- All articles are fully supplemented, searchable, and downloadable—see http://environ.annualreviews.org
- Access links to the reviewed references (when available online)
- Site features include customized alerting services, citation tracking, and saved searches

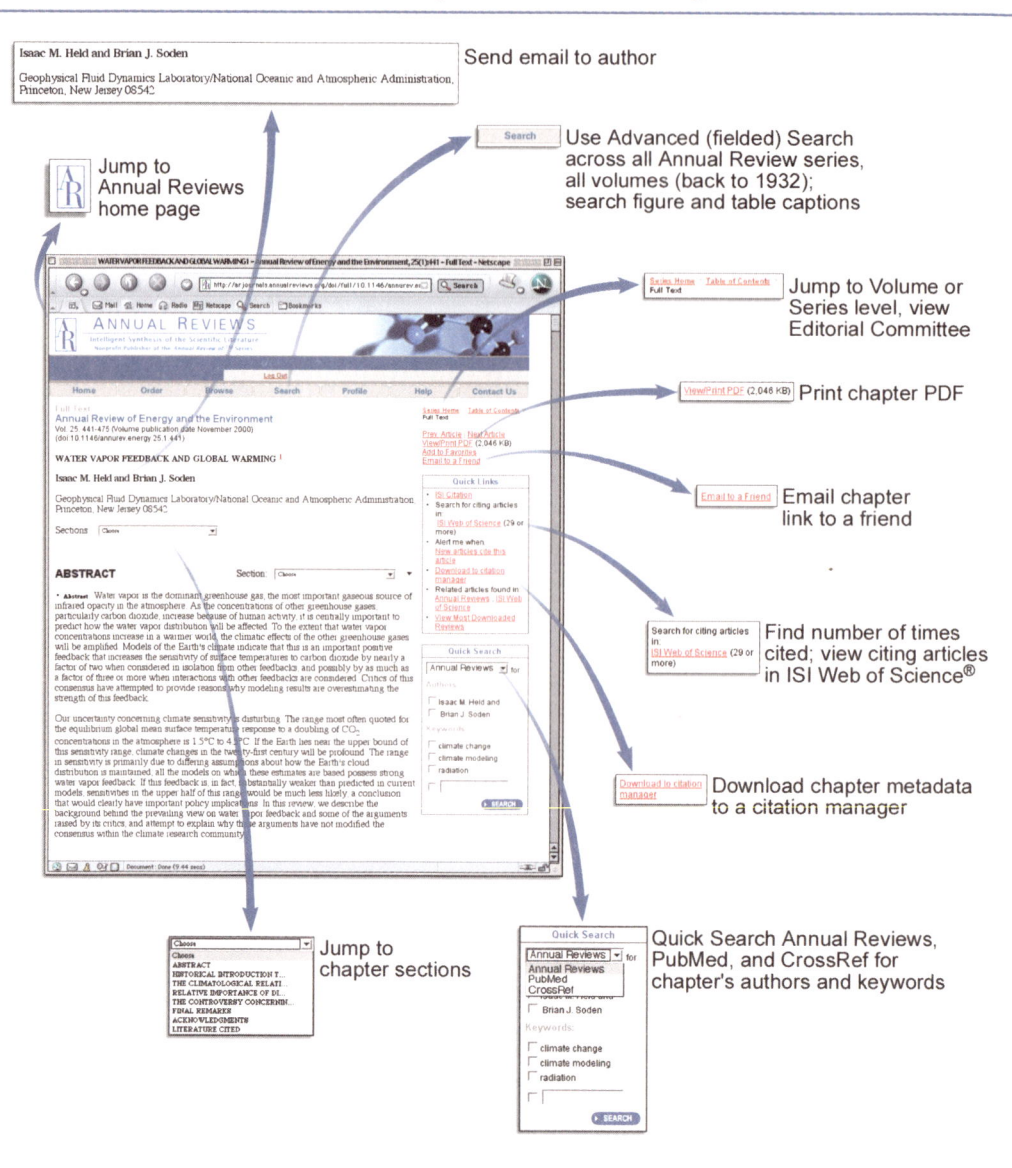

Send email to author

Use Advanced (fielded) Search across all Annual Review series, all volumes (back to 1932); search figure and table captions

Jump to Annual Reviews home page

Jump to Volume or Series level, view Editorial Committee

Print chapter PDF

Email chapter link to a friend

Find number of times cited; view citing articles in ISI Web of Science®

Download chapter metadata to a citation manager

Jump to chapter sections

Quick Search Annual Reviews, PubMed, and CrossRef for chapter's authors and keywords

Copyright © 2004 Annual Reviews, Nonprofit Publisher of the *Annual Review of* ™ Series